Readings in Ethology and Comparative Psychology

Core Books in Psychology Series
Edward L. Walker, Editor

Psychology: A Story of a Search
W. Lambert Gardiner, Sir George Williams University

The Uptight Society: A Book of Readings
Howard Gadlin, University of Massachusetts
Bertram E. Garskof

Human Socialization
Elton B. McNeil, The University of Michigan

Readings in Human Socialization
Elton B. McNeil, The University of Michigan

The Scope of Motivation: Environmental, Physiological, Mental, and Social
Wilson McTeer, Wayne State University

Psychological Theories and Human Learning: Kongor's Report
Guy R. Lefrancois, The University of Alberta

Comparative Animal Behavior
Richard A. Maier, Loyola University, Chicago
Barbara M. Maier

An Introduction to Cognitive Psychology
Melvin Manis, The University of Michigan

Experimental Contributions to Clinical Psychology
Erasmus L. Hoch, The University of Michigan

Readings in Ethology and Comparative Psychology
Michael W. Fox, Washington University

Readings in Ethology and Comparative Psychology

MICHAEL W. FOX
Washington University

BROOKS/COLE PUBLISHING COMPANY
MONTEREY, CALIFORNIA
A division of Wadsworth Publishing Company, Inc.

ISBN: 0-8185-0055-7
L.C. Catalog Card No: 72-82198
Printed in the United States of America
1 2 3 4 5 6 7 8 9 10–77 76 75 74 73

PREFACE

This selection of readings is designed to supplement class texts in Animal Behavior and, at the same time, to accomplish two other things: (1) to introduce the student to various experimental techniques; (2) to give the student an opportunity to begin in-depth study of various areas of ethology and comparative psychology, such as social organization, communication, behavior genetics, and effects of early experience on behavior development.

The various readings have been selected to give the reader a survey of the rich and diverse field of animal behavior. Some of the readings provide a prerequisite and basic understanding of the concepts and terminology of the European school of ethology.

The readings, covering many facets of ethology and comparative psychology, are organized into five general areas. The first section, the history of ethology and an introduction to the study of animal behavior, is followed by a basic methodology section, in which selected readings illustrate various experimental techniques that may be used effectively in the laboratory to answer certain questions about animal behavior. Subsequent sections include readings that provide further examples of techniques applicable to research in both the field and the laboratory. The areas covered in these later chapters introduce the student to social behavior, organization, and communication and to aspects of behavior genetics, behavior development, and learning. The reader should be able to use this sample of readings, as well as the many references and further suggested readings, as a starting point for in-depth specialization.

It has been said that man is two things: as a "human" he is the center of the universe; as a "being" he is a creature of circumstance. The reflective human side of his nature motivates him to explore the world around him; and with increments of experience, man increases his self-awareness. Creative inquiry, one of the most satisfying and self-actualizing experiences, is part of the essence of being human. Such satisfaction has been found by many through the study of animal and human behavior. To these ends this collection of readings is dedicated.

The editor gratefully acknowledges the advice and encouragement of Professors Bennett G. Galef, Dale F. Lott, Richard A. Maier, F. J. Mortenson, Robert M. Murphey, James M. Polt, Fred P. Valle, and Edward L. Walker in drawing up this selection of readings.

M. W. Fox

CONTENTS

I ETHOLOGY, AN INTRODUCTION 1

Ethology as a New Branch of Biology, *W. H. Thorpe* 5
The Place of Animal Behavior in Undergraduate Education, *M. W. Fox* 24
The Comparative Study of Species-Specific Behavior, *R. A. Hinde & N. H. Tinbergen* 30
Instincts and Chromosomes, What Is an "Innate" Act? *Peter H. Klopfer* 49
Suggestions for Further Reading 55

II METHODOLOGY: THE ANALYSIS OF BEHAVIOR 57

An Analysis of the Social Behaviour of the Male Laboratory Rat, *E. C. Grant* 61
Socio-infantile and Socio-sexual Signals in Canids: A Comparative and Ontogenetic Study, *M. W. Fox* 87
Effects of Morphological Variations of Chicken Models on Sexual Responses of Cocks, *Blair T. Carbaugh, M. W. Schein, & E. B. Hale* 116
Role of the Mate in the Elicitation of Hormone-induced Incubation Behavior in the Ring Dove, *R. H. Bruder & D. S. Lehrman* 125
Modification of Motivated Behavior Elicited by Electrical Stimulation of the Hypothalamus, *E. S. Valenstein, V. C. Cox, & J. W. Kakolewski* 132

Neuroethology and the Motivation of Agonistic Behavior, *Jerram L. Brown & Robert W. Hunsperger* 139
Displacement Activities and Arousal, *Juan D. Delius* 162
Suggestions for Further Reading *167*

III SOCIAL BEHAVIOR, ORGANIZATION, AND COMMUNICATION 169

The Analysis of Social Organization in Animals, *J. P. Scott* 173
The Development of Social Organisation in the Domestic Chick, *A. M. Guhl* 192
Behaviour and Life History of the Wildebeest, *Richard D. Estes* 234
Endocrines, Behavior, and Population, *John J. Christian & David E. Davis* 241
Ritualization of Animal Activities in Relation to Phylogeny, Speciation and Ecology, *J. M. Cullen* 272
Developments in the Study of Animal Communication, *P. Marler* 290
The Behavioral Significance of Pheromones in Vertebrates, *Kathryn K. Gleason & James H. Reynierse* 347
Suggestions for Further Reading *376*

IV BEHAVIOR GENETICS 377

Genes and the Evolution of Insect Behavior, *Aubrey Manning* 381
Effects of Genotype on Mouse Behaviour, *J. H. F. van Abeelen* 408
Inheritance of Behavioral and Physiological Characters of Mice and the Problem of Heterosis, *Jan H. Bruell* 421
The Effect of Reciprocal Cross-Fostering on the Behaviour of Two Species of Rodents, *Mus Musculus* and *Baiomys Taylori Ater, David M. Quadagno & Edwin M. Banks* 448
Suggestions for Further Reading *472*

V BEHAVIOR DEVELOPMENT AND EFFECTS OF EARLY EXPERIENCE 473

The Development of Ritualized Displays in Junglefowl, *J. P. Kruijt* 477
Imprinting in Birds and Primates, *Eric A. Salzen* 486
Play in Mammals, *Caroline Loizos* 513
Neurobehavioral Development and the Genotype-Environment Interaction, *M. W. Fox* 524
Suggestions for Further Reading *553*

VI COMPARATIVE PSYCHOLOGY OF LEARNING 555

Experience I: Learning, *R. A. Maier & B. M. Maier* 559
Experience II: Higher Processes, *R. A. Maier & B. M. Maier* 573
Phyletic Differences in Learning, *M. E. Bitterman* 587
Primate Learning in Comparative Perspective, *J. M. Warren* 609
Suggestions for Further Reading 647

INDEX 649

Readings in Ethology and Comparative Psychology

I ETHOLOGY, AN INTRODUCTION

The readings in this chapter provide historical background for current ethological terms and concepts. The paper by W. H. Thorpe gives a historical view of ethology emerging as a new branch of biology. The place of ethology in undergraduate education, especially as it relates to psychology and biology curricula, is then discussed by the editor. The Hinde and Tinbergen paper introduces the reader to the conceptual world of the ethologist; it shows how the science of animal behavior has developed out of a naturalistic approach to the study of various species in the field. Klopfer's short article grapples with one central issue: What is an innate or inborn act?

Ethology grew out of a combined interest of zoologists and field naturalists in the behavior of animals. The approach of Konrad Lorenz and Nikko Tinbergen, who may be regarded as founders of ethology, consisted primarily of observing the animal in its natural habitat so that its behavior could be interpreted in relation to social and ecological factors; the stimuli that evoked or released certain actions were also sought. Because behavior tends to be *adapted* to the socioenvironmental milieu, ethologists study the processes of behavior development (otogeny) and evolution (or phylogeny)–often by making comparisons between sympatric species (species that share the same habitat) and the same or closely related species adapted to different habitats or ecological niches. By means of an *ethogram* (a detailed descriptive listing of an animal's behavior in various contexts) the survival value or adaptive function, the causation, and the development of a particular behavior is elucidated. Through the species-comparison approach, exemplified by Lorenz's studies on ducks and geese, actions may be classified and species-characteristic activities used as a taxonomic basis for behavioral comparisons between species. The evolution of similar actions in the various species selected for study can then be ascertained, as well as the adaptive function of such action patterns.

Fixed-action patterns, actions that appear to be unlearned or innate, can be elicited by particular stimuli. These stimuli, known as *releasers* or sign stimuli, were studied extensively by ethologists. For example, Tinbergen found that the red belly of a male stickleback is a sign stimulus that releases aggression under certain circumstances in other males. Even a crude model of a stickleback will release this behavior if the ventral surface of the model is painted red. If the model is presented with the head pointing downward, an additional element in the aggressive display of the stickleback, it evokes an even more sustained attack. Thus, two releasers—red belly and head-down posture—can have an additive effect, which Tinbergen termed *heterogenous summation*. He also showed that some models are better releasers than the normal object; for instance, a bird might ignore its own eggs and attempt to incubate a clay egg that is ten times larger. The term *supranormal releaser* is applied to such models.

Lorenz proposed that an *innate releasing mechanism* (I.R.M.) is involved in mediating, neurophysiologically, the release of an appropriate action by a sign stimulus. The animal seems to have an innate preference for specific elements in its environment. These elements (which constitute the animal's Umwelt, or perceptual world) are the sign stimuli that evoke predictable actions via the appropriate I.R.M. Lorenz also proposed that each action pattern has its own *reaction-specific energy*, or *specific-action potential*. This "energy" tends to build up during periods when the animal is not exposed to the sign stimulus. Thus, if an animal has been deprived of food or sex for a long period, eating or sexual behavior may be evoked by a subnormal releaser. A hungry anemone will even seize sand grains dropped onto it, which it normally ignores; a bird may attempt to copulate with a tussock of grass. A leerlauf (or *vacuum*) reaction may even occur; that is, the behavior in question is apparently discharged spontaneously, in the absence of an external releaser. When the animal is approaching a state of satiation or habituation (that is, when the reaction-specific energy is depleted), a much more potent (or supranormal) releaser is required to trigger a response. Even then, an *incomplete movement* or response might occur, indicative of a low "drive" or motivational state—or, in Lorenz's frame of reference, a lowering of reaction-specific energy.

These early concepts will be explored in later chapters in the light of more recent findings.

Many of the fixed-action patterns serve a communication function as *displays*, which play an important role in social behavior such as courtship and aggression. Some displays, such as the push-ups of lizards, occur at a particular amplitude or frequency; others, such as the dog's variations in tail wagging and aggressive facial expressions, show a shift in amplitude or frequency according to the degree of arousal. (In Chapter III, the communicative function of displays is discussed in some detail.) Displays may take the form of derived actions, compromise movements, or displacements.

Derived actions are displays that are shifted, through the hypothetical evolutionary process of emancipation, from one social or motivational context to another. For example, a female bird during courtship may show infantile food-begging behavior, soliciting food and attention from the mother. Another hypothetical evolutionary process, referred to as *ritualization* (see Chapter III), is proposed to account for the stereotype of displays within members of the same species. Thus in courtship, male ducks preen in front of the female (this is displacement preening). Structural changes may also take place, so that the ritualized display is further enhanced by bright colors or by longer feathers, hair, or skin folds. In male ducks, displacement preening is coupled with wing movements and flash displays of feathers that have evolved to become bright and gaudy so as to enhance the display. Through ritualization, ambiguity is reduced and communication is enhanced.

Compromise movements are simultaneously combined actions, which through evolution have become part of the animal's behavior repertoire. A good example is the simultaneous combination of attack and flight postures in many birds; in the courtship display of the albatross, for instance, a compromise posture derived from these two actions is manifest. The courtship waltz of cock jungle-fowl contains successive and simultaneous combinations of approach and flight, and a complex series of ritualized displays, made up of derived compromise actions, is seen.

Displacement behavior may occur when an animal is in a conflict or state of ambivalence. For instance, an aggressive animal, inhibited from attacking a higher-ranking one, may begin to preen itself or peck the ground as though it were eating. If the animal, in this same state of conflict, were to attack an innocent inferior or even a tuft of grass, he would be displaying *redirected behavior*. More details and examples about these fascinating actions are given in later chapters.

Ethology as a New Branch of Biology

W. H. THORPE

The word ethology is certainly not very new. It was at least in occasional use as a zoölogical term by the end of the last century. But it is now widespread and popular use is certainly something new, and moreover many at least of those who use it are convinced that it denotes a new approach to the study of animal behavior. I propose to start by considering briefly various ways of approaching the study of animal behavior, to inquire how far any of them is new or embodies new techniques, and to consider the prospects for further development and application of such methods in one or two fields of marine biology.

There are three scientific ways of probing into the behavior of animals. Briefly, they may be called the way of the naturalist, the way of the psychologist, and the way of the physiologist. Certainly none of these three ways is new. Let us look at them a little closer and see how they have developed. Before Darwin there was very little of the scientific approach to the study of animal behavior. The physiology of that day had hardly got to the point where behavior as such was coming above its horizon. Similarly, psychology, insofar as it was scientific, was concerned solely with human beings, and naturalist writers were primarily anecdotal. Anyone who doubts this latter statement has only to look at books such as Bingley's *Animal Biography* (1829) and Couch's *Illustrations of Instinct* (1847) to be made aware how little there was, apart from straight-forward

In A. A. Buzzati-Traverso (Ed.), *Perspectives in Marine Biology*, University of California Press, 1958, pp. 411-428. Reprinted by permission.

descriptions of life history, to interest the modern zoölogist. Even Romanes, writing much later in 1882, shows similar defects, although as a physiologist he was highly and justly valued in his day. So in considering the present position of animal behavior studies, we shall not go far wrong if we start with Charles Darwin.

The publication in 1872 of *The Expression of the Emotions in Man and Animals* was an important milestone in natural history, and ultimately had a big influence on the behavior study that was to come. We will return to that a little later. Let us first consider what was happening in the physiological and psychological spheres. Thomas Willis (1664) was the real father of the concept of reflex as a scientific rather than a philosophical idea, and it would take too long and be too far removed from our present interests to attempt to trace the development of this concept, until in the hands of the nineteenth-century Russian physiologists Sechenov, Pavlov, and Bekterev it flowered into a general theory of the origin and development of the fixed inherited behavior patterns of animals. So it was that by the end of the nineteenth century, the physiological view of animal behavior was primarily that of a coördination of a very large number of simple, quick muscular movements, executed in an immediate response to simple environmental stimuli of varying degrees of complexity. The problem of the adaptation of behavior by the individual organism in response to changing conditions experienced within its life span was largely beyond the scope of physiological theory until Pavlov developed his work on the conditioning of the reflex. Then, for the first time, the reflex theory seemed to be within sight of providing a reasonably complete physiological explanation of animal behavior, and the philosophical idea of reflex, which started with Descartes and had been translated into scientific terms by Whytt, at last came into its own as a major scientific concept. Looking at it in this way, we see the justice of Sherrington's summing up of Pavlov as "Descartes' greatest successor." Perhaps the greatest merit of Pavlov's great contribution was that he isolated by his experimental procedure a single element of behavior, and was able to produce it at will in the laboratory under controlled conditions, to measure its intensity, and to measure the strength of the various stimuli influencing it. The systematic and quantitative study of reflex conditioning has of course given rise to an immense body of knowledge. R. S. Woodworth (1938) justly says,

"The conditioned reflex is perhaps no more simple than other types of learned response, and we cannot regard it as an element out of which behavior is built. But it does open a window into the dynamics of behavior and it furnishes an outlet for the investigation of the senses of animals." It is hard to exaggerate the importance of this step in the scientific study of animals. But it would be a disservice to a very great physiologist to suggest that study of the conditioned reflex in the original simple sense of both words is the only scientific way of studying the action of animals. The simplest reflex is in fact now seen as something very different from what it was originally thought to be, as well as much more complicated, and we realize now that instinctive behavior, far from being merely chain reflex, includes characteristics that cannot be derived from reflex in anything like the original sense of the term. Great as was the advance made by Pavlov, we now realize that instinct is more than reflex and learning is more than conditioning, and it is idle to pretend that they are the same.

The nineteenth-century psychologists were, as I have said, solely concerned with human beings, and almost the whole of their outlook and technique was centered upon the problems of the human mind, its feelings and emotions, and did not provide the tools required for the scientific study of animal behavior. But toward the latter part of the nineteenth century, a change began to appear in that psychologists became imbued with the concept of association which had arisen from the philosophical writings of Hobbs, Hume, and James Mill, which were slowly working through two centuries to their theoretical climax as a principle of philosophical associationism or the mechanical compounding of stimuli. Ebbinghaus (1885) was the pioneer in making practical experimental use of these ideas, and his study of human learning of nonsense syllables was an important landmark in the development of the scientific and objective study of human behavior. Thorndike was the first to undertake similar studies with animals. Whether he was influenced by Ebbinghaus or whether he evolved his ideas and methods for himself is not clear, but his studies of the behavior of cats and dogs in puzzle boxes led to a theory of animal behavior which was taken up by Watson, and became known as Behaviorism. This was fundamentally associationist or mechanist in outlook, and prided itself on being purely objective; with the implication perhaps that it was more nearly a physiological than a psychological system. Perhaps we should not have heard so much of Watson's Behaviorism had it not been that, within a few years of its publication, the work of Pavlov and Bekterev began to be known outside Russia, and so, for the first time, there seemed to be a physiological system that could be related in detail to the superficially physiological ideas behind behavioristic psychology. Behaviorism received much violent criticism, not all of it justified; for it was in some ways a laudable attempt to be objective and to purge behavior study of the uncritical anecdotal writing, so much of which was still being passed off as science at the time. But Behaviorism as a general theory of animal behavior was woefully inadequate in its original rather crude form, and in this form its day was short–although it may be said to have given rise by a long process of development, refinement, and extension to the vast system of comparative psychology, which will always be associated with the name of Hull, and may be perhaps not too unfairly paraphrased in the single sentence, "Learning only proceeds when it leads to reduction of need." "Need" in this context is not usually defined, but it is a physiological need that is implied.

The obvious deficiencies of the existing mechanist physiological approach to the study of animal behavior first became apparent to those workers who were studying the more highly developed perception of animals and man, and so it was that Wertheimer (1912), working on the visual perception of movement, and later his disciples Wolfgang Köhler and Koffka, were led to propound the concepts and theories which in due course came to be known as the Gestalt psychology. These in their turn had a far-reaching influence upon our ideas of animal behavior, and, through a quarter of a century of debate, had, in the form of various field theories, a great influence on the development and fate of Behaviorism itself.

The various schools of workers we have been discussing up to now were concerned almost exclusively with the laboratory approach. Perhaps 95 per cent of the work of physiologists was done with dogs and cats, and 99 per cent of that of the comparative psychologist with the white rat. This being so, it is hardly surprising if the picture of animal nature and behavior which emerged was distorted and incomplete. What had happened to the naturalists? Darwin was a field naturalist; yet, as Elton has shown, his promulgation of the natural-selection theory had the extraordinary result of sending students of terrestrial animals indoors for fifty or more years where, as embryologists, comparative anatomists, and at length comparative physiologists, they attempted to work out with techniques, which at the time were fresh and exciting, the full implications of the new and tremendous generalization. And natural history for the time being suffered much neglect, and it needed the stimulus of a "new" discipline, ecology, to bring naturalists interested in the terrestrial animal and its environment out into the open once again, and to make them observe and experiment in the field. With marine natural history the response was fortunately just the reverse. Darwin's oceanographical speculations offered so much promise to the marine explorer that they were never subject to quite the same danger of becoming purely laboratory zoölogists and indeed his writings gave the impetus for the founding of a number of marine stations. The effect of Darwin's work on that aspect of field natural history which used to be called bionomics until its rebirth as ecology, is seen to be closely paralleled when we look at behavior studies. It is generally true to say that field studies of behavior suffered an even longer neglect, and it was not until the reformulation of our ideas about instinct in 1935 that the field investigation of behavior once again began fully to come into its own. Just as with ecology, so the adoption of a comparable term, ethology, had an important effect in bringing this about. So we shall see that ethology in some sense represents the rebirth of one-half of a scientific natural history, and although there has been a strong tendency to reserve it for application to the particular school of behavior students who happened to be most active in bringing this rebirth about, it is in my view most undesirable to restrict it in this way. The only limitation permissible is one that stresses the fact that both animal ecology and animal ethology are branches of zoölogy, with the implication that the ethologist is looking at his problems from the point of view of one primarily interested in the animal kingdom as a whole, and not as adjunct to the study of human psychology or social relations. So I consider that ethology means the scientific study of animal behavior. And insofar as the vastly greater part of modern experimental psychology is concerned, not with theorizing about emotions, feelings, and states of mind, but with the objective study of behavior, the term can be justifiably used to cover it too.

As usual with new ideas, those about animal behavior and the new attitude accompanying them arose independently with three or four different workers. Some of the essential concepts can be found in the writings of Heinroth in Germany, Wallace Craig and Lashley in America, and Lorenz in Austria but it was only Lorenz who succeeded in welding his concepts together to form a thoroughgoing theory of animal behavior, and consequently he is rightly regarded as the founder of the new movement.

The new workers were concerned primarily with instinct, and it is easy to see the reason for this. Previous to Lorenz' appearance on the scene, hardly any scientific work on the genesis and implications of the elaborate inherited behavior patterns of animals was being carried out. Those groups that might have been expected to have developed scientific studies of instinctive behavior were either halted by an inadequate and misleading theory of instinct, or else were, perhaps for that very reason, busy with other things. The physiologists should, one thinks, have been able to make progress in this field, but they were curiously constrained by the dead hand of Pavlov. Pavlov did in fact widen the use of the term reflex so that it became first synonymous with response, and then practically meaningless. Nevertheless, he handicapped his followers by his retention of it, and by his contention that instincts are nothing but reflexes. He urged indeed that the investigation of instincts was the next important task, but none of his followers heeded this, for the simple reason that the idea of reflex did not alone provide them with the concepts necessary for the work. Perhaps partly for the same reason the "rat psychologists" were devoting all their energies to the study of learning, and the older type of comparative psychologist had, as Lorenz showed, become entangled in a rather stultifying vitalistic approach which in extreme cases tended to look upon "instincts" as something "given," to be accepted as such, and to be impossible of further analysis. Instincts were generally looked upon as directed in some mysterious teleological way toward ends that were desirable for the specific race or species to achieve. Instinct had in fact become something of a dirty word and the reaction of respectable scientific workers to it was to turn up the nose, and change the subject. Lorenz' main argument is that in each example of true instinctive behavior there is a hard core of absolutely fixed and relatively complex automatism, an inborn movement form. This restricted concept is the essence of the instinct itself; it is now usually referred to as the *fixed action* or the *fixed-action pattern*. Such action patterns are items of behavior in every way as constant as are anatomical structures, and potentially just as valuable for phylogenetic and systematic studies. Where such action patterns constitute an end point or climax of either a major or a minor chain of instinctive behavior, they have come to be known as *consummatory acts*. The internal coördination mechanism of these consummatory acts is assumed to be generating some *Specific Action Potential* (SAP). This is the internal drive, which is of the very essence of the word instinct. Both Lashley and Lorenz had realized that instead of trying to study this mysterious drive itself, and utter vague generalities about tension, nervous energy, and so forth (which were in any case useless both as explanatory concepts and as guides for future research), the way out was to describe and analyze the complex and stereotyped action systems themselves. These and their coördinating mechanisms were assumed to be the fundamental things, and the conviction was felt that a study of the mechanisms themselves might eventually throw further light on the problems of drive and of motivation. Woodworth (1938), in the field of human psychology, had already pointed out that habit mechanisms may become drives, and the similarities between habit and instinct had of course been commented upon by many workers. So it was felt that the *activation* of rigid instinctive actions was the result of the activity of specific mechanisms behind them, and the first thing to do was therefore to make as complete an inventory as possible of these fixed action patterns, study their relation to one another, the circumstances in which they appear, and as far as possible analyze them experimentally into their constituent units.

Although instinct is characterized by an internal drive, and is not simply a response to external stimulation, yet obviously instincts would be useless without an appropriate system ensuring adjustments to the external situation. So we have the concept of the *Innate Releasing Mechanism* (IRM), which assumes that within the central nervous system, there is a series of mechanisms coördinated with the more complex sense organs, which effectively inhibits or blocks all discharges of activity unless the animal encounters the right environmental situation or stimulus to remove or release the block. Furthermore, since, as everyone knows, instinctive behavior is not entirely rigid but is sometimes remarkably adaptable, the distinction was made between the preliminary adjustable introductory phrase of instinct known as *appetitive behavior* and the rigid *consummatory act*. It is in this preliminary, flexible, searching behavior that learning ability is most likely to be manifest, and intelligence has the opportunity to show itself. In a simple animal it may consist of little more than random wandering governed by simple kinesis or taxis as of the hungry wireworm (*Agriotes*), burrowing at random in search of its food. On the other hand, appetitive behavior may contain subsidiary consummatory acts, and searching behavior of great elaboration. This division into appetitive behavior and consummatory act, while as we now see relative only and not absolute, resulted in substantial experimental advance. One could now plan experiments for the investigation of both fixity and flexibility, whereas before there was no real clue as to how to begin. Moreover, by separating the taxis or steering component of behavior, which in lower invertebrates is largely reflex, from the internally activated locomotory behavior, much of the mystery and confusion associated with complex orientation began to be dispelled, and experiments became far easier and more profitable than before. Another main attraction of the scheme lay in its apparent avoidance of the vitalistic approach; for the objective of the animal is now no longer the attainment of the final biological goal or result, which it is of course inconceivable in most cases that it could know about; rather is it the performance of the rigid consummatory acts themselves. So we have a physiologically reasonable system replacing an obviously untenable vitalistic one. Finally, Lorenz' idea of internal drive, arising from the activation of the specific coördination mechanisms of the consummatory act, but held back by the block or inhibitory action of the innate releasing mechanism until the right *releaser* is encountered, at once attracts the field naturalist. For it supplies a ready explanation for a vast amount of puzzling behavior–displacement and vacuum activity–which it seems otherwise extremely difficult, if not impossible, to interpret. This theoretical system of instinct led almost directly to the hierarchy scheme of Tinbergen, according to which there are a number of tiers or levels within the total organization which makes up an instinct, and incorporated in each level are one or more innate releasing mechanisms. On the receptor side, these are in some way attuned to the biologically right stimuli or situations in the environment, as for example the appearance of the sexual partner or the specific prey, and are as it were unlocked by the appropriate environmental releasers and only by them, thus allowing behavior to proceed to the levels below only in the biologically right situation. These lower levels in their turn incorporate blocks that, although they remain unmoved, prevent action of these lower centers proceeding. So long as such lower centers remain blocked, the action potential will activate the appetitive behavior—which is directive, in the sense that it tends to bring the animal into the kind of environment where the appropriate releaser is likely to be encountered.

Since this scheme was proposed our ideas on many details of it have changed. The term center is no longer thought of, if indeed it ever was thought of, as a physically localized region in the central nervous system. The blocks are not merely blocks, but more probably antagonistic coördination mechanisms, and the channels represent causal relations of behavior and not nervous communications. Again, appetitive behavior and consummatory act are two extremes of one concept rather than two incompatible systems. Nevertheless, in spite of, or perhaps because of, these modifications, the system seems to be more valuable now in promoting and coördinating research than it has ever been.

Although many of the essential ideas of Lorenz' system can be found in the writings of earlier and contemporary writers, as a system, the whole is new in a number of respects; and it is the new relations, which it displays, rather than the novelty of its separate components which have rendered it so valuable.

The techniques of ethology, insofar as they are new, are extremely simple. From the ethologist's point of view it is important to be able to study closely the whole sequence of acts which constitute an animal's behavior. If we are studying the relation between instinct and learning, we cannot get very far without being able to rear the animal in isolation from its associates, for without this we cannot be sure we are observing the performance of a given act for the first time. Ethology, then, must be done not only in the field but also with tame and captive animals kept in the best and most natural conditions. Again, because the whole sequence of acts must be investigated, it is essential to recognize the same individual animal and observe its behavior for a significant part of its individual life. Therefore, simple forms of individual marking are essential. Since the innate releasing mechanism is one of the most important new concepts put forward, experiments must be carried out with models in which the different components or sign stimuli making up the full releaser can be tested, singly and in combination, on the animal. Since also minute investigation and inventory of the animal's actions are essential, recording by cinematograph, sound-recording apparatus, etc., are necessary.

Modern ethology has a particular interest in the fishes, for this group has provided material for some basic and highly critical studies on the hierarchical organization of instinctive behavior and on its analysis in terms not of chain reflexes but of reaction chains. Harris and Whiting (1954) have recently confirmed the conclusions of Wintrebert (1920) that the earliest contractions of the skeletal musculature of the embryo dogfish are of almost constant rhythm and entirely myogenic in origin and control. At this stage the active myotomes on the right and left sides behave as two entirely different units. Presently, although the two sides are still independent in frequency and phasing, each side may show sudden changes in frequency; this apparently being evidence of the first participation of the nervous system. Later still, coordination of the two sides appears, suggesting the first development of central nervous excitation and inhibition. From the work of Holst (1935-1937), Lissman (1946), and others it appears that the locomotory movements of the mature fish are not necessarily to be interpreted as pure instincts in the sense that the "locomotory centers" are completely independent of proprioceptive and other peripheral stimulation. Thus any "locomotory drive" which may exist must be the expression of the activity of the sensory-motor coördination system as a whole, not exclusively of the C.N.S. Moreover, the coördination of the various movements into an economical and effective locomotory pattern may well be learned as a result of mechanical necessity, and the drive itself thus be acquired. But leaving aside locomotion itself, we may ask whether there is any behavior more completely inborn.

A very thorough analysis of instinctive behavior has been provided by the work of N. Tinbergen on the mating behavior of the three-spined stickleback (*Gasterosteus aculeatus*). The male must first receive the appropriate internal and external stimuli for setting up a territory, among which stimuli the sight of green vegetation is necessary. He next constructs a nest, in choosing material for which green is again the preferred color (Wunder, 1930), and is then ready to receive and conduct a female thither for the purpose of egg-laying. The male's first reaction, the zigzag dance, is dependent on the sight of a female having the swollen abdomen which shows that she is ready to lay eggs. At this stage the special swimming movements made by the female also play a part. She in her turn reacts to the red color of the male and to his zigzag dance by swimming directly toward him. This action enables him to "lead," which simply consists of swimming rapidly toward the nest. This in turn induces the female to follow and again stimulates the male to the next action, which is to show her the nest entrance by pointing his head at it. And so the chain of behavior patterns of the two individuals proceeds, each one dependent on releasers or sign-stimuli, mostly visual, which are different for each of the links and are essential in order to enable the behavior to proceed to the next action in the series. From an example such as this it will be seen that it is perhaps not the basic *locomotory* movements themselves, but the ground plan of the overall *coördination* and *orientation* of these locomotory movements that must be inborn.[1] Some of these movements which are less specifically locomotory can probably also be regarded as inborn; for although they may have been ritualized from locomotory components, they do not themselves seem necessitated by stimuli explicable in terms of the mechanical necessities of the fluid environment. On the contrary, they seem to demonstrate much more clearly the concept of the pure instinct or "erbkoördination." Thus in the case of the three-spined stickleback the characteristic expression of the territorial phase of the reproductive instinct consists of the particular orientation of movements in patrolling and fighting activities. In the next phases it similarly consists largely of correct coördination and orientation of the movements we have just been describing. But since the orientation or taxis component is shown to be such an important part of the instinctive organization, we must inquire as to how much of the releaser system which mediates it is inborn. It now seems fairly clear from the work of Baerends, Seitz, Tinbergen, Morris, and many others that in these

[1] Dr. D. Morris tells me that if the normal nest-building pattern is continually interfered with, quite large modifications in orientation may be made.

fishes the inborn releasers are very simple sign-stimuli. These may be chemical, as Frisch has shown, for the broken cuticle of an injured minnow (*Phoxinus laevis*) may release a chemical substance that causes the school to congregate and immediately go into hiding. The releasers may also include a particular movement—such as the trembling of the courting stickleback or the typical slow, jerky swimming movement characteristic of the cichlid parent leading away its young (Baerends and Baerends-van Roon, 1950). Baerends again has shown that relative size may be an inborn releaser, for in the same cichlids the angle at which the young have to see the parent when following is fixed for a given age, and this probably prevents the young from following objects too small or too large to be a parent.

Besides movement and size, visual releasers display two other features often less easy to evaluate precisely, namely configuration and color. As an example of configuration alone providing a stimulus we may mention the outline of the breeding female stickleback and the threatening attitude adopted by a male at the boundary of his territory and directed toward an intruder of the same sex. This consists of standing in a vertical position, head pointing downward; but it is by no means the configuration only which supplies the stimulus here but probably to an even greater extent the displacement "picking" movements the male continually makes on the floor of the aquarium. In a great many instances configuration is also linked with color. Much of the earlier work on color vision in the fishes is suspect owing to lack of understanding of the difficulties of designing critical experiments, but that color vision does exist in many fishes is now well enough established. An excellent summary of the earlier work will be found in the paper by Warner (1931). Noble and Curtis (1939), in their studies of the jewel fish, found that the young were attracted to red and suggested that this attraction was related to the breeding colors of the adults. The females were found to recognize their own males as individuals by means of the color pattern on the head, for if the whole body of the male except the head were covered, the female still recognized her mate. If, however, the faces were painted and the rest of the body left its natural color, the recognition was no longer shown. The parent fish were found to distinguish their own young from those of other species by the color of the face, for if the young fish were stained an abnormal color, they were rejected by their parents. These authors succeeded in inducing *Hemichromis* to rear the young of *Cichlasoma bimaculatum* and produced evidence that the color preference of these young was very largely learned. That conditioning in the early life can affect the response to colors of several species of cichlids seems to be fairly clear both from the work of Noble and Curtis and from Baerends and Baerends-van Roon. But there seems little doubt, from the work of the latter authors, that in some species there is a strong inborn preference for a particular color and this preference can be affected only very slightly by experience. Seitz (1940), studying the genus *Tilapia* (mouth-breeders in which there is a marked difference between the reproductive color patterns of male and female), has shown that simple models do not release courting in the male, which apparently has a very detailed and presumably conditioned knowledge of female characters. It is assumed that this learning process can take place in the schools of immature fishes showing markings very similar to the color pattern of the ripe female. The *Tilapia* male, however, apparently cannot recognize the reproductive markings of a male of its species, nor indeed can the female, for a male that assumes this color immediately isolates itself in a territory. In *Astatotilapia* also Seitz found that fighting could be released by quite simple models and both male and female in this genus possess an inborn knowledge of the form and probably the color pattern of the male. But although, as such studies show, learning abilities may play an important part even in such closely organized instinctive behavior chains as these, nevertheless extraordinarily few cases have as yet been investigated. There is an immense field of work now open to the student both of marine and fresh-water forms.

The schooling behavior of fishes is certainly one of the most characteristic features of the life of the group, and a study of its course naturally leads on to the investigation of visual releasers; for it is clear that vision is the chief sense governing social behavior in this group. Critical studies of social behavior have long been under way in this country, particularly by Parr, Breder, and his associates at the Marine Laboratory at Bimini in the Bahamas. It was my good fortune to visit this station four years ago and see something of its work in progress, but I feel sure that many of you here are quite as familiar with it as I am, so I shall pass it over lightly. But I think we can summarize the subject very briefly by saying that although there is abundant evidence for the development of the schooling response by a learning process, it is in most cases extremely difficult to distinguish between the effect of this and the possibility that an inborn recognition of the species pattern is slowly maturing. Most young fish school heterogeneously and very strongly; an aquarial life of a few months as an adult is often sufficient to inhibit this, and it would seem fairly clear that the concepts both of learning and of maturation are necessary to account for the many variations of behavior which have been described. The schooling is of interest also in that it seems to be such a distinct behavior pattern, and one not necessarily linked with any of the main instinctive urges. I feel convinced that one must at present regard it as evidence of a distinct social instinct, sufficient in itself and in some species at least, independent of the instincts of feeding and reproduction–although no doubt likely to be valuable in both these connections. This is an important conclusion for our science, for ethologists, notably Tinbergen, have been reluctant to allow the existence of social instinct in its own right. So I should like to see much more investigation directed toward unraveling the complex interrelations of inborn and learned responses in the schooling behavior of fish. I also hope that the new techniques in marine biology will soon give us more information about the survival value of school formation. The advantages of schooling for fish with poor vision might well be that the species is safer in a group since many pairs of eyes are better than one; but is there a real advantage when it comes to feeding behavior? One would like to know whether species that feed on large particles, which have to be searched for but when found can provide food for many individuals, may be more successful when hunting in groups; just as the feeding flock is an inefficient technique for birds that have to survive the nonbreeding season under hard conditions. There is already impressive evidence that fish learn more rapidly and efficiently when the individuals are grouped (Welty, 1934).

The territorial behavior of fishes is another subject that strikes me as particularly promising for future investigation. The term "territory" should strictly be reserved for a defended area, and as far as I know, the evidence for area defense by fish in the nonreproductive state is still somewhat inconclusive. It is certainly an important aspect of the biology of inshore fishes. Territory holding, as apart from territorial defense, is common in fresh-water fishes, and is certainly very obvious in many marine species that dwell in nooks and crannies of coastal rocks and coral reefs. The evidence that territorial recognition is normally based on vision is so overwhelming that it need hardly be discussed, but of course there are exceptions, particularly among fresh-water fish living in very turbid water. It is interesting that the electric fishes *Gymnarchus* (Lissmann, 1958) can use their electric organs and electric sensitivity to aid territorial recognition. The tendency to take up residence in a particular spot, even though the fish is not in the reproductive phase, is of course already well known to aquarists, and there is evidence (Braddock, 1949) that prior residence in an area gives an individual of the species *Platypoecilus maculatus* greater potentiality for dominion over its fellows than it would otherwise have. The effect is mainly upon the initial contacts with other individuals, and tends to fade as time passes. The exploits of aqualung divers have already indicated how widespread is this habit of establishing nonreproductive territories, and the workers at the Lerner Marine Station at Bimini are familiar with the extraordinary spectacle of subtropical reef fishes in the marine enclosures seeking out the same "sleeping places" night after night.

What has already been said about schooling will have made clear that there is much behavior suggesting social facilitation in fishes. Gudger (1944) has given a number of interesting records of follow-my-leader behavior in both swimming and leaping fish, although in most of these cases no particular advantage appears to accrue from the behavior. Breder and Halpern say that it is common knowledge among aquarists that in order to get a fish to feed it is often necessary to show it a companion feeding, a companion that need not necessarily be of the same species. Baerends and Baerends-van Roon (1950) report that the cichlids they had kept appeared to live in schools till they reached maturity and that it was typical of those schools that the members continually showed a preference to perform the same action simultaneously. "Sometimes they are all engaged in foraging on the bottom, and then again we will find them all scraping *algae* from the glass walls, floating quietly in the water, or lying together on the bottom. That they can experience the same emotional reaction simultaneously is illustrated by the following observations on *Tilapia natalensis*. These fish, when immature and living in schools, show either a pattern of vertical bars or two longitudinal bands. The latter pattern they assume when not disturbed, the former when they feel anxiety. Now, as soon as we brought a small *Hemichromis* into a tank containing a school of *Tilapias* showing the longitudinal bands, all at once assumed the cross bands. From this we conclude that they all became anxious irrespective of whether they individually had been affected or not. When living together in a territorial society such sharp, simultaneous reactions to events in a certain territory do not occur." The most careful experiments on the group learning of fishes have been those of Welty (1934). He found that a maze was learned by goldfish more quickly when they were grouped than when they were isolated. Putting a trained fish in the maze will speed up the learning of untrained fish. This group facilitation is attributed to three related causes: (1) group cohesion based on vision, (2) mass-habituation (which the author describes as "interreassurance"), and (3) group-interaction stimulating exploratory activity. However, none of these three categories can be considered as evidence of true imitation; rather they are three special cases of social facilitation. Welty, however, has some further observations rather more puzzling. Thus, for instance, he found that a goldfish learns to run a simple maze more rapidly after having seen another goldfish run it. This seems to be owing (*a*) to reassurance that the stimulus was not followed by harmful results, so that there was a mutual quietening effect, and (*b*) to learning, through visual cohesion, to move forward at the time the stimulus was presented. Untrained fishes were sometimes seen even to precede the trained fish in moving toward the stimulus in their respective chambers. It seems fairly clear that this latter group of observations, (*b*), can again be explained as social facilitation together with local enhancement. There does, however, remain a doubt as to the first class, (*a*), of observations. This, at first sight, seems to be owing to an appreciation by one fish of the lack of harmful results subsequent to the behavior of the other fish. If this could be established it would seem to be evidence of true imitation, but there seems to remain the possibility that the quiet behavior of the fish being tested had a quietening effect on its associate. Morrow (1948) considers that the shape of Welty's learning curves indicates typical trial-and-error learning, which would not be expected if imitation were actually in operation. Welty also found that numbers of goldfish *retain* motor responses better than do isolated fishes, but the explanation of this retention is not understood. Besides these and many similar experiments with goldfish, Welty found that paradise fish (*Macropodus opercularis*), the zebra fish (*Brachydanio rerio*), and shiners (*Notropis atherinoides*) eat more per fish when in groups than when kept singly. Welty's work on the superiority of groups of fishes over single fishes in maze-learning experiments has been confirmed by Greenberg (1947) in work with the green sunfish (*Lepomis cyanellus*). He found that the biggest individual tends to be the leader, although leadership at the maze shifted at almost every trial. Subordinates appear to lessen tension among territory-holding fishes, and removal of the "omega" from aquaria with three territories increased aggressive behavior among those remaining, whereas the introduction of a new fish led to their attacking it instead of one another.

Before leaving the subject of the evidence for psychologically higher types of behavior in fish, I would like to make a brief reference to behavior we describe colloquially as play. Behavior that appears playlike can often be seen in fishes, particularly in nest building—as in the stickleback (Iersel, 1953)—but there seems good reason for thinking that many such examples represent only the simplest transference activity, and do not require any concepts as elaborate and subtle as those implied by the term play. But there do seem to be some well-authenticated examples of what seem like true play in addition. Thus Brahm has a long account of the apparently playful squirting of water by "shooters" (*jaculator*) at an aquarium keeper personally known to them. Such a record may savor too much of anecdote and I may be thought unwise to quote it. But many other naturalists and psychologists have described other examples suggestive of true play and some of these accounts seem sufficiently precise to suggest that a critical investigation of the subject in fish would be well worthwhile.

In what I have said, I have cast a brief glance at a few types of investigation which seem to me to be particularly promising for ethologists who have at their disposal the facilities and techniques supplied by the modern marine biological station. But I could have chosen many other examples for mention, and it has largely been a matter of personal choice and interest. I hope, however, I have said enough to show that ethology, although only new in a rather limited and special sense of the word, has great significance for the future of marine biology, and I hope that this conference may be a means of securing coöperation and understanding between the two groups of investigators.

REFERENCES

Baerends, G. P., and J. M. Baerends-van Roon, 1950 An introduction to the ethology of cichlid fishes. *Behavior Supplement.* 1: 1-243.

Bingley, W., 1829 *Animal biography*, 7th ed.; London, Ribington. 4 vols.

Braddock, J. C., 1949 The effect of prior residence upon dominance in the fish *Platypoecilus maculatus. Physiol. Zool.* 22: 161-169.

Couch, J., 1847 *Illustrations of instinct*. London, John Van Voorst, 343 pp.

Darwin, C., 1872 *The expression of the emotions in man and animals.* London, John Murray, 387 pp.

Ebbinghaus, H., 1885 *Uber das Gedachtnis: Untersuchungen zur experimentellen Psychologie*. Leipzig. (Translated as *Memory: a contribution to experimental psychology*.) New York, Teachers' College, 1913.

Greenberg, B., 1947 Some relations between territory, social hierarchy and leadership in the green sunfish (*Lepomis cyanellus*). *Physiol. Zool*. 20: 267-299.

Gudger, E. W., 1944 Fishes that swim heads to tails in single file. *Copeia.* 1944: 152-154.

Harris, J. E., and H. P. Whiting, 1954 Control of rhythmical activity in the skeletal muscle of the embryonic dogfish. *J. Physiol.* 124: 63.

Holst, E. von, 1935-1937 Vom Wesen der Ordnung im Zentralnervensystem. *Naturwiss.* 25: 625-631, 641-647.

Iersel, J. J. A. van, 1953 An analysis of the parental behaviour of the male three-spined stickleback. *Behaviour Suppl.* III: 1-59.

Lissmann, H. W., 1946 The neurological basis of the locomotory rhythms in the spinal dogfish (*Scyllium canicula, Acanthias vulgaris*). I. Reflex behaviour. II. The effect of de-afferentiation. *J. Exp. Biol.* 23: 143-161, 162-176.

Lissmann, H. W., 1958 (Untitled; in press.)

Morrow, J. E., 1948 Schooling behaviour in fishes. *Quart. Rev. Biol.* 23: 27-38.

Noble, G. K., and B. Curtis, 1939 The social behaviour of the jewel fish, *Hemichromis bimaculatus*, Gill. *Amer. Mus. Nat. Hist. Bull.* 76: 1-46.

Seitz, A., 1940 Die Paarbildung bei einigen Cichliden. I. Die Paarbildung bei Astatotilapia strigigena. *Z. Tierpsychol*. 4: 40-84.

Warner, L. H., 1931 The problem of colour vision in fishes. *Quart. Rev. Biol.* 6: 329-348.

Welty, J. C., 1934 Experiments on group behaviour of fishes. *Physiol. Zool.* 7: 85-127.

Wertheimer, M., 1912 Experimentelle Studien über das Sehen von Bewegung. *Z. Psychol.* 61:161-265.

Wintrebert, P., 1920 La contraction rhythmée aneurale des myotemes chez les embryons de sélaciens. *Arch. Zool. exp. gen.* 60:221-245.

Woodworth, R. S., 1938 *Experimental psychology*. New York, Columbia Univ. Press, 889 pp.

Wunder, W., 1930 Experimentelle Untersuchungen am Driestachligen Stickling (*Gasterosteus aculeatus*) während der Laichzeit. *Z. Morph. ü Ök. Tiere.* 16. 453-498.

The Place of Animal Behavior in Undergraduate Education

M. W. FOX

Psychology and biology undergraduate curricula have changed significantly since the days of mazes and memory drums, pickle-pots and smoke drums. Until recently there has been respectively an overemphasis on the molecular approach to biology and, in psychology, an artificial laboratory approach to the analysis of pigeon and male rat "behaviorisms" that evaluates more the dexterity and imagination of the experimenter than of the animal's behavioral repertoire. Without integration with other related areas, such reductionistic pursuits are of very limited value. Educational programs may become fragmented into unstructured and unrelated "packets" of information. The final product of this programming is an overspecialized technologist who, as a teacher, carries on a tradition that effectively turns off many bright students from electing a career in biology or psychology.

Not only because of these reasons, the biology and psychology curricula are also being examined and revised in the light of increased public and political concern about the state of the biosphere and the quality of life: pollution, overpopulation, conservation, depletion of natural resources, mental health, child development, and so on. Biology and psychology are undoubtedly two disciplines most relevant to man's current problems.

Animal Behavior is one field that can give students a feel for the intrinsic complexities of organismic and socioecological systems,

Adapted from M. W. Fox, "The place of animal behavior in the biology curriculum." In *Bioscience*, 1971, 21, 977-980. Reprinted by permission of the publisher, American Institute of Biological Sciences.

and at the same time enable them to acquire the skills for research. This field also bears upon several relevant issues, which will be briefly enumerated below, and also integrates many diverse aspects of biology and experimental psychology, including endocrinology, neurophysiology, genetics and evolution, natural history, ecology, communication, and social organization. Animal behavior is poorly represented in many departments, for few educators are aware of the scope of the subject. In essence, animal behavior enables the teacher to bring in the facts of physiology as well as behavioral adaptation to the environment. Another way of looking at animal behavior studies is to regard the field as providing a holistic picture of the evolution and ecology of the individual and of social groups. A course in ecology or social psychology would therefore be inadequate without reference to ethological studies, and vice versa.

Scherba (1965) in his survey reports that "the manner and extent to which animal behavior is currently presented in General Biology (texts) is grossly inadequate, frequently outdated, and occasionally absurd." Reference to animal behavior often occurs as a final adjunct to sections on ecology or structure and function of the nervous system, and Scherba finds that the antiquated dichotomy "Is the behavior innate (or instinctive) or is it learned?" is unfortunately still being presented to students as a vital question. Similarly, in introductory psychology texts animal behavior is often passed over as a side issue—when historically, in fact, psychology began partly as a philosophic and naturalistic approach to animal and human behavior. Many contemporary experimental psychologists use the animal as part of the experimental equipment to test some hypothesis, but to give students prematurely this one perspective is not good education: merely a technologist may emerge. The student should be encouraged to observe the behavior of his subject before generating certain questions. The ethologist looks at an animal and discovers many questions while the experimental psychologist finds a suitable animal to answer his own questions. Both conceptual approaches are not mutually exclusive, but it is logical that a student should begin with some degree of objectivity and first look at the animal. A succession of generations of researchers testing and modifying each other's hypotheses, moving further away from the realities of behavioral adaptation and organization which they originally studied, might then be avoided.

Scherba also notes with surprise that an area of biology which is of great interest to professional biologists receives inadequate treatment in modern introductory tests. The reason for this, he feels, lies in the formerly widely held view that details about behavior lie in the province of psychology. (And yet psychology texts contain little about behavior outside of the laboratory setting.) The ethologist does use some of the research methods of the psychologist, but the questions asked and the philosophy behind his research is closer to biology than to classical psychology.

Behavior may be defined as a response to a change in the internal or external environment. In order to explain it, one must bring in many of the basic branches of biology and psychology, including genetics, physiology (especially neuroendocrinology), embryology, ecology, taxonomy, and learning theory. Animal behavior, therefore, provides a means by which a functional course in general biology or psychology might be organized, as emphasized by J. P. Scott (1962).

Scherba (1965) suggests that students in general biology (and in introductory psychology) should be confronted with data which pertain to the following generalizations.

1. That the behavioral repertoire exhibited by an animal is closely dependent upon the kind and complexity of its nervous system, including receptors and the nature of its anatomical structures.

2. That the expression of behavioral response is dependent upon stimuli, often quite specific; upon the environmental setting in which the animal finds itself; and upon the internal state of the animal. A close relationship exists between physiological determinants, such as hormones, and the expression of behavior, as in sexual behavior of vertebrates.

3. As in other fundamental characteristics of organisms, the expression of behavior alters with changes in development, with maturational changes, and also with experience. The extent to which experience affects behavior varies continuously from behavioral acts which are not altered by experience to those whose expression is completely guided by experience. It is an important task of the scientist in analyzing behavior to determine the extent of the contribution of experience to the expressions of a behavioral act or pattern.

4. Behavior is adaptive and functions indispensably in the survival of animals—as in orientation, nest building, feeding, defense, parental care, etc.

5. Many patterns of behavior in a wide array of animals are periodic with variations in periodicity from circadian rhythms to annual and several-year cycles.

6. The capacity for the expression of behavioral patterns is inherited.

7. Behavior has evolved, and the expression of behavior can affect the evolution of a species, as in the isolating effects of courtship and activity patterns.

At the population level, students should become aware of the nature and organization of several kinds of interspecific and intraspecific groups and relationships, including parasitism; symbioses; aggregations; herds, flocks, and schools; families and societies.

Despite the enormous diversity of animal groups, certain widespread characteristics are prevalent. These include the existence of dominance hierarchies, the establishment of territories, and a division of labor. Probably all animals communicate at some point in their life, and the role of communication mechanisms in social behavior needs to be presented.

Finally, students should be alerted that the study of animal behavior is in an incipient state and that there remains much to be learned (Scherba, 1965).

A few specific examples of some of the ways that an understanding of animal behavior may help a person to understand his own life and society better than he can do through a traditional introductory biology or psychology course will now be offered. Over the past five years several popular books—*The Naked Ape* and *The Human Zoo* by Desmond Morris, *On Aggression* by Konrad Lorenz, and Robert Ardrey's *African Genesis, The Territorial Imperative*, and *The Social Contract*—have stimulated a great deal of interest in animal and human behavior among the general public. These writings, which essentially "ethologize" many objective animal studies into often sensational but unfounded analogies of human behavior, deserve some rigorous and critical analysis. There is much to learn from studying the human animal; and in the correct, disciplined, and cautious comparative approach, animal studies can provide the student with some understanding of the evolution of social behavior and adaptive significance of certain rituals, which in animals are largely inherited but which in man are also acquired culturally.

A knowledge of nonhuman primate social organization and communication would give the student a clearer picture of the biological basis for many aspects of human behavior. His thinking would then be less superficial and his knowledge more competent for dealing with some of the unfounded speculations and analogies that are being currently published and which generally remain unchallenged. A knowledge of the biological evolutionary antecedents of human behavior would also put the cultural influences on human behavior in a clearer and more logical perspective. The student would then be cognizant of the "biology versus culture" dichotomy, which, like the "nature versus nurture" controversy, causes a polarization of interacting and interdependent processes and merely poses a sterile pseudo-question. Awareness of such interacting processes would serve to educate the student toward a more mature and sophisticated approach to the understanding of living (rather than conceptual) systems.

But why study the sex life of sticklebacks, the courtship displays of ring doves, or the pecking patterns of barnyard hens? Some anthropocentric critics feel that this is frivolous indulgence by eccentrics that even claim sometimes to gain some insight into human nature from wolves, geese, sticklebacks, and fruitflies. In reality such studies, like any basic science topic, are rewarding in their own right and provide sufficient intellectual stimulation and personal creative involvement to warrant neither defense nor criticism. But, as emphasized earlier, criticism is necessary when tenuous analogies are drawn between animal and human behavior. Some behavior studies are more relevant, notably problems of population regulation, communication, social organization, aggression, crowding stress, effects of early experience such as "handling," environmental "enrichment," imprinting, and socialization. It is here that the enlightened student could bring his knowledge to bear upon current problems of society: such knowledge could potentially reveal important variables which might otherwise be overlooked, because man is not only a cultural being but also a social animal. It is perhaps through the comparative and interdisciplinary approach that we may increase our knowledge and awareness of the phenomenon of life and, in particular, enhance the development of our own species where potentials have been neither explored nor fully developed. Animal studies are essential, for without such basic research no findings on human development could be safely put into an evolutionary perspective. Culture is a phenomenon almost unique to the higher primates and most highly evolved in man. Animal studies will reveal precultural or basic biological developmental phenomena which might then be looked for and dissected from interacting cultural influences in man. Cross-cultural studies, analogous to interspecies comparative studies in animals and at present almost the exclusive domain of a few social anthropologists, could also be investigated from the ethologist's perspective.

There are many advantages in the interdisciplinary (and interdepartmental) approach to education, and the integrative science of animal behavior can do much to structure this kind of teaching program. It is hoped that this introduction has demonstrated the relevance of animal behavior to undergraduate education, where the student, be he a science major or not, may profit by the factual and conceptual enrichment that can be gained in this field.

REFERENCES

Scherba, G. M. (1965) Animal behavior in the general biology course. Paper presented at Symposium on Undergraduate Instruction in Animal Behavior, Berkeley, Calif. Sponsored by Animal Behav. Soc. of America.

Scherba, G. M. (1967) Animal behavior in the introductory biology course. *Amer. Biol. Teacher,* **29**: 523-527.

Scott, J. P. (1962) Animal behavior as a biological discipline. *Amer. Biol. Teacher,* **24**: 91-95.

The Comparative Study of Species-Specific Behavior

R. A. HINDE

N. TINBERGEN

INTRODUCTION. AIMS AND METHODS

Aims

Species-specific behavior is in part the product of evolutionary processes. Likewise, the behavior of a species must influence the course of its evolution. These two interrelated problems—the influence of evolutionary processes on behavior and of behavior on evolution—comprise a large field about which little is yet known. This chapter is concerned mainly with the first, namely how behavior changes in evolution. It is also confined primarily to behavior which is more or less characteristic of the species, and thus discusses only one aspect of the whole problem.

Methods

In studying evolution, the ethologist is in a different position from the morphologist. Direct evidence about the ancestral species, which morphologists can obtain from paleontology, is not available; and ontogenetic evidence has so far been little help, though it may be more widely used in future. Comparison between living taxonomic units is thus the only method available, and this is naturally indirect.

However, by comparing the behavior traits of species whose phylogenetic relationships are established, it is possible to make hypotheses about the probable origins of that behavior, and thus about the course of its evolution.[1] In doing this, the ethologist must start by relying on the currently accepted classification of the group he is studying. This is usually satisfactory, but sometimes the results of behavior study clash with the classificatory scheme previously in use. In such cases a reappraisal of all characters, morphological and behavioral, may lead to a revision of the classification. Circular arguments are thus avoided by the same method that is used by comparative morphologists, namely the use of independent sources of evidence about the systematic relationships of the species studied.

Use of the comparative method in studying the evolution of behavior then involves several distinct steps. First, formal similarities in the behavior patterns of the species concerned must be recognized. Since the species are believed to be closely related on other grounds, such similarities suggest that the behavior elements have a common evolutionary origin. However, similarity between behavior elements does not necessarily mean identity,[2] for minor differences between species will occur. Examination of these differences, together with evidence about the causation and function of the behavior elements, enables hypotheses to be erected about which behavior form is the more primitive (i.e. phylogenetically older). This in turn permits hypotheses about the probable origins of the behavior elements, and the differences between their present condition and their probable origin can be described. The result is a tentative description of the

[1] The use of the comparative method in the study of behavior owes much to the pioneering studies of Whitman (1919), Heinroth (1911, 1928) and Lorenz (1935, 1939, 1941). Among the groups now being studied are salticid spiders (Crane, 1948-50), grasshoppers (Jacobs, 1950; Faber, 1953), mantids (Crane, 1952), *Drosophila* (Spieth, 1950, 1952), spider wasps and digger wasps (Evans, 1953, 1955), fiddler crabs, (Crane, 1941), cichlid fish (Seitz, 1940, 1941, 1949; Baerends and Baerends, 1950), sticklebacks (Tinbergen, e.g. 1951; van Iersel, 1953; Morris, 1958), ducks and geese (Heinroth, 1911, 1928; Lorenz, 1941), fringilline and cardueline finches (Hinde, 1953, 1954, 1955, 1956; Marler, 1956), old world buntings (Andrew, 1956b), estrildine finches (Morris, in press), and gulls (Goethe, 1937; Tinbergen, 1953; Tinbergen and Broekhuysen, 1954; Moynihan, 1955a; Cullen, 1957).

[2] The precise meaning to be attached to "similarity" will vary with the nature of the behavioral character and the diversity of the taxonomic group. Since the gaps between the units within a taxonomic group are usually smaller than the gaps between groups, "similar" usually means less different within the group than between the group and other groups. A comparable difficulty of course arises in morphological work and is met in the same way.

way the behavior has changed in evolution; this is the most that can be expected from descriptive comparative studies.

A knowledge of the probable course of evolution prompts further enquiry as to why evolution has taken that course and not some other. It is thus desirable to know whether the changes are adaptive and can have been brought about by selection. This involves a study of the survival value of the behavior elements and of the inter-species differences, as well as further investigation into the causal and functional relationships between the behavior elements.

Selection of Characters for Study

As in morphology, successful use of the comparative method depends on the selection of the characters to be compared. A major problem is one of level of complexity: how far is the behavior to be analysed before its parts are compared? Both because there is no direct evidence about the behavior of extinct forms, and because convergences are widespread, most of the studies made hitherto have dealt with relatively small behavior elements within groups of closely related species. The conclusions drawn from such studies thus refer at most to microevolution. Although quite complex behavior traits, such as the communal nesting habits of the Crotophaginae (Davis, 1942) and the parasitic habit in cuckoos (Friedmann, 1929), have sometimes been used successfully in comparative work, the results of such studies are often difficult to assess until a further analysis of the characters has been undertaken.

Ultimately it will be desirable to make comparative studies not only of overt behavior but also of the causal mechanisms underlying it. However, since the motor patterns are directly observable, it is these which have been studied most often. Heinroth and Whitman were among the first to point out that species-characteristic movements (the "fixed action patterns") can be isolated from the total motor behavior, and the results obtained by many later workers have confirmed the value of these for comparative work.

One further point about the selection of characters for comparative study must be discussed. All characters of the living animal, behavioral and morphological, are products of environmental factors as well as of inherent potentialities. The student of evolution must therefore always ensure that the differences he is investigating are in fact indicative of genetic diversity and not merely of dissimilar environments. Special care is needed in behavior studies because of the plasticity introduced by learning processes.

In the past, as Lehrman (1953), Beach (1955), and others have pointed out, ethologists have often been too ready to assume that learning does not enter into the development of "instinctive" patterns. (But see also Koehler 1954.) Recently, for instance, it has been shown that an inexperienced ring dove (*Streptopelia risoria*) will not walk up to its chick in order to feed it: this has to be learned (Lehrman, 1955). Similarly, Craig (1912) showed that drinking is not elicited in young doves by the sight of water; the response to the visual characteristics of water has to be conditioned.

On the other hand, the opposite tendency has also occurred: many authors have overestimated the part played by learning and underestimated the widespread occurrence of "unlearned" behavior. To cite but two examples, Sauer's (1956) very detailed observations on *Sylvia borin* show that the complete repertoire of species-characteristic movements and calls is performed by birds raised without their parents. Second, female canaries which have never manipulated anything but fine grain show all the movements of nest building before they have had material to build with, and treat such material appropriately as soon as it is presented. Of course such observations do not show that learning processes do not enter into the development of the elements of the behavioral patterns in question, but only that the species-characteristic patterns develop and are given appropriately in the absence of example or reward.

However, for the present purpose the relevant problem is not whether a given character is independent of learning or not but whether and to what extent behavioral differences between species are due to hereditary differences, that is whether they are innate.[3] This can be decided by raising two species in the same environment: if specific differences persist, then these must ultimately be due to hereditary differences. For instance, the Heinroths (1928) have given numerous examples of interspecific differences in behavior which persist even in individuals reared in the same artificial environment.

[3] Some semantic clarification is perhaps required here. In the past the term "innate" has been applied in ethology to both characters and the differences between characters. Various critics (Beach, 1955; Lehrman, 1953; Spurway, 1953) have pointed out that the application of the term to characters is misleading, since these are the result of continuous interaction between environment and inherent potentialities throughout development. In this paper, therefore, "innate" is applied only to differences (Tinbergen, 1955).

To cite another example, great tits (*Parus major*) or blue tits (*Parus caeruleus*) taken from the nest eight days after hatching and reared by hand deal with large food items (e.g. mealworms) by placing them under their feet and pecking at them. The use of the feet appears first, in an incomplete form, at about seventeen days, and learning clearly enters into its perfection. Chaffinches bred from eggs which were hatched and reared for eight days by tits, and subsequently fed by hand, only rarely use the foot in feeding.[4] Thus this difference in the use of the foot is basically hereditary, even though learning plays an important part in its development.

This exemplifies a principle of great importance: many of the differences between species do not lie in the first instance in stereotyped behavior sequences but consist in the possession of a propensity to learn. Thus the production of the species-characteristic song by chaffinches (*Fringilla coelebs*) depends on learning from other singing males, but a chaffinch will not imitate any sound it hears—only those having certain characteristics in common with normal chaffinch song (Thorpe, 1954, 1956; see also Heinroth, 1928; Sauer, 1954). However, although the ontogeny of behavioral characters is as yet largely unexplored, there is a wealth of material showing that interspecies differences in motor patterns of the kind most commonly used in comparative studies are almost invariably innate. On the other hand, differences in responsiveness to releasing stimuli are sometimes due to conditioning and sometimes innate. A check on the relative roles of inherent and environmental factors in the production of interspecies differences is thus even more necessary when comparing responsiveness than when comparing motor patterns.

THE EVOLUTION OF COURTSHIP AND THREAT DISPLAYS IN BIRDS

To exemplify the use of these methods in comparative work we will now consider some of the conclusions reached about the evolution of the threat and courtship displays of birds. Courtship behavior has been much used in comparative studies because of the rela-

[4] Of course the intra-egg environment differed, but even this is presumably ultimately largely under genetic control.

tively stereotyped postures involved and the extent of interspecies diversity.

A Preliminary Causal Analysis of the Displays

It is first necessary to consider some results obtained in the causal analyses of such displays. Recent studies of both fishes and birds have shown that a threatening animal has two incompatible tendencies: to attack its rival and to flee from it. Similarly a courting bird has three incompatible tendencies: to attack, flee from, and behave sexually toward its mate (e.g. Tinbergen, 1952, 1953; Hinde, 1952, 1953). The nature of the behavior shown at any stage in the courtship depends on the strengths and relative strengths of these conflicting tendencies.

Among fishes and birds species differ in the relative importance of these tendencies. In some the male is markedly aggressive to the female throughout the reproductive season (e.g. three-spined stickleback, *Gasterosteus aculeatus*, Tinbergen and van Iersel, in preparation; river bullhead, *Cottus gobio*, Morris, 1954b), while in others he is afraid of her most of the time (e.g. chaffinch, *Fringilla coelebs*, Hinde, 1953; Marler, 1956; zebra finch, *Poephila guttata*, Morris, 1954a). Among many passerines the male is dominant early in the season and the female later, the time at which the change in dominance occurs varying between species: as the relative strengths of these tendencies change, there are correlated changes in the courtship displays (Tinbergen, 1953; Hinde, 1955). In a few species the male's tendencies to attack and flee are relatively insignificant and the courtship is primarily a result of sexual thwarting (e.g. Mexican swordtail, *Xiphophorus helleri*, Morris, 1955). Among fringilline and cardueline finches most of the components (e.g. wing raising, tail spreading, etc.) of the courtship displays are associated with one or the other of these three tendencies. The relations between display components and tendencies are similar in all the species and interspecific hybrids so far studied, and are probably widespread among passerines. The species differences in display thus lie primarily in the relative intensities of components.

The Evolutionary Origin of Display Movements

Comparison of the display movements of related species leads to the establishment of homologies. Behavior elements from the different species can thus be grouped together as having a similar evolutionary origin. Examination of the diversity shown by the homologous elements, coupled with the results of causal and functional analyses, provides indications of the evolutionary origins of the movements. This method has so far revealed three primary sources of display movements. From these the displays as seen today have become elaborated, presumably through the action of selection on genetic variability.

1. Intention movements. These are the preparatory and incomplete movements which often appear at the beginning of an activity; for instance, a bird about to fly crouches, raises its wings and tail, withdraws its neck, and then reverses these movements as it springs off. Many avian displays have been elaborated from such movements (Daanje, 1950).

2. Displacement activities. This term is used here in a broadly descriptive sense for activities which appear at first sight irrelevant in the situation in which they occur; for instance, the bill wiping, preening, and feather movements which often appear during avian courtship. (Tinbergen, 1952). Their causation is still poorly understood, but there seems little doubt that many displays have been elaborated from them. In each case the evidence that present-day display postures have evolved from these sources is comparative. Often the display movement can be compared with the unritualized movement as it occurs in the same species. In other cases species can be found in which the evolutionary changes undergone by a particular display movement are relatively slight, and which therefore form a link between the highly elaborated cases and their presumed source.

3. Redirection activities. When the expression of behavior toward the object which elicited it is inhibited, it is sometimes redirected onto another object. Thus the aggressive behavior of the male black-headed gull, elicited by its mate, is often redirected onto other nearby gulls (Moynihan, 1955a, 1955b).

Sometimes a display posture of one type becomes secondarily modified into another. Thus some threat postures, themselves derived from intention movements, have become secondarily modified for courtship. Here the evidence is partly comparative and partly ontogenic; in the chaffinch the threat behavior of the male toward the female changes gradually into courtship as his sexual tendency increases (Marler, 1956).

Elaboration of Display Movements in Evolution

When the evolutionary origins of the display movements have been provisionally identified, the changes which they have undergone in evolution can be described. Although the precise ways in which intention movements and displacement activities have become elaborated into display are still imperfectly understood, some principles are becoming clear (Tinbergen, 1954).

1. Development of conspicuous structures and further correlation of the movement with the structures. Most display movements show off a conspicuous structure. Although it is often found that a similar movement shows off quite different structures in related species, so that the movement appears to be primary and the structure secondary, there has probably always been a parallel elaboration of structure and movement. Thus among tits (*Parus* spp.) there is a correlation between the degree of elaboration of the "head-up" threat posture and the development of a conspicuous throat and breast coloration (Hinde, 1952). Further, the blue tit (*Parus caeruleus*), in which the head-up posture is relatively inconspicuous, makes much use of a head-forward posture in reproductive fighting, and can raise the cheek feathers in a special way to make this conspicuous (Tinbergen, 1937).

2. Schematization of the movement. Usually the actual nature of the movement itself becomes changed in the course of evolution. The changes which occur have been classified by Daanje (1950) as follows:

a. Exaggeration of certain components of the movement. Thus the magpie (*Pica pica*) makes exaggerated tail movements in display. These represent an elaborated form of the up-and-down tail movements before flight and probably serve as a social releaser.

b. Changes in absolute and relative thresholds of components. This may result in marked accentuation of one component of, for instance, an intention movement of take-off and a virtual suppression of others. Similar changes result in the movement becoming increasingly stereotyped, a given intensity of response being elicited by a wider range of strengths of the eliciting factors. As we have seen, in many finches and other passerines the various components of the displays are linked with one or other of the conflicting tendencies. There have so far been no studies in other groups to determine how far relative changes in the components of the displays are related to changes in the associated tendencies.

c. Changes in the coordination of components. Thus a component of the first stage of taking off (e.g. crouching) may be combined with one from the springing-off phase (e.g. tail lowered).

The above three categories are, of course, to be regarded only as a means of classifying the changes that can be observed. The changes in the mechanisms underlying them are still unknown, and it seems unlikely that the categories have any causal validity. All the changes in the movements and the accompanying structures can be understood as adaptations to the signal functions[5] of the movement; they make it more conspicuous and, in some cases, more different from other movements. The genetic changes involved are undoubtedly rather complex: the displays of cardueline F_1 inter-species hybrids are intermediate between those of the parents (Hinde, 1956a; see also the detailed work of Clark, Aronson, and Gordon, 1954, on Xiphophorin fishes), and most plumage characters conspicuous in display are polygenic (references in Hinde, 1956b).

3. Emancipation. In addition to the changes in absolute and relative thresholds mentioned above, it has been suggested that there are more marked motivational changes such that the movement comes in evolution to be governed by causal factors different from those which governed it originally. Although such changes may be important in some groups (e.g. Lorenz, 1951), their general importance is not yet established. Thus it has recently been suggested that the feather postures of birds, much used in display and always apparently well correlated with one or other of the tendencies underlying it, may be under the same type of autonomic control as when they are used for cooling or warming (Andrew, 1956a; Morris, 1956). Even courtship feeding, which seems to be a clear-cut case of emancipation from parental/juvenile to sexual behavior (for the female may beg while actually holding food in the beak), may in fact be partly a secondary result of other (e.g. dominance) changes such that common factors between the parental and sexual situations are introduced.

[5] The diverse functions which displays may cover, and the ways in which signal movements have been elaborated to serve these functions, have been reviewed recently by Baerends (1950) and Tinbergen (1954).

The Function of Display

Now that we have made a provisional sketch of the evolutionary radiation of display movements within a group of closely related species, it remains to assess their functional significance. Here it is necessary to consider the biological significance both of the differences between a given display movement and its origin and of the differences (and similarities) between the displays of the present-day forms. The principal functions of the displays used in fighting and courtship have recently been reviewed by Tinbergen (1954), and will be mentioned only briefly here:

1. Fighting. Displays reduce the amount of actual combat and help to limit fighting to intraspecific encounters.

2. Courtship. (a) Synchronisation of the behavior of the sexes. This may be long term, involving, for instance, hormonal changes (Craig, 1911; Matthews, 1939), or short term, synchronising the mating activities of the pair. (b) Orientation. Some displays have primarily a guiding function (for instance the song of many passerines, the nest site display of the great tit and other hole-nesting species). The highly coloured patches round the genitalia of many baboons and chimpanzees may guide the male to the female's copulatory organs. (c) Suppression of nonsexual responses. "Submissive" postures in passerines help to suppress the aggressive behavior of the mate. (d) Maintenance of reproductive isolation. Thus sympatric closely related species of birds usually differ markedly in display, color, or song (Huxley, 1942; Skutch, 1951).

As Lorenz has pointed out, all these functions require that the display should be effective in eliciting responses in other individuals. This has led to progressive adaptation for signaling. Apart from this, divergence between species is enhanced by the need for maintaining reproductive isolation. This does not mean, however, that selection acting through the disadvantageous consequences of hybrid pairings is the only cause of evolutionary divergence in displays. Since the various characters of an animal are developmentally, causally, and also functionally interrelated, selection for change in any one character will have repercussions on many others. Thus not all differences in displays are necessarily the product of selection for divergence in the displays themselves (see below; Hinde, 1955; Mayr et al., 1956; Cullen, 1957).

THE EXTENT OF INTERSPECIES DIFFERENCES IN BEHAVIOR

In general, the behavior of closely related species is more similar than that of distantly related ones. To mention but one example of this well-known fact, all gulls feed their chicks by regurgitating food and presenting it in their bills, carduelines by regurgitation into the gape of the young, *Parus* spp. by dropping insects and so forth directly onto the gape of the young without previously swallowing them themselves. On the other hand, there are constant differences even between closely related species: thus the alarm calls of all gulls are a series of staccato cries, but the number, pitch, and frequency of the calls vary between species.

The nature and extent of such interspecies differences very often seem to be adaptive. For instance, the motor patterns used in maintenance activities such as preening, bathing and feeding, and in nest building, are closely similar in all carduelines so far studied. All species use the head-forward threat posture, though there are slight interspecies differences in the relative intensities of components. In song and courtship, however, the interspecies differences are conspicuous, a fact presumably related to their function in promoting reproductive isolation. In general it is in the earlier phases of courtship that interspecies differences are most marked; the female's soliciting posture and the copulatory behavior of the male vary little among species. This suggests that it is these earlier phases of courtship—i.e. pair formation and the immediately subsequent period—which are most important in effecting reproductive isolation.

Supporting evidence for this conclusion is given by the fact that if pair formation is forced under conditions of captivity breeding success of mixed pairs between closely related species may be comparable with that of pure species. Similar generalizations could be made for other groups of closely related species. Thus where the motor patterns of courtship, song, and so on play a role in maintaining reproductive isolation there has been selection for interspecies divergence (Huxley, 1942). Usually, however, the color patterns shown off by the displays have diverged more than the displays themselves (Morris, 1954a; Hinde, 1956b); and this in its turn implies that the releasers for courtship behavior have diverged more than the motor patterns. In other spheres, also, the stimuli eliciting the behavior show greater interspecies divergence than the motor patterns. Thus the behavior used in hunting for, catching, preparing, and swallowing food is usually similar in closely related species, but there is seldom much overlap in the kind of food eaten (references in Lack, 1954). However, in cases where one species is exploiting a food niche different from those of its relatives there may also be marked divergence in the method of hunting (contrast, for instance, the avocet, *Recurvirostra avosetta*, with other waders). Interspecies differences in the eliciting stimuli are the rule in other aspects of behavior which have important ecological implications. Often, as with habitat selection, this is probably the direct result of selection for interspecies divergence.

Convergence in behavior can be seen in the feeding behavior of unrelated species exploiting similar niches, for example fly-catchers (*Muscicapidae*), drongos (*Dicruridae*), and some American warblers (*Compsothlypidae*); swifts (*Apodidae*) and swallows (*Hirundinidae*). Among display postures, the widespread distribution of the head-forward threat among passerines probably indicates that it is primitive and not the result of convergence, but since interspecific disputes over food, roosting sites, and so forth often arise there may have been selection against divergence. Further, since there are selective forces governing the precise way in which intention movements and displacement activities are elaborated into displays, some degree of convergence in the broader features of the displays of unrelated species is to be expected. Among vocal utterances, Marler (1955) has shown that the similarities among the "flying predator" alarm calls of many passerines are probably due to convergence toward a pattern which is difficult for a hawk to locate. Marler also gives an important discussion of many of the selective factors affecting animal calls.

Convergence in color patterns is of course common in predominantly cryptic species. Occasionally unrelated species show some degree of convergence toward conspicuous patterns which are presumably particularly effective in display; e.g. the great tit, Java sparrow (*Padda oryzivora*), and white-cheeked bulbul (*Pycnonotus leucogenys*).

THE USE OF CHARACTERS OF BEHAVIOR IN SYSTEMATICS

In spite of their ephemeral nature, characters of behavior have been used successfully in studies of the systematics of a number of groups. The problems involved are parallel to those entailed in the use of morphological characters.

It is of course necessary to choose characters in which the interspecies differences are innate. Next, the characters must have an interspecies variability suitable for the particular problem. In general, those which have been either markedly conservative or divergent within a group are of little use for assessing relationships within that group, though characters which are conservative within a group may be useful for assessing the relationship of that group with others. For instance, the various *Parus* species all nest in holes and use moss for nest construction, differing in these characters from the other genera frequently included in the Paridae: these characters could thus be used to characterize the genus but would be useless for elucidating relationships within it (Hinde, 1952). Threat postures, and some courtship displays, on the other hand, are very valuable in studying relationships between closely related species or genera but are too divergent for determining relationships between families. The precise patterns of "tail flicks" made by passerine birds when moving through foliage and so forth have proved to be rather conservative within families, and can therefore provide useful evidence in assigning genera to families and in assessing relationships between families (Andrew, 1956c).

As with morphological characters, it is not desirable to use characters which change rapidly and could have been acquired independently in different groups for establishing phylogenetic relationships: when unrelated species acquire superficially similar characters, they may have different origins. However, if the character is analyzed sufficiently, the danger of false homologizing disappears. It is extremely difficult to find characters where there is no danger of convergence. Although, as Lorenz claimed, the courtship postures of birds depend on an "inherited" convention among the members of the species and are thus especially useful for systematic work, even in these movements convergences are by no means absent. There must be some reason for the elaboration of this intention movement other than its being a social signal, and the most effective type of ritualization will depend upon the context. The dangers of being misled by convergent characters can of course be reduced by making comparisons first between species believed to be closely related on other grounds: similarities then found are reasonably likely to be due to homologies.

It is often difficult to assess the systematic significance to be attached to behavioral characteristics because functional relations between characters are frequently more difficult to trace than those between morphological ones (Hinde, 1955). For instance, in passerine birds, selection for territorial behavior, distinctive song, sexual dimorphism in color and behavior, and suppression of male aggressiveness in courtship may all be linked, so that a trend in the direction of one of them will influence the selective advantages of all the others.

An excellent example of the ramifying effects of selection of one characteristic throughout the whole adaptive complex is given by the work of E. Cullen on the kittiwake (*Rissa tridactyla*); we are grateful to her for allowing us to quote her unpublished work. Kittiwakes are the only gulls that select steep cliffs for breeding. This enables them to nest out of reach of both mammalian and avian predators. The following characteristics of the kittiwake are undoubtedly connected with this: (1) They are extremely tame while on the ledges, as shown by their very short fleeing distance and the high threshold of the alarm call. (2) They do not attack predators as other gulls do. (3) They defecate just over the rim of the nest (other gulls walk or fly several yards from the nest), and as a result the nest, though not itself fouled, is extremely conspicuous, the whole rim being white. (4) Neither the eggs nor the chicks are camouflaged. (5) The egg shells are not carried off after hatching, and their white inner surface contributes still more to making the nest conspicuous. (6) The chicks do not run when alarmed, and are thus protected from falling over the cliff. (7) Regurgitated food is not dropped on the ground (nest), so that fouling of the nest is avoided. (Unlike other gulls, which leave the nest soon after hatching, young kittiwakes stay on the nest until fledging.) (8) Prior to building the nest itself, kittiwakes construct a mud platform which broadens and flattens the narrow and often slanting substrate. This involves collecting of mud and trampling it down by "foot paddling." (9) In a contest over food the young bend the head away from the attacker, instead of either fighting back or fleeing as other gulls do; this head bending stops the attack. The gesture also exposes the black neckband. Neither the movement nor the band is found in chicks of other gulls.

Many of the difficulties involved in the use of behavioral characters in systematics can be avoided by a broad approach: the importance of a knowledge of the natural history of the animal and of the causation and function of the behavior cannot be over-emphasized.

CONCLUSION

We see, then, that the comparative study of behavior can yield the same type of results as comparative anatomy—a tentative description of the course evolution has taken. Furthermore, in both cases the method depends basically on the establishment of homologies, that is the grouping together of elements having a common evolutionary origin. The fertility of the comparative method is, however, enormously enhanced when it is coupled with studies of function and causation. These enable us to distinguish between homology and convergence, give us insight into the origin and later adaptation of "derived" movements, and permit a more accurate description of the true innate differences between species.

All this work, tentative though it may be, provides the necessary basis for an attack on the ultimate problem of the dynamics of behavior evolution. Comparative study itself cannot contribute directly to the solution of this problem, but as a phase of research it is indispensable; it alone can supply us with a formulation of the problems to be solved.

REFERENCES

Andrew, R. J., 1956a Some remarks on behaviour in conflict situations, with special reference to *Emberiza* spp. *Brit. J. Anim. Behav.*, 4, 41-5.

Andrew, R. J., 1956b The aggressive and courtship behaviour of certain *Emberizinae. Behaviour*, 10, 255-308.

Andrew, R. J., 1956c Intention movements of flight in certain passerines, and their use in systematics. *Behaviour*, 10, 179-204.

Baerends, G. P., 1950 Specializations in organs and movements with a releasing function. In *Physiological mechanisms in animal behaviour.* Sympos. Soc. Exp. Biol., No. 4. Cambridge, Eng., Cambridge Univ. Press, pp. 337-60.

Baerends, G. P., and J. M. Baerends, 1950 An introduction to the ethology of cichlid fishes. *Behaviour*, Suppl. 1, pp. 1-242.

Beach, F. A., 1955 The de-scent of instinct. *Psychol. Rev.*, 62, 401-10.

Clark, E., L. R. Aronson, and M. Gordon, 1954 Mating behaviour patterns in two sympatric species of Xiphophorin fishes: their inheritance and significance in sexual isolation. *Bull. Amer. Mus. Nat. Hist.*, 103 (2), 135-225.

Craig, W., 1911 Oviposition induced by the male in pigeons. *J. Morphol.*, 22, 299-305.

Craig, W., 1912 Observations on doves learning to drink. *J. Anim. Behav.*, 2, 273-9.

Crane, J., 1941 Crabs of the genus *Uca* from the West Coast of Central America. *Zoologica*, 26, 145-208.

Crane, J., 1948-50 Comparative biology of salticid spiders at Rancho Grande, Venezuela. *Ibid.*, Vols. 33-5.

Crane, J., 1952 A comparative study of innate defensive behaviour in Trinidad mantids. *Ibid.*, 37, 259-93.

Cullen, E., 1957 Adaptations in the kittiwake to cliff-nesting. *Ibid*, 99, 275-302.

Daanje, A., 1950 On the locomotory movements of birds, and the intention movements derived from them. *Behaviour*, 3, 48-98.

Davis, D. E., 1942 The phylogeny of social nesting habits in the Chrotophaginae. *Quart. Rev. Biol.*, 17, 115-34.

Evans, H. E., 1953 Comparative ethology and systematics of spider wasps. *Syst. Zool.*, 2, 155-72.

Evans, H. E., 1955 An ethological study of the digger wasp, *Bembecinus neglectus*, with a review of the ethology of the genus. *Behaviour*, 7, 287-304.

Faber, A., 1953 *Laut und Gebärdensprache bei Insekten*. Staatl. Museum fur Naturkunde in Stuttgart.

Friedmann, H., 1929 *The cowbirds*. Springfield-Baltimore, Thomas.

Goethe, F., 1937 Beobachtungen und Untersuchungen zur Biologie der Silbermöwe auf der Vogelinsel Memmertsand. *J. f. Ornithol.*, 85, 1-119.

Heinroth, O., 1911 Beiträge sur Biologie, namentlich Ethologie und Physiologie der Anatiden. *Verh. 5 Int. Ornithol. Kongr.* Berlin.

Heinroth, O., and M. Heinroth, 1928 *Vögel Mitteleuropas*. Berlin.

Hinde, R. A., 1952 The behaviour of the great tit, and some other related species. *Behaviour*, Suppl. 2, pp. 1-201.

Hinde, R. A., 1953 The conflict between drives in the courtship and copulation of the chaffinch. *Ibid.*, 5, 1-31.

Hinde, R. A., 1954 The courtship and copulation of the Greenfinch. *Ibid.*, 7, 207-32.

Hinde, R. A., 1955 A comparative study of the courtship of certain finches. *Ibis*, 97, 706-45; 98, 1-23.

Hinde, R. A., 1956a The behaviour of certain cardueline interspecies hybrids. *Behaviour*, 9, 202-13.

Hinde, R. A., 1956b Breeding success in cardueline interspecies pairs and an examination of the hybrids' plumage. *J. Genetics*, 54, 304-10.

Huxley, J. S., 1942 *Evolution: the modern synthesis*. London, Allen & Unwin.

Iersel, J. J. A. van, 1953 An analysis of the parental behaviour of the male three-spined stickleback. *Behaviour*, Suppl. 3, pp. 1-159.

Jacobs, W., 1950 Vergleichends Verhaltensstudien an Feldheuschrecken. *Z. f. Tierpsychol.* 7, 169-216.

Koehler, O., 1954 Review of Lehrman (1953) in *ibid*., 11, 330-34.

Lack, D., 1954 *The natural regulation of animal numbers*. London, Oxford Univ. Press.

Lehman, D. S., 1953 A critique of Konrad Lorenz' theory of instinctive behavior. *Quart. Rev. Biol.*, 28, 337-63.

Lehrman, D. S., 1955 The physiological basis of parental feeding behaviour in the ring dove (*Streptopelia risoria*). *Behaviour*, 7, 241-86.

Lorenz, K., 1935 Der Kumpan in der Umwelt des Vogels. *J. f. Ornithol.*, 83, 137-213, 289-413.

Lorenz, K., 1939 Vergleichende Verhaltensforschung. *Zool. Anz.*, Suppl. Band. 12, 69-102.

Lorenz, K., 1941 Vergleichende Bewegungsstudien an Anatinen. *J. f. Ornithol.*, 89, Sonderheft, 19-29.

Lorenz, K., 1950 The comparative method in studying innate behavior patterns. In *Physiological mechanisms in animal behaviour*. Sympos. Soc. Exp. Biol., No. 4, Cambridge, Eng., Cambridge Univ. Press, pp. 221-68.

Lorenz, K., 1951 Uber die Entstehung auslösender "Zeremonien." *Die Vogelwarte*, 16, 9-13.

Marler, P., 1955 The characteristics of some animal calls. *Nature*, 176, 6.

Marler, P., 1956 The behaviour of the chaffinch. *Behaviour*, Suppl. 5.

Matthews, L. H., 1939 Visual stimulation and ovulation in pigeons. *Proc. Roy. Soc. London*, Series B., 126, 557-60.

Mayr, E., R. J. Andrew, and R. A. Hinde, 1956 Die systematische Stellung der Gattung *Fringilla*. *J. f. Ornithol.*, 97, 258-73.

Morris, D., 1952 Homosexuality in the ten-spined stickleback (*Pygosteus pungitius*). *Behaviour*, 4, 233-62.

Morris, D., 1954a The reproductive behaviour of the zebra finch (*Poephila guttata*), with special reference to pseudofemale behaviour and displacement activities. *Ibid.*, 6, 271-322.

Morris, D., 1954b The reproductive behaviour of the river bullhead (*Cottus gobio*) with special reference to fanning activity. *Ibid.*, 7, 1-32.

Morris, D., 1955 Courtship dance of the swordtail. *Aquarist*, 19, 247-9.
Morris, D., 1956 The feather postures of birds and the problem of the origin of social signals. *Behaviour*, 9, 75-113.
Morris, D., 1958 The reproductive behaviour of the ten-spined stickleback (*Pygosteus pungitius* L.). *Ibid.*, Suppl. 6, pp. 1-154.
Moynihan, M., 1955a Some aspects of reproductive behaviour in the blackheaded gull (*Larus ridibundus*) and related species. *Ibid.*, Suppl. 4, pp. 1-201.
Moynihan, M., 1955b Remarks on the original sources of displays. *Auk*, 72, 240-6.
Sauer, F., 1954 Die Entwicklung der Lautäusserung vom Ei ab schalldichtgehaltener Dorngrassmücken. *Z. f. Tierpsychol.*, 11, 10-23.
Sauer, F., 1956 Ueber das Verhalten junger Gartengrasmücken *Sylvia borin* (Bodd.) *J. f. Ornithol.*, 97, 156-89.
Seitz, A., 1940-41 Die Paarbildung bei einigen Cichliden. *Z. f. Tierpsychol.*, 4, 40-84; 5, 74-101.
Seitz, A., 1949 Vergleichende Verhaltensstudien an Buntsbarschen. *Ibid.*, 6, 202-35.
Skutch, A. F., 1951 Congeneric species of birds nesting together in Central America. *Condor*, 53, 3-15.
Spieth, H. T., 1950 Mating behaviour and sexual isolation in the *Drosophila virilis* species group. *Behaviour*, 3, 105-45.
Spieth, H. T., 1952 Mating behaviour within the genus *Drosophila* (*Diptera*). *Bull. Amer. Mus. Nat. Hist.*, 99, 401-79.
Spurway, H., 1953 Territory and evolution in sticklebacks. Penguin *New Biology*, 4, 33-43.
Thorpe, W. H., 1954 The process of song-learning in the chaffinch, as studied by means of the sound spectrograph. *Nature,* 173, 465.
Thorpe, W. H., 1956 *Learning and instinct in animals.* London, Methuen.
Tinbergen, N., 1937 Über das Verhalten kämpfender Kohlmeisen. *Ardea*, 26, 222-3.
Tinbergen, N., 1948 Social releasers and the experimental method required for their study. *Wilson Bull.*, 60, 6-52.
Tinbergen, N., 1951 *The study of instinct.* London, Oxford Univ. Press.
Tinbergen, N., 1952 Derived activities; their causation, biological significance, origin and emancipation during evolution. *Quart. Rev. Biol.*, 27, 1-32.
Tinbergen, N., 1953 *The herring gull's world.* London, Collins.
Tinbergen, N., 1954 The origin and evolution of courtship and threat display. In A. C. Hardy, J. S. Huxley, and E. B. Ford, eds., *Evolution as a process.* London, Allen & Unwin.
Tinbergen, N., 1955 Psychology and ethology as a supplementary parts of behaviour. In *Group processes*, Trans. 1st Conf. Sponsored by Josiah Macy, Jr., Foundation.

Tinbergen, N., and G. J. Broekhuysen, 1954 On the threat and courtship behaviour of Hartlaubs' gull. *Ostrich,* 25, 50-61.

Weidmann, U., 1955 Some reproductive activities of the common gull, *Larus canus* L. *Ardea*, 43, 85-132.

Whitman, C. O., 1919 *The behaviour of pigeons*. Carnegie Inst. Wash. Publ., No. 257, 1-161.

Instincts and Chromosomes: What is an "Innate" Act?

PETER H. KLOPFER

If chicks of a yellow and of a black variety are reared together and their individual preferences for one or the other variety then determined, of those that do evince a preference, most will select chicks of their own hue as companions. Since the animals have been reared together under identical conditions, we can say that this difference in their preferences is genetically determined (see Kilham, Klopfer, and Oelke 1968). Such a formulation cannot easily be paraphrased without doing violence to its content. It is not identical, for instance, with the statement "preference for own kind is genetically determined." I wish to examine the reason behind this assertion of nonequivalence.

The experiments alluded to above are far from complete. They were originally designed merely to test the validity of conclusions summarized by Howell and Vine (1940) that there are strain differences in the perceptual preferences of chicks; second, they were intended to identify the relevant cues by which chicks make the requisite discriminations and on which their preferences are based; and, finally, they were intended to discover how apparently innate perceptual preferences are programmed by the nervous system. For example, if the discrimination between own strain and alien strain is based on color (but it was not insisted that this is so), we can ask whether this is due to the differential distribution of retinal oil droplets, to sensitivity of the retinal cells, or to central

From *The American Naturalist*, Vol. 103, No. 933, September-October 1969, pp. 556-560.

mechanisms. Fortunately, some of the different answers to such questions have been provided in a study by Hailman (1967) which affords an example of what a careful analysis of "innate" behavior may reveal. The stereotyped species-common behavior pattern he examined is the feeding behavior of chicks of the laughing gull, *Larus atricilla*. Typically, gull chicks remain near the nest after hatching and are fed by the parents, which regurgitate semidigested food. Regurgitation by the parent is apparently stimulated by the chicks pecking at the tip of the parental bill. (The tip is colored and contrasts with the rest of the bill.) Field observations show that as long as the chick pecks at the bill tip, the parent regurgitates the food onto the ground. While the chick continues pecking, the parent takes the food back into its own bill and, after a time, reswallows it. The hungrier the chick is, that is, the longer since its previous feeding, the more intensely it pecks. Thus, this behavior ultimately brings the chick's bill in contact with the food. Once contact is made, the food is quickly swallowed. Thereafter, pecking is preferentially directed to the food. The analysis of movies of this pecking behavior by the chicks shows that the movement itself consists of four discrete, recognizable elements: a forward and upward movement of the head, an opening of the bill, a rotation of the head, and a push with the legs. There seems to be a considerable inter- and intraindividual variation both in the duration of these different components of the total movement as well as in their synchronization. Rearing the chicks under conditions of darkness and force-feeding them, thus denying them many of the usual visual and motor adjustments of normally reared chicks, affected some, but not all of the components. Similarly, the chicks that were kept in the dark until an initial exposure to a variety of simple models that mimicked one or another of the characteristics of the parental head and bill, were shown to respond differently to quite a number of features of the model. The experiments with models show that the important features of the parental head include the figure-ground contrast, the orientation (whether vertical or horizontal), diameter of the simulated bill, its rate of movement, and its color; many of these attributes could be manipulated in a compensatory manner without affecting the overall rate of pecking.

The act of pecking seems as simple and "instinctive" an act as any that has been described. Indeed, it has long served as a paradigm for ethologists (Tinbergen and Perdeck 1950). But, from the foregoing, we can see that pecking is not a unitary affair. The final outcome, the contact of the chick's bill with bill tip of a parent, may appear to represent a relatively simple and stereotyped behavioral response; but in fact it is a response composed of a multiplicity of movements and choices, many of which can vary without the final result being altered. And the analysis of the pecking could certainly be pushed further along a reductionist path! There is no reason to believe that in the forward movement of the chick's head the same muscle bundles are invariably involved. And, even within one bundle, different fibers doubtless fire at different times. Indeed, the more closely one approaches the molecular level, the more probabilistic and nondeterministic our description must become. Recall how the gas laws of physics permit precise statements regarding pressure-volume-temperature relations while taking for granted indeterminancy in the behavior of the individual gas molecules. The question, then, whether pecking is genetically determined, has to be rephrased; in fact, what is represented on the genome? Surely not the final result of the many motor and perceptual phenomena listed above. A separate gene for each motor element of pecking? And for the color and the speed-of-movement preference, perhaps? Ultimately, must we postulate genes for virtually every nerve or muscle fiber which contributes to a response? The difficulty in relating behavior, however stereotyped it may seem, to genetics actually stems from an obsolete and incorrect notion of gene action. This notion, which, in its essentials, holds the chromosome to be a biochemical homunculus is derived from the one-gene-one-enzyme hypothesis, which is itself an oversimplification.

Consider again the preference of the chick for a particular color. Color preferences in gulls depend, at least partially, on the presence and distribution of oil droplets in the retinal cells. How is their distribution and appearance controlled by the genes? The most reasonable assumption, superficially stated, appears to be that, at a particular locus of a chromosome, a synthetic process is initiated which leads to the formation of certain enzymes which react with substances derived extrachromosomally to produce other substances that lead (eventually) to formation of certain oil soluble pigments. Obviously, this description is but a small distance of the way to a color-coding and perceiving mechanism. But the question of what in fact has been inherited becomes even more difficult to answer when we recognize the complexities of the mechanisms that underlie color preferences.

We might make studies of heritable differences in behavior more intelligible if we view the gene not as a repository of data or a blueprint from which an organism can be constructed, that is, as an inchoate homunculus, but rather as an information-generating device which exploits the predictable and ordered nature of its environment (or in Schroedinger's terms [1951], which feeds on negative entropy). This view accords well with current models of gene action, such as that advanced by Jacob and Monod (1961), among others, or that of Waddington (1966). A segment of the alpha helix specifies a particular species of RNA which ultimately, and in an appropriate environment, leads to the synthesis of a particular enzyme, which in turn may repress or activate further synthetic activity by that portion of the helix, or repress or activate another segment. "Wheels within wheels," and all depends as much on substances external to the helix as on the structure of the helix itself. Hormones, for instance, whose synthesis can be traced ultimately back to the action of particular segments of the alpha helix, are now known to activate genetic transcription at other portions of the helix. The transcription products may further feedback and regulate development (Schneiderman and Gilbert 1964).

It is intriguing to see how Erikson (1968), in his discussion of human development, has perceived parallel situations at the cultural level. He writes: "The human infant is born preadapted to an *average expectable environment* [my emphasis]. Man's ecology demands constant and natural historical and technological readjustment which makes it at once obvious that only a perpetual, if ever so imperceptible, restructuring of tradition can safeguard for each new generation of infants anything approaching an average expectability of environment. . . . In other words the human environment as a whole must permit and safeguard a series of more or less discontinuous and yet culturally and psychologically consistent developments, each extending further along the radius of expanding life tasks."

The implication that human behavior is the outcome of epigenetic processes expressed in the context of a stable environment is profound. For one thing, greater developmental stability is assured than by a homunculus, for the epigenetic system is buffered and self-correcting at many points. At the same time, the system is far more responsive to changes in environmental conditions than a homunculus would be. (Note particularly Waddington's [1966] reference to this labile aspect of epigenetic systems, and his discussion on canalization.)

In short, *behavior* is not a noun, defined and determined by a discrete locus on a DNA molecule. It is a process that derives from a series of interactions, some stochastic, some perhaps deterministic, which at times can achieve a certain level of predictability and stereotypy. At some point this degree of inevitability and sameness become so great that we speak of "an instinct." But let us not neglect that acts, or behavior, are sequences of movements and perceptions and are best described in terms of latencies, frequencies, durations, and intensities. They must be analyzed with a view to unraveling a skein of interactions which tie together particular stimuli and particular responses, for example, in the case of the gull chicks, the sight of the parent, the lunge forward, and the open bill.

A *gene* refers to inheritable differences. But, while it is nonsense to talk about the inheritance of behavior, it is true that behavior may be more or less stereotyped. One can imagine a continuum with acts, perceptions, or responses ranging from highly plastic and variable at one end to highly constrained or stereotyped at the other. Further, it is of interest to ask how behavior falling at either end of this spectrum develops, or to make inquiries about its evolutionary history, the mechanisms which underlie it, or the functions which it serves. The answers to such queries will reveal interesting differences between those kinds of behavior which we know to be highly plastic, falling at one end of the continuum, and those kinds of behavior which we know to be more stable, less flexible, falling at the opposite end. The hope of finding an instinct in a chromosome, in any event, is illusory.

REFERENCES

Erikson, E. 1968. Identity: youth and crisis. Norton, New York.

Hailman, J. P. 1967. The ontogeny of an instinct. (Behaviour Suppl. 15.) E. J. Brill, Leiden.

Howell, T. H., and D. O. Vine, 1940. The innate differential in social learning. J. Abnormal Soc. Psychol. 35: 537-548.

Jacob, F., and J. Monod. 1961. Genetic regulatory mechanisms in the synthesis of proteins. J. Mol. Biol. 3: 318.

Kilham, P., P. Klopfer, and H. Oelke. 1968. Species identification and color preferences in chicks. Anim. Behav. 16: 238-245.

Schneiderman, H. A., and L. I. Gilbert. 1964. Control of growth and development in insects. Science 143:325.

Schroedinger, E. 1951. What is life? Cambridge Univ. Press, New York.

Tinbergen, N., and N. C. Perdeck. 1950. On the stimulus situation releasing the begging response in the newly hatched herring gull chick. Behaviour 3: 1-39.

Waddington, C. H. 1966. Principles of development and differentiation. Macmillan, New York.

SUGGESTIONS FOR FURTHER READING

Eibl-Eibesfeldt, I. *Ethology: The biology of behavior*. New York: Holt, Rinehart & Winston, 1970.

Ewer, R. F. *Ethology of mammals*. New York: Plenum Press, 1968.

Fox, M. W. *Behaviour of wolves, dogs and related canids*. London: Cape, 1971.

Hafez, E. S. E. (Ed.) *The behaviour of domestic animals*. London: Balliere, 1969.

*Hess, E. H. Ethology: An approach toward the complete analysis of behavior. In T. M. Newcomb (Ed.), *New directions in psychology*. New York: Holt, Rinehart & Winston, 1962. Pp. 159-266.

Hinde, R. A. *Animal behaviour*. (2nd ed.) New York: McGraw-Hill, 1970.

*Johnsgaard, P. A. *Animal behavior*. Dubuque, Iowa: Wm. C. Brown, 1967.

Klopfer, P. H., & Hailman, J. P. *An introduction to animal behavior*. Englewood Cliffs, N.J.: Prentice-Hall, 1967.

*Maier, R. A., & Maier, B. M. *Comparative animal behavior*. Monterey, California: Brooks/Cole, 1970.

*Manning, A. *An introduction to animal behavior*. Chicago: Aldine, 1968.

Marler, P., & Hamilton, W. J. *Mechanisms of animal behavior*. New York: Wiley & Sons, 1966.

**Psychobiology, The biological bases of behavior*. Readings from *Scientific American*. Introductions by J. L. McGaugh, N. W. Weinberger, & R. E. Whalen. San Francisco: W. H. Freeman, 1967.

*Scott, J. P. *Animal behavior*. (2nd ed.) Chicago: University of Chicago Press, 1970.

Thorpe, W. H. *Learning and instinct in animals.* (2nd ed.) Cambridge, Mass.: Harvard University Press, 1963.

*Tinbergen, N. *Curious naturalists.* Garden City, N.Y.: Doubleday & Co., 1968.

*Tinbergen, N. *The study of instinct*. New York: Oxford University Press, 1969.

*Wiedman, U. Innate behavior. In *Topics in animal behavior, ecology and evolution*. New York: Harper & Row, 1971. Pp. 3-12.

*Introductory texts and reviews

II METHODOLOGY: THE ANALYSIS OF BEHAVIOR

In the recording and interpretation of data, objectivity is essential—objectivity in describing and categorizing behaviors, in measuring frequency and duration, and in investigating the factors responsible for the elucidation or cessation of certain behaviors. The ethologist or naturalist of 20 years ago used binoculars and note pad for observing and recording, and to this day there is no finer recording equipment available. Data collection may also be facilitated by the use of such equipment as an Esterline-Angus digital event recorder, which provides a valuable time base and records duration and frequency; video and sound tape recordings, enabling slow-motion frame-by-frame analysis of vocalizations; time-lapse photography, for sampling movements and changing spatial relationships; and photo cells or pressure sensors, for monitoring the activity of animals in a particular area. In addition, operant devices—for example, a bar that the animal must press in order to receive food—may be used for measuring motivation. Finally, biotelemetry equipment for monitoring physiological activity (heart rate, temperature, and so on) in free-moving animals, and also for tracking and locating, has given the ethologist and ecologist a new tool.

Once a base line of predictable sequences of behavior has been obtained, the experimenter may study such factors as *social* influences (effects of addition or removal of a subject from a social group) or *stimuli releasing* or eliciting certain behaviors (use of live prey, or model "sign stimuli"). In both examples he is investigating *context.* A second approach to this situational analysis is to manipulate certain variables such as temperature or food intake; here the experimenter is beginning to question what internal changes in the animal may be affecting behavior in a particular situation, the context of which must be kept as constant as possible. A third approach is to effect changes within the animal, as by injecting hormones (e.g., testosterone or estrogen) or by destroying or electrically or chemically stimulating certain parts of the brain.

What does the investigator decide to select for analysis from the animal's repertoire? From the ethogram, certain components of behavioral systems may be investigated; rating scores–giving graded measurement scales for latency, frequency, duration, and intensity (e.g. amplitude of movement)–may be drawn up. The temporal sequence in terms of probability of evocation of certain responses can be determined, and also the response decrement (fatigue, satiation, or habituation) and response recovery may be assessed.

Marler and Hamilton (1966), in discussing the descriptions of behavior in space and time, emphasize the following points:

1. Select the "apparently" most relevant aspects for recording and analysis.
2. Identify stereotyped fixed-action patterns.
3. Identify underlying motivation or "mood hierarchy" and the social, environmental, ontogenetic, endocrine, and genetic influences.
4. Use descriptive rather than speculative functional terms in describing qualitatively what the animal does.
5. Attempt to find the temporal organization within a sequence. The sequence of actions of one animal varies with external stimuli, such as the responses of its mate. The dominant sequence patterns may vary at different times, as during the progressive phases of courtship, nest building, and care of the young.
6. Quantify and compute clusters of action patterns. Some behavior patterns are not restricted to one type of temporal grouping or motivational context. For example, biting the scruff of the neck is seen during copulation, carrying offspring, and killing prey in the cat.

The readings in this chapter represent these various approaches and levels of procedural analysis in terms of extracting meaningful and quantifiable data from the behavior repertoire. (For general details concerning experimental design and statistical treatment of data, the reader is referred to the excellent review by

Denenberg and Banks, 1968.) The readings cover four major aspects of behavior research methodology: observation, the use of models, hormonal analysis (socioendocrinology), and neuroethology.

Grant's detailed study of the social behavior of the male laboratory rat exemplifies the ethologist's approach: observing, categorizing, situationally eliciting, and predicting behavior; and analyzing temporal sequences (or ongoing chains of related actions). This study should also give the psychology student a certain respect for the talents of the common laboratory rat.

The second paper, dealing with certain *derived* behavior patterns in canids, combines many methods of the ethologist: the use of models, social deprivation (hand-rearing in isolation), and straightforward observation of animals interacting socially. The developmental and comparative methods are also employed (for example, as methods, studying the gradual unfolding of behavior from infancy and comparing the behavior of different species can give valuable insights into the origins and evolution of behavior).

The paper by Carbaugh, Schein, and Hale explores stimuli that elicit sexual responses in the cock and demonstrates the use of models to analyze the releasing properties of complex sign stimuli.

The paper by Bruder and Lehrman illustrates another approach employed by ethologists: the identification of internal (hormonal) changes triggered by social stimulation and affecting subsequent behavior.

The studies by Brown and Hunsperger and by Valenstein and coauthors utilize brain-stimulation techniques for investigating the causes and control of behavior. Delius's paper explores some of the theoretical interpretations of displacement behavior on the basis of his intriguing findings on the effects of selected brain stimulation in gulls.

An Analysis of the Social Behaviour of the Male Laboratory Rat

E. C. GRANT

INTRODUCTION

A number of authors, e.g. Davis (1953), Hall & Klein (1942), have classified the social behaviour of the rat into groups of elements with a view to simplifying the analysis of "fighting" behaviour and a number have also attributed motive to particular elements or postures, but in no case has a detailed analysis preceded such a grouping. This, combined in many cases with loose descriptions of the elements, has led to difficulties in the interpretation of these results. Therefore, it was felt that a detailed ethological study of the social behaviour of this species was desirable. In the first place it would give basic information on the normal behaviour of the rat, which is still lacking despite several decades of intensive psychological research. Secondly, it would demonstrate the practicability of an ethological analysis of mammalian behaviour of a similar type to that which has been previously carried out on the lower vertebrates. Finally, it would form a basis for comparable studies on other laboratory rodents.

The first necessary step in such an analysis is to become familiar with, describe and name the elements of behaviour used by the animal. In another paper, Grant and Mackintosh (1963), these

From *Behaviour*, 1963, **121**(3-4), 260-280.

elements, recognised in the rat, were described in some detail and compared with those shown by other laboratory rodents. In that paper these elements were classified into groups, within which there were motivational similarities, e.g. aggressive and flight postures. This grouping, as opposed to the description of the elements, was dependent on the analysis to be described in this paper and does not, of course, precede such an analysis.

MATERIALS AND METHODS

Materials

The animals used were random bred male laboratory rats (*Rattus norvegicus*) of an agouti strain bred in our own laboratories. When observed, the rats were between ten and sixteen weeks old, that is, sexually mature but still young. In any one test they were within ten days of each other in age. From weaning until the beginning of the experiments the rats were kept in small monosexual groups of three to six animals in wire cages 18″ x 11″ x 9″, resting on metal trays covered with sawdust.

At least a fortnight before the beginning of observation the animals were taken into the experimental rooms, and ten days before the observations, they were put into separate cages. The animals were marked by a commercial black hair dye so that individuals could be distinguished. The lighting in the experimental rooms was reversed, i.e. a strong white light was switched on from 7.30 p.m. until 9.30 a.m. and was replaced by dim red light during the day. This has the effect of reversing the diurnal activity cycle of the rats so that they are awake during the day.

Introduction

One animal was placed into the home cage of another and the two were observed for a period of about 15 minutes after which the intruder was put back into his own cage. This "introduction" gives a period of fairly intense social activity. An experiment normally consisted of about 24 introductions.

Method of Recording

In each experiment there were two observers each watching one of the animals. When a rat performed any social act its observer made a note of the code word for that act and at the same time depressed a button activating a pointer writing on a kymograph. The pointer operated by one observer lay precisely below that operated by the other, so that they drew concurrent parallel paths on the drum. A time marker made a one-second time trace between the other two traces.[1]

Analysis of the Trace

The relationships between the postures can be determined by the frequency with which one posture is followed by any other. I felt that if a considerable period of time elapsed between two postures it would not be possible to suppose that they would be consecutive steps in the same series. Therefore, an arbitrary maximum time of three seconds was considered not to belong to the preceding sequence. A sequence would then be any two or more acts performed in series by one animal with a maximum time lapse of three seconds between the end of one act and the beginning of the next. The method of presenting the results allowed only sequences of two acts to be tabulated. For example, the sequence A-B-C was tabulated as A-B and B-C.

The effect of the acts of one animal on the behaviour of the other can be determined by the frequency with which any particular posture, when shown by one animal, is followed by any particular posture shown by the other. As the two traces are being recorded simultaneously on parallel lines this is much the same problem as the previous one; thus a Cross-Correlation Sequence is any two or more acts, each act performed by alternate animals and with a maximum time lapse of three seconds between the end of one act and the beginning of the next.

This time period of three seconds may seem rather short and one can see obvious continuations of behaviour sequences after

[1] Recently this method had been improved on by the use of a two-track tape recorder instead of paper and pencil, and a moving paper pen-recorder in place of the kymograph.

longer pauses than this in many species. In a more diverse or larger environment this may also be true of the rat. However, in a cage where the main feature of the environment is the other rat, three seconds is a considerable period of time.

Analysis of the Sequences

The first stage in the analysis of the sequences is to transfer the data from the traces and notes and make it available in tabular form. This is done by arranging all the acts in columns and rows. The rows are acts preceding acts in sequences and the columns are acts following acts in sequences. A diagram of a small part of such a table will help the explanation:

	Threat	*Attack*	*Agg. Posture*	*Agg. Groom*	*Total*
Threat	–	12	44	75	131
Attack	0	–	52	14	66
Agg. Posture	0	0	–	19	19
Agg. Groom	14	1	15	–	30
Total	14	13	111	118	246

Thus, from the sequence table Aggressive Posture is shown by a rat 44 times after it has shown Threat but Threat is never shown after Aggressive Posture. In this analysis I have not recorded the occurrence of the same act being repeated, although this happens quite frequently. It does not, however, imply any change in motivation and, therefore, I have disregarded it. I will take this point up later in the Results, where I will try to show that the behaviour is motivated by opposing drives and that any one posture indicates certain levels of these drives. A row total of any one act gives a measure of the number of times that that particular act precedes all other acts and the column total of that act the number of times it follows other acts. If any act is recorded as having a large number of acts following it and a small number preceding it, or *vice versa*, it indicates that this act is either a beginning or end point of a sequence of social behaviour. This, of course, depends on an evaluation by the experimenter of what behaviour is relevant to the social situation and what is not. This decision, particularly in the early stages of a study, is rather arbitrary as it depends on a knowledge of the behaviour, i.e.

the end point of the study. A working hypothesis, which could be modified as experience was gained, allowed a start to be made in the investigations. This was that any action that a rat will perform alone in its own cage will not be relevant to a social encounter.

From a comparison of the totals of the rows an "expected value" can be obtained for the number of times any act should precede any other, e.g. in Table I, if the acts were being shown in a random sequence, Threat would be preceded by Attack, Aggressive Posture and Aggressive Groom in the ratio 66: 19: 30, i.e. the ratio in which acts lead to all other acts. This can be compared with the ratio 0 : 0 : 14 in which they are observed to lead to Threat. Any major discrepancy between "expected" and "observed" will give indications of affinity or otherwise between the acts. A similar procedure can be followed for the columns for acts leading to acts. The complete table contains 42 acts and postures with a grand total of over 9,000 entries; for its analysis the two procedures can be combined and an "expected" value for each cell obtained from the ratio (row total x column total)/grand total; this can then be compared with the observed total for that cell. Davis (1960) used this method to analyse the relationships between seven acts in the mutual feeding behaviour of ants.

Another example will demonstrate the final point I wish to make. After Bite was shown, the following posture on ten occasions was Upright Posture and on ten occasions was Aggressive Posture. The expected values for these two sequences were Bite-Upright Posture 5 and Bite-Aggressive Posture 2. Two statements can then be made:

a) In actual behaviour, a rat that has just bitten another will be just as likely to next give an Upright Posture as an Aggressive Posture.

b) Bite is more closely related to the Aggressive Posture than to Upright Posture, as the observed value for the sequence Bite-Upright Posture is closer to the expected value than that of the sequence Bite-Aggressive Posture.

From b) I would predict that the motivation of Bite was nearer that of Aggressive Posture than to that of Upright Posture.

RESULTS

The postures (static) and the acts (involving movement) have been described in detail in another paper, Grant and Mackintosh (1963), and I will only describe them briefly as they arise. In most cases the names given to them are descriptive.

Most of the elements shown by rats can be separated into two groups, those occurring when the animals are close together or in contact and those occurring when they are apart. I will examine first those occurring when the animals are close together.

In a previous paper, Grant and Chance (1958), the Submissive Posture was taken as indicating that the rat showing this posture had submitted and had lost that particular encounter. This particular posture was used because it was easily recognised and there was a strong subjective feeling that the animals showing it had submitted. The following points indicate that this assumption was correct.

It is now recognised that agonistic social behaviour is motivated by two main drives, Aggression and Flight: a submissive posture should then be an expression of the Flight drive. If the occurrence in sequences of Submissive Posture is compared with that of the more overt form of flight, Retreat, they are shown to occur in similar positions. Defensive Upright Posture and Defensive Sideways Posture lead to both Submissive Posture and Retreat at higher than the expected level.

Defensive Upright	Submissive Posture	102	(expected 24)
Defensive Upright	Retreat	96	(expected 43)
Defensive Sideways	Submissive Posture	105	(expected 19)
Defensive Sideways	Retreat	41	(expected 33)

On the other hand, the overt forms of Aggression, Attack and Bite, do not occur before or after Submissive Posture.

The final part of the evidence from the behaviour of the animal performing the Submissive Posture is that this posture is one of the few that occur as end points of social behaviour, the ratio of acts preceding it to acts following it is 454 : 195.

It is also possible to make deductions from the behaviour of the other animal. The cross-correlation sequences show that Submissive Posture occurs much more frequently as a response than it is responded to; the other rat usually stops acting socially and moves away. Also from the cross-correlation it can be seen that it occurs in response to the overt form of aggression, Attack.

Attack responded to by Submissive Posture 27 (expected 4)

These facts seem to show that the Submissive Posture is an expression of submission motivated by a flight drive. If this is accepted, the Aggressive Posture, the equivalent posture of the aggressive animal in which it positions itself at right angles over the body of an animal in the Submissive Posture, can then be thought of as an expression of dominance motivated by an Aggressive Drive. Other evidence for this is its positive relationship with the more overt forms of aggression, Attack and Bite.

Attack → Aggressive Posture 52 (expected 5)
Bite → Aggressive Posture 10 (expected 2)

There is also a marked lack of correlation with the flight postures. Defensive Upright Posture and Defensive Sideways Posture lead to Aggressive Posture only once each as compared with expected values of 23 and 17.

Aggressive Posture and Submissive Posture are, therefore, expressions of aggression and flight occurring as end points of sequences.

Morris D. (1958) and Moynihan M. (1955), working with sticklebacks and gulls respectively, drew diagrams showing the interaction of these two drives. The basic diagram is as shown in Fig. 1. Increase in the flight drive is shown on the abscissa and increase in aggression on the ordinate. Along the diagonal both drives are at the same level and postures showing ambivalence between them will be shown. The intensity of this ambivalence increases from the bottom left to the top right of the diagram. I have shown that the Aggressive Posture and the Submissive Posture are expressions of the aggressive drive and the flight drive. The ambivalent postures should then lead equally to both of them.

Upright Posture and Sideways Posture, Defensive Upright Posture and Defensive Sideways Posture lead to Submissive Posture. Upright Posture and Sideways Posture, Offensive Upright Posture

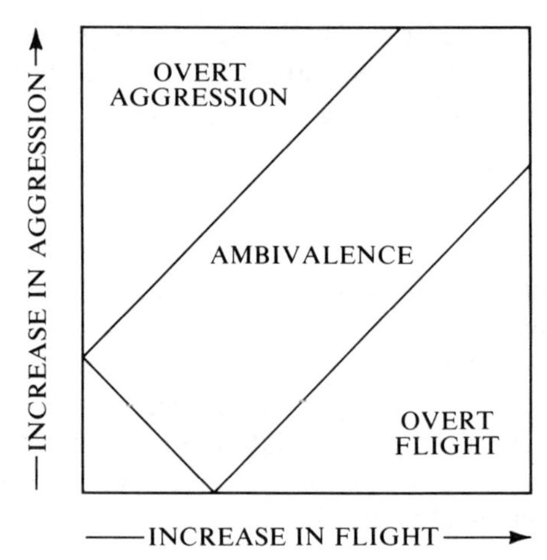

Figure 1. Basic diagram of interaction of Aggression and Flight. (After Morris, 1958.)

and Offensive Sideways Posture lead to Aggressive Posture. Attend and Approach also lead to Aggressive Posture and Submissive Posture equally, but at a much lower level.

Upright & Defensive Upright	→ Submissive 151	(expected 69)
Upright & Offensive Upright	→ Aggressive 118	(expected 53)
Sideways & Defensive Sideways	→ Submissive 116	(expected 34)
Sideways & Offensive Sideways	→ Aggressive 91	(expected 21)

The sexual postures Mount and Attempted Mount also lead to both Aggressive Posture and Submissive Posture but they seem to be a special case and will be dealt with later. The Upright Postures and Sideways Postures are then the ambivalent postures.

There is evidence that the Upright Posture occurs at a lower level of intensity than the Sideways Posture. This evidence is:

1) Postures that start sequences, Attend (ratio of acts preceding to acts following 189 : 651) and Approach (ratio 285 : 734), lead more often to Upright Posture than to Sideways Posture. That is, Upright Posture occurs earlier in the sequence of behaviour than does Sideways Posture.
2) There is a relatively higher correlation of Sideways Posture with Displacement Activities.

3) In the less intense situation of a small stable group of animals, the Sideways Posture is very infrequent.
4) The Upright Posture occurs more frequently than the Sideways Posture in all situations.

Two other postures occur as end points of sequences; these are Aggressive Groom (ratio of acts preceding to acts following 336 : 133), a posture similar in appearance to Aggressive Posture but in which the rat at the same time vigorously grooms the other animal, and Crouch (ratio 312 : 168). These are strongly associated in the cross-correlation. Crouch is generally recognised as part of flight behaviour. There are similarities in the relationships of Crouch and Submissive Posture. Defensive Upright Posture and Defensive Sideways Posture occur before Crouch with the following values:

Defensive Upright → Crouch 32 (expected 17)
Defensive Sideways → Crouch 28 (expected 13)

Although the similarity in the relationship of Crouch and Submissive Posture with the Defensive Upright and Sideways Postures is strong enough to indicate similar motivation, there are interesting differences in the use of the two postures which will be discussed later.

In the same way it can be shown that Aggressive Groom is similar to Aggressive Posture:

Offensive Upright	→ Aggressive	73	(expected 11)
Offensive Sideways	→ Aggressive	35	(expected 7)
Offensive Upright	→ Agg. Groom	21	(expected 9)
Offensive Sideways	→ Agg. Groom	13	(expected 5)

Bite is also similar to Aggressive Posture in its position in sequences but only follows Sideways Posture and not Upright Posture. This indicates, as might be expected, that Bite only occurs at the higher intensities of Aggression.

Finally associated with this group of agonistic postures we have the head and body movements towards and away from the other animal. The movements of the head, Threat, and the head and body, Thrust, towards the other animal would appear to be intention movements of aggression, as they lead to Aggressive Posture and Aggressive Groom.

Threat → Aggressive posture 25 (expected 19)
Threat → Aggressive Groom 37 (expected 15)

They would be expected to indicate a low level of intensity of aggression. However, as well as occurring at low levels of intensity they occur associated with Sideways Posture and the preceding Bite, both of which we have already decided are occurring at high levels of intensity. It seems, therefore, that these intention movements indicate a low level of available aggressive drive; that is to say, they occur just to one side of the diagonal ambivalent line. Similarly, the head away and body away postures, Flag and Evade, can be interpreted as intention movements of flight. They are followed by the more complete movements of flight, Submissive Posture and Crouch.

Flag → Submissive Posture 15 (Expected 6)
Flag → Crouch 24 (Expected 4)

As mentioned before, sequences start with acts which indicate a focusing of attention on the other animal, Attend and Approach. These lead to all the postures already mentioned but most

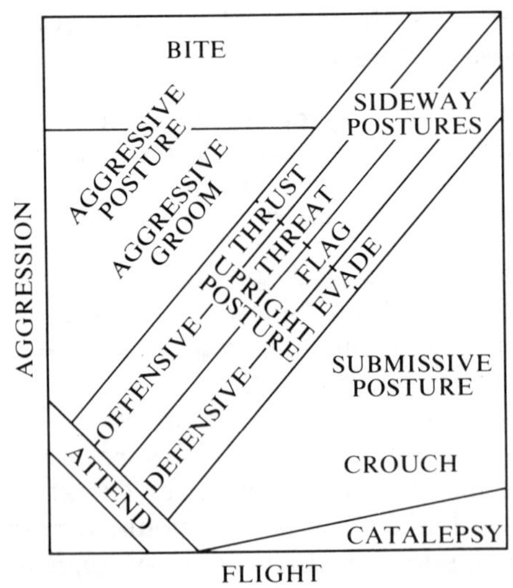

Figure 2. The completed ethogram.

significantly to the intention movements and the Upright Posture; that is, the postures occurring at the lower intensity levels. They can probably be interpreted as indicating arousal of any one or more of the social drives.

The ethogram can now be completed (Fig. 2).

Pathway Analysis

There is a large amount of overlapping of position in the ethogram, Crouch and Submissive Posture overlap on the flight side of the diagram, and on the aggressive side Aggressive Groom and Aggressive Posture overlap. Although Upright Posture and Sideways Posture lead directly to these postures it is also found necessary to put Threat and Flag at each side of the diagonal so that they too overlap with the ambivalent postures. Although it is obviously impossible to fix these positions accurately, this overlapping does seem to be correct. This means that at any given position the rat has at least two motor patterns available.

It is possible to draw a pathway diagram showing the inter-connections of the postures in the ethogram. For convenience I have divided this into two diagrams, one showing the predominantly flight motivated postures and the other showing the aggression motivated postures. The breadth of the arrows between the postures is roughly proportional to the number of times that particular sequence was recorded. The actual number is also shown. On the flight diagrams (Fig. 3) it can be clearly seen, despite a certain

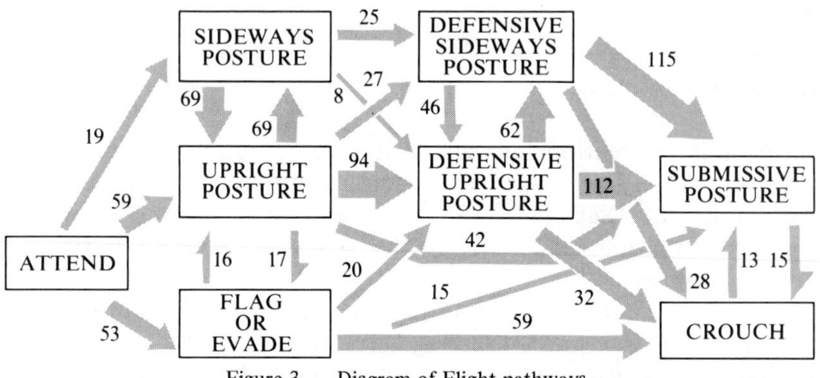

Figure 3. Diagram of Flight pathways.

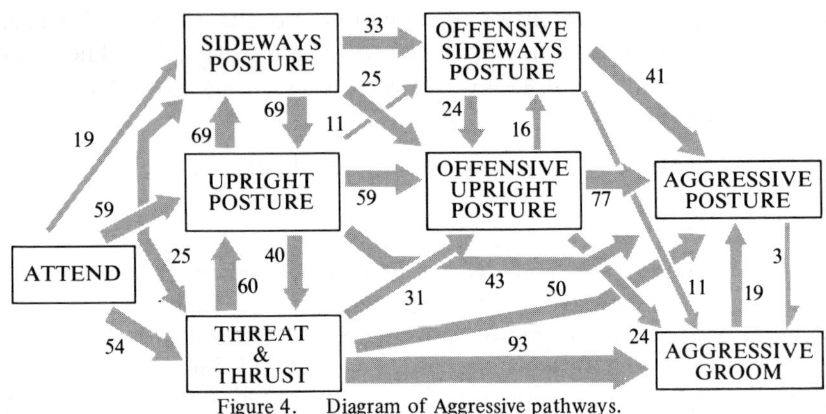

Figure 4. Diagram of Aggressive pathways.

amount of crossing over, that there are two well defined pathways of activity. One pathway leads from attention through the structured ambivalent postures to Submissive Posture and the other leads from attention through the intention movements of flight to Crouch.

The diagram of the aggressive postures again shows two pathways (Fig. 4). In this case, however, the crossing over is much more pronounced. This is probably due to the response of the aggressive animal being much more dependent on the action of the submissive animal. Thus, although the commonest response to Threat or Thrust is Flag or Evade, Upright Posture and Defensive Upright Posture are also frequent.

If Threat is responded to by an Upright Posture the threatening rat will then most likely also show one of the structured postures.

Displacement Activities

During this interaction between male rats, a number of apparently irrelevant activities occur. The most common of these are Self-Grooming and Digging. These activities when performed in this agonistic situation differ from the autochthonous activity in a number of ways.

When a rat self-grooms normally, it starts by washing its face with its licked fore-paws, drawing the fore-paws down its face from the base of the ears to the tip of the snout. It then licks the fur, starting with the fore-part of the body and working back to the tail. It finally scratches vigorously with its hind legs. This is, of course, an ideal sequence. When self-grooming is performed during a social encounter only the face washing is seen. This may be reduced to only one or two movements of the fore-paws. Each individual movement appears to be much faster and the complete pattern has a staccato effect. Occasionally orientation is disturbed and the fore-paws are observed to miss the front of the snout.

Similarly, only the first part of the normal digging pattern of scraping with the fore-paws, kicking back with the hind paws and, finally, turning round and pushing with the fore-paws is seen and again the actions are briefer and faster.

Much less commonly, drinking and eating are also seen, again in an abbreviated form.

This description is what would be expected for displacement activities, as described by Bastock, M., Morris, D., and Moynihan, M. (1952). That is, irrelevant activities that are performed when two mutually inhibiting drives are activated or when one strongly activated drive is frustrated.

The relative frequencies of these displacement activities are very different–Displacement Groom 221, Displacement Dig 89, and Displacement Drink 9, but there is no evidence that they occur in different situations, as, for example, Clarke (1956) has described in voles. For the purposes of this analysis they will be considered as a group.

In the sequences these activities occur at a higher level than the expected values after the ambivalent postures Upright Posture and Sideways Posture and also after Aggressive Groom.

Although the observed numbers are higher after Upright Posture the association is actually much stronger with Sideways Posture:

Upright Posture → Displacement Activities 30 (expected 24)
Sideways Posture → Displacement Activities 22 (expected 9)

This is, of course, expected as I have already indicated that Sideways Posture is occurring at a higher level of activation of the two drives, flight and aggression, and is consistent with that interpretation.

The association of displacement activities with Aggressive Groom is less expected:

Aggressive Groom → Displacement Activities 7 (expected 4)

I have already shown that Aggressive Groom is an expression of fairly complete aggression. If my interpretation is correct, the explanation for the occurrence of displacement activities after this posture must be that the aggressive drive is being frustrated. Evidence for this can be obtained from the cross-correlation data. As I have said before, the posture in the other animal associated with Aggressive Grooming is, very significantly, Crouch. If we then examine the responses to Crouch it can be seen that they vary quite widely and include a considerable number of displacement activities. On the other hand, there are only a few responses to Submissive Posture mainly Aggressive Posture and Sniff. This point will be discussed later but it suggests that, whereas Submissive Posture has a signal value indicating submission and thereby reducing the aggressive drive in the other animal, Crouch has no signal value and leaves the aggressive drive high without affording any opportunity to act aggressively.

Displacement activities also occur at a significantly high level after Retreat. This will be discussed when examining acts and postures performed at a distance from the other animal.

Mounting

In all of these male-male situations sexual acts are seen. The full mounting pattern, moving round to the back of the other animal, putting the fore-paws on the back of the other animal and palpating with them, executing pelvic thrusts and, finally, throwing itself back on its haunches and grooming its own genitals, is described as Mount. Any other attempt, from simply putting the paws on the back to the full pattern with the wrong orientation, is called Attempted Mount.

This behaviour would also appear to be irrelevant in a male-male situation, but it differs in several significant ways from the displacement activities described in the last section. The points of difference from displacement activities are the following:

1) The total occurrence of mounting is much higher than all the displacement activities together.

2) Although still occurring after the ambivalent postures Upright Posture and Sideways Posture, it does occur after the consummatory postures Aggressive Posture and Submissive Posture.
3) Within the ambivalent postures it occurs more after the lower intensity Upright Posture than the higher intensity Sideways Posture.

   Upright Posture → Mount & Attempted Mount 104 (expected 67)
   Sideways Posture → Mount & Attempted Mount 17 (expected 24)

   This is the reverse of the occurrence of displacement activities.
4) Quite frequently the complete pattern of sexual behaviour is shown, apart from intromission, and the speed of the performance is no higher than that seen in normal sexual behaviour.

It seems, therefore, that the appearance of mounting in the male-male situations cannot be explained as a displaced activity. The alternative to this is that the sexual motivation is separately aroused in these social situations. This hypothesis accounts for its appearance after the consummatory postures of the other drives and after the lower intensity elements of the other drives.

Mounting is also strongly associated with Follow and Sniff:

Follow → Mount 86 (expected 23)
Sniff → Mount 78 (expected 38)

In male-female situations this group of activities, Sniff, Follow, Attempted Mount and Mount is very much increased. This suggests that these elements are also part of male sexual behaviour.

Distance Ambivalence

From time to time during the agonistic behaviour one or other or both animals will break off the encounter and move away for a certain distance. At that point, one or more of a number of activities may or may not be performed and the animals will then return to the encounter. In its simplest and commonest form this activity consists of the sequence Retreat-Approach.

Retreat → Approach 147 (expected 16)

This sequence is quite often immediately repeated:

Approach → Retreat 84 (expected 64)

Very commonly Attend comes between Retreat and Approach:

Retreat → Attend 30 (expected 9)
Attend → Approach 50 (expected 23)

This simply means that the animal stops for a short time at the end of the retreat and watches the other animal before approaching.

A number of other acts can be performed at this point. These are:

1) Walk Around: a movement round the arc of a circle whose centre is the other animal.
2) Hunch: standing broadside to the other animal on tip-toes and with the back arched.
3) Side: as Hunch but without being on tip-toes and with the back flat.
4) To-Fro: a short movement back and forward along the line between the animals.
5) Figure-of-Eight: similar to To-Fro but stylised into a tight figure-of-eight.
6) Tail Rattle: a sinusoidal movement of the tail.
7) Stretched Attention Posture: a stretching of the body towards the other animal.

All of these postures show clear indications of conflict between approach and avoidance. This conflict is resolved into ambivalent postures in Hunch and Side, into a vector in Walk-Around and into alternating movements of both tendencies in To-Fro and Figure-of-Eight. In Stretched Attention Posture approach is slightly dominant, but the slowness of this approach and the long stretching of the body show the effect of avoidance.

The occurrence of the individual postures is rather low and this makes analysis difficult. However, it is possible to examine them as a group, which I have called Distance Ambivalence. This group occurs after Retreat and Attend significantly more than expected by chance.

Retreat → Distance Ambivalence 67 (expected 28)
Attend → Distance Ambivalence 71 (expected 40)

It leads to Attend and Approach at levels higher than expected by chance.

Distance Ambivalence → Attend 30 (expected 12)
Distance Ambivalence → Approach 31 (expected 21)

This places the group at that point in the sequence I have described.

Certain differences can be seen within the group: Walk Around and To-Fro lead mainly to Threat, Aggressive Groom and Mount; Side and Figure-of-Eight lead to Crouch. This is evidence that these postures can be divided into two sub-groups, one of which is slightly approach dominated and the other slightly avoidance dominated. The figures also show Stretched Attention Posture as leading to Retreat and Crouch, contradicting my previous statement that it is slightly approach dominated. This is because it has been redefined since the end of this study. The original definition included the approach component, that is, a stretching of the body towards the other animal followed by a slow approach towards it. This does then frequently lead to Retreat. However, I now feel that these two components should be separated.

As mentioned before, Displacement Activities occur at a significantly high level after Retreat.

Retreat → Displacement Activities 44 (expected 13)

They also lead to Approach and are quite strongly associated with Attend and Distance Ambivalence.

Displacement Activities → Approach 42 (expected 8)
Displacement Activities → Attend 24 (expected 5)
Distance Ambivalence → Displacement Activities 32 (expected 16)

Again suggesting that there is conflict at this point.

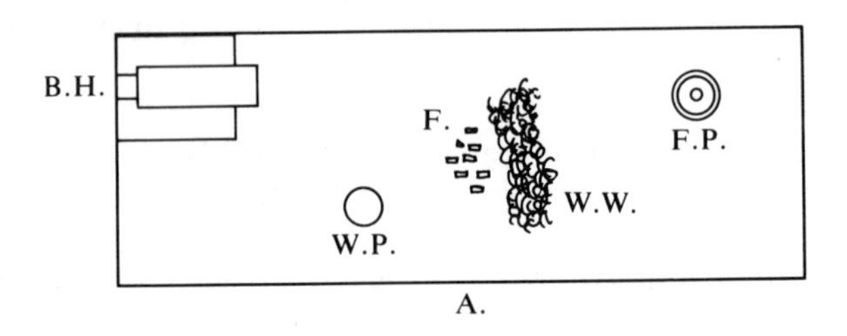

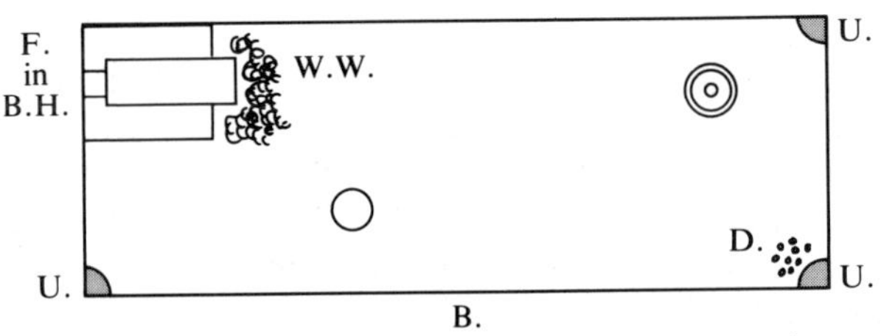

Figure 5. General layout of runs. A. Before occupation by rat. B. After occupation by rat. B.H.–Brick House, F.P.–Flower Pot, W.P.–Water Pot, F.–Food, W.W.–Wood-wool, U.–Urine, D–Droppings.

A number of observations were made with the rats in a larger space–runs 8′ x 2′ with a number of objects in them: an upturned flower pot, a few bricks and a water pot. Fig. 5 shows the general layout of these runs. In this situation[2] an activity that I call Crawl over Obstacles occurs, consisting of crawling over and urinating on these objects. They occur in the same part of the sequence as Distance Ambivalance, commonly after Retreat and leading to Attend and Approach. They also occur after one another, a typical sequence being: Retreat-Over Flower Pot-Over Water Pot-Approach.

[2] The behaviour described in this paper was observed in a number of different experimental situations. In all cases, however, the actual sequence of behaviour and the relationships of the postures remained constant. The changes that did occur were due to tendencies to use some of the postures more than others. It is hoped that these differences will be the subject of a future paper. For the purposes of this paper the results from these different situations have been taken together.

Crawling over and Crawling under

In these acts the rat moves over or under the other animal in such a way as to maintain body contact. Very often during Crawling Over the animal passes a drop or two of urine, leaving a wet patch on the fur of the other rat.

Barnett, S. A. (1958), has described Crawling Under and interprets it as a "friendly" gesture shown by a subservient "beta" animal to an intruder. I find that it occurs before and after all the agonistic postures, but is strongly connected with Sniff, Follow and Approach. This is a group of postures that is associated with mounting and I feel that Crawl Under may be an expression of sexual motivation. Against this there is the fact that it is not positively connected with mounting, occurring before and after mounting at about chance level.

In the same paper Barnett also mentions Crawl Over but does not think it a clearly defined act. I must disagree with this. When performed by the aggressive animal and combined with urination, it is very clear and deliberate.

Crawling Over occurs most frequently after Aggressive Posture, Aggressive Groom, Attempted Mount, Approach and Sniff, and leads to Aggressive Groom, Retreat, Follow and Sniff. Crawling Over seems, therefore, to be connected with aggressive and sexual tendencies. There may be two forms, one associated with urination and the other not, but it is very difficult to be sure of seeing the urination and I have no data on this point. However, when urination was clearly observed the act was performed by the more aggressive animal.

Other Acts

This leaves a group of postures which are not necessarily related to each other, which I will only describe briefly.

Freeze: This occurs as a response to a movement by the other animal that is, or could be, aggressive. The cross-correlation table shows that it occurs in response to Threat, Offensive Upright Posture, Aggressive Posture, Approach, Sniff and Attend. It occurs in connection with the more submissive postures in the animal showing it. It has some inhibiting effect on the social behaviour of the other animal, as it occurs as a response 70 times but is only responded to 47 times. The most common responses are Mount and Aggressive

Groom. The mounting is probably due to the fact that it is a frequent part of the behaviour of the oestrus female where the sequence Run-Freeze is a stimulus for mounting by the male.

Pull: This act consists of gripping the skin of the other animal with the teeth and then pulling. Again it is not strongly connected with any particular set of activities. It occurs in the sequence Approach-Pull. During observations it seems to occur when the opponent is not reacting socially and the actor is aroused.

Kick: Kicking with the hind foot; most commonly occurs as a response to the genital sniffing of the other animal. It is performed by the submissive animal, frequently when it is on its back in the Submissive Posture. It is also a very common act in the female, again in response to genital sniffing.

Finally, it is possible to draw a pathway diagram for the complete series of postures. However, if all the connections are put in, this becomes so full of intercrossing lines that it is very difficult to get any meaning from it. If only the commonest postures preceding and following each posture are used, the resultant diagram gives an idea of the total relationships between the groups of postures (Fig. 6).

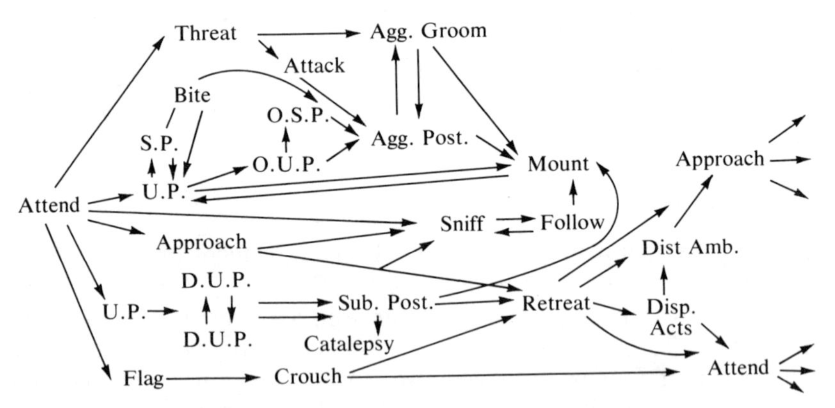

Figure 6. Pathway diagram showing the connections of the main postures. U.P.–Upright Posture. O.U.P.–Offensive Upright Posture. D.U.P.–Defensive Upright Posture. S.P.–Sideways Posture. O.S.P.–Offensive Sideways Posture. D.S.P.–Defensive Sideways Posture. Agg. Post.–Aggressive Posture. Sub. Post.–Submissive Posture. Dist. Amb.–Distance Ambivalence. Disp. Act.–Displacement Activities.

DISCUSSION

The structure and motivation of many of the elements shown by male rats in social situations can be discussed in terms of different levels of arousal of two main drives, Aggression and Flight. These two drives are opposed to each other and when aroused together, cause conflict in the animal. As described here, this conflict is evident in many of the postures shown. If one or other of these drives is at a much higher level than the other, then the elements shown reflect that tendency only.

Another distinct motive that appears to be separately aroused, though at a lower level in these situations, is a tendency to behave sexually towards the other animal and to mount it. This is again incompatible with other drives and adds to the conflict. It does, however, share an approach component with Aggression.

Morris, D. (1954), has described the courtship behaviour of some birds and fishes as being structured by the simultaneous arousal, in what he calls the F.A.M. complex, of the three tendencies: to flee from, to attack or to mate with the other animal. I have shown here, in a mammal, that social behaviour in non-courtship situations can be analysed in the same way and we have evidence that this is true of a number of laboratory species. Although the female behaviour has not been studied to the same extent it would also seem to be motivated in the same way, with the interesting point that the "M" tendency is still shown overtly as male sexual behaviour, i.e. attempted mounting.

In the previous section, the elements were analysed in these terms. There is, however, a major point that cannot be explained in this way, that is the availability of more than one motor pattern at, apparently, the same level of motivation. When in contact, the rats can either assume postures, Upright or Sideways, that were shown by the pathway analysis to lead most frequently to the end points Aggressive Posture and Submissive Posture, or perform intention movements, Threat and Flag, that usually lead to Aggressive Groom and Crouch. When at a distance from the other rat a completely different set of acts, apparently due to a similar balance of motives, were performed, Distance Ambivalence.

I suggest that there are actually only two alternative behaviour patterns and that Crouch, which does not seem to indicate submission in the same way that Submissive Posture does, is performed by an animal that would normally retreat, but due to the physical restriction of the cage, is unable to. If it could retreat it might, as the distance from the other animal increased and the flight drive was reduced, show Distance Ambivalence and approach once more (Fig. 7). Evidence for this is available from observations on

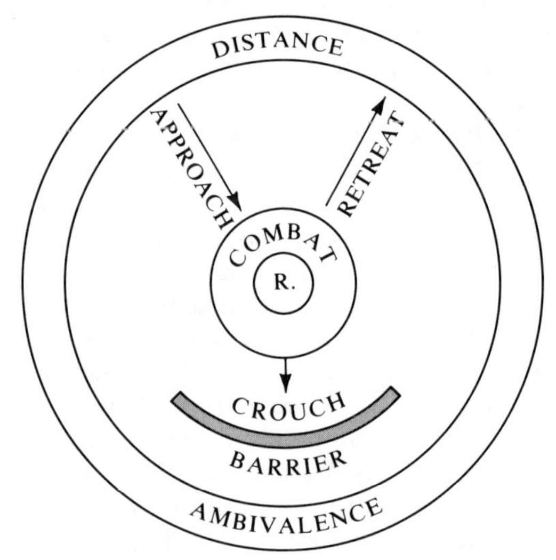

Figure 7. Diagram showing relationship of Crouch to Retreat.

behaviour in runs 8′ x 2′ when the incidence of Crouch decreased and that of Retreat and Distance Ambivalence increased. This will be discussed in a future paper dealing with the differences in behaviour seen in different situations.

These two alternatives may perhaps be related to the behaviour of the wild rat, *Rattus norvegicus*. Trapping, marking and recapture reports during ecological studies seem to indicate that rats live in groups within a well defined area. Calhoun (1948) showed that when strange rats were introduced into these areas there was a high mortality among both alien and resident rats and most of the aliens moved out of the area. None of the marked residents moved away from their home. Steiniger (1950) observed colonies of wild rats and reported that members of these colonies will defend the area against strangers. Barnett (1958) reported similar behaviour in artificial colonies of wild rats. Within the colony there is very little fighting and, although Steiniger says that he saw no evidence of rank order, it is obvious that some sort of social stability is obtained. Barnett mentions a form of social rank in his experiments, in that some of the animals adapted themselves to a submissive role. Calhoun (1948b) also showed some kind of ranking in that certain animals occupied favourable positions within the colony and retained them by combat, while we ourselves have demonstrated rank order in caged rats (Grant and Chance, 1958).

From these findings there is evidence of two systems of social behaviour. The first occurs as a response to a strange animal of the same species and has a territorial function. The second occurs in response to a familiar animal of the same species and has a social function, allowing the submissive animal to remain within the colony. I relate the two patterns of behaviour that I have observed in the laboratory rat directly to these two systems. The Submissive Posture, which reduces the intensity level of the encounter and allows the rat to remain near the aggressor, is associated with dominance-submission relationships within the colony. On the other hand, the losing animal in a territorial situation will retreat out of the social situation. In the wild rat this flight tendency would not be so strong as to take the rat completely out of the territory or, if this was not possible, would possibly cause complete breakdown and death, as reported by Barnett. With the laboratory rat the intensity of an encounter normally stays well below this level and an area the size of the run usually allows it to get far enough away from the other rat for the flight to come into conflict with opposing approach tendencies.

Some of the activities occurring during this conflict may themselves have territorial functions. Crawl Over Obstacles and sprinkling urine on them is evocative of olfactory territory marking as described by Hediger (1950). The points marked in this way often seem to act as bases for the retreating animal. Other acts seem to be simple ambivalent responses to the conflict, Side and Walk Around being vectors and To-Fro and Figure-of-Eight being alternating movements of the two tendencies.

A number of elements combine to give rise to this approach tendency. Among these are: aggression, which is always aroused to some extent by the presence of another rat; sexual approach, very obvious when the other animal is a female but also playing some part between males; and what appears to be a positive attraction towards the aggressive animal. This last gives rise to slow approach movements performed by animals with a high flight drive. It was also noted and recorded by Seward (1945), who said, "One trait characteristic of all stages (of submission) is a constant preoccupation with the other animal–apparently trying to keep as near him as possible"; and by Barnett, who said, "There is a continued tendency of intruders to approach the alphas, even after being beaten." No attempt was made by either of these authors to explain this behaviour.

A similar aspect of behaviour has been observed in monkeys. Kummer (1957) says that baboons will run to the nearest dominant animal when frightened, even when this animal is the cause of fear. He suggests that the mother-seeking behaviour of the young is transferred to the dominant males when the mother-young relationship is broken up. Chance (1956) described similar behaviour in the macaque, which he suggests might be due to an attractive element in threat. He also suggested that this type of behaviour might have a considerable effect in keeping the colony together in the face of strong disruptive forces present during sexual fighting.

Approach behaviour in these conditions would seem to indicate a tendency with the adaptive function of keeping these essentially social animals together. Functionally, the Submissive Posture can be thought of as an expression of Flight, which allows the rat to remain within the social situation; causally it is necessary to indicate what approach motive is present. In the more ambivalent postures this may well be aggression, but in the Submissive Posture and Catalepsy it is difficult to find any evidence of either aggressive or sexual motivation sufficient to overcome the overt reaction of flight. We might here have an example of a "social drive" such as has been postulated by Tinbergen (1950) and Allee (1939), coming into direct conflict with the agonistic behaviour.

SUMMARY

An analysis is made of the social behaviour of the male laboratory rat using the following methods.

One rat is introduced into the home cage of another. One observer records the series of elements shown by each rat. These results are tabulated in sequence tables of elements. The tables are analysed by calculating an "expected" value for each cell and comparing this with the observed value.

An ethogram is built up showing the relationships of the elements seen when the rats are close together and indicating the possible motivation of these elements in terms of the interaction of Aggression and Flight.

It is shown that the Flight motivated elements fall into two groups, one leading to Crouch and the other leading to Submissive Posture.

The occurrence of grooming and digging as displacement activities is shown and is contrasted to the occurrence of mounting which appears to be separately aroused in male-male situations.

A group of elements occurring when the rats are at a distance from each other, and showing conflict between approach and avoidance, is described.

It is suggested that there are two main Flight pathways, one leading to a Submissive Posture and the other to Crouch or Retreat, the occurrence of these is related to two types of behaviour seen in the wild, intra-colonial and territorial.

Finally, the possible occurrence of an Approach component other than Aggression or Mating, which might be called a social drive, is suggested.

REFERENCES

Allee, W. C. (1939). The Social Life of Animals. Heineman, London.

Barnett, S. A. (1958). An Analysis of Social Behaviour in Wild Rats. Proc. Zool. Soc. Lond., 130, p. 107-152.

Bastock, M., Morris, D. & Moynihan, M. (1953). Some Comments on Conflict and Thwarting in Animals. Behav. 6, p. 66-84.

Calhoun, J. B. (1948a). Mortality and Movement of Brown Rats (*R. Norvegicus*). J. Wildlife Management 12, p. 167-171.

——— (1948b). The Development and Role of Social Status among Wild Norway Rats. Anat. Rec. 101, p. 694. (Abs.)

Chance, M. R. A. (1956). The Social Structure of a Colony of *Macaca mulatta.* Brit. J. Animal Behav. 4 (1), p. 1-13.

Clarke, J. R. (1956). The Aggressive Behaviour of the Vole. Behaviour 9, p. 1-23.
Davis, F. C. (1933). The Measurement of Aggressive Behaviour in Laboratory Rats. J. Genet. Psychol. 43, p. 213-217.
Grant, E. C. & Chance, M. R. A. (1958). Rank order in Caged Rats. Animal Behav. 6, p. 183-194.
——— & Mackintosh, J. H. (1963). A Description of the Social Postures of Some Laboratory Rodents. Behaviour 21, p. 246-259.
Hall, C. S. & Klein, S. J. (1942). Individual Differences in Aggressiveness in Rats. J. Comp. Psychol. 33, p. 371-383.
Hediger, H. (1950). Wild Animals in Captivity. Butterworths, London.
Kummer, H. (1957). Soziales Verhalten einer Mantelpavian-Gruppe. Beiheft Zur schweizerischen Zietschrift für Psychologie und ihre Anwendungen, No. 33. Verlag Hans Huber, Bern und Stuttgart.
Morris, D. (1958). An Analysis of the Reproductive Behaviour of the Ten-spined Stickleback (*Pygosteus pungitius* L.) Behaviour Supplement No. 6.
———(1954). The Function and Causation of Courtship Ceremonies. Extract from "L'Instinct dans le comportement des animaux et de l'homme." Fondation Singer-Polignac, Masson et Cie, Paris.
Moynihan, M. (1955). Some Aspects of Behaviour in the Black-headed Gull (*Larus ridibundus ridibundus* L.) Behav. Suppl. No. 4.
Seward, J. P. (1945). Aggressive Behaviour in the Rat. 1. General Characteristics; Age and Sex differences. J. Comp. Psychol. 38, p. 175-179.
Steiniger, F. (1950). Beiträge zur Soziologie und sonstigen Biologie der Wanderratte. Zs. für Tierpsychol. 7, p. 356-379.
Tinbergen, N. (1950). The Study of Instinct. Clarendon Press, Oxford.
Wallis, D. I. (1961). Food Sharing Behaviour of the Ants *Formica sanguinea* and *Formica fusca.* Behaviour 17, p. 17-47.

Socio-infantile and Socio-sexual Signals in Canids: A Comparative and Ontogenetic Study

M. W. FOX

PART I: SOCIAL SIGNALS, INVESTIGATION AND INTERACTION

Introduction

Wickler (1967) and Anthoney (1968) have shown in primates that certain behavior patterns associated with infant responses to the mother may subsequently be incorporated (as "derived" activities) into social and sexual contexts in the adult. Wickler (1967) also emphasizes that certain patterns of adult sexual behavior may be employed as social signals in the absence of specific sexual motivation. This investigation is focused on an identification and ontogenetic analysis of such socio-sexual and socio-infantile patterns in canids. The significance of various body markings and secretions will also be discussed.

Materials and Methods

Observations were made on several litters of domesticated dogs, *Canis familiaris*, and on hand-raised pairs of coyotes, *C. latrans*, wolves, *C. lupus*, and grey foxes. *Urocyon cinereoargenteus.* Three red foxes, *Vulpes vulpes fulva*, four Arctic foxes. *Alopex lapopus*, and

From *Z. fur Tierpsychologie*, 1971, 28, 185-210.

two grey foxes obtained at a later age were also studied. Data were collected from in-cage observations, and during social interaction in an 8′ x 8′ arena equipped with one-way observation windows (see Fox 1970). A total of over 200 hr. of observations during development and at a later age, when subjects were reacting to prey and to strange conspecifics of approximately the same age, provided significant qualtitative and quantitative data to permit some developmental and cross-species comparisons of a variety of behavior patterns.

The following categories of behavior in relation to the situation were recognized:

1. Social investigation of a familiar conspecific after 24 hr. social deprivation, or of a strange conspecific.
2. Social interaction or contactual behavior in neonatal life, with conspecific (and with mother in domesticated dog subjects).
3. Social interaction or contactual behavior post weaning, associated with (a) play or play soliciting, (b) agonistic behavior, fighting, dominance and submissiveness, (c) sexual behavior, socio-sexual investigation, (d) lying down together, mutual licking and grooming.

A group of domesticated dogs were tested with a "whole dog" painting as a cross-sectional sample, being observed with the model for 3 min. only. These subjects were crossbreed mongrels, six aged 4 weeks, six aged 8-10 weeks, four aged 20 weeks, and six adults.

The test consisted of placing each subject in an 8′ x 8′ arena equipped with one-way observation windows, with the stimulus attached to one wall of the arena and illuminated with a floodlight (200 W). A score was made by two observers each time the subject approached and made contact with its nose or tongue on any region of the model (see Fox and Wiseman 1969, and Part II, for more extensive observations).

It was not difficult to score regional interactions with the model, for interaction was usually preceded by a clearly oriented, visually guided approach. Some difficulty was encountered when the subject would approach the model and sweep past it, in contact throughout. This occurred only rarely, and in such cases a score was given only to the initial region contacted. Occasionally, the subject would approach, contact the head, and then clearly orient and contact a forelimb, then move across the model and turn and contact the inguinal area or tail and then move away. In such cases, a score was given for each contact following a single approach. Observer bias was controlled by averaging scores of the two observers: without exception, there was a high degree of concordance in the records of trained observers.

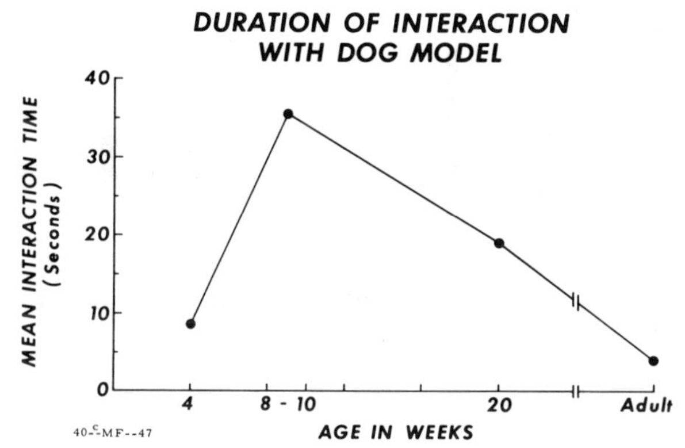

Fig. 1. Greatest interaction time in pups aged 8-10 weeks when first exposed to conspecific model (see Fig. 3).

Results

The results are described according to the above categories, and discussion is supplemented with observations of social responses of dogs of various ages toward the dog model.

In the cross-sectional group of dogs tested only once with the "whole dog" painting, the greatest duration of interaction lay between 8-10 weeks of age (Fig. 1). There were significant differences in the frequency of interaction with different parts of the model, highest scores to the hind leg and inguinal regions being seen at 8-10 weeks of age; interaction with the mouth and face, shoulder and foreleg were also highest at this age, but the differences were not statistically significant (Fig. 2, Fig. 3). In dogs aged 20 wks., and in adults, highest scores were associated with high interaction frequencies with the ear and anal areas. These areas are normally investigated by conspecifics and may provide important olfactory cues associated with individual identity; cerumen from the ear and

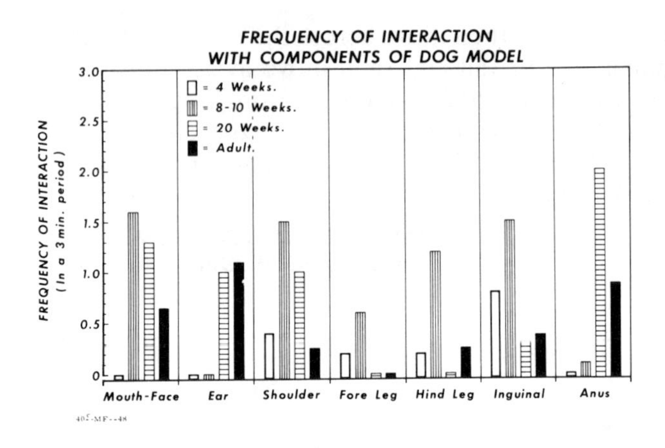

Fig. 2. Frequencies of interaction with various regions of the conspecific model.

secretions from the perianal or circumanal glands may therefore be of social significance to more mature dogs. The 20 wk. old dogs also showed a higher interaction frequency toward the mouth-face and shoulder regions than the adult subjects.

SOCIAL INVESTIGATION. In the Canidae, both genitalia and anal areas are investigated and presented during initial social encounters. The ears, mouth and supracaudal gland situated beneath a dark patch of hair one third down the tail are also closely investigated by conspecifics. In the Arctic fox the tail gland is very well developed, being circular (approx 3 cm. in diameter) and producing a sweet ambrosia-like odor in contrast to the rancid pervading odor of the anal gland secretion. Tail gland secretion increases in Arctic foxes after engaging in group play for a period of 15-30 min. In the grey fox, the tail (supracaudal) gland extends along the entire length of the tail beneath a dark dorsal line of hair (Fig. 4), and has a strong musklike odor. The red fox has a similar but weaker odor to the Arctic fox, and both wolf and coyote possess a very faint ambrosia-like smell beneath the dark patch of hair on the dorsum of the tail. In the wolf, this dark hair is seen as a thin stripe, and in the coyote as

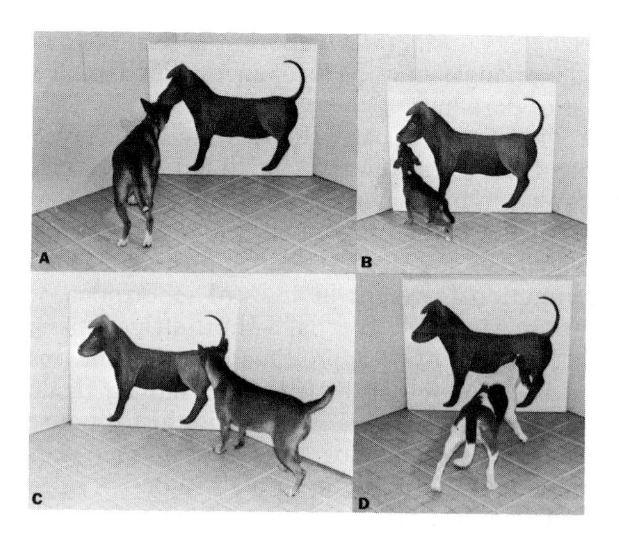

Fig. 3. Face-oriented investigation in adult and 10 wk. old dogs (a and b), and anal (c) and inguinal (d) investigation of model, in adult dogs.

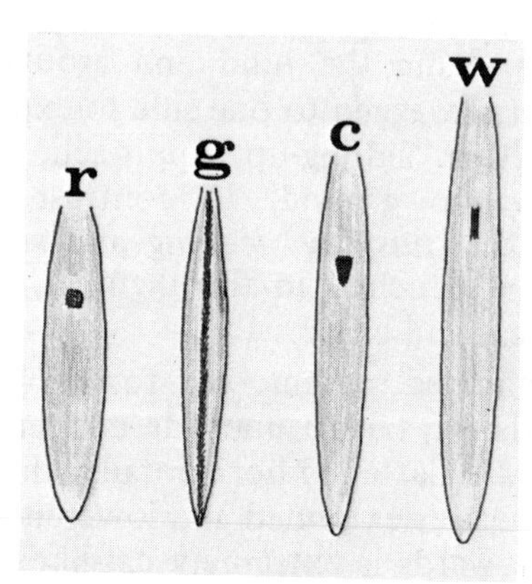

Fig. 4. Typical supracaudal gland markings in red fox (r), grey fox (g), coyote (c) and wolf (w).

an inverted triangle. Considerable variation is seen in the coyote tail gland mark; the triangle may be broken or blend with vertical or horizontal rings of dark hair.

Wickler (1967) was apparently unaware of the presence of this supracaudal gland and suggested that the round black spot on the tail of canids lies over the black perineum to provide an orienting cue as to the position of the perineum, which lies directly beneath it when the tail is lowered. In the domestic dog, this supracaudal gland is rarely if ever functional, except in cases of seborrhoea, when some hypertrophy occurs. In a few breeds, a short stripe, triangle, or oval area of dark hair is present in approximately the same position as in wild Canidae. Dissection reveals little or no glandular tissue except in older subjects, especially in those with a prior history of seborrhoea. In many breeds of domestic dog, this supracaudal gland mark is absent, or is present early in life (as in the Rhodesian ridgeback) and disappears as the adult coat develops. During social investigation, sniffing of the supracaudal gland area has not been observed in the domestic dog, and only occasionally in the wolf. This area is regularly investigated in the red, Arctic and grey fox. Frequency of investigation in the coyote tends to be intermediate between wolf and foxes, the odor being stronger in coyote than in wolf.

SOCIO-SEXUAL PATTERNS. The domestic dog, the coyote and wolf, when handled, will often lean toward the handler and push with the shoulders, bringing the hind end around in an inguinal presentation with the tail wagged to one side to expose the anus (and genitalia in the ♀). In this "sidling-up" approach, the hind end may be lowered, even to the ground, in contrast to the elevation characteristic of the cat; *pushing, leaning* and *standing still when contacted* (especially if touched in the inguinal area) are to some extent comparable in cat and canid.

When being handled, a tame red fox crouches, elevates the hind end slightly, curls the tail to one side and leans slightly toward the handler. The ears are flattened horizontally, the lips are retracted horizontally and the head is extended and lowered. This low intensity lordosis and leaning towards is extremely cat-like and may represent a comparable socio-sexual display in the red and Arctic fox. In the red and Arctic fox, a clear lordosis or elevation of the hind end occurs, coupled with whisking or curling of the tail in the direction of trunk flexion; and leaning or pushing with the shoulders or hips is seen during play and in play-soliciting. A similar pattern is seen in actual fighting when one fox attempts to avoid the check-oriented bites of the other, but does not run away.

The lateral "flagging" with the tail and leaning in the direction of body contact, and even turning of the trunk to present the genitalia, has been observed in the ♀ wolf, dingo and in many domestic dogs when in heat. Comparable patterns are seen during non-sexual (i.e., social) greeting between conspecifics and with a handler. The estrus display is enhanced by enlargement and reddening of the vulva and by bleeding, which is copious in the wolf and provides a strong, far-carrying visual cue against the white-cream hairs of the thighs.

Wickler (1967) and Leyhausen (1956) describe in both primates and cats the erect tail and elevated hind-end posture as socio-sexual presentation functioning as an appeasement or greeting gesture. In the domestic cat, this presentation, together with leaning or pushing and facial rubbing against a handler or nearby inanimate object, is seen when the cat is being petted or spoken to. The cat may roll over, scratch the ground with the forelimbs and groom itself and then orient again towards the handler. Similar displays are seen between conspecifics during social (greeting) and sexual encounters. Comparable patterns in the Canidae are less exaggerated, and many of the components are omitted (see Part II for further discussion).

SOCIO-INFANTILE PATTERNS. In grey fox, coyote and wolf (cubs), the same reflexes and neonatal responses described earlier for the domestic dog (Fox, 1964) were observed from birth onwards, namely the rooting and body righting responses, negative geotaxis, positive thigmotaxis and thermotaxis, reflex urination and semi-circular locomotion with the head moved from side to side as a thermotactile sensory probe. This side-to-side "searching" movement became unidirectional as a warm or soft tactile object was placed near or on one side of the face: this has been termed the *auriculonasocephalic* (ANC) *reflex* (Fox 1964). When the subjects were hungry, sucking intention movements and rooting toward the side of stimulation could be elicited in all canid species by simply handling them. The side-to-side head movements continued until a teat or finger was seized. This side-to-side head movement persists in dogs and wolves into maturity as a derived ANC reflex, along with teat searching activity during approach to the handler or in greeting a conspecific (Fox 1970). Pushing or stabbing with the nose and upward elevation of the head are seen when the neonate is nursing: the same movements, often coupled with side-to-side rooting, are seen in adults as a social greeting, while nose-pushing or stabbing may solicit attention or play.

In the hand-raised neonate canid, a good deal of self-sucking (or of a conspecific) occurred, notably on the prepuce, vulva or fore or hind paws. When observed together from birth onwards, the ANC reflex and rooting response resulted in mutual contactual circling which increased when the subjects were aroused by cold or hunger. When cold, this circling ceased when a tight "pile" of pups had been formed and is thus an important mechanism for heat conservation and thermal conductance in a partially poikilothermic neonate.

This *contactual circling* persisted as a social response in older canids long after they had become homiothermic (Fig. 5).

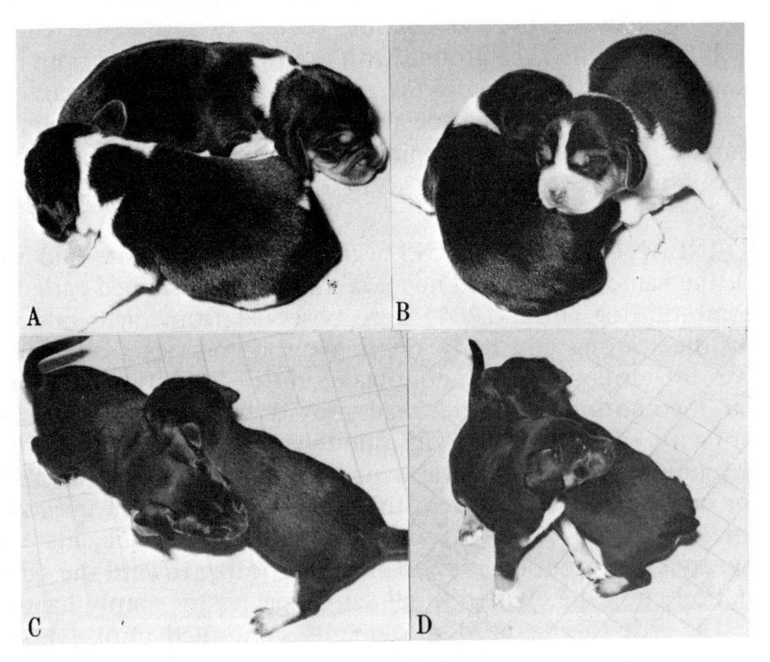

Fig. 5. Contactual circling (a) and circling with chin-resting (b) in neonate pups persisting in 5 week old pups respectively (c and d).

Table 1. Neonatal and infantile derived activities in adult canids.

Neonatal & Infantile Patterns	*Adult Behavior*
Contactual circling	Circling, leaning
Chin resting	T posture
Successive paw-raising (nursing)	Playful approach and play soliciting? (or merely exaggerated approach)
Side to side lateral head swinging–rooting to nurse	Social greeting, active submission
Vertical, upward head movements 'butting', nose-stabbing–nursing	Social greeting, play soliciting
Unilateral paw-raising, to reach up to teat, to paw mother's face	Play soliciting, as directed pawing or pawing intention
Face-mouth oriented licking to solicit food from mother	Social greeting, active submission
Licking intention prior to feeding: licking intention while approaching to lick face of mother	Social greeting, active submission and slower in passive submission
Passivity during ano-genital stimulation by mother, and passivity with inguinal contact during such stimulation	Passivity during social investigation. Submission, social greeting with inguinal presentation ('C' posture), submissive urination
Visually guided approach to inguinal area of mother to feed	Inguinal orientation and contact during social investigation
Distress vocalizations (whines and yelps) when cold or in pain	Passive submissive vocalizations, 'cut-off'
Distress vocalizations (whines) when hungry (care soliciting)	Care-soliciting vocalizations, active submission, social greeting
Nursing with tail down but arched away from anus	Eating or drinking, with tail down but arched away from anus
Eyes closed or partially closed during consummatory behaviors–eating, drinking, urinating, defecating and scratching	Eyes closed or partially closed during consummatory behaviors–eating, drinking, urinating, defecating, scratching and copulating
Squatting low on hind legs with tail out to urinate in male and female; female squats lower than male	Female and male show same urination patterns as in infancy but may raise one hind leg; more usual in male

Other social activities in canids are in part derived from patterns associated with earlier motivation-specific categories (Table 1). Most canids regurgitate food for their offspring, and the offspring readily approach and solicit food by pawing, nosing and licking the sides of the mouth of the parents. In the domestic dog, this food regurgitation is often absent, although mouth-oriented licking and greeting are still present. Licking, as part of social greeting, may therefore be unrelated to food-soliciting. Hand-raised wolves and coyotes readily lick the face and mouth of the handler, and this pattern persists in the absence of reinforcement with regurgitated food. Repeated extrusion of the tongue and smacking sounds are seen in all neonate canids when approaching the mother to nurse, or while being handled just prior to bottle-feeding. Such licking intention movements prior to nursing persist as a social greeting in some species. The duration and intensity of intention licking and actual licking, while approaching and greeting, are much greater in the dog and wolf than in the coyote. Intention licking has not been observed in any of the fox species during approach, but when contact is made, licking as a greeting response is seen at low frequency. According to Kühme (1965) regurgitation of food, following mouth-oriented soliciting, is not restricted to early life as in other canids, but persists as a highly ritualized ceremony in adult Hunting dogs (*Lycaon pictus*). Reciprocal food-soliciting (active submission) and food-giving have evolved in this species as a socially integrative phenomenon at the expense of the more usual social dominance hierarchy.

URINATION IN SOCIAL CONTEXTS. In all species of canid studied, urination is evoked as a reflex response by stimulation of the external genitalia during the first 3-4 weeks of age. After this age, tactile stimulation of the external genitalia does not result in urination. During social greeting toward the handler, a dominant conspecific or an adult, the submissive animal will frequently urinate. In the young domesticated dog, this can become a problem when the animal is petted, disciplined or even stared at (Fox 1965). Some dogs eventually grow out of this behavior, but others (notably ♀♀) may retain this into maturity. In the young ♂ dog, penile erection frequently occurs during handling, and this may have some relationship to general arousal involving the autonomic nervous system. The submissive dog will often roll over into lateral recumbency, elevate the uppermost hind leg and "display" the tumescent glans penis, and occasionally urinate. From the situational context it appears that urination is a submission signal and may be derived from earlier mother-infant interaction. Such urination during submissive greeting has been observed in the domestic dog and wolf, occasionally in the coyote, but not in any of the fox species. Urination (and defecation) in other contexts associated with fear, with marking of unfamiliar objects or strange conspecifics and with marking particular "scent" posts have been discussed by Kleiman (1965). There is no evidence that these activities are in any way derived from earlier activities, as in the case of submissive urination. During submissive urination, the animal does not adopt the normal urination posture. Urination occurs while the animal is approaching with the hind end lowered to the ground and the inguinal region presented toward the dominant individual, or when the animal lies in lateral recumbency with the uppermost hind leg elevated.

Wickler (1967), in his review of socio-sexual signals, also refers to certain infantile behavior patterns which may be seen in the adult, notably social grooming in primates. Anthoney (1968) has postulated that greeting, grooming and sexual motor patterns in the baboon are ontogenetically related to, or derived from, infantile nursing patterns. Lip-smacking is first associated with nursing, and later with sexual behavior and social greeting; embracing and mounting are derived from the grasping reflex of the infant; grooming is first seen after weaning when the contact-comfort seeking infant comes to groom its mother instead of seeking her breast, and social grooming may be derived from nursing and teat-seeking behavior. This latter phenomenon is supported by the fact that more obvious motor patterns seen in the infant occur in variations of adult grooming—oral-grooming, saliva-licking, plucking and hair-pulling. Such mutual care-giving and care-soliciting behavior may evolve from infancy and become an integral part of adult social behavior. These persistent infantile patterns may be regarded as *socio-infantile signals* in adults, which may be used as attention-seeking, assurance, greeting or appeasement signals. There are, however, some intermediate forms. It has been suggested that such "regressive" infantile signals in an adult may appease or remotivate the aggressor: they are frequently exhibited during courtship by the ♀ towards the ♂. In many avian species, the ♀ may "present" sexually, but also flutter the wings, gape and vocalize like a food-soliciting fledgling. Ritualized or token feeding may then follow. Such infantile signals of submission during sexual encounters may remotivate the aggressive ♂, and represent a transitional class of *socio-infantile-sexual signals.*

PAW-RAISING. Sustained raising of one paw may represent an incomplete intention to roll over into submissive lateral recumbency, and (together with licking intention, horizontal retraction of the lips and depression of ears and tail) provides an unambiguous visual signal. This complex signal may also be accompanied by whining vocalizations and occasionally by urination. Successive raising and lowering of each paw, occurring especially in play-soliciting, may be derived from the alternate paw movements seen during nursing (Table 1) but are more probably related directly to adult locomotor patterns (alternate stepping). They serve as an exaggerated signal of intention to approach: during this display, the hind end is often elevated, and the hind feet remain stationary. The animal may alternate this display with forward, backward or sideways leaps or runs, and show the characteristic "play face" expression. Barking at the conspecific on such occasions has only been recorded in the domestic dog. These two categories of paw-raising (which have not been observed in foxes) are to be distinguished from directed pawing or stabbing with the fore-paws at the face or shoulders of a conspecific during play or (especially in the coyote) during intimidation of a subordinate.

PART II: ONTOGENY OF INGUINAL APPROACH AND PRESENTATION

Introduction

One of the most intriguing phenomena of behavioral development is the apparent persistence of neonatal or infantile responses and their incorporation into adult behavior patterns. Some of these neonatal responses belong to a distinct category, having characteristics of taxes (thigmotaxis, thermotaxis, negative geotaxis; Fox 1964), being influenced by the internal or motivational state of the animal (e.g. cold or hunger). Following Scott & Fuller's (1965) classification of behavior patterns into motivational systems, these neonatal responses may be grouped under et-epimeletic or care-soliciting behavior. Many of these responses are highly adaptive (survival-promoting) and are related to the environment of the neonate at birth (Fox 1966). Anokhin (1964) and Schneirla (1965) have respectively formulated the highly significant hypotheses of heterochronous systemogenesis and approach-withdrawal processes in relation to the ontogeny of many of these neonatal responses.

These responses, within the motivational system of et-epimeletic behavior, may subsequently be incorporated into other systems later in life (Fox 1967), notably social contactual, care-giving and care-soliciting behavior. Schenkel (1967) has shown that the submissive behavior patterns (both passive and active greeting) of the adult wolf can be recognized earlier in life, and these neotenous or regressive infantile patterns form an important part of the social behavior of the adult. Fox (1968) has shown how such infantile behavior in the pet dog ("perpetual puppy syndrome") may be reinforced by excessive care-giving by over-indulgent owners.

A highly predictable sequence of inguinal (groin) presentation and inguinal contact resulting in submission or passivity was noted some years ago by the author while handling adult dogs. Comparable behavior was observed also during social interaction between adults. On the basis of earlier studies on the reflex and behavioral development of the dog (Fox 1964) the following developmental and comparative study of inguinal contact and presentation was carried out with various species of Canidae.

Materials and Methods

The following observations were made on several litters of domestic dogs of various breeds, and on two wolves, three coyotes and two grey foxes which were hand-raised. In addition, four Arctic and four red foxes, acquired at weaning age, were studied, and also two grey foxes aged 4 months.

Visually guided approach to the inguinal area in the domestic dog, *Canis familiaris*, is first seen between 3-4 weeks of age, when the pups approach to feed from the mammae of the bitch, which are most productive in the inguinal area. These mammae usually continue to produce milk, when the glands in other regions have ceased to lactate. (In rare cases, an axillary teat may continue to lactate. In this case, the pup approached the axillary area of a dog model instead of approaching the inguinal area.) This approach behavior was tested with various models (Fig. 6), in three groups of dogs raised under various degrees of maternal and peer deprivation.

A test consisted of placing the subject in an 8′ x 8′ arena equipped with one-way observation windows, with the stimulus

B. Grzimek (1943) used comparable models in his studies of equine social behavior; Tierpsychol. 5, 466-480.

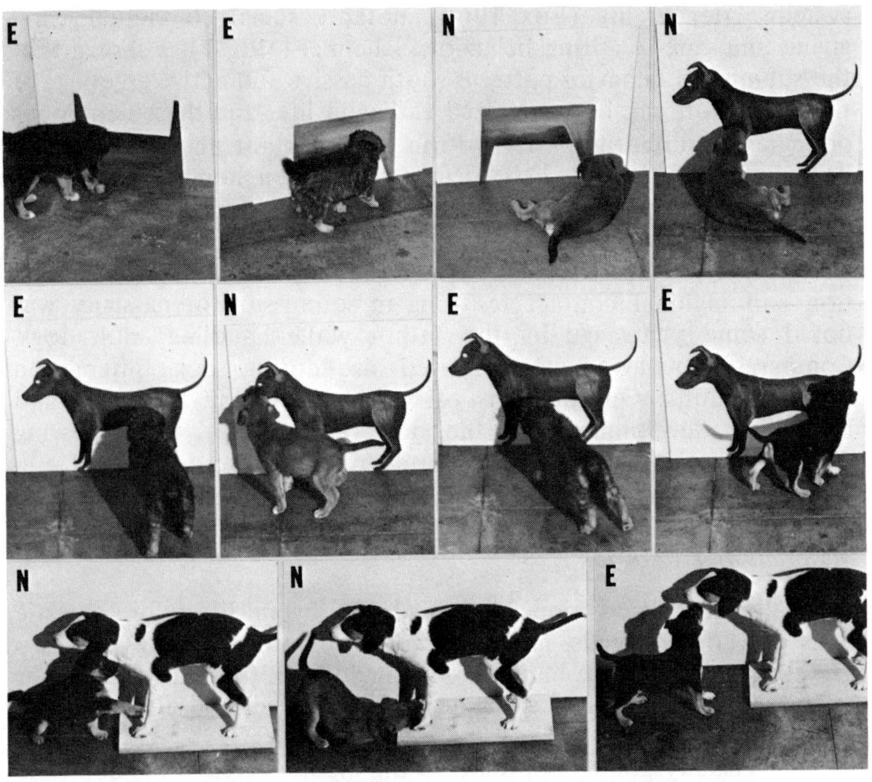

Fig. 6. Reactions of visually deprived (E) and normally reared pups (N) at 5 wks. towards various models (I-IV) described in text: 'inguinal' approach towards models I and II, and simply lying close to the model (proximity comfort?). With model III, shoulder, inguinal, facial and tail approaches are shown, and with model IV, paw-raising and play soliciting (also seen with model III) are shown as well as face-oriented contact.

attached to one wall of the arena and illuminated with a floodlight (200 W). A score was made by two observers each time the subject approached and made contact with its nose or tongue on any region of the model. Duration of interaction was not recorded. With all models, duration was ½-2 sec. with the exception of the stuffed dog, in which case duration increased to 5-10 sec. when the subject would lie down, and chew one of the feet of the model. Even with this model, duration of interaction was generally brief, for the subject would alternate from licking and chewing one leg and then another. [See Part I for further details of this test.]

Approach to mother may be reinforced transmodally during the transition period when the pup begins to respond to visual cues; prior association with tactile, thermal, olfactory and gustatory stimuli may contribute to the organization of approach processes, as emphasized by Schneirla (1965). To test this hypothesis, eight pups were visually deprived by bandaging the eyes from the time of opening of the eyes until weaning at 4 weeks of age. These pups were kept with the mother and experienced play and other social interactions with control littermates. These visually deprived pups (VD group) and the controls (C group), were kept in separate cages visually isolated from each other from 4 until 5 weeks of age, at which time various tests outlined below were conducted. During this period of isolation, essentially intended to allow recovery of visual function, the pups only had visual experience with the experimenter. They were not prevented from seeing their own bodies (by the use of collars, as employed in cats by Hein & Held 1967), but were fed a gruel and no water so as to prevent the possibility of them seeing their own reflections in the water bowl. Six pups were hand-raised by stomach tube from one day of age after they had received maternal colostrum. These (HR group) were kept isolated from each other in incubators and were visually deprived at the time of eye-opening and were subsequently treated as the visual deprived group described earlier. This HR group was included in order to eliminate all modalities of stimulation and reinforcement associated with maternal and peer interaction. They received a regime of no handling or petting except for feeding by stomach tube, and reflex stimulation of urination (six times daily, approx. 8 min. of total contact). It should be emphasized that these HR pups provided themselves with some degree of stimulation, in that they would crawl and root into the sides of the incubator and turn to suck their genitalia, paws or tail. These activities were of course not reinforced in the normal manner by food, but demonstrated the autonomous or endogenous motivation of various components of ingestive behavior; HR pups continued to root and self-suck even after stomach loading. Ross et al. (1957) and Stanley & Bacon (1963) have considered these phenomena in some detail.

Both HR and VD pups developed the visually guided placing

response precisely on the third day after removal of bandages. Between the fourth and fifth day they developed an avoidance of a visual cliff and on the fifth and sixth days when placed in the observation arena for habituation or shaping, readily approached and followed the experimenter. Control subjects were also shaped to the empty arena at 33 and 34 days of age.

On the 35th day each subject was tested for 3 minutes with each model (in the order shown in Fig. 6), at intervals of approximately 20 min. between each model. They were then allowed 45 min. play together and then re-tested 24 hr. later. The following regions of the various models were categorized:

> Models I & II—forelimb; hind-limb; inguinal; flank.
> Models III & IV—forelimb, hind-limb, shoulder-neck; flank, inguinal; anal; tail; head (face) and ear.

Between each test, both model (except Model IV) and the arena floor were wiped with Airkem R to mask any odors from earlier subjects which might interfere with the test.

Results

Reactions to the various models shown in Fig. 6 were as follows (see also Tables 2, 3, 4 and 5).

With *Model I*, the control (C) pups had the highest interaction frequency with the "inguinal" region, compared to their interactions with other regions. Visually deprived (VD) pups interacted more with the "forelimb" and "inguinal" regions. Reactions of hand-raised (HR) pups were diffuse, no regional preferences towards the model being seen.

With *Model II*, both C and VD pups interacted more with the "forelimb" and "inguinal" regions, while again the HR pups showed no regional preferences.

With *Model III*, the "whole dog" painting, the C pups reacted more to the head-face region of the model than to any other area. Their reactions to the head were greater than in either the VD or HR groups. (It should be emphasized that these pups are all 5 weeks of age at the time of testing and consequently their reactions to the whole painting cannot be directly correlated with those of earlier studies where subjects reacting to the same model were of a different age and had a different life-history prior to testing, i.e., were not socially isolated for 1 week or more prior to testing, Fox & Wiseman 1969.)

When retested with Model III, the whole dog painting, 24 hr. later after 45 min. play with each other, the HR pups (only) showed a significant difference in their reactions, as a result of this social experience with peers. Their frequency of interaction with the head-face and shoulder-neck region of the model increased dramatically (Table 4).

With *Model IV*, the "stuffed" dog, all subjects had a high interaction frequency to the fore and hind-limbs. Between-group comparisons show that the C pups reacted more to the head and hind-limb and inguinal area of the dummy than the HR or VD pups.

Table 2. Model I.

	FL.	*HL.*	*Flk.*	*Ing.*
C (9)	1.3	1.5	1.4	* 2.4
VD (8)	* 3.1	1.1	2.2	* 4.2
HR (6)	0.6	0.5	0.8	0.6

Table 3. Model II.

	FL.	*HL.*	*Flk.*	*Ing.*
C (9)	2.1	1.2	0.4	* 3.6
VD (8)	2.5	1.1	2.5	* 2.9
HR (6)	1.0	1.2	1.2	1.1

Table 4. Model III.

	Hd.		*Sh.*		*FL.*		*HL.*		*Flk.*		*Ing.*		*TL.*	
C (9)	* 4.1	* 3.6	2.0	1.5	1.5	1.1	1.3	1.0	1.4	0.8	1.5	1.1	1.2	1.0
VD (8)	1.4	1.7	* 2.7	1.7	1.4	1.1	1.2	1.7	1.4	0.6	1.7	1.5	1.1	0.5
HR (6)	0.2 →	2.5 *	0.5 →	2.3 *	1.2	1.5	1.5	1.6	0.5	1.0	0.7	0	0	0.3

(Scores for *test* and *retest* 24 hr. later after 45 min. play.)

Table 5. Model IV.

	Hd.	*Sh.*	*FL.*	*HL.*	*Flk.*	*Ing.*	*TL.*
C (9)	2.3	2.5	* 4.2	* 6.5	1.2	2.4	1.0
VD (8)	1.5	2.6	* 3.4	* 4.7	1.5	1.4	0.2
HR (6)	0.3	0.8	* 5.1	* 4.8	0.3	0.3	0.5

Tables 2-5 show average approach frequencies of control (C), visually deprived (VD) and hand-reared pups (HR) to the forelimb (FL), hind limb (HL), flank (Flk), inguinal (Ing), shoulder (Sh), head-face (HD) and tail (TL) regions of the models 1-4. Highest interaction frequencies in visually deprived pups are with foreleg and inguinal region of model, while normally reared pups show more interaction with the dummy inguinal region than with other areas. All scores of hand-reared pups are consistently low and diffuse or non-selective. Table 3: Consistently low and diffuse scores in hand-reared pups, while both control and visually deprived pups show highest interaction frequencies with inguinal region of model 2. Table 4: Consistent increase in approach frequencies in hand-reared pups towards head of model when retested after 45 min. social experience with peers. Control pups show highest interaction with the head-face on initial test and on retest, while visually deprived pups show no obvious change in reactivity (but note high approach scores to shoulder on initial test—see text). Table 5: All subject-groups show highest interaction frequencies with fore and hind limbs of model; hand-reared pups have lowest approach scores to other regions of model, while the control pups approach the head and inguinal regions at a higher frequency than recorded in the other two groups.

In all tests with the various models, the frequency of interaction in the HR pups was lower than in either VD or C pups, and their reactions showed little orientation towards any specific region of the model, except after a brief period of socialization when retested with the "whole dog" painting.

Discussion

The high approach scores to the "inguinal" area of models I and II may simply be due to the fact that this area was the center of the painting, evoking non-specific orientation. It may alternatively be homologous with the inguinal area of the mother, and approach to that (or comparable) area be associated with some prior reward. This argument may be supported by the lack of preference for any specific region of models I and II in the HR pups that had only contact with the inguinal and mammary regions of the mother for the first 24 hr. of life. The increase in head-face and shoulder approach in these latter subjects clearly demonstrated the effects of even very brief social experience. The overall low approach scores of the HR pups in contrast to the VD pups implies that visually guided approach to "social" stimuli or conspecific models is facilitated by prior associations of social experiences via other sensory modalities. Schneirla (1965) has hypothesized that experiences in one modality (thermal, tactile) early in life may influence approach (or withdrawal) reactions to stimuli providing auditory or visual cues later in life, in addition to evoking earlier (tactile, thermal) associations. This hypothesis appears to be confirmed: intermodal associations may be involved in the ontogeny of social behavior.

It may be argued that the HR pups had a lower preference for stimulus complexity because they had been raised in an experientially impoverished environment. This might account for their low approach scores to the various models prior to the brief period of social interaction. It is more probable, however, that the lack of prior associations with conspecific social stimuli was the major contributing factor, and this contention is supported by the re-test scores with Model III 24 hr. after 45 min. social interaction.

It is intriguing that, in spite of play with conspecifics, the VD pups did not show a marked increase in specifically oriented reactions towards this whole dog painting. This might imply that, in spite of prior visual deprivation, these pups had developed some type of schema of a conspecific which was not affected (or the direction of change was not revealed) by play with conspecifics and subsequent retesting with the "whole dog" model. A dramatic change in reactivity was shown in the HR pups, presumably because they were socially naive and had developed no schema (Sollwert) of a conspecific. It should be added that the VD pups during play with conspecifics were more contactual (see later) and this behavior, or the interaction effects of visual deprivation during earlier socialization and play with conspecifics, may have contributed to their rather diffuse reactions to the whole dog painting even on retesting after a short period of play with conspecifics.

PLAY OBSERVATIONS. As observed in an earlier study (Fox & Stelzner 1966) HR pups immediately made contact with each other during the 45 min. play period in the same contactual circling pattern observed in neonates, and this was followed within seconds by scruff-oriented biting. Subsequently following, chasing, facially oriented pawing, licking, biting (and intention movements thereof) tail and ear biting and mutual scruff-wrestling were seen. Inguinal contact and inguinal rooting, and inhibition when inguinal contact was made, were observed. Only toward the end of the play period were more sustained bouts of interaction longer than 15 sec. observed. The C and VD pups essentially shared similar action patterns but more sustained and coordinated reciprocal social interaction, less contactual circling and clear play-soliciting behavior were noted. The VD pups were indistinguishable from the C pups, with the exception that chin-resting on the shoulder of a conspecific frequently preceded scruff-oriented biting in the VD pups. This may be a remnant of contactual circling, which persisted in the VD pups in which social interaction was preceded by contact-seeking approach (as in the neonate) rather than by visually-guided approach. In the C pups, contactual circling and leaning occurred during social interaction (which is normal, even in adults) while scruff-biting was entirely visually oriented and was not preceded by chin-resting contactual behavior. (See Part I, for further discussion of the ontogeny of contactual circling.)

COMPARATIVE OBSERVATIONS. During social interaction between dogs, one individual initiates inguinal contact and genital investigation while the other, remaining largely passive, elevates the hind leg. This latter pattern is thought to be derived from remaining passive earlier in life, while the mother stimulates urination and cleans the anogenital area (Fig. 7a, 7b). It is most readily elicited between 3-5 weeks of age. The adult individual which makes inguinal contact is usually dominant over the one which stands still and allows inguinal contact and genital investigation. During active submission (greeting) in dog, wolf and coyote, one side (inguinal) may be presented as the animal approaches (the "C" posture); during passive submission in these species, the uppermost hind limb may be raised to expose the inguinal (genital) area and urination may occur as the animal rolls over on to its side. In these three species, and especially in the coyote, between 3-5 weeks of age, "accidental" inguinal contact with a peer during play or with a chair leg (for example) caused inhibition, and the animal would remain still for several seconds; occasionally the hind leg on the side of stimulation would be raised. Such responses to "non-specific" stimulation subsequently disappeared, except during social investigation (inguinal contact) initiated by a peer or human being (Fig. 7c, 7d). Lateral

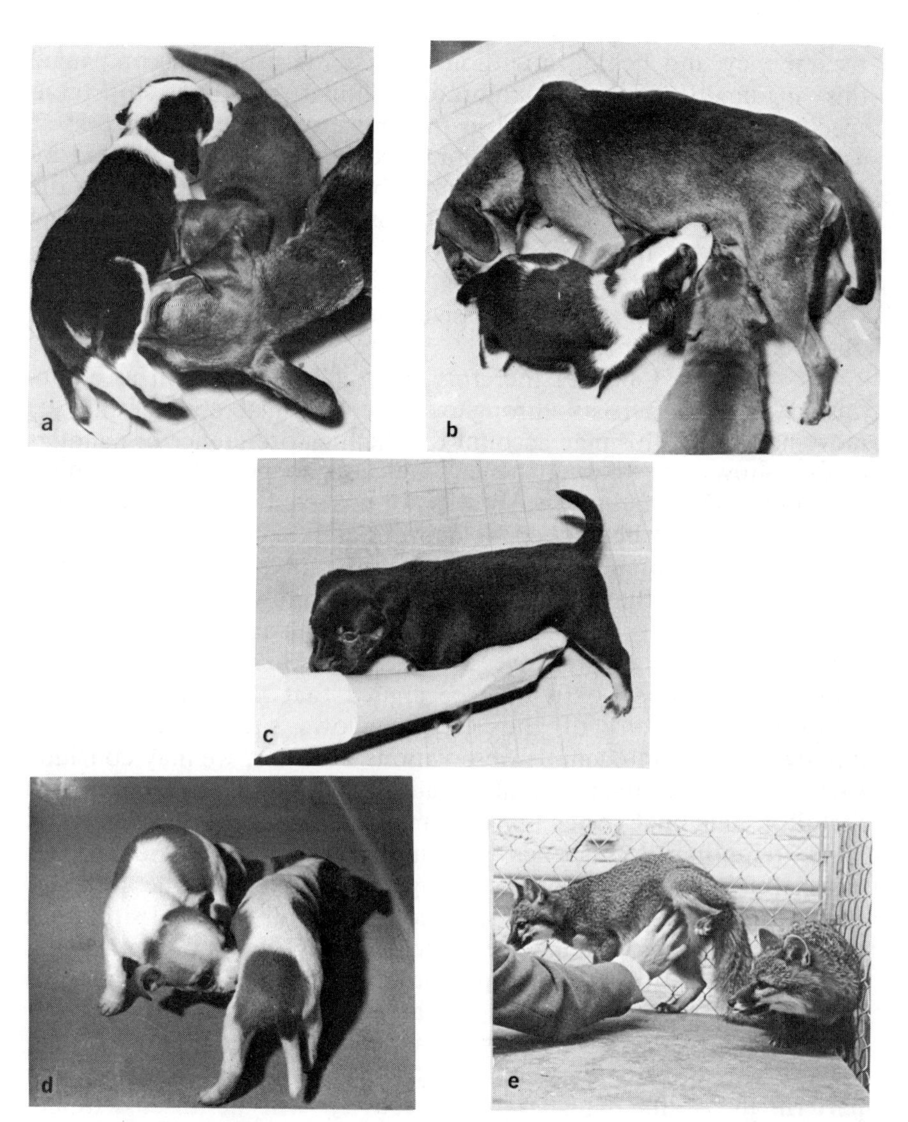

Fig. 7. (a) Inguinal contact initiated by mother, licking genital region of pup, who remains passive. (b) Visually guided inguinal oriented approach in pups to most productive teats of bitch. No anal 'presentation' (cf. Fig. 3) as bitch licks anal region of one pup. (c) Inhibition of pup following inguinal contact by handler. (d) Inguinal contact initiated during social investigation results in inhibition or passivity of conspecific. (e) Iguinal contact in adult grey fox results in passivity and elevation of the hind leg to form a clear inguinal presentation.

recumbency and licking intention movements usually accompanied this inguinally initiated inhibition. Similar responses to "non-specific" stimuli also occurred in the grey fox between 3-5 weeks of age, but persisted as a greeting or appeasement gesture elicited by inguinal contact from a peer or human being (Fig. 7e). Raising of the hind leg and inguinal presentation was seen frequently, following agonistic play in the grey fox between 5-8 weeks of age; occasionally both kits would stand head to tail, each with one hind leg raised ("position 69"). Passive-submissive lateral recumbency was not observed in the grey fox.

In some Canidae, therefore, inguinal presentation as a submissive gesture persists throughout life; inguinal contact inhibits movements, and this may account for the high preference of handlers at dog shows for holding the inguinal area to position and inhibit their dogs. The inguinal display was not observed in the red or Arctic fox, nor could it be elicited by appropriately touching the inguinal region. Inguinal presentation as a submissive or appeasement gesture was observed in the wolf, coyote, dog and grey fox, and in these same species light inguinal contact by a human hand resulted in behavioral inhibition (passive submission). Such stimulation may evoke this response, or it may be argued that the behavioral state (passive submission) of the subject allows such contact to be initiated. From ontogenetic observations however, we may conclude that inguinal contact actually causes behavioral inhibition, for fortuitous inguinal contact with inanimate objects or with a human hand temporarily suspends ongoing behavior in these species, especially between 3-5 weeks of age. Subsequently, the response becomes stimulus-specific or specific in relation to social situations involving submission and appeasement during inguinal contact and genital investigation by a conspecific of established social rank. This pattern may be derived from remaining passive while the mother stimulates urination and cleans the anogenital area earlier in life, and may be regarded as a derived activity which persists as socio-infantile pattern in adults. This type of activity will be discussed and compared with socio-sexual patterns which have been identified especially in Primates as socially integrative activities derived from sexually-motivated displays. The fact that the inguinal response can be elicited in hand-reared canids implies that development of the response is not dependent upon stimulation by the mother in early postnatal life, but rather that this social response is phylogenetically determined. During development, there is some ontogenic change in relation to the social situations in which the response is seen: the response of the adult, though phylogenetically determined, may therefore be ontogenetically derived from some earlier situational or motivational context (i.e., phylogenetically determined, ontogenetically derived or emancipated).

It should be noted that the bilateral inguinal stimulation of the ♀ by the ♂ when mounting prior to and during copulation (in which the ♂ clasps the ♀ around the waist) may inhibit the ♀ from moving. Receptivity during "heat" may greatly lower the threshold of this response to the ♂. Bilateral inguinal clasping is not seen in the cat, *Felis domesticus*, in which species the scruff-biting immobilization response is present (and can be identified in the neonate; Fox 1969).

Conclusions

SOCIO-INFANTILE AND SOCIO-SEXUAL SIGNALS. It is pertinent here to briefly consider socio-sexual signals and to compare and contrast these with the inguinal display and presentation of canids. Wickler (1967) has reviewed such derived sexual signals which become incorporated into the normal family and social life of Primates. There is consequently a change in motivation and context of sexual signals into non-sexual situations, associated with greeting, appeasement and assertion of dominance. Wickler (1967) also stresses that patterns other than sexual ones tend to stabilize the group; notably, brood-care patterns such as lip-smacking, mouth-to-mouth greeting and grooming persist throughout life. It is similarly argued that inguinal contact and inguinal presentation, possibly derived from two distinct motivational contexts early in life, persist as a socially integrative action and reaction between conspecific canids.

The outward rotation of one hind limb and inguinal presentation to expose the erect penis is a social display well documented by Ploog (1966) in the squirrel monkey. This may be comparable to the inguinal presentation in canids, in which the canid may assume a lateral recumbent posture and elevates the uppermost hind limb to expose the genitalia. The derivation of this activity in primate and canid may be quite different. For the canid, it has been suggested in this paper that it is derived from remaining passive while the mother stimulates urination and cleans the anogenital areas of the pups. Indeed in the adult and juvenile dog and wolf, urination is frequently associated with passive or active submission, at which times inguinal presentation also occurs. In the young ♂ domesticated dog, penile erection frequently occurs when the animal is being handled. Tumescence of the bulbus glandis and extrusion of the glans penis are invariably accompanied by inguinal presentation, and may be the result of non-specific (i.e., non-sexual) excitement involving autonomic arousal. In this case autonomic arousal results in penile erection, while in other more timid or frightened cases it may trigger relaxation of the sphincters and discharge of anal glands and of urine. Morris (1955) has discussed some of these autonomic aspects of social displays in detail and concludes that many are at first the result of general or non-specific or motivationally unspecified categories.

ANAL PRESENTATION AND DISPLAY. In the striped hyena, the author has observed reciprocal anal extrusion (which may result in discharge of anal-gland secretions), in which the anus is prolapsed up to 3 cm. and is presented to a conspecific with the tail elevated over the back and the hind end raised and the front end of the body lowered. This ritual frequently occurred after play-fighting in a pair of young striped hyenas; one would present and extrude the anus and the other would sniff it, and in turn present for its conspecific (Fig. 8).

This display may be derived from maternal-infant interaction, when the latter remain passive as the mother cleans the anal region. Such a possibility should be evaluated in a developmental study of this species, in which no inguinal display has been observed. It is conceivable that this display represents an extreme of the ano-genital presentation (with vertical tail) of felines, which, being present in the infant and being associated with maternal care (ano-genital licking), may be regarded as a socio-infantile pattern (which is also seen as a socio-sexual display in felines). In the Canidae, there is no such comparable anal display. In submission, the tail is depressed, covering the anal region, while in assertion of dominance the tail is held high. Exposure of the anal region may be quite fortuitous and of questionable significance in terms of social display in canids. Tail-

Fig. 8. In contrast to the development of inguinal presentation in canids as a social display, some carnivores have instead developed pronounced anal display. The anus is extruded, as in the polecat while being handled (a) and in young striped hyenas (b and c), coupled with elevation of the tail, occurring frequently after a bout of fighting or play-fighting.

wagging *per se* is seen during social greeting and in active submission in all canids observed in this study, being less frequently seen in the less social canids (i.e., foxes). Tail-wagging in the wolf, dog and coyote also occurs, at a different frequency and position, during general arousal (prey-chasing) and in agonistic encounters.

This social ritual may involve comparable autonomic elements associated with penis and pseudopenis erection in the ♂ and ♀ spotted hyena. In this species, genital display accompanied by elevation of the hind leg nearest to the conspecific, and mutual investigation (often in "position 69") is associated with appeasement and greeting ceremonies.

In conclusion, inguinal presentation in canids (namely in the grey fox, wolf, coyote and domestic dog) is a social display associated with social interaction and investigation, submission and appeasement; it is also seen in ♀♀ subordinate to ♂♂ and may be confused with a primary sexually-motivated display. In ♀♀ during the breeding season, a variety of other displays within the context of sexual behavior are manifest. The inguinal response, however, may play a significant role in receptive ♀♀ when they are mounted by the ♂. Bilateral inguinal stimulation by the clasping forelimbs of the ♂ around the ♀ may effect some degree of inhibition, so that the ♀ remains motionless so that intromission can be accomplished. In the domesticated cat, comparable inhibition is induced by the ♂ seizing the nape of the neck of the ♀; in this species, neither inguinal presentation nor inguinal clasping occurs.

Inguinal presentation is thought to be derived from remaining passive while the mother stimulates the offspring to urinate, and cleans the anogenital area. Inguinal presentation, and allowing a conspecific to make inguinal contact with the nose, are correlated with submission and appeasement. A dominant dog will rarely allow a subordinate to initiate inguinal contact. The author has been attacked on numerous occasions when attempting to initiate inguinal contact (by hand) with dominant dogs on their own territory. More friendly or subordinate dogs allow such contact, remain passive, and may even roll over and urinate. Dogs of equal dominance (or strangers) will circle each other until one stands still and allows the other to sniff the perianal region and genitalia. Inguinal approach towards a ♂ is oriented toward olfactory and gustatory investigation of the preputial area of the conspecific. Inguinal approach and orientation earlier in life is thought to be derived from food-reinforcement by the productive inguinal mammae of the mother. The motivation to approach the inguinal area clearly changes during the animal's lifetime, but the effect of inguinal contact, namely inhibition of on-going behavior, does not. This effect, derived from mother-infant interaction, persists as a greeting and appeasement response, especially in dominant-subordinate interactions. In essence, the adult is displaying regressive (or neotenous) infantile behavior in greeting or subordination, during both active and passive submission. Schenkel (1967) draws similar conclusions from his studies of other categories of active and passive submissive behavior in wolves.

SUMMARY

Part I

A study was made of the development of social investigatory behavior in dogs, and of its orientation towards conspecifics. In domesticated dogs, responses to a conspecific model or "social releaser" were also evaluated for different age classes. The orientation of social investigation is discussed in relation to the presence of scent glands and of other body secretions in the various Canid species.

A number of behavior patterns observed in adults during non-sexual, social interaction may also be observed during sexual interaction, or alternatively may closely resemble similar patterns present in infancy (i.e. these represent, respectively, *socio-sexual* and *socio-infantile* patterns). Socio-sexual behavior patterns are described and compared, and a number of behavior patterns present in infancy which become incorporated into adult social behavior patterns are detailed. The ontogeny of these derived, socio-infantile patterns is outlined.

Part II

Light contact on the inguinal area, initiated by a handler or by a conspecific, causes passivity or inhibition in the domestic dog, wolf, coyote and grey fox, but not in the red fox or the Arctic fox. In social interactions, inguinal presentation and elevation of the hind leg nearest to the conspecific occur as a submissive or appeasement gesture. This has evolved as a mutual display in the grey fox. The ontogeny of the response is described for these species.

The response to inguinal contact may be derived from remaining passive early in life while the mother stimulates urination. Bilaterial inguinal contact during copulation in Canids may result in behavioral inhibition; similar unilateral or bilateral contact is used by dog handlers to position and restrain show dogs.

The motivation of initiation of inguinal contact, and the effects of early experience, were investigated in domestic dogs. Food reinforcement from the mother is postulated as a positive conditioning agent. 23 subjects were tested at 6 weeks of age after one of the three following treatments: rearing in isolation from birth; visual, but not social deprivation; rearing under normal conditions. Reactions towards four different models or "social releasers" presented in succession were evaluated. It was found that social experience contributed to the orientation towards and frequency of interaction with various parts of these models.

The ontogenetic, phylogenetic and social significance of the inguinal response is discussed and compared for various Canidae.

REFERENCES

Anokhin, P. K. (1964): Systemogenesis as a general regulator of brain development; pp. 54-86, In: Progress in Brain Research **9**: The Developing Brain (Eds.: Himwich, W. A., & Himwich, H. E.).

Anthoney, T. R. (1968): The Ontogeny of greeting, grooming and sexual motor patterns in captive baboons (super-species *Papio cynocephalus*). Behaviour **31**, 358-372.

Fox, M. W. (1964): The ontogeny of behavior and neurologic responses of the dog. Anim. Behav. **12**, 301-310.

Fox, M. W. (1965): Canine Behaviour. C. C. Thomas, Springfield, Ill.

Fox, M. W. (1966): Neuro-behavioural ontogeny. A synthesis of ethological and neurophysiological concepts. Brain Res. **2**, 3-20.

Fox, M. W. (1967): Postnatal neuro-ontogeny and behavioural development of the dog. Ph. D. Thesis, University of London (unpub.), now published (1971), Integrative Development of Brain and Behavior in the Dog. Chicago, Chicago University Press.

Fox, M. W. (1968): Socialization, environmental factors and abnormal behavioral development in animals; pp. 332-335, In: Abnormal Behavior in Animals (Ed.: Fox, M. W.), W. B. Saunders, Philadelphia.

Fox, M. W. (1970): Comparative development of facial expressions in canids. Behaviour **36**, 49-73.

Fox, M. W. (1969): Reflex development and behavioral organization. Chap. 17 in: Developmental Neurobiology (Ed.: Himwich, W. A.), C. C. Thomas, Springfield, Ill.

Fox, M. W., and D. Stelzner (1966): Behavioral effects of differential early experience in the dog. Anim. Behav. **14** 362-366.

Fox, M. W., and R. Wiseman (1969): Development of responsiveness to a social releaser in the dog: Effects of age and hunger. Develop. Psychobiol. **2**, 277-280.

Hein, A., and R. Held (1967): Dissociation of the visual placing response into elicited and guided components. Science **158**, 390-392.

Kleiman, D. (1965): Scent-marking in the Canidae. Symp. Zool. Soc. London **18**, 167-177.

Kühme, W. (1965): Communal food distribution and division of labor in African hunting dogs. Nature **205**, 443-444.

Leyhausen, P. (1965): Verhaltensstudien an Katzen. Z Tierpsychol., Suppl. 2.

Morris, D. (1955): The feather postures of birds and the problem of the origin of social signals. Behaviour **9**, 75-113.

Ploog, D. W. (1966): Biological bases for instinct and behaviour: studies on the development of social behaviour in squirrel monkeys. pp. 199-224 in: Recent Advances in Biological Psychiatry, **8**, Plenum Press, New York.

Ross, S., A. E. Fisher and O. King (1957): Sucking Behavior: a review of the literature. J. genet. Psychol. **91**, 63-81.

Schenkel, R. (1967): Submission: its features and functions in the wolf and the dog. Amer. Zool. **7**, 319-330.

Schneirla, T. C. (1965): Aspects of stimulation and organization in approach/withdrawal processes underlying vertebrate behavioral development; pp. 949-958, In: Advances in the study of behavior **1** (Eds: Lehrman, D. S., R. A. Hinde and E. Shaw), Academic Press, New York.

Scott, J. P., and J. L. Fuller (1965): Genetics and Social Behavior of the Dog. University of Chicago Press, Chicago.

Stanley, W. C., and W. E. Bacon (1963): Suppression of sucking behavior in non-deprived puppies. Psychol. Rep. **13**, 175-178.

Wickler, W. (1967): Socio-sexual signals and their intra-specific imitation among primates. pp. 89-189 in: Primate Ethology (Ed.: Morris, D.), Aldine, Chicago.

Effects of Morphological Variations of Chicken Models on Sexual Responses of Cocks

BLAIR T. CARBAUGH

M. W. SCHEIN

E. B. HALE

INTRODUCTION

The stimuli releasing sexual behaviour of birds are often studied with the aid of models, which have the advantage of providing a constantly controlled stimulus to all individuals tested. A stuffed dummy hen (*Gallus domesticus*) mounted in a squatting position was used by Domm & Davis (1948) to elicit sexual responses from normal and from intersexual domestic fowl. Wood-Gush (1957) found that a stuffed pullet in a crouched position effectively released sexual behaviour of young cockerels. The posture of a model may play an important role in the type of response (i.e. sexual or aggressive) elicited from cocks (Fisher & Hale, 1957). Cocks respond more readily to birds or models of the same colour as the birds with which the cocks have been associated with than to those of a different colour (Fisher & Hale, 1957; Hale, 1957).

Various parts of the model may be effective in releasing sexual responses: Lorenz (1937) describes the interaction between a Shell Parakeet (*Melopsittacus undulatus*) and a small celluloid ball, wherein the bird reacted socially and sexually as if the ball were the head of another bird. Schein & Hale (1958) reported that a head alone provided both sexual arousal and orientation cues to the male turkey, and Schoettle & Schein (1959) determined that variations in the characteristics of the head, ranging from detailed carved features to a simple featureless teardrop shape, did not adversely affect sexual responses of the male turkeys. The effectiveness of the head in eliciting sexual behaviour in chickens has not been tested, but in agonistic encounters the head was more important for individual recognition than other parts of the body (Guhl & Ortman, 1953).

The ability to modify morphological features of the model permitted a search for the specific characteristics releasing sexual behaviour. The objectives of this study were: (1) to discover which morphological features of chickens (*Gallus domesticus*) were of primary importance as *releasers* of sexual behaviour patterns of cocks; (2) to determine the effect of variations of positions and presence or absence of body structures on *arousal* of sexual behaviour and *completeness* of sexual pattern.

METHOD

Twenty sexually experienced White Leghorn cocks, maintained in all-male groups and not permitted access to females for at least 6 weeks previous to this experiment were exposed for one minute each to complete and partial models of White Leghorn hens. Sexual responses of each male to the model during the one minute test were recorded at 6-second intervals. Responses of the males to a model ranged from complete sexual patterns (Guhl, 1961) with copulatory attempts to complete indifference to the model.

A scoring system was devised to serve as an index of the level of sexual response. Arbitrary values of 1, 2, 3, 4, and 5 were assigned to the components of sexual behaviour patterns pertinent to this study: *approach, grab, mount, tread,* and *copulatory movements*, respectively. A component that occurred at any point during the one minute test was scored as if it persisted throughout the remainder of the test unless it was replaced with a higher value component. Thus, if the approach occurred in the first 6-second time block, a value of 1 would be assigned to this first block *plus* each of the succeeding 9 blocks, for a total score of 10. If the approach was followed by a grab, mount, tread, and copulatory movements in the *2nd* time block, then a score of 46 resulted: 1 + (9 x 5). Maximum scores of 50 points occurred when copulatory attempts (i.e. a complete sexual pattern) were made in the first 6-second time block. Responses to the models were usually made within the first 5 time blocks; in only 5 per cent of the cases was the resulting score higher for an incompleted pattern than for a completed sexual pattern.

A model of a hen in sex crouch position (Foreman & Allee, 1959) was used as a standard to valuate the daily fluctuations of sexual behaviour levels during the course of testing. Pretesting indicated that this position of the model elicited consistently high levels of sexual responses from the roosters. In the evaluation of a test model, cocks were individually exposed to either the test model or to the standard. At the completion of the run, the birds were re-exposed, this time to the other model. Thus each cock was exposed both to the test model and to the standard during the trial period, and at least one hour elapsed between the two exposures. All trials were run in one of the two adjoining rooms in which the cocks were housed; each room was 9 feet x 9 feet. Testing was limited to between 4 P.M. and 6 P.M., since these hours are within the late afternoon period of high sexual activity (Wood-Gush & Osborne, 1956).

The observer brought a cock into the testing room in such a way as to prevent it from seeing the model, and a time clock was started as the bird was released. Each cock was attentive to the model and ignored the observer unless the latter made some loud noise or movement. At the end of the trial the cock was returned to the holding room and the procedure repeated with another cock and the alternate model.

RESULTS

For each test, the mean of the raw scores and one standard deviation from the mean were calculated for both the test model and the standard. The percentage of correctly orientated partial or complete sexual patterns was also calculated: a 100 per cent score indicates that all the sexual responses on that test were correctly orientated (an anterior-posterior alignment which would lead to copulation). These data are presented in Fig. 1.

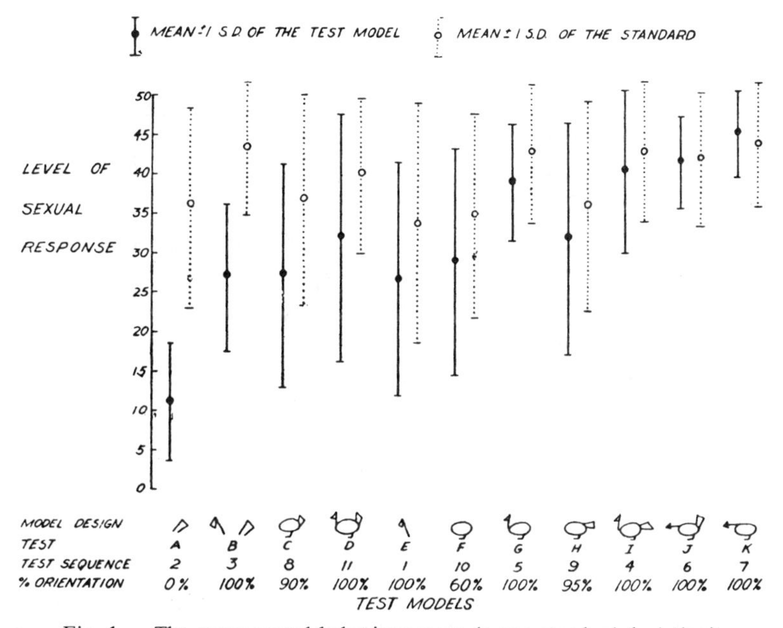

Fig. 1. The mean sexual behaviour score (± one standard deviation) for each test model and the standard model tested that day. On the bottom is shown: a diagram of each test model; the test letter designation; the sequence of testing; the percentage of tests in which correct anterior-posterior orientation was demonstrated.

The number of complete patterns elicited by the test model and the standard for each test are compared in Fig. 2. In no trial did all twenty roosters respond with complete patterns to either the test model or the standard. The drawings at the bottom of Figs. 1 and 2 show each model as it was used in the test. The sequence of testing is shown by the numbers at the bottom of Figs. 1 and 2.

DISCUSSION

The proportion of test scores to standard scores can be expressed as a percentage, calculated by the formula:

$$\frac{\text{test score} \times 100}{\text{standard score}} .$$

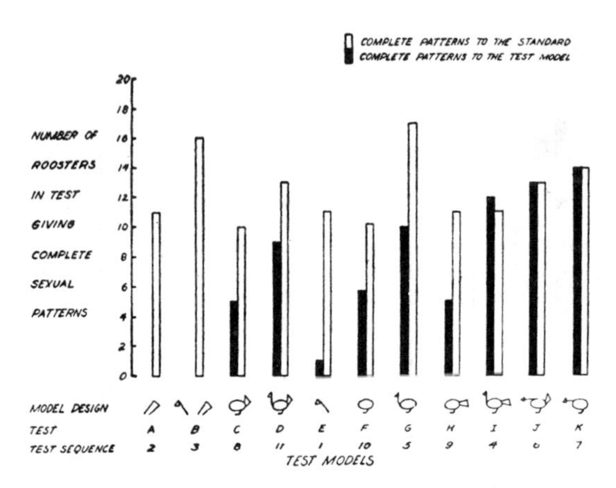

Fig. 2. The number of complete sexual patterns elicited by the test model as compared to the standard for each test.

These values, which afford a method of comparing different test models, are presented in Table 1. It is clear that the arousal value of the head was about the same as that of the body, but the head is not as adequate as the body in releasing complete patterns. The body with a head elicited the greatest amount of sexual arousal, while the highest percentage of complete patterns occurred when the entire model was present.

The effect of the presence and position of the head on arousal levels and on complete patterns was estimated by comparing the percentage values of models without heads to those with heads.

Table I. Relative scores as related to completeness of the model. The scores are expressed as the percentage of test model scores to standard scores (see text).

Model	*Arousal score* %	*Complete patterns* %
Tail (A)	31	0
Head (E)	82	9
Head + Tail (B)	62	0
Body (F)	80	60
Body + Tail (C & H)	81*	48*
Body + Head (G & K)	97*	80*
Body + Head + Tail (D, I, & J)	92*	93*

* Average of percentage scores obtained from the several models.

Table II. Effect of presence and position of head on arousal and completeness of the sexual pattern.

Models without heads	Models with heads	Increment in arousal*		Increment in complete patterns*	
		Prone	Erect	Prone	Erect
A	B		32		0
C	D		7		19
F	G		11		−1
H	I		6		64
C	J	27		50	
F	K	22		40	

* Expressed as the differences in percentages.

Table III. Effect of presence and position of the tail on arousal and completeness of the sexual pattern.

Models without tails	Models with tails	Increment in arousal*		Increment in complete patterns*	
		Prone	Erect	Prone	Erect
F	H	9		−15	
G	I	4		50	
K	J		2		0
F	C		−7		−10
G	D		−11		10

* Expressed as the differences in percentages.

Again, percentage values were calculated as for Table I; these data are shown in Table II. In all 6 cases, an increase in *arousal* percentages occurred when the head was present, regardless of its position. However, the prone position may elicit sexual arousal more effectively than the erect position. In 4 out of 6 cases *complete patterns* were more effectively elicited when the head was present than when it was absent; in the other two cases, neither an increase nor a decrease of complete patterns was evident with respect to presence or absence of the head.

Similar comparisons, aimed at determining the effect of the presence or absence and position of the tail, showed that a prone tail position may possibly serve as a better arousal stimulus than an erect tail position (Table III). The effect of tail position and its presence or absence on completeness of sexual patterns revealed no consistent

Table IV. Relative stimulus functions of the head, body and tail in turkeys and chickens (maximum value = ++++).

		*Turkey**	*Chicken*
Head	Arousal	++++	+++
	Complete pattern	++++	+
Body	Arousal	+++	+++
	Complete pattern	+	+++
Tail	Arousal	No	+
	Complete pattern	Data	0

* Data from Schein & Hale (1957, 1958).

trends. In one comparison (G to I), an increment of 50 per cent in complete patterns occurred; the other four comparisons showed that the presence of the tail, regardless of position, was not related to the number of complete patterns expressed.

In observing the orientation of the male to the model, it was found that in every case where the head was present all the patterns were properly oriented. A comparison of tests C & H to test F (Fig. 1) indicated that the tail facilitated correct orientation. Where the tail alone was presented (Test A), no correct anterior-posterior orientation was evidenced; however in 45 per cent of the trials in this test, the birds responded to the tail as if it were a head, i.e. made grabs and oriented to it.

The value of the head, body, and tail in releasing sexual behaviour of turkeys and chickens is compared in Table IV. Schein & Hale (1957, 1958) showed that the head was the primary factor in sexual arousal and orientation of turkeys, while the body provided some arousal. In the rooster the head and body seem to have equal arousal values. With respect to complete patterns, the head was the primary releaser in the turkey, while the body was the primary releaser in the cock.

SUMMARY

Twenty sexually active White Leghorn males were individually confronted with modified taxidermic models of receptive White

Leghorn hens. Test models varied in terms of presence or absence of a body, a head, and a tail, and in terms of the position of the head or tail. Responses of each male to the test models were recorded. A standard model was incorporated into each test to facilitate comparisons and to indicate the performance level of the roosters in each trial.

The presence or absence of the tail had little effect on the level of sexual response or the completeness of sexual patterns. When present, a prone position of the tail tended to raise the level of sexual behaviour; its presence aided in orientating the sexual pattern.

The body or head were primary factors releasing sexual behaviour and as such their presence or position on a model determined the level of behaviour. If the head was in a prone position on the body, it seemed to have more stimulus value than when erect. Test results suggest that the body was necessary for releasing complete sexual patterns. In addition, proper orientation of the sexual pattern occurred when the head was present.

REFERENCES

Domm, L. V. & Davis, D. E. (1948). Sexual behavior of intersexual domestic fowl. *Physiol. Zool.*, **21**, 14-31.

Fisher, A. E. & Hale, E. B. (1957). Stimulus determinants of sexual and aggressive behavior in male domestic fowl. *Behaviour,* **10**, 309-323.

Foreman, D. & Allee, W. C. (1959). A correlation between posture stance and outcome in paired contests of domestic hens. *Anim. Behav,* **8**, 180-188.

Guhl, A. M. (1961). The effects of acquaintance between the sexes on sexual behavior in White Leghorns. *Poult. Sc.*, **40**, 10-21.

Guhl, A. M. & Ortman, L. L. (1953). Visual patterns in the recognition of individuals among chickens. *The Condor,* **55**, 287-298.

Hale, E. B. (1957). Breed recognition in the social interactions of domestic fowl. *Behaviour,* **10**, 240-254.

Lorenz, K. Z. (1937). The companion in the bird's world. *The Auk,* **54**, 245-273.

Schein, M. W. & Hale, E. B. (1957). The head as a stimulus for orientation and arousal of sexual behavior of male turkeys. *Anat. Rec.*, **128**, 617-618, (abstr.).

Schein, M. W. & Hale, E. B. (1958). *Stimuli Releasing Sexual Behavior of Domestic Turkeys.* 16 mm. film, Psychological Cinema Register, PCR 114K, Pennsylvania State University.

Schoettle, H. E. T. & Schein, M. W. (1959). Sexual reactions of male turkeys to deviation from a normal female head model. *Anat. Rec.*, **134**, 635 (abstr.).

Wood-Gush, D. G. M. (1957). Aggression and sexual activity in the Brown Leghorn cock. *Brit. J. anim. Behav.*, **5**, 1-5.

Wood-Gush, D. G. M. & Osborne, R. (1956). A study of differences in the sex drive of cockerels. *Brit. J. anim. Behav.*, **4**, 102-110.

Role of the Mate in the Elicitation of Hormone-Induced Incubation Behavior in the Ring Dove

R. H. BRUDER

D. S. LEHRMAN

When progesterone-injected and prolactin-injected doves were tested, more individuals incubated when the birds were tested in pairs than singly ($p < .001$). Progesterone-injected birds were tested in pairs twice, 4 wk. apart; in the 2nd test, some pairs were birds which had made the same response (both or neither incubated) on the 1st test, while others were birds making opposite responses on the 1st test; more birds changed their response when tested with a "mate" which had responded differently than with one which had responded the same as S ($p < .02$). Thus, presence and behavior of the mate significantly influence hormone-induced incubation responses.

Ring doves with previous breeding experience may be induced to incubate eggs by injections of progesterone (Lehrman, 1958; Riddle & Lahr, 1944) or, in a smaller percentage of cases, of prolactin (Lehrman & Brody, 1961).

In all of these previously reported studies, the birds were tested in pairs, since in this species (as in all species of pigeons and doves) both members of the pair incubate the eggs. The beginning of any episode of incubation by either the male or female during the normal breeding cycle involves some interaction with the mate; since the eggs are almost never normally left unattended, the sitting bird

From *Journal of Comparative and Physiological Psychology,* **63**, 1967, 382-384.

leaves the egg at the moment when its mate is to begin incubating (Lehrman, 1965).

Observation of pairs of ring doves which are about to sit on eggs as a result of hormone treatment strongly suggests that each bird reacts to the presence of the other. The purpose of the present paper is to consider the question of whether interaction with the mate is a significant factor in determining whether a ring dove will sit on an available nest and eggs. We shall approach this problem by (*a*) testing hormone-injected birds in the presence and in the absence of similarly treated birds of the opposite sex, and (*b*) testing hormone-treated birds in the presence of birds of the opposite sex which have previously incubated eggs in a similar situation or have failed to do so when given the opportunity.

METHOD

Subjects

The *S*s were ring doves (*Streptopelia risoria*) hatched in the laboratory.

Caging and Rearing Conditions

HOUSING. Experimental cages were of wood, each 32 x 18 x 14 in., with wire-mesh front doors. They were provided with dispensers for water, food, and a grit-and-mineral mixture, and (when required) a glass bowl 4¼ in. in diameter in which *S*s built their nests. These cages were illuminated by strips of fluorescent lights mounted on a wall 5½ ft. in front of the doors. Stock cages were 35-in. cubical cages built with wooden frames and wire-mesh sides. Isolation cages were metal rat cages 16½ x 9½ x 7 in., mounted in racks.

Water, food, and grit were continuously available in all cages. Nesting material, when present, consisted of pine needles or hay placed on the floor in a corner of the breeding cage. Breeding cages, stock cages, and isolation cages were kept in separate rooms. Lights in all rooms were clock controlled, being turned on at 6 A.M. and off at 8 P.M. Temperature in all rooms was 72-74°F., except for brief and irregularly distributed periods of malfunctioning of the temperature-control apparatus.

EXPERIENTIAL BACKGROUND. All *S*s were hatched in breeding cages. They were separated from their parents at 21 days of age, marked for identification with leg bands, and placed in stock cages in groups of 6-10 birds. At the age of approximately 4 mo., they were placed, singly, in isolation cages. At approximately 6 mo. of age, their sex was determined by an exploratory laparotomy, and they were placed in breeding cages in male-female pairs. When they had gone through a breeding cycle, and had successfully reared young to the age of 21 days, they were removed from the breeding cages and again placed, singly, in isolation cages. After a minimum of 4 wk. in the isolation cages, they were considered available for use in the present experiments. Pairs for use in the present experiments were constituted of males and females which had not previously mated. In summary, experimental birds were doves with breeding experience, but not with each other, that had been in isolation for at least 4 wk. before the beginning of the experiment.

Experimental Procedures

HORMONE INJECTIONS. Progesterone[1] was administered in seven daily injections each of .1 mg., in .1 cc of sesame oil, injected into the pectoral muscle on alternate sides on successive days. Prolactin (Armour "Panlitar," lot No. R10109)[2] was administered as a total of 400 IU, divided into seven daily doses, each dissolved in .1 cc of physiological saline solution, and injected intracutaneously over the pectoral muscles, on alternate sides on successive days, All injections were given in the morning.

INCUBATION TESTS. Between 9:00 A.M. and 11:00 A.M. on the morning following the last hormone injection, *S* (or the pair of *S*s) was placed in a breeding cage with a nest bowl containing a dove nest and two eggs. The cage was observed continuously for 10 min. following introduction of the bird(s) and visited every 10 min. thereafter to determine whether incubation behavior had begun. If no incubation behavior was observed within 3 hr., the test was discontinued and scored as negative. If any bird began incubating within this 3-hr. period, it was removed from the cage. If there was another bird in the cage, the second bird was allowed to remain for

[1] Provided through the courtesy of Ciba Pharmaceutical Co.

[2] Provided through the courtesy of the Endocrinology Study Section, National Institutes of Health.

an additional 3 hr., during which it was observed every 10 min. We therefore secured data for each bird separately in the pair test. The criteria for scoring an incubation response were (*a*) the bird must be sitting on the eggs with the feathers on the ventral side of its body erected around the eggs, and (*b*) it must allow *E* to insert his hand under the bird's breast without deserting the eggs. These are the same criteria that have been used in all work in this laboratory.

EXPERIMENT I

If interactions with the mate are a factor in establishing incubation behavior under appropriate hormonal conditions, then we would expect that tests of hormone-treated birds in pairs would result in incubation responses by a higher number of individual birds than would be obtained from the same number of *S*s tested singly.

Method

The *S*s were 160 ring doves, 20 males and 20 females in each of four groups. Prolactin pairs were injected with prolactin and tested in pairs. Prolactin singles were injected with prolactin and tested singly. Progesterone pairs were injected with progesterone and tested in pairs. Progesterone singles were injected with progesterone and tested singly.

Results

Table 1 shows the results of this experiment. Since there were no significant differences between males and females, either within any

Table 1. Number of ring doves incubating when tested singly or in pairs.

Hormone	*Test conditions*		χ^2
	Single	*Pairs*	
Progesterone	10	27	12.87*
Prolactin	1	16	14.64*

Note.–$N = 40$ *S*s per cell.
* $p < .001$.

group or over all groups, male and female *S*s have been combined in each cell of Table 1. It is apparent that, under either progesterone or prolactin administration, a significantly higher number of individual doves sat on the eggs when tested with another bird of the opposite sex than when tested singly.[3]

EXPERIMENT 2

When progesterone-injected ring doves are tested in pairs for incubation behavior, there are always a certain number of non-incubators (30-50% in different replications). If the behavior of the mate is a factor in determining whether a hormone-injected bird will sit on the eggs, it should be possible to demonstrate this by comparing the behavior, on a second test, of birds arranged into pairs on the basis of their performance on the first test. Specifically, we would expect that birds tested for the second time in pairs both members of which had reacted in the same way on the first test would show unchanged reaction on the second test; on the other hand, a bird tested in a second test with a mate that reacted on the first test differently than *S* would show a greater tendency to reverse its response, by comparison with the first test. This would indicate that the tendency of the mate to incubate, or not to incubate, was a factor affecting the probability that *S* would incubate.

Method

All 67 male and 67 female ring doves (*Streptopelia risoria*) were progesterone injected.

Following the last progesterone injection, all *S*s were tested in male-female pairs. At the conclusion of the test, *S*s were returned to isolation cages where they remained for 4 wk. The *S*s were divided for the second time into four groups: (*a*) ++ ($N = 22$)-pairs in which both *S*s had incubated on the first test; (*b*) –– ($N = 44$)-pairs in which neither *S* had incubated on the first test; (*c*) –+ ($N = 30$)-pairs in

[3] This experiment incidentally corroborates a point made by Lehrman and Brody (1961): at the dosage level used here, progesterone is more effective in inducing incubation behavior than is prolactin, whether the birds are tested in pairs ($\chi^2 = 5.03, p < .03$) or singly ($\chi^2 = 6.74, p < .01$).

Table 2. Number of ring doves making the same or opposite response to eggs on two successive tests.*

Type of pair on second test	*N*	*Response on second test*	
		Same	*Opposite*
Homogeneous	66	59	7
Heterogeneous	68	48	20

* χ^2 (1 *df*) = 6.24, $p < .02$

which only the male had incubated on the first test; and (*d*) +– (*N* = 38)-pairs in which only the female had incubated on the first test. All *S*s were injected with progesterone and tested on the day following the last progesterone injection.

Results

The results are set out in Table 2. Since ++ and –– pairs did not differ significantly from each other, they are grouped as "homogeneous" in the table, and similarly +– and –+ are grouped as "heterogeneous." Males and females are also treated together, since there was neither a significant difference between males and females overall nor a significant interaction between sex and nature of response.

The significant χ^2 for Table 2 ($\chi^2 = 6.24$, $p < .02$) indicates that there was a significantly higher tendency for the doves to change their response to the eggs on the second test if they were, on the second test, tested with a mate whose response on the first test had been different from their own. The great preponderance of "same" responses, even in the heterogeneous pairs ($\chi^2 = 15.6$, $p < .001$), means, of course, that there were stable differences between birds which did, and those which did not, tend to incubate eggs under the type of hormone treatment used here. However, the significant 2×2 χ^2 is additional evidence that the reaction of the mate was a significant factor in determining the response of *S*.

DISCUSSION

Both of the experiments reported here indicate that the effect of the progesterone is not merely to alter the ring dove's reaction to the nest and eggs, with the result that it incubates, but rather that the effect of the treatment is to alter the reaction of the bird to the situation including the mate and the eggs, with the result that the eggs are incubated. Further, it is not merely the presence of the mate which is a relevant factor influencing the response of *S*, but also the nature of the mate's own response to the nest and eggs.

REFERENCES

Lehrman, D. S. Effect of female sex hormones on incubation behavior in the ring dove (*Streptopelia risoria*). *J. comp. physiol. Psychol.,* 1958, **51,** 142-145.

Lehrman, D. S. Interaction between internal and external environments in the regulation of the reproductive cycle of the ring dove. In F. A. Beach (Ed.), *Sex and behavior*. New York: Wiley, 1965. Pp. 355-380.

Lehrman, D. S., & Brody, P. Does prolactin induce incubation behaviour in the ring dove? *J. Endocrinol.,* 1961, **22**, 269-275.

Riddle, O., & Lahr, E. L. On broodiness of ring doves following implants of certain steroid hormones. *Endocrinology*, 1944, **35**, 255-260.

Modification of Motivated Behavior Elicited by Electrical Stimulation of the Hypothalamus

E. S. VALENSTEIN

V. C. COX

J. W. KAKOLEWSKI

Abstract. Previous reports demonstrated that hypothalamic stimulation may elicit either eating, drinking, or gnawing and emphasized both the specificity of the neural circuits mediating these behaviors and the similarity to behavior during natural-drive states such as hunger and thirst. We find that, after a period of very consistent elicitation of one of these behaviors, the animal may exhibit an equally consistent alternate behavior. A learning component is implicated in the association of hypothalamic stimulation with a particular behavior pattern.

Hypothalamic stimulation in the rat may elicit behaviors such as eating, drinking, and gnawing (*1, 2*); previous reports have emphasized both specificity of the neural structures activated and similarity of the behavior to that occurring during natural-drive states. As satiated animals exhibit the behavior only during the period of stimulation, the term "stimulus-bound" behavior has been applied. From the fact that animals that exhibit such behavior will perform some learned task (instrumental behavior) to obtain a relevant goal,

From *Science*, Vol. 159, pp. 1119-1121, 8 March 1968.

it has been concluded that the stimulation does not trigger a stereotyped motor act, but activates a motivational state such as hunger or thirst.

We studied the development of "stimulus-bound" behavior and the possibility of modifying the elicited behavior in the absence of any change in stimulation site or stimulation parameters. Our results indicate that there is a learning component involved in the association of hypothalamic stimulation with such behavior as eating, drinking, or gnawing. Hence, we question those theoretical positions based on the conclusion that electrical (and perhaps chemical) stimulation activates fixed neural circuits mediating natural-drive states.

Bipolar electrodes (*3*) were implanted in the lateral hypothalamus of mature Holtzman albino rats of both sexes. With the dorsal surface of the skull level between bregma and lambda, the electrodes were positioned 2.50 to 3.50 mm posterior to bregma, 1.25 to 1.50 mm lateral, and 8.25 to 8.50 mm below the top of the skull (*4*). Animals were stimulated with either 30-second trains of 60-cycle sine waves or biphasic rectangular pulses (frequency, 100 pulses per second; pulse duration, 0.2 msec). The stimulus parameters used with each animal are provided in Table 1. All stimulation was programmed by automatic equipment and was not delivered under the experimenter's control.

After surgery but before any stimulation, the animals were placed individually in Plexiglas cages which served as living quarters and testing chambers. Light in the room was on from 7:00 A.M. to 7:00 P.M. each day. The cages contained three goal objects: pellets (Purina Lab Chow), a water bottle with a metal drinking tube, and a pine wedge mounted either on the wire-mesh floor or one of the walls. During preliminary screening to determine an appropriate stimulus intensity, animals were stimulated for a 30-second period followed by a 60-second interstimulus interval. The intensity was adjusted until the stimulus elicited a forward-moving "searching" behavior. If, after a period of time, the animal did not exhibit either eating, drinking, or gnawing in response to stimulation, the intensity was raised or lowered to what appeared to be a more promising level. If no specific behavior pattern emerged, the animal was stimulated throughout the night for 30 seconds every 5 minutes (night schedule). If no "stimulus-bound" behavior was evident, the

Table 1. Eating (E), drinking (D), and grawing (G) behavior elicited during hypothalamic stimulation.

		Test series						
		First series			*Second series*			*Stimulus parameters*
Animal	*Behavior*	*1*	*2*	*3*	*1*	*2*	*Competition*	*(μa)*
	E	0	0	0	15	17	11	RP, 80
60S	D	20	20	20	–	–	14	RP, 80
	G	0	0	0	0	0	0	RP, 80
	E	0	0	0	20	20	15	RP, 120
61S	D	20	20	20	–	–	12	RP, 120
	G	0	0	0	0	0	0	RP, 120
	E	0	0	0	0	0	0	RP, 500
63S	D	0	0	0	20	20	12	RP, 500
	G	20	20	20	–	–	8	RP, 500
	E	0	0	0	20	20	12	SW, 20
74S	D	20	20	20	–	–	13	SW, 20
	G	0	0	0	0	0	0	SW, 20
	E	19	16	12	–	–	10	RP, 120
80S	D	1	5	8	19	16	10	RP, 120
	G	0	0	0	2	2	6	RP, 120
	E	0	0	0	18	20	16	SW, 24
89S	D	19	19	20	–	–	4	SW, 24
	G	0	0	0	0	0	0	SW, 24

Each test had 20 stimulation periods. Maximum score for any behavior is 20, but the animal could exhibit different behaviors during each period. The dash (–) in the second series of tests indicates which goal object had been removed. RP, rectangular pulses; SW, sine wave. All animals except 80S were males.

sequence was repeated during at least one additional night before the animal was rejected. With this procedure, approximately 25 percent of the animals exhibited "stimulus-bound" eating, drinking, or gnawing on the pine wedges.

The animals that exhibited "stimulus-bound" behavior were then given a series of three standard tests (30 minutes in duration, with twenty 30-second stimulation periods, each separated by a 60-second interstimulus period). There was a minimum of 30 minutes between each test. During these tests, the three goal objects were present. After this first series of tests, the goal object to which the rat oriented was removed, and the animal was left overnight with the other two goal objects and stimulated on the night schedule. If, for example, the rat exhibited "stimulus-bound" drinking during the first series of tests, the water bottle was removed during the night, and only the wood and food pellets were left in the cage. *The stimulus parameters remained unchanged.* If the animal did not exhibit a new "stimulus-bound" behavior, it was stimulated additionally on consecutive nights. In most cases, however, one night was sufficient time for a new behavior to emerge, although for animals 60S and 89S several nights were necessary. In general, the earlier the onset of the first behavior during the preliminary stimulation sessions and the more consistently this behavior was displayed, the sooner the animal switched to a second behavior pattern when the first goal object was removed. Animals were then given two additional standard tests with the initial goal object still absent. Finally, the animals were given a competition test with all three goal objects present. Prior to all tests, animals were provided with an opportunity to satiate themselves on food and water.

Eating and drinking were scored only when there was clear evidence of consuming the food or water (Table 1). The food pellets were held with the front paws, and pieces were bitten off; the drinking tube was lapped, and the animal could be observed ingesting the water. Gnawing consisted of biting off pieces of wood from the wedge. In most cases, the animal began the "stimulus-bound" behavior within 1 to 2 seconds after the onset of the stimulus and stopped abruptly after its termination. The duration of the "stimulus-bound" behavior was variable. In a number of instances, the animal ate, drank, or gnawed for the entire 30-second stimulation period, and in a few cases the behavior was observed for only a 5-second period. Only in rare instances was any scoreable behavior observed during the interstimulus period. Table 1 illustrates that the "stimulus-bound" behavior during the first series of tests was exhibited consistently with almost every stimulus presentation. The second series was administered after the animal spent a variable amount of time receiving stimulation without the first goal object present. In most cases the second "stimulus-bound" behavior was exhibited as consistently as the first behavior (Table 1). During the competition test, when all three goal objects were present, approximately equal amounts of the two "stimulus-bound" behavior patterns were displayed in most instances, although the second behavior–eating–dominated the behavior of 89S during the competition test. In the case of 80S (an animal that exhibited two behaviors initially), a third behavior pattern–gnawing–was observed during the second series of tests and the competition test. This animal had been placed on the night schedule for two consecutive nights with only wood and water present. In addition to eating, drinking and gnawing, other behavior was observed to be elicited by the stimulation in some animals: for example, 80S frequently positioned itself in one part of the cage, and with the onset of stimulation a specific path was traversed on the way to the drinking bottle.

There were no cases of "stimulus-bound" behavior which could not be switched to another behavior with the stimulus parameters held constant. We cannot be certain that such a case might not exist, but, in addition to the data in Table 1, there were a number of instances in which there were "spontaneous" switches from one "stimulus-bound" behavior to another. For example, an animal that might exhibit "stimulus-bound" gnawing approximately 50 percent of the time might switch to drinking with approximately the same consistency. We regard these cases of "spontaneous" switching as additional evidence of the lack of specificity of the behavior evoked by electrical stimulation. This conclusion is also supported by animal 80S, as well as others that did not complete the test series, which exhibited more than one behavior from the beginning of stimulation.

In stressing the lack of specificity between a given behavior pattern and lateral hypothalamic stimulation, we are not advancing a position of neural equipotentiality. We were not able to evoke either eating, drinking, or gnawing from a number of lateral hypothalamic sites. Furthermore, in several animals in which electrodes were placed in somewhat different lateral hypothalamic sites on the left and right side, the animal exhibited "stimulus-bound" behavior only when stimulated on one of the sides.

It might be argued that all the animals used in our experiment were special cases in which stimulation activated simultaneously the neural circuits mediating two motivational systems. We disagree for several reasons. We did not select the animals, and we studied all that exhibited any "stimulus-bound" behavior. Only one of the animals exhibited more than one behavior pattern before our effort to modify their responses. Of the animals exhibiting only one behavior initially, those that displayed the most vigorous pattern (judged by the brief latency, long duration during stimulation, and great consistency) required the least amount of training for a second pattern to emerge.

As far as we could determine, most investigators of "stimulus-bound" behavior focused on a specific behavior. As a result, the animals received either or both special training or limited opportunity to display different patterns. These few instances in which an animal was given a brief "competitive" test with another goal object present usually followed an extensive amount of opportunity to display the initial behavior pattern. We found that the more opportunity an animal has to exhibit a specific "stimulus-bound" behavior, the longer it may take for a new pattern to emerge.

A number of experiments demonstrated that animals exhibiting "stimulus-bound" eating, drinking, or gnawing have much in common with animals under the influence of natural drives such as those induced by deprivation. Animals will work to obtain appropriate goal objects and appear willing to tolerate aversive stimulation, such as shock or quinine additives, in order to obtain the desired objects (*2*). However, the fact that in our experiment animals that were "stimulus-bound" drinkers appear just as motivated to obtain food, for example, raises the question of whether thirst and hunger motives are involved at all (*5*). Apparently, there is considerably more plasticity in establishing connections between hypothalamic circuits and motivated behavior than commonly advanced interpretations of "stimulus-bound" behavior suggest.

REFERENCES AND NOTES

1. E. E. Coons, thesis, Yale University (1964), (microfilm obtainable from University Microfilms, Inc., Ann Arbor, Mich., order 64-13, 166); ———, M. Levak, N. E. Miller, *Science* **150**, 1320 (1965); L. Fantl and H. Schuckman, *Physiol. Behav.* **2**, 355 (1967); M. A. Greer, *Proc. Soc. Exp. Biol. Med.* **89**, 59 (1955); J. Mendelson, *Science* **157**, 1077 (1967); ——— and S. L. Chorover, *ibid*, **149**, 559 (1965); N. E. Miller, *Fed. Proc.* **19**, 846 (1960); P. J. Morgane, *Nature* **191** 672 (1961); G. J. Mogenson and J. A. F. Stevenson, *Physiol. Behav.* **1**, 251 (1966); ———, *Exp. Neurol.* **17**, 119 (1967); W. W. Roberts and R. J. Carey, *J. Comp. Physiol. Psychol.* **59**, 317 (1965); E. A. Steinbaum and N. E. Miller, *Amer. J. Physiol.* **208**, 1 (1965).

2. P. J. Morgane, *Science* **133**, 887 (1961); *Amer. J. Physiol.* **201**, 838 (1961); S. S. Tenen and N. E. Miller, *J. Comp. Physiol. Psychol.* **58**, 55 (1964).
3. E. S. Valenstein, W. Hodos, L. Stein, *Amer. J. Psychol.* **74**, 125 (1961).
4. The electrode tips were located in neural sites previously reported to yield "stimulus-bound" behavior. The electrode tips of animals 60S and 61S were located in the zona incerta dorsal to the fornix, and the electrode tips of animals 74S, 80S, and 89S were located in the dorsal part of the lateral hypothalamus. No histology is available for 63S due to dislodgement of its electrode pedestal.
5. Animals that were switched from "stimulus-bound" drinkers to "stimulus-bound" eaters have been observed to eat the dry pellets in the absence of water almost to the point where they appeared to be choking.
6. Supported by NIH grants M-4529, career scientist award MH-4947, and research grant NsG-437 from NASA. We thank Laura Lande and Debra Singer for assistance.

Neuroethology and the Motivation of Agonistic Behavior

JERRAM L. BROWN

ROBERT W. HUNSPERGER

I. INTRODUCTION

The aim of this paper is to bring to the attention of ethologists some findings on the neural bases of agonistic behaviour and to interpret them in relation to some commonly held ethological concepts of motivation. It is hoped that in doing so a better understanding between conventional ethologists and those who experiment directly with the central nervous system will result. Both of these groups depend on each other's findings for the understanding of their own problems; and both share common goals in the study of the mechanisms of behaviour.

The central problems confronting both ethology and neurological sciences concern the mechanisms by which information coming from outside the nervous system is received and evaluated, and by which responses are selected and programmed to result in co-ordinated and typically adaptive effector performance throughout ontogeny and phylogeny.

The methods of investigating these problems characteristic of ethology and the neurological sciences are fundamentally different. Ethological techniques are generally confined to manipulations and observations external to the organism. In contrast, the neurological sciences investigate directly neural structure and function.

Although ethologists may study such internal phenomena as releasing mechanisms and motivation, their method is essentially that of *drawing correlations between externally observable events* and using these correlations to characterize phenomena which are internally mediated.

For example, some ethological studies have concentrated on effector performance and the "internal motivation" of it, such as the study of Baerends, Brouwer & Waterbolk (1955) on the sexual behaviour of the male guppy (*Lebistes reticulatus*). In this study test females of standardized sizes were presented to the males and the resulting behaviour was correlated with the colour pattern of the male (which reflected its "internal motivation"). Both the colour pattern of the male and his behaviour to the test female may be considered effector responses which were correlated with each other.

A more complex example of concentration on effector performance is the factor analysis of the behaviour of the bitterling (*Rhodeus amarus*) performed by Wiepkema (1961) in which the occurrence of many types of behaviour were correlated with each other and the correlations mathematically attributed to a relatively small number of common factors.

In contrast to the methods used in conventional ethology a common experimental procedure for neuroethology is to make an alteration of some part of the nervous system, for instance, by activating or inactivating a specific part of it, and then to correlate changes in the behaviour with the alteration. The most common means of activation for neuroethology at the present time is the electrical stimulation of circumscribed small areas of the brain. By this means specific neural areas may be implicated in the mechanisms of the behaviour resulting from their stimulation. The neuro-behavioural work in the cat will be considered as a specific example of this general approach.

The methods used by the authors are based on the original technique of Hess (1932, 1957), further developed in its electrical part by Wyss (1945, 1950, 1957) and Hunsperger & Wyss (1953).

The term *agonistic behaviour* includes all types of behaviour thought to contain elements of *aggressiveness, threat*, or *fear*.

II. NEUROBEHAVIOURAL INVESTIGATIONS OF AGONISTIC BEHAVIOUR IN THE CAT

The programme of research in this laboratory on neural mechanisms in agonistic behaviour of the cat attempts to correlate various aspects of agonistic behaviour with both anatomical and physiological properties of the brain. This paper is based primarily on the findings of Hess & Brügger (1943), Hunsperger (1956), Fernandez de Molina & Hunsperger (1959, 1961), and Brown, Hunsperger & Rosvold (in preparation). The relevant literature including contributions by other workers has been reviewed by Hunsperger (1959).

A. Agonistic Behaviour Elicitable by Localized Stimulation

A considerable range of agonistic behaviour patterns may be elicited in the cat by electrical (or chemical; MacLean & Delgado, 1953) stimulation of small areas in the brain. The elicited behaviour depends on the site of stimulation in the brain, the intensity of activation, and the environment. It generally follows one of four patterns. These are (1) threat alone, (2) threat followed by attack, (3) threat followed by escape, (4) escape alone.

Some typical components of threat alone as elicited through brain stimulation are listed below (not in order of appearance, intensity, or other classification).

Opening of eyes
Pupillodilatation
Piloerection
Folding down of ears
Folding back of ears
Crouching
Forward rotation of whiskers
Lowering of the head
Protrusion of claws
Arching of back
Straightening and stiffening of legs
Faster and deeper respiration
Urination, defaecation
Growling and yowling
Shrieking
Hissing
Standing up
Tail quivering
Tail whipping
Erection of tail base

It is not uncommon to obtain every component in this list from a single brain locus; however, partial coverage of the list is more often obtained.

These components may be fully integrated into a behaviour which cannot be distinguished from the normal behaviour which cats show towards other cats, and sometimes toward other, larger species, such as dogs or humans. A second normal cat placed together with a cat stimulated to show such threat behaviour, reacts to the stimulated cat as it would under normal circumstances.

The behaviour described above is referred to as threat behaviour because it has that general function in social communication.

In the pattern, threat followed by attack, the cat performs threat as described above followed by an attack if a dummy is present or by a short forward rush and an explosive forward extension of the forepaws with claws protruding when no suitable object is present. Attacks on dummies commonly consist of striking the dummy's face with one or both forepaws with sufficient force to knock it over. But in some instances the cat has leaped upon the dummy, bitten it in the nape and ears, and used the hind feet in knocking the dummy over. Thus, the attacks vary in their execution, some appearing more aggressive than others.

In threat followed by escape the cat performs threat as described above followed by jumping off the experimental table, often accompanied by hissing.

In escape alone the cat first looks in all directions and then jumps off the table without any previous growling, hissing, or other actions especially characteristic of threat. The pupils may be dilated and there may be piloerection. When prevented from escaping by enclosure on the table, the cat runs rapidly back and forth looking for an exit.

B. Neuroanatomical Localization of Threat, Attack, and Escape Behaviour

No two items in the list of components of threat behaviour above have identical patterns of anatomical localization in the brain, but they all overlap in the general region from which threat behaviour is elicitable. Growling and hissing are generally characteristic of the threat pattern and the areas from which they have been elicited have been plotted in Fig. 1.

Fig. 1 (from Fernandez de Molina & Hunsperger, 1959)

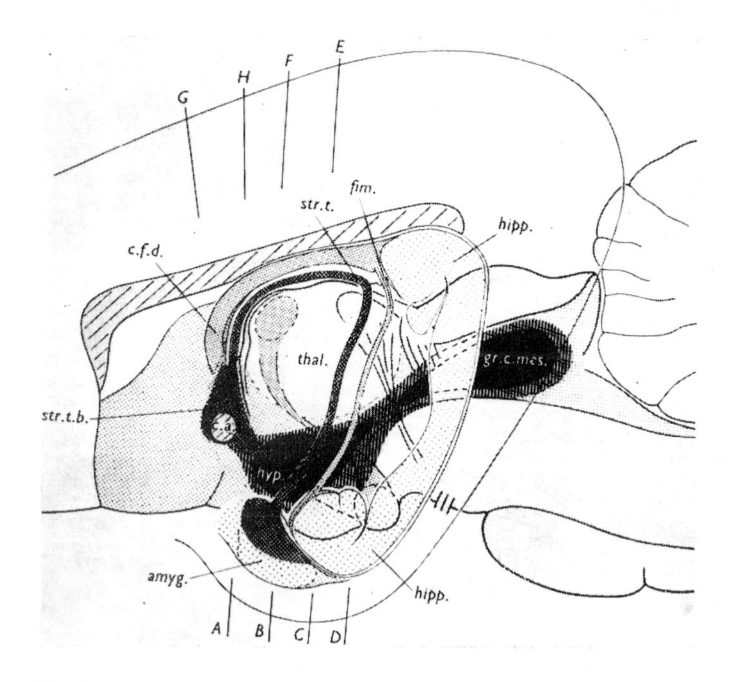

Fig. 1. Sagittal section through the brain stem of the cat with amygdala and other more lateral forebrain structures superimposed illustrating the threat and escape areas of brainstem and forebrain. This schematic representation is based on histological examination of over 800 sites of stimulation. (From Fernandez de Molina & Hunsperger, 1959. Reprinted by permission.)

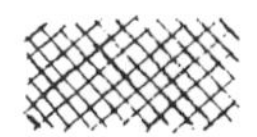

Active field of amygdala, stria terminalis, and stria terminalis bed, continuing into:

Active field of the hypothalamus and the central gray of the midbrain. Black inner zone yielded hissing; hatched outer zone yielded escape.

amyg.	= amygdala
c.a.	= anterior commisure.
c.f.d.	= dorsal column of fornix.
fim.	= fimbria.
gr. c. mes.	= midbrain central gray substance.
hipp.	= hippocampus.
hyp.	= hypothalamus.
str. t. b.	= stria terminalis bed.
thal.	= thalamus.

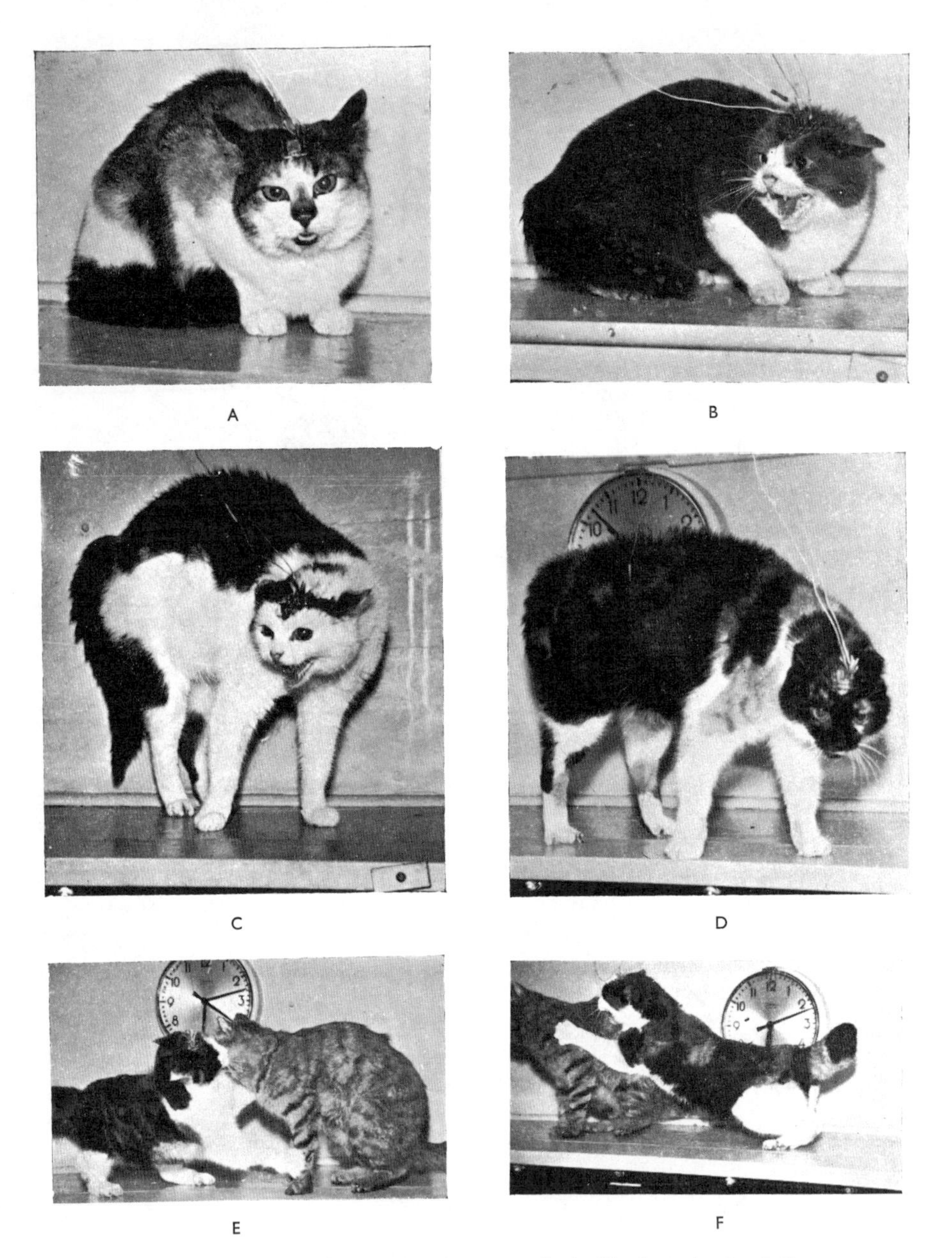

Fig. 2. Some of the various postures obtainable through stimulation of the hypothalamix part of the threat-attack system. (A) Low intensity threat; note turning back of ears, crouched posture. (B) Middle intensity threat with hissing and depressed ears. (C) High intensity threat; standing with arched back, hissing, and piloerection. (D) High intensity threat with lowered head. (E & F) Attacks on stuffed dummy cat.

represents a parasagittal section of the cat brainstem with, superimposed upon it, some structures of the forebrain lying more laterally, such as the amygdala and hippocampus. It is a diagrammatic summary of many localization experiments and provides an overall view of the agonistic behaviour system in relation to the brain as a whole. In black and cross hatching are shown the areas from which threat behaviour was obtained, using as criteria growling and/or hissing integrated in a reaction involving other threat components. The areas from which escapes were obtained are indicated by vertical lines. Stimulation in other brain areas has not established that any other areas are so intimately concerned with the integration of threat behaviour. These results are in general agreement with those of other authors, such as Nakao (1958; see review by Hunsperger, 1959).

The figure illustrates that anatomically the system for threat behaviour is *not unitary* but *multirepresentational.* It has principal representation at three brain levels: the midbrain, the hypothalamus, and the amygdala.

There is no justification for the argument that the effects are primarily dependent on activation of areas lying outside the threat system. Indeed, the evidence is that activation of the neurons located in these areas is directly responsible for the threat behaviour elicited. Each of these three areas where threat behaviour is elicitable is an area of high cell density, and with the exception of the amygdala, long myelinated fibres are generally absent. The co-ordinated nature of the elicited behaviour, the absence of agonistic responses from stimulations in other brain areas, and the anatomical evidence (including lesion studies; see below) have led to acceptance among neurophysiologists and neuroanatomists of the concept that these areas are integrative in function, concerned with motivation, and depend on the population of neurons located in these areas for their properties.

The threat behaviour patterns elicited from the amygdala, hypothalamus, and midbrain have many elements in common, such as lowering of the head, laying back of the ears, piloerection, pupillodilatation, deepened, more rapid respiration, hunching of the back, hissing, and growling. Differences in the behaviour elicited from these three areas are present, however. The most striking of these is in the vocalizations: from the midbrain hissing is the predominant vocalization; from the amygdala growling predominates although hissing has also been elicited in addition to growling from about half of the points which gave growling. From the hypothalamus the reactions are usually characterized by mixed growling and hissing, thus intermediate behaviourally and anatomically between midbrain and amygdala.

Since growling is correlated more with aggression, and hissing with defense (Leyhausen, 1956), the possibility arises that this difference in behaviour elicitable from anterior and posterior ends of the threat system might reflect an anterior-posterior gradient in aggressiveness of the threat. It would be interesting to know if a similar anterior-posterior gradient in aggressiveness of the elicited threat behaviour occurs in other species.

Another anatomical finding of importance to ethology is that the areas from which escapes may be elicited are located adjacent and overlapping with those for threat. This is consistent with the principle often encountered in neuro-anatomy that similar functions are represented close together in the brain. Escape and threat in the cat may both function in self-protection, whether from other cats or other species. In the brainstem escape reactions are elicitable from regions just anterior and posterior to the threat areas in the hypothalamus and midbrain and also to a lesser extent from a thin layer surrounding and inter-connecting the threat areas (Hunsperger, 1956). Combinations of threat and escape are often obtained from the border areas. In the amygdala the escape responses are obtained from areas which are also closely related anatomically to those for threat responses (Fernandez de Molina & Hunsperger, 1959; Ursin, 1960).

C. Threat Behaviour as a Function of Intensity of Activation

In addition to being dependent on the *locus* of stimulation the nature of the elicited threat behaviour is also greatly influenced by the *intensity* of stimulation. Raising the intensity of stimulation either through frequency or voltage has the effects of (1) activating the area under direct stimulation more intensely and/or (2) activating a larger area. The more conspicuous effects of increasing the voltage are seen not only in latencies but also in the intensities or rates of expression of the component elements of threat and in the behaviour as a whole. For example, with increasing voltage pupillodilatation and piloerection may become extreme, the ears fully lowered, the rate of growling or hissing may increase, and the loudness and pitch of growling may increase; at near maximum activation the legs are rigidly extended, the tail rigid or whipping, and explosive attacks with the forepaws may be made. The elicited behaviour may also change in character, for example, from growling alone to growling and hissing.

D. Modification of Centrally Elicited Behaviour by External Environment

Of the various types of physiological and behavioural changes which can be elicited by central stimulation in the vertebrates ranging from the movement of a finger in man to whole series of natural integrated behaviour patterns in many species it is the latter type which is of special interest in regard to motivation. The neural areas from which natural integrated behaviour may be elicited do not seem to be just motor co-ordination centres, for stimulation of these areas appears to cause real changes in the pre-disposition of the animal. When humans are stimulated in the amygdala, for example, "the strong emotional response is conscious and integrated in the thinking of the patient. . . ." (Heath, Monroe & Mickle, 1955). Similar findings have been reported for the human hypothalamus and midbrain (Sem-Jacobsen & Torkildsen, 1960; Heath & Mickle, 1960).

The basic mood or *motivation, which may be considered as neural activity*, is rather specific to the locus stimulated and appears to be relatively independent of the presence or absence of particular objects in the environment. However, such objects may play a role in the orientation of the behaviour and may bring out some external expression of the elicited motivation which might not otherwise have appeared. Just as the neurosurgeon can characterize the emotions of a patient during stimulation better by talking with him, the neuroethologist can characterize the motivation underlying the elicited behaviour better by varying the external environment through the presence of stuffed or live animals during stimulation and other means.

The independence of the basic motivation elicited during stimulation of areas which elicit threat and escape from various aspects of the external situation is striking. The threat and escape reactions appear in the "neutral" experimental room and require no special factors in the environment. They have appeared in a blind cat and in cats which could not see the experimenters as readily, or more so, as in normal cats in full view of the experimenters.

Sex, age, the individual temperament of the cat (tameness, wildness, submissiveness) and the particular behaviour in which the cat was engaged just before stimulation influence the occurrence of centrally elicited threat and escape relatively little compared to the location of the electrode, in the experience of the authors. The elicited threat and escape behaviour take precedence over apparently all other forms of activity when the appropriate areas of the brain are stimulated. The adaptive value of this attribute of agonistic behaviour is obvious. It also makes agonistic behaviour one of the easier to study of the categories of complex behaviour patterns which may be elicited by brain stimulation.

In many experiments the cat has been stimulated while it was in the presence of a stuffed cat, dog, fox, or pigeon. In order for the dummy to have an effect upon threat behaviour some part of the neural substrate for threat behaviour had apparently to be activated electrically. The dummy had no effect alone. In almost all cases where the presence of the dummy strengthened threat behaviour or brought in an attack it was with electrode placements where stimulation was capable of eliciting elements of threat behaviour even in the absence of any dummies. In a few cases elements of threat and sometimes attacks were brought in by stimulation in the presence of the dummy from loci which elicited escape but did not elicit threat behaviour. In these it seemed likely because of the anatomical location of the electrodes next to the threat zone and the nature of the behaviour which was elicited that part of the threat substrate was being activated but at subthreshold levels.

The behaviour towards the dummies during stimulation at loci where escape but not elements of threat were elicited consisted primarily of investigative sniffing, especially in the nasal and facial regions (Nasenkontrolle). Unlike the agonistic responses, this sniffing waned rapidly with a few repetitions using the same dummy. The loci lay mostly lateral and posterior to the hypothalamic threat substrate.

Where there was an effect of the dummy on threat behaviour, it consisted of more extreme development of the whole pattern, sometimes with shortened latencies and quickened rates, and in some cases attacks on the dummy with the forepaws.

In order for the elicited threat behaviour to be directed toward the dummy, the species of dummy seems not to be critical. Strong threat reactions with much hissing and growling and apparent fear of the opponent have been given toward the stuffed fox, dog, cat, and pigeon and also toward a live guinea pig and a live kitten. The motivation elicited by the electrical stimulus, therefore, does not depend in our experience on the species of dummy but primarily on the location of the electrode.

It was at first thought that the strengthening effect was dependent on the cat's perception of the dummy as an enemy. However, in several cases cats directed startling threats and attacks at dummies which they seemed to completely ignore before stimulation. Recent evidence of a preliminary nature indicates that with weak stimulation in the threat zone the perception of the dummy as an enemy (as judged by the cat's behaviour when not stimulated) and the strengthening effect of the dummy on the elicited threat behaviour may wane together. But with strong stimulation in the same area the dummy may acquire new meaning to the cat as a dangerous enemy even when it was ignored beforehand. Thus, the strengthening effect of the dummy may require that the cat regard it as an enemy; but when such regard is absent, it may be generated by the electrical stimulus itself in conjunction with the dummy. Long after-reactions of growling toward the dummy which sometimes occurred are evidence for this view.

In some ways the presence of the dummy had an effect similar to the simultaneous stimulation of a second area eliciting hissing and associated threat elements (see below). This was apparent in the shortened latencies and fuller, more intense development of the threat sequence.

E. Interrelations

As the nervous system functions on the principle of interdependence of cells and of populations of cells, dynamic aspects of the neural activities mediating the motivation of agonistic behaviour are of primary importance. Unfortunately, however, they are poorly understood. For example, whether the threat areas, or parts of them, in amygdala, hypothalamus, and mid-brain are normally differentially activated according to different motivations and what spatio-temporal patterns of activation occur during different motivations are largely unknown. Also the exact neural paths of input and output to these areas, whether inhibitory or excitatory are poorly known. Since so little is actually known about these questions only a few aspects can be mentioned.

Some aspects of interdependence have, however, been studied. The work in which a lesion in one area was combined with stimulation of another area (Hunsperger, 1956; Fernandez de Molina & Hunsperger, 1961) illustrates some aspects of thc interdependence of the various parts of the threat system. After acute lesions at some levels of the system the threat or escape behaviour elicited from remaining levels was eliminated. The elimination of threat behaviour elicited in one area after lesioning in another area was strikingly dependent on the location of the lesion. Damage to the anterior part of the threat system (amygdala, bilateral) had no effect on the threshold of the threat and escape behaviour elicited more posteriorly; while damage to the posterior parts (midbrain and hypothalamus) eliminated threat behaviour elicited anterior to the lesion immediately after coagulation. Two weeks later it could again be elicited without apparent change in character but at a higher threshold. These studies also indicate that threat behaviour may be elicited from the midbrain area independently from the anterior parts of the system.

Work using the technique of simultaneous stimulation of two brain areas concerned with agonistic behaviour (domestic fowl, von Holst & von St. Paul, 1958, 1960; cat, Hunsperger & Brown, 1961) has not reached a stage where generalizations concerning the whole threat system can be made. However, studies in this laboratory indicate that within the hypothalamus of the cat are areas which when stimulated strengthen threat and escape reactions elicited and areas which weaken them. Generally when one response may be elicited by each of two electrodes, that response, such as growling, hissing, piloerection, ear-flattening, or escaping, is strengthened by simultaneous stimulation with the two electrodes. Threat behaviour elicited from the hypothalamus is generally strengthened and changed in character by simultaneously elicited escape behaviour, and in these combinations escape behaviour is often delayed.

Since areas for "pure" attack have not been found in the cat brain, it has not been possible to perform the interaction experiment so long desired by ethologists, namely the simultaneous activation of "pure" attack and escape mechanisms. The failure to find these areas is of significance in itself, however, and will be discussed below.

III. ATTACK-ESCAPE THEORY

The neural bases of agonistic behaviour have not been investigated in detail for many species; and until the results of studies in other vertebrate classes are published, the mammals, especially the cat, remain the principal source of information. Knowledge of the neural bases of agonistic behaviour in the cat is only suggestive of the situation in other species; but because of the existence of basic homologies in the anatomy of the brainstem among vertebrate classes it is reasonable to suppose that *some* of the *general* properties of the neural bases of agonistic behaviour will be found to be similar in other species, despite difference in detail. Evidence for basic similarities between bird and mammal in the brainstem organization of certain physiological and behavioural regulatory mechanisms has been given by Akerman *et al.*, (1961). The more general implications of the works discussed above will be considered as an aid in improving the working hypothesis underlying ethological motivation studies.

Attack-escape theory has apparently never received formal definition in its entirety, nor has it been customarily referred to in print by any name. Rather, it has developed in stages and is best known through the investigations in which it has been applied. The theory became strongly influential on ethological analyses of the motivation of agonistic behaviour through the works of Tinbergen (1952), Hinde, (1952), Moynihan (1955) and others. No attempt to assign credit for each development of the theory to individual authors will be made in this paper.

In each of the following four sections we shall attempt briefly to first state the principal conclusions of attack-escape theory, second, mention the types of behavioural observations which have given rise to each conclusion, third, examine the neurological correlations, which may be made with these observations, and fourth, compare the neurological experimental results with the conclusions of attack-escape theory.

The principal inferences characterizing attack-escape theory follow:

(*a*) The motivation of behaviour may be understood through the use of *unitary drive concepts*.

(*b*) Threat behaviour has *dual* rather than unitary motivation; the two drives being those for *attack* and *escape*.

(*c*) Threat behaviour is caused to appear by the simultaneous activation and *mutual inhibition* of attack and escape drives.

(*d*) The motivation of different types of threat and other behaviour patterns of a species may be *characterized* by the intensities and relative strengths of attack and escape drives.

(*a*) *Unitary Drives*. Ethological motivation analyses of agonistic behaviour have been in recent years frequently founded on unitary drive concepts. These allow behaviour to be interpreted in terms of attack, escape, sex, parental, hunger drives, etc. The dangers of unitary drive concepts in ethology have been ably reviewed by Hinde (1959), and the reader is referred to that paper for a detailed discussion. In ethology such concepts have been inferred primarily from the common observation that different behaviour patterns with similar functions (e.g. obtaining of food) frequently occur in close spatio-temporal proximity with each other. This observation has led to the postulating of a common causal mechanism for the behaviour patterns concerned, and this mechanism has in some cases been hypothesized to be a neural "centre." For the central nervous system concepts of unitary centres have a history of inadequacy in the explanation of various physiological and behavioural functions. Fig. 1 reveals that anatomically the concept of central nervous centres for attack and escape has little meaning in the cat. In any case the assumption that unitary mechanisms exist is unnecessary for the investigation of neural mechanisms, and it seems equally unnecessary in purely behavioural investigations.

(*b*) *Dual Motivation of Threat*. That threat behaviour has dual rather than unitary motivation has been concluded from inferences that both attack and escape drives are active during threat. Such inferences concerning the existence of subthreshold activation of attack and escape drives during threat have been made from three types of observation (Tinbergen, 1959). These are:

(1) occurrence of threat in close *temporal proximity* with the acts of attack and escape.

(2) occurrence of threat in spatial and temporal *contexts* where attack and escape drives would both be expected to be subthreshold, and

(3) the involvement of acts and *postures* in threatening which are related to or identical with those used in actual attack and escape.

Similar observations can be made in the cat. For example, growling occurs frequently in temporal proximity with attack and hissing with defense and escape (Leyhausen, 1956). Gradations in posture and facial expression between attack behaviour and various kinds of threat behaviour have been shown by Leyhausen (ibid.). Threat and escape behaviour in the cat have in common pilo-erection and pupillodilatation.

The postulating of unitary attack and escape drives to explain such observations is unnecessary. For such close relationships between threat, attack and escape may be correlated simply with the extensive coincidence of the neural areas where threat and attack may be elicited and the considerable overlap of the neural areas where threat and escape may be elicited.

It has been established that there are in the cat brain definite areas from which threat behaviour may be consistently elicited. This fact appears to contradict the theory that threat behaviour results from simultaneous activation and conflict of neural mechanisms for attack and escape, since *only one area needs to be directly stimulated, not two*. In birds threat can be elicited with one electrode also (von Holst & von Saint Paul, 1958). Furthermore, no anatomical or physiological provisions have been shown in any species for the motivation of threat behaviour by means of antagonistic interaction between neural mechanisms for pure attack and escape. Thus, although the occurrence of threat behaviour may be correlated with simultaneous activation of hypothetical attack and escape drives in some species, it can in the cat and chicken also be correlated with activation of an experimentally demonstratable neural substrate for threat behaviour.

(*c*) *Mutual Inhibition*. The inference that both attack and escape drives are active during threat was drawn from the three types of observations discussed above (temporal proximity, spatio-temporal contexts, postures). The failure of attack and escape to appear during threat even though active has been attributed to their mutual inhibition and conflict. The normally observed mutual exclusion of the acts of attack and escape has probably been most responsible for the concept that they are mutually inhibitory or conflicting. For the present we cannot investigate this particular conflict in the cat, if it exists, with neurological methods because it has not been possible to elicit an attack which is not preceded by threat. Stimulation in the threat-attack zone of the hypothalamus often retards escape elicited from the hypothalamus. But stimulation in the escape zone generally strengthens and prolongs simultaneously elicited threat behaviour. In the two cases investigated to date stimulation in the escape zone hastened simultaneously elicited attacks preceded by threats. Present results, therefore, indicate that *mutual* inhibition between threat-attack and escape zones does not occur.

(*d*) *Characterization of Threat Displays*. Characterization of the specific threat displays of a species according to the intensities and relative strengths of attack and escape drives has become widespread in recent ethological literature. Such characterizations have been inferred through the three types of observations mentioned above.

For example, from the observations of Leyhausen (1956) on the cat it can be deduced that growling occurs typically and more often than hissing in temporal proximity with attack and that hissing occurs more often than growling in temporal proximity with escape and defence. From these observations the inference could be made according to attack-escape theory that the attack drive was higher during growling than the escape drive and the escape drive higher during hissing than the attack drive.

These observations may also be correlated with experimental findings for the brain: Attacks elicited by brain stimulation are characteristically preceded by growls and hisses. In contrast, escapes elicited from regions of overlap of escape and threat are characteristically preceded by hisses without growls. In addition, growls are characteristically elicited from the amygdala and hypothalamus while hisses are characteristically elicited from the midbrain and hypothalamus. This evidence suggests that the spatial pattern of neural activation within the threat-attack system is different during these two types of threat vocalization. Furthermore, the extensive overlap of the areas where growling and attack may be elicited correlates with the close temporal relationships of growling and attack in normal behaviour. And the overlap of the areas where hissing and escape may be elicited correlates with the close temporal relationships of hissing and escape in normal behaviour. Thus, for the cat different types of threat and their temporal relationships with attack and escape can be correlated with different spatial patterns of central nervous activity.

In summary, when attack-escape theory as discussed above is compared with present knowledge of the structure and function of the nervous system, little direct agreement is found. However, many of the behavioural observations for which attack-escape theory has been invoked may now be correlated directly with the structure and function of the brain.

IV. TERMINOLOGY

Attacks are easily elicited by brain stimulation in the cat, but "pure attacks" are not. According to attack-escape theory "pure attacks" should be those attacks which have no elements of fear or threat motivation in them. In the cat this might be equivalent to catching a mouse or to attacking in situations where the cat has learned not to be afraid. Such confident attacks do not result from stimulation of the threat-attack zone under the conditions of our experiments. On the contrary, stimulation there has caused cats to threaten in apparent self-defence such harmless objects as a live guinea pig and a small kitten and to attack the guinea pig defensively.

In discussing "pure attack" in the cat Leyhausen (1956) wrote, "Das reine, durch teilweise Ueberlagerung mit anderen Verhaltensweisen nicht gestörte Angriffsverhalten des Katers sieht man nur selten." However, he also referred to the same behaviour as in "extreme threat position" ("in extremer Drohstellung"). From his own statements, photographs, and descriptions it is clear that this is a threat posture rather than a "pure attack." Moreover, it is not the extreme threat posture obtained by stimulation of the threat zone in the cat brain but a partial development of it. It is similar to some attacks made on dummies during stimulation of the border area between threat-attack and escape zones.

Some clarification of the ontogenesis of "pure attack" may be gained by consideration of established social hierarchies among groups of vertebrates. Under these conditions supplanting attacks are often seen devoid of external signs of fear or threat. The absence of fear evinced in these attacks is specific to the opponent or the location and depends on previous establishment and stabilization of a dominant-subordinant relationship. If the opponent is slow in leaving, a mild threat may occur; and if it stays, strong threat followed by fighting often results. It would appear probable from this relationship that the more hesitant the attack and the more resistance of the opponent, the more activation of a threat system in the attacker.

Conditioning to specific opponents or situations is probably necessary for such attacks, and they could probably also be conditioned in the cat. It is known that mice can be trained to attack or not (Scott, 1958: 18) and rats to be killers of mice or not (Heimstra & Newton, 1961). In 14 of 16 such killer rats bilateral amygdalectomy eliminated the killing response (Karli, 1956) thus implicating a structure known to be part of the threat-attack system in the cat in a learned attack behaviour. In man anger and attack have also been eliminated by ablation of temporal lobe structures including the amygdala (cases reviewed by Ursin, 1960). Work on the cat amygdala in relation to attack is in progress in this laboratory.

Although much has been said about a "threat system" or "threat-attack system," *one should not infer that it is a unitary system* and that all varieties of threat behaviour in the cat are merely the result of quantitatively different levels of activation of a unitary threat system. The term "threat system" has been used in reference to the basic similarities in the behaviour patterns elicited from all parts of it. It should be stressed, however, that important differences also exist in the behaviour elicited from various places in the threat system. Virtually no two component elements of threat behaviour have exactly the same pattern of localization in the brain; and just which combination of elements is elicited appears to vary from place to place within the threat-attack zone.

All factors which affect motivation in the vertebrates, whether external stimuli or integral stimuli and conditions must work through the central nervous system. It follows from this relationship that ethological motivation theories have value primarily through their relevance to actual events in the central nervous system. The terms and concepts employed in such theories are, thus, of critical importance to the understanding of the relationship between the nervous system and behaviour.

Some ethologists may prefer to refrain from making inferences about nervous processes on the basis of their behavioural observations. If so, then to be consistent with neural concepts of motivation the terms "tendency," "drive" and their substitutes would become unnecessary. These terms, which are used interchangeably in this paper, have received two basic types of definition in ethology. One type defines them as reflecting "the state of an animal. . . ." (Tinbergen, 1959: 29); the other type, purposely even less explicit, defines them as "the complex of internal and external factors leading to a given behaviour" (van Iersel & Bol, 1958: 5).

If "tendency" is confined in its meaning to external stimulus factors, then with adequate and accurate description of them the concept of a tendency becomes superfluous and misleading. If "tendency" is defined as including internal factors (both definitions above), then by definition it concerns the state of the central nervous system. If "tendency" is meant to describe explicitly only the behaviour and not to imply anything about the nervous system, then the description would better be made in terms of the units of observation and the correlations between the different measures (these need not be mathematically stated); "tendency" in this case is also superfluous and misleading.

Since confusion is at present inevitable in this subject it would seem advisable either to be explicit in making statements about the theoretical neural state in motivation by using a term such as "neurobehavioural mechanism" (NBM) or not to mention neural states and to restrict the discussion to the units of observation actually used and the correlations between the different observations. In both cases "tendency" and "drive" need not be used at any time and ambiguity would be reduced.

V. CONCLUSION

Ethologists have been confined primarily to observations of external events. Their form, their quantitative variation, and the correlations between them as analysed by ethologists are some of the phenomena which the neurobehavioural sciences seek ultimately to explain. In the case of agonistic behaviour explanations are sought especially for behavioural relationships concerning (1) temporal proximity and sequence, (2) postural similarities and differences, and (3) general environmental and discrete stimulus contexts. When such phenomena are objectively and clearly described and correlated by ethologists they become more useful to the neurobehavioural sciences. It is hoped that ethologists will provide detailed and quantitative information of these types for the cat, monkey, and other species in common use in the neurobehavioural sciences.

Conversely, ethology may also make use of the contributions of the neurological sciences. Because the motivation and organization of behaviour are mediated through the nervous system, whatever is known about neural mechanisms in behaviour should be utilized by ethologists in the improvement of research hypotheses and theories. The existence in the brain of a multirepresentational system which when activated leads to threat followed sometimes by attack and the existence in close anatomical relationship to it of areas which when activated lead to escape are neuro-behavioural facts of direct relevance to ethology.

SUMMARY

1. The methods of ethological investigations are primarily concerned with drawing correlations between externally observable events. Neuroethology concerns additionally direct correlations with activity and structure of the nervous system.

2. Integrated threat behaviour may be elicited from three different brain areas: in the amygdala, hypothalamus, and midbrain of the cat. The neural substrate for the "motivation" of threat behaviour is, therefore, not unitary but multi-representational.

3. The neural substrate for "motivation" of threat behaviour in the cat overlaps that for escape. This overlap helps to explain the temporal, postural, and situational similarities of threat to escape behaviour.

4. Attacks may be elicited with high intensity stimulation at some places which at the same and lower intensities of stimulation first yield threat. This functional relationship helps to explain the temporal, postural, and situational similarities of threat to attack behaviour.

5. The basic "mood" elicited by stimulation in these motivation areas is primarily determined by the intensity and locus of stimulation. Dummies and other aspects of the external environment (conversations in the case of man) play a role in the orientation of the behaviour and may bring out some external expressions of the elicited motivation which might not otherwise appear.

6. The attack-escape theory and the terms "drive," "tendency," and "neurobehavioural mechanism" are discussed. Nonneural concepts of drive or tendency are considered to be superfluous and misleading.

REFERENCES

Baerends, G. P., Brouwer, R. & Waterbolk, H. T. J. (1955). Ethological studies on *Lebistes reticulatus* (Peters). I. An analysis of the male courtship pattern. *Behaviour,* **8**, 249-334.

Fernandez de Molina, A. & Hunsperger, R. W. (1959). Central representation of affective reactions in forebrain and brain stem: electrical stimulation of amygdala, stria terminalis, and adjacent structures. *J. Physiol.,* **145**, 251-265.

Fernandez de Molina, A. & Hunsperger, R. W. (1962). Organization of the subcortical system governing defence and flight reactions in the cat. *J. Physiol.,* **160**, 200-213.

Heath, R. G. & Mickle, W. A. (1960). Evaluation of seven years experience with depth electrode studies in human patients. In *Electrical Studies on the Unanesthetized Brain*. New York: Hoeber, Inc., 214-247.

Heath, R. G., Monroe, R. R. & Mickle, W. A. (1955). Stimulation of the amygdaloid nucleus in a schizophrenic patient. *Amer. J. Psychiat.,* **111**, 862-863.

Heimstra, N. W. & Newton, G. (1961). Effects of prior food competition on the rat's killing response to the white mouse. *Behaviour,* **17**, 95-102.

Hess, W. R. (1932). *Beiträge zur Physiologie des Hirnstammes. I. Die Methodik der lokalisierten Reizung und Ausschaltung subkortikaler Hirnabschnitte*. Leipzig: Georg Thieme.

Hess, W. R. (1957). *The Functional Organization of the Diencephalon*. New York, London: Grune & Stratton.

Hess, W. R. & Brügger, M. (1943). Das subkortikale Zentrum der affectiven Abwehrreaktion. *Helv. physiol. Acta,* **1**, 33-52.

Hinde, R. A. (1952). The behaviour of the Great Tit (*Parus major*) and some other related species. *Behaviour*, Suppl., **2**, x & pp. 201.

Hinde, R. A. (1959). Unitary drives. *Anim. Behav.,* **7**, 130-141.

Hunsperger, R. W. (1956). Affektreaktionen auf elektrische Reizung im Hirnstamm der Katze. *Helv. physiol. Acta,* **14**, 70-92.

Hunsperger, R. W. (1959). Les représentations centrales des réactions affectives dans le cerveau antérieur et dans le tronc cérébral. *Neuro-Chirurgie,* **5**, 207-233.

Hunsperger, R. W. & Brown, J. L. (1961). Verfahren zur gleichzeitigen elektrischen Reizung verschiedener subcorticaler Areale an der wachen Katze. Abwehr- und Flucht-reaktion. *Pflügers Arch. ges. Physiol.,* **274**, 94.

Hunsperger, R. W. & Wyss, O. A. M. (1953). Quantitative Ausschaltung von Nervengewebe durch Hochfrequenzkoagulation. *Helv. physiol. Acta,* **11**, 283-304.

Holst, E. von & Saint Paul, U. von (1958). Das Mischen von Trieben (Instinktbewegungen) durch mehrfache Stammhirnreizung beim Huhn. *Naturwissenschaften*, **45**, 579.

Holst, E. von & Saint Paul, U. von (1960). Vom Wirkungsgefüge der Triebe. *Naturwissenschaften,* **18**, 409-422.

Iersel, J. J. A. van & Bol, A. C. A. (1958). Preening of two tern species. A study on displacement activities. *Behaviour,* **13**, 1-88.

Karli, P. (1956). The Norway rat's killing response to the white mouse: an experimental analysis. *Behaviour,* **10**, 81-103.

Leyhausen, Paul (1956). Verhaltensstudien an Katzen. *Z. Tierpsychol.*, Beiheft 2.

MacLean, P. D. & Delgado, J. M. R. (1953). Electrical and chemical stimulation of fronto-temporal portion of limbic system in the waking animal. *Electroenceph. clin. Neurophysiol.,* **5**, 91-100.

Moynihan, M. (1955). Some aspects of reproductive behavior in the Black-headed Gull (*Larus Ridibundus ridibundus* L.) and related species. *Behaviour*, Suppl. 4, x & pp. 201.

Nakao, H. (1958). Emotional behavior produced by hypothalamic stimulation. *Amer. J. Physiol.,* **194**, 411-418.

Okerman, B., Andersson, B., Fabricius, E. & Svensson, L. (1961). Observations on central regulation of body temperature and of food and water intake in the pigeon (*Columba livia*). *Acta physiol. scand.,* **50**, 328-336.

Scott, J. P. (1958). *Aggression*. University of Chicago Press.

Sem-Jacobsen, C. W. & Torkildsen, A. (1960). Depth recording and electrical stimulation in the human brain. In *Electrical Studies on the Unanesthetized Brain*. New York: Hoeber, Inc., 275-287.

Tinbergen, N. (1952). "Derived" activities; their causation, biological significance, origin, and emancipation during evolution. *Quart. Rev. Biol.,* **27**, 1-32.

Tinbergen, N. (1959). Comparative studies of the behaviour of gulls (Laridae): a progress report. *Behaviour,* **15**, 1-70.

Ursin, H. (1960). The temporal lobe substrate of fear and anger. *Acta psychiat. neurol. scand.,* **35**, 278-396.

Wiepkema, P. R. (1961). An ethological analysis of the reproductive behaviour of the Bitterling (*Rhodeus amarus* Bloch). *Arch. Néerl. Zool.,* **14**, 103-199.
Wyss, O. A. M. (1945). Ein Hochfrequenz-Koagulationsgerät zur reizlosen Ausschaltung. *Helv. physiol. Acta,* **18**, 18-24.
Wyss, O. A. M. (1950). Beiträge zur elektrophysiologischen Methodik. II. Ein vereinfachtes Reizgerät für unabhängige Veränderung von Frequenz und Dauer der Impulse. *Helv. physiol. Acta,* **8**, 18-24.
Wyss, O. A. M. (1957). Nouveaux appareila éléctrophysiologiques (VII). *Helv. physiol. Acta,* **C49**-C50.

Displacement Activities and Arousal

JUAN D. DELIUS

In 1940 Tinbergen[1] and Kortlandt[2] independently drew attention to a behavioural phenomenon which has since been called displacement activity and has received a good deal of attention.[3,4] Although no binding rules exist by which displacement behaviour can be recognized, the term is applied to behaviour patterns which appear to be out of context with the behaviour which closely precedes or follows them, either in the sense that they do not seem functionally integrated with the preceding or following behaviour or that they occur in situations in which causal factors usually responsible for them appear to be absent or at least weak compared with those determining the behavioural envelope. Displacement activities occur in three situations: motivational conflict, frustration of consummatory acts and physical thwarting of performance. Several theories have been put forward to explain the causal mechanism involved.[5-8] A variety of behaviour patterns have been reported as displacement activities,[9] even in a single species, but this variety needs revision.[10] Monographic treatments of the behaviour of any one species usually indicate only two or three activities which according to the judgment of the observer occur commonly as displacement. None of the theories on displacement activities gives cogent reasons why particular behaviour patterns should be more common than others as displacement activities, apart from stating that the causal agents which usually elicit them in non-displacement situations can also be presumed to be present, if only weakly, in the displacement context, or remarking that these patterns are prepotent in the repertoire of the animal.

In the course of a systematic exploration of the forebrain and brainstem of herring and lesser black-backed gulls (*Larus argentatus* and *L. fuscus*) with electrical stimulation, information was obtained which may bear on this particular issue. The gulls with chronically implanted monopolar electrodes (conical active area ~ 0.25 mm^2)[11,12] were stimulated with a sine current at 50 c/s ranging between 10 and 150 μamp root mean square current, in repeated trains lasting 30 sec-5 min for several testing sessions, over 2 or more months. The electrode tip locations were checked histologically.

A great variety of responses have been obtained, but here we will only consider a behavioural syndrome which is characterized by preening and staring down, and more rarely by pecking, yawning, squatting, relaxation (fluffing of plumage, shortening of the neck, general diminution of activity, intermittent closure of eyes) and occasional sleep. We find that several, and sometimes all, these component patterns can often be elicited from single loci with the same stimulation strength, usually less than 50 μamp, either as a result of a single stimulation train or more frequently in the course of several consecutive trains. In Table 1 all 202 loci so far explored

Table 1

	N	*Staring down*	*Pecking*	*Yawning*	*Squatting*	*Relaxing*	*Sleeping*
Loci eliciting preening (%)	37	27	16	49	43	54	8
Loci not eliciting preening (%)	165	5	4	4	7	10	0

Fisher's or χ^2 one d.f., P <0.001 ≈ 0.001 <0.001 <0.001 <0.001 <0.01

have been classified into those which gave preening and those which did not. Within each class of loci the percentage which yielded the different other components is shown. All the component patterns were associated with electrodes eliciting preening rather than with those which did not, and the association is significant. A similar relationship may also hold for mandibulation, shaking the body and head, wagging the tail and shaking the foot, but because these patterns are also frequent during control periods without stimulation, a decision is difficult. No such association could be detected for some twenty-five other various behaviour patterns examined.

It is significant that the preening positive points clustered in several discrete anatomical areas of the telencephalon and diencephalon and that ten electrodes responsible for more than half the entries in the non-preening class also lay within or close to these areas. There is not sufficient information to decide whether the associations of components are stronger in some areas than in others, although some evidence points in this direction.

The conclusion that these diverse behaviour patterns reflect the activation of a more or less unitary system leading to de-arousal, and are not a result of the simultaneous stimulation of contiguous but otherwise unrelated neural systems, is supported by observations on unstimulated normal gulls which suggest a high temporal and sequential association between the component patterns including sleep. Furthermore, preliminary experiments indicate that at least two hypnotic drugs, pentobarbital sodium and tribromoethanol, given systemically, reliably elicit the syndrome just described. Preening, staring down and pecking the ground are also the patterns most often involved in displacement behaviour in gulls.[13,14] A similar relationship seems to hold in some other species.

In the cat Parmeggiani[15] stimulated several different and separate areas of the forebrain and brainstem and obtained a behavioural complex consisting of sniffing, grooming, yawning, lying down, curling up, dozing and sleeping. He emphasizes that this behaviour is normal in unstimulated cats. Rowland and Gluck[16] present some evidence that in a certain conditioning procedure grooming replaced the synchronization of the electroencephalogram shown by sleeping cats when these were tested awake. Again, Leyhausen[17] lists grooming, sniffing and lying down as displacement behaviour for the cat.

For the rat, Caspers[18] has shown that grooming and some other unfortunately unspecified "motorautomatisms" are associated with shifts in the cortical d.c. potential making the surface positive, which otherwise are typical of sleep, while shifts towards a negative surface are characteristic of the waking animal. Grant[19] mentions grooming, digging and sniffing as typical displacement activities of rats.

These facts suggest that grooming or preening and certain

other movements are largely controlled by neurophysiological mechanisms which are also responsible for de-arousal and sleep. On the other hand they are often involved in displacement behaviour. There is little doubt, however, that the behavioural situations leading to displacement, that is, conflict, frustration and thwarting, are effective in increasing arousal.[20,21] I suggest that the occurrence of at least some displacement activities is the reflexion of a homeostatic process operating towards cancelling the arousal increment so generated, through the activation of an arousal inhibiting system. The existence of arousal homeostasis has been suggested by Berlyne,[22] who also marshals supporting empirical evidence. Such regulation appears logically necessary if arousal is correlated with the rate at which information is handled and if the nervous system is considered as a communication channel of restricted and specific capacity where for maximum efficiency the information handling rate must be held with certain limits.[23,24]

The striking occurrence of sleep as displacement in several species[5] may be regarded in this context as a regulatory overshoot. Why grooming and other patterns should be activated by a neural de-arousal system is functionally not obvious, but perhaps these types of activities are conducive to de-arousal in a similar way to other activities possibly through stimulus reduction (cut-off[28]), switch of attention to stimuli of little novelty[22] or generation of repetitive stimulation.[29,30]

REFERENCES

1. Tinbergen, N., *Z. Tierpsychol.*, **4**, 1 (1940).
2. Kortlandt, A., *Arch. Neerl. Zool.*, **4**, 442 (1940).
3. Zeigler, H. P., *Psychol. Bull.*, **61**, 362 (1964).
4. Hinde, R. A., *Animal Behaviour* (McGraw-Hill, 1966).
5. Tinbergen, N., *The Study of Instinct* (Oxford University Press, 1951).
6. Bindra, D., *Brit. J. Psychol.*, **50**, 263 (1959).
7. Sevenster, P., *Behaviour*, suppl. 9 (1961).
8. McFarland, D. J., *Z. Tierpsychol.*, **23**, 217 (1966).
9. Tinbergen, N., *Quart, Rev. Biol.*, **27**, 1 (1952).
10. Beer, C. G., *Behaviour*, **18**, 62 (1961).
11. Delius, J. D., *J. Small Anim. Pract.*, **7**, 605 (1966).
12. Delius, J. D., *Med. Biol. Eng.*, **4**, 393 (1966).

13. Tinbergen, N., *Behaviour,* **15**, 1 (1959).
14. Goethe, F., *Behaviour,* **11** 310 (1957).
15. Parmeggiani, P. L., *Helv. Physiol. Pharmacol. Acta,* **20**, 347 (1962).
16. Rowland, V., and Gluck, H., *Rec. Adv. Biol. Psychiat.* (edit. by Wortis, J. 96 (Grune and Stratton, 1960).
17. Leyhausen, P., *Z. Tierpsychol.,* suppl. 2 (1956).
18. Caspers, H., *Brain Function* (edit. by Brazier, M. A. B.), 177 (University of California Press, 1963).
19. Grant, E. C., *Behaviour,* **21**, 260 (1963).
20. Bindra, D., *Motivation, a Systematic Reinterpretation* (Ronald Press, 1959).
21. Johnson, H. J., *Decision Making, Conflict and Physiological Arousal.* (PhD thesis, Illinois, 1962).
22. Berlyne, D. E., *Conflict, Arousal and Curiosity* (McGraw-Hill, 1960).
23. Welford, A. T., *Nature,* **194**, 365 (1962).
24. Broadbent, D. E., *Brit. J. Math. Stat. Psychol.,* **18**, 145 (1965).
25. Hutt, C., and S. J., Lee, D., and Ounsted, C., *Nature,* **204**, 908 (1964).
26. Delgado, J. M. R., *Intern, Rev. Neurobiol.,* **6**, 349 (1964).
27. Freeman, G. L., *Psychol. Rev.,* **47**, 491 (1940).
28. Chance, M. R. A., *Symp. Zool. Soc. Lond.,* **8**, 71 (1962).
29. Gastaut, H., and Bert, J., *The Nature of Sleep* (edit. by Wolstenholme, G. E. W., and O'Connor, M.), 260 (Churchill, 1961).
30. Pompeiano, O., *Aspects anatomo-fonctionels de la physiologie du sommel* 309 (C.N.R.S. 1965).

SUGGESTIONS FOR FURTHER READING

Beach, Frank A. Analysis of the stimuli adequate to elicit mating behavior in the sexually inexperienced male rat. *Journal of Comparative Physiological Psychology,* 1942, **33**, 163-207.

*Denenberg, V. H., & Banks, E. M. Techniques of measurement and evaluation. In E. S. E. Hafez (Ed.), *The behaviour of domestic animals.* London: Balliere, 1969. pp. 192-234.

*Johnson, J. I., Jr., Hatton, G. I., & Goy, R. W. The physiological analysis of animal behavior. In E. S. E. Hafez (Ed.), *The behaviour of domestic animals.* London: Balliere, 1969. pp. 131-191.

Stokes, A. W. (Ed.) *Animal behavior in laboratory and field.* San Francisco: W. H. Freeman, 1968.

Von Holst, E., & Von Saint Paul, U. On the functional organization of drives. *Animal Behaviour*, 1962, **11**, 1-20.

*Introductory reviews

III SOCIAL BEHAVIOR, ORGANIZATION, AND COMMUNICATION

The ways in which animals communicate is related to their social behavior and organization, which in turn are influenced by the habitat or niche that the species occupies. In this chapter, the readings provide in-depth reviews of these interrelationships between animal and environment. Species and individual differences in communication and behavior may vary according to place, season, and age. For example, with increasing age, young red foxes become increasingly intolerant of each other's proximity; this intra-litter aggression serves to disperse individuals and so regulate population density; it also insures that they will live a more or less solitary existence. As adults, foxes tend to communicate by way of olfaction and highly stereotyped vocal calls; in contrast, the more sociable wolves communicate by subtle and variable visual signals. Wolves are gregarious and their social behavior and communication reflect a very different pattern of adaptation to the environment compared to the fox. *Socioecology* is the study of such interactions and interrelationships. Interactions between *age* (development), *time* and *place* (ecology), and *context* (social milieu) also must be considered. For example, the sexually mature male grouse engages in courtship displays in early spring at a particular place—the lek—in the company of other males.

The use of space by animals is also relevant to social organization and communication. Depending upon the species, sex, and season, many vertebrates possess a territory (which they may

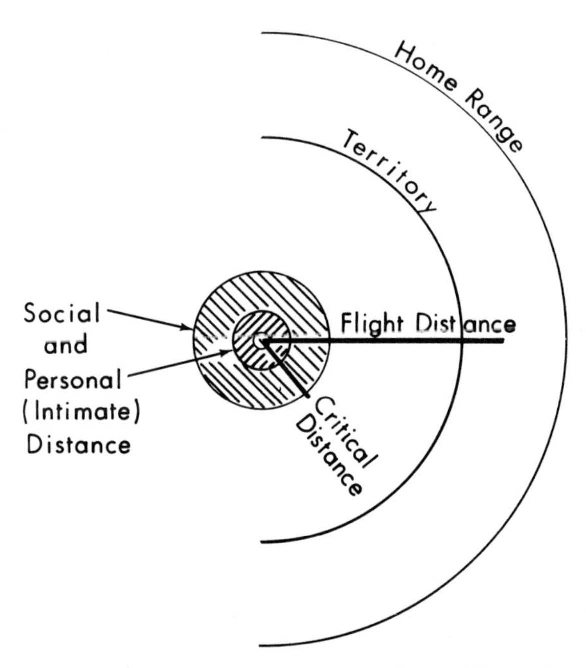

Fig. 1. Approximate concentric zones in the spatial world of an animal are arbitrarily depicted. If a predator (or strange person) moves into flight distance, the animal will run away; if critical distance is crossed, it may turn and attack, especially if cornered. When socialized to man and with its own kind, these responses are not seen; close proximity and even contact can be made within social and personal distance.

scent-mark and defend) and a home range, where they gather or catch food (Fig. 1). Dr. H. Hediger* was the first to propose the phenomena of *flight distance* and *critical distance*. A wild animal will begin to move away when an approaching observer reaches a certain distance from it—namely, the flight distance. If its escape is blocked and the observer crosses over the next threshold, the critical distance, the animal may attack. In hand-raised, socialized animals, critical and flight distances are usually absent, and one may enter the social distance and make contact at the personal (or intimate) distance. Similarly, when animals interact, they emit signals (e.g., tail

* Author of *Wild Animals in Captivity*. New York: Dover, 1964.

wagging or a snarl and direct stare in the wolves) that serve to control or modulate these distances. Signals may increase, decrease, or maintain a certain distance or proximity (the term *proxemics* being coined by E. T. Hall* for the study of spacing patterns). Signals may also signal *intentions*—for instance, to approach and to reduce social distance. Personal and social distances between conspecifics may vary according to *species* (e.g., contact and "noncontact" species) and with *age* (young of many species are more contactual than adults). Personal and social distances and proximity tolerance also vary according to *social rank, sex*, and *season* (in the red fox, for instance, social distance between sexes is reduced during the breeding season and care of young). Environmental factors such as temperature, availability of food, and shelter also influence social distance and spacing patterns in many vertebrates and invertebrates. The study of social organization therefore includes an analysis not only of communication signals but also of spacing patterns (i.e., solitary or gregarious) and ecological influences.

This section of readings begins with Scott's general classificatory paper, in which various categories of social behavior are described. Guhl and Estes then describe the methods and results of their studies: Guhl's, on the social organization of the domestic chick; Estes', on the ethology of the African wildebeest. These two papers amply demonstrate the research that can be done on domestic and wild species.

The paper by Christian and Davis shows how hormonal changes are affected by and in turn influence the population dynamics of rodents.

Marler reviews the field of zoosemiotics (animal communication) and gives many examples of tactile, olfactory, visual, and auditory communication in various species. The problem of ritualization of signal displays and behavior, in relation to evolution and ecological adaptation, is then discussed by Cullen. One of the most unexplored but fascinating topics is the olfactory world of animals. In their paper, Gleason and Reynierse review the effect of pheromones (chemical signals) on social organization and communication.

* Author of *The Hidden Dimension*. New York: Doubleday, 1969.

The Analysis of Social Organization in Animals

J. P. SCOTT

INTRODUCTION

Following Darwin's emphasis on the principle of adaptation in organic evolution, biologists became strongly interested in the study of individual animal behavior. Adaptation could only be inferred from fossils, but could be observed directly in living forms. Up till 1900 a great many biologists concentrated their efforts in this field, which was at that time almost as popular as comparative anatomy and embryology. Shortly afterwards two discoveries were made which strongly influenced this type of research. One was the rediscovery of Mendelian heredity, and a great many workers who were interested in general evolutionary problems shifted their attention to genetics. The other was the establishment of general laws of learning following Pavlov's studies of conditioned reflexes, and those workers with psychological interests tended to elaborate these findings with studies of behavior in the rat.

About 1920 a new era in behavioral research began with the description of social organization in birds. Elliot Howard (1920) wrote on the significance of song and territory in birds and Schjelderup-Ebbe (1922) discovered the existence of social dominance in chickens. Shortly afterward Allee approached the problem from a more general viewpoint with his review on animal aggre-

From *Ecology*, 1956, 37, No. 2, 213-221.

gations (1927) and later book by the same title (1931). Since that time a large body of information has been accumulating around the problem of social organization, and this paper will briefly describe some general methods and the kinds of results to be expected from its study.

The study of the social organization of a species may be delimited by the natural units of social organization, which are usually species populations and their subgroups. It differs from a general ecological study in which the unit of organization is the animal and plant community, which may be composed of many different sorts of animal and plant populations. It also differs from psychological analysis in which the unit of organization is the individual and where the primary interest lies in internal organization. So defined, the analysis of social organization occupies an intermediate position between the sciences of ecology and psychology, and overlaps with both at many points.

At the present time we have only a few definite standard techniques for the study of social behavior and organization (Scott, 1950). However, there are certain general methods which have achieved wide use and which can be recommended to anyone working in the field. The analysis of social organization in any animal should begin with a thorough descriptive study in which the seasonal and daily cycles of behavior are thoroughly surveyed. An essential part of this study is the identification of individuals, since without this information the details of social organization can only be surmised. Descriptive study should also include a study of the development of social behavior and organization from birth to maturity, since behavior and organization change with age. This systematic descriptive information naturally leads to certain hypotheses which can be studied experimentally, and it is found that many types of factors can affect social organization. These may be described as ecological, psychological, physiological, and genetic; and appropriate techniques used for the examination of each.

CLASSIFICATION OF GENERAL BEHAVIOR PATTERNS AND THEIR COMPARATIVE STUDY

In relating genetic factors to social organization it has been found that each species has certain characteristic ways of adapting to the environment and that these "patterns of behavior" in part determine the nature of social organization which can be developed in the species. As a guide to the study of characteristic patterns of behavior the author has developed a general scheme of classification. This scheme is intended to include the kinds of behavior generally recognized by students of animal behavior rather than to conflict with them, and has been found useful in making general descriptive studies of the type described above (Scott 1945, 1950a). It was developed originally by attempting to classify the behavior patterns described in several species of animals by other authors, as in Allen's (1911-1914) study of the blackbird and Dean's (1896) study of the river dogfish.

The chief rule for any good scheme of classification is that it should be natural and conform to discontinuity which exists in nature and which can be recognized by independent observers. The scheme of classification should be logical, and one which includes all related phenomena. Terms in common usage may be employed, provided their meanings are clear and describe the observed phenomenon correctly, but they should not be redefined with new meanings as this leads to great confusion. Finally, terms should be descriptive and not imply some theoretical interpretation of the facts.

These rules for classification and terminology conform to general usage in biological science. In addition, the author feels that one should be conservative about forming new terms inasmuch as they add to the labor of acquiring a scientific vocabulary, but that one should not hesitate to form new ones where necessary. Those which are useful will stand the test of time and those which are not useful will tend to be discarded.

The following classification includes all the major patterns of social and semi-social adaptation which have so far been described.

Contactual Behavior. This may be defined as simply maintaining bodily contact and, as Allee (1931) has shown, the formation of simple aggregations through behavior of this sort occurs very widely throughout the animal kingdom. The adaptive significance of the behavior may vary a great deal. A group of mammals may huddle together for warmth whereas a group of Paramecia may form because the bodies of their fellows afford protection against unfavorable chemical conditions. This extremely simple type of social behavior affords a possible basis for the evolution of higher types of behavior.

Ingestive Behavior. This may be defined as behavior concerned with the taking of solids and liquids into the digestive tract and is found very widely although not universally throughout the animal kingdom. It may have an important social significance in animals which feed their young, and becomes highly social in the nursing behavior of mammals.

Eliminative Behavior. This is defined as behavior associated with the elimination of urine and feces from the body. Special behavior is rarely seen in aquatic animals but highly elaborate patterns may be developed in terrestrial species which build nests or lairs. In such forms as wolves and the prong-horned antelope, it may acquire considerable social significance.

Sexual Behavior. This may be defined as behavior connected with the fertilization process and includes the usual courtship and copulation behavior of animals. It occurs very widely though not universally in the animal kingdom and is undoubtedly one of the most primitive forms of social behavior.

Epimeletic Behavior (Gr. *epimeleteon,* care-giving). This may be defined as the giving of care or attention. It has been called maternal behavior but is also found in males in animals like the ostrich which incubates the eggs, and in many other animals where there is biparental care of the young. It could be called parental behavior except for the fact that in many species it is done by animals other than the parents as, for example, the mutual grooming of adult primates, and the care of the young by worker females in the social insects. This behavior includes what has been called by the more specific terms of attentive behavior and nurturance.

Et-epimeletic Behavior (Gr. *aeteo*, beg, + epimeletic). This is defined as calling and signaling for care and attention and is very widely found in animals which give some care to the young. The behavior may be vocal, as in infant mammals, or simply be some sort of movement, as in the larvae of bees and ants. This behavior could be called infantile except that it also occurs in adult animals. In most cases it is used as a substitute for direct adaptation by an individual which is itself helpless or unable to adapt.

Agonistic Behavior (Gr. *agonistikos*, combative). This is defined as any behavior associated with conflict or fighting between two individuals. The term fighting behavior was originally used, but it was found that patterns of behavior involving escape or passivity were very closely related and could not be included under the narrow term of fighting. This type of behavior occurs principally in the arthropod and vertebrate phyla.

Allelomimetic Behavior (Gr. *allelo*, mutual, + *mimetikos*, imitative). This is defined as any behavior in which animals do the same thing with some degree of mutual stimulation and consequent coordination. It is seen developed to a high degree in schools of fishes, flocks of birds and herds of mammals. It could be called imitative behavior except that to most people this implies some degree of learning, which is not necessarily involved, and the idea of a model and a mimic rather than mutual stimulation. Such behavior in birds has been described as mimesis by Armstrong (1952) and as contagious or infectious behavior by other authors. The two latter terms appear to be somewhat undesirable in that they suggest that the behavior is transmitted in the manner of a disease.

Investigative Behavior. This may be defined as sensory inspection of the environment. This has been called exploratory behavior in the rat, where the animal actively explores the environment with nose and whiskers. However, in an animal with highly developed eyes, such behavior may consist merely of glancing around without movement of the whole body. The more general term of investigation appears preferable.

When the above classification is used to organize descriptive data the result is a detailed list of activities under each category which gives the characteristic ways in which a species responds in relation to major behavioral functions (Scott 1950a). Many of these exist in playful or immature forms as well as adult patterns.

It is also possible that patterns of behavior grouped in the above or similar categories may reflect an underlying nervous organization. For example, the behavior of an inexperienced male mouse of the C57 Black strain attacked by a superior fighter follows a regular and predictable sequence (Scott and Fredericson 1951). He first fights back, and when this is not successful he attempts to escape. If he fails in this he adopts a defensive posture, and if cornered he may lie on his back with feet in the air. We may eventually come to think of "systems of behavior" organized around a particular function, but general evidence still needs to be obtained on the point.

The categories may also be used to check the completeness of a descriptive study, leading to the discovery of behavior which has passed unnoticed. Sometimes a major category of behavior is almost or entirely absent, and this affords an opportunity for characterizing the social life of the species. For example, allelomimetic behavior is highly developed in the sheep and almost entirely absent in the mouse, which results in two very different types of social organization (Scott 1945a).

Species differences can also be found within a category of behavior. For example, the agonistic behavior of sheep and goats consists largely of butting. Sheep back off and run together head on, but goats typically rear up and butt with a sideways thrust of the head. A scheme of classification can be used as a systematic framework for such comparative studies of species differences in behavior, as well as making it easier to do a complete descriptive job. A high standard of scholarship requires such a complete systematic method, which has too often been missing in past studies of comparative behavior.

Comparative studies lead to the conclusion that the presence or absence of a given type of social behavior affects the type of social organization developed by the species. Stated more specifically, the presence of a given behavior pattern defines the types of social relationships which may be developed from it.

SOCIAL RELATIONSHIPS

Social organization may be analyzed in terms of social relationships. Such a relationship is defined as regular and repeatable behavior between two or more individuals, and it in turn may be described in terms of the patterns of behavior exhibited by the individuals taking part. The classical example of a social relationship is the peck order in hens in which one individual regularly threatens or pecks the other which just as regularly dodges or submits to pecking. Social behavior is not identical with social organization. In the case of two strange hens, behavior at first consists of unorganized fighting, and it is only after several encounters that behavior is organized through learning and habit formation into a regular dominance-subordination relationship. Even in the social insects, where heredity seems to play a relatively stronger role, social organization is not automatic. Experience in early life determines the species with which social relationships are formed by larvae taken by slave-raiding ants. Social behavior may therefore be considered an important but not the sole determiner of social relationships, and this should be kept in mind in making analyses of the two phenomena.

A great many types of social relationships are theoretically possible if all types of social behavior are considered. The number of possible combinations of behavior patterns in a species which shows all of the 9 types of behavior classified above may be theoretically calculated as follows. There are 9 possible combinations where both members of the relationship exhibit the same type of behavior and 36 possible combinations where the individuals exhibit unlike behavior, making a total of 45 (Scott 1953). Some of these combinations are frequently seen, such as the dominance order in which behavior of both individuals is agonistic. Some of them may be commonly overlooked as, for example, the combination of sexual and agonistic behavior exhibited by male and female rodents when the female is not in heat, and many of them are yet to be described. It is possible, of course, that certain ones are only theoretical and do not occur in nature. Some of them which have been widely observed are described below, using the names commonly applied to them.

Simple Aggregations. In this type of relationship the behavior of both animals is contactual. As Allee has shown, such relationships exist very widely in the animal kingdom, but their occurrence is apt to be irregular and nonspecific because of their dependency on environmental conditions.

Dominance-Subordination Relationships. In this type of relationship the behavior of both individuals may be described as agonistic. That of one individual consists of a threat or actual fighting while the other individual remains passive or attempts to escape. Evidence gathered by Allee (1950) and his students and summarized by Collias (1944) shows that this type of relationship is widespread in the vertebrates and occurs in at least some arthropods. It does not occur in many of the lower animals which are incapable of fighting.

Leader-Follower Relationships. The behavior of both individuals may be classed as allelomimetic, but there is an unequal degree of stimulation so that one tends to lead and the other follow. This has been described in sheep (Scott 1945), deer (Darling 1937) and ducks (Allee *et al.* 1947) and deserves more extensive study. It should not be confused with cases in which a dominant animal drives a group before him, as in the case of a stag and does in the rutting season.

Sexual Relationships. The behavior of both individuals is sexual. Although sex behavior has been extensively described in many species, very few analytic studies of the resulting social relationships have been made. Dominance and sexual relationships may be interdependent in both chickens (Guhl and Warren 1946) and chimpanzees (Nowlis 1942).

Care-Dependency Relationships. In this case the behavior of one individual is epimeletic while the behavior of the other individual may be one of several different types. An infant animal may exhibit et-epimeletic behavior, as when a young lamb is separated from the flock, or it may exhibit ingestive behavior in the process of nursing. In animals like dogs which regularly clean the young, the latter may exhibit eliminative behavior. This type of relationship has been widely described but subjected to very little experimental analysis in animals.

Mutual Care. In this case the behavior of both individuals is epimeletic, and an example is seen in the mutual grooming of primates. In spite of its theoretical importance for considerations of basic human sociology, such relationships have been little studied in animals.

Trophallaxis. This is a complex relationship described by Wheeler (1923) in the social insects. Both individuals may exhibit investigative behavior, and one usually exhibits epimeletic behavior in providing food from the crop while the other ingests the food. On subsequent occasions the roles may be reversed.

Mutual Defense. This is another complex relationship in which the members exhibit both agonistic and allelomimetic behavior. It has been described in such animals as muskoxen, wolves, baboons and many kinds of birds in reaction to hawks, but has not been subjected to analysis.

It would appear from the above presentation that the complete analysis of the social organization of a species can be an extremely complex affair, and that the simple description of the dominance-subordination relationships does not give the whole story by any means. However, the task is not hopeless since in any actual case the number of important relationships turns out to be relatively small.

BIOLOGICAL CLASSIFICATION OF SOCIAL RELATIONSHIPS

As described above, analysis of the social organization of an animal species consists of a systematic description of the basic patterns of behavior and their organization into social relationships. If an animal gave the same responses to all individuals the relationships would be simple to describe and a low degree of social organization would result. As indicated above, the behavior of individuals is frequently unlike and the concept of differentiation (Tinbergen 1953) becomes a useful one. Behavior may be differentiated by biological factors such as age and sex on the one hand and by psychological factors involving learning on the other. As Carpenter (1934) has pointed out, there are three biologically determined types of individuals in mammals: males, females and young. When these are combined in all like and unlike combinations, a total of six basic relationships can be established. These are essentially super-categories under which those relationships mentioned in the previous section may be grouped. For example, male-male relationships can include dominance-subordination and mutual care relationships as well as many others. This general scheme can be applied to other animals as well as primates and is particularly useful in studying groups of wild animals where it is difficult to distinguish individuals except by age and sex.

In the case of the social insects which have biologically differentiated castes, the scheme may be amplified to include greater numbers of basic relationships. A similar extension must be made when social relationships are developed between two different species, as commonly occurs in domestication (Scott 1953).

ANALYSIS OF SPECIFIC SOCIAL RELATIONSHIPS

So far, the analysis of social organization has been considered in terms of behavior of the whole organism and relationships between organisms. It is also possible to investigate the internal processes which in part determine behavior and through it influence social organization. Since the methods used are well known to physiologists and psychologists, the scope of such investigations will be described only briefly here.

One basic field of study is the analysis of the complex network of physiological factors which is associated with any major pattern of behavior (Scott and Fredericson 1951). Available information of this sort tends to be scattered and unequal. The physiology of sexual and ingestive behavior has been widely studied, but our knowledge of agonistic behavior comes largely from the domestic cat. The physiology of certain types of behavior, such as investigative and allelomimetic, is almost completely unknown.

A related field of investigation is concerned with the physiological genetics of social behavior and social relationships. As Collias has shown (1943), dominance-subordination relationships may in part be determined by such physiological factors as weight and hormones, which in turn may depend on the genetic differentiation of sex. Further genetic variability in physiological factors affecting social behavior introduces an individual specificity into social relationships. Those of the genetic variant will fall into the usual broad categories but will also show certain unique and specific differences.

In animals which are capable of learning, social behavior becomes differentiated on the basis of mutual adaptation and habit formation as well as on the basis of biological differences. As shown by Ginsburg and Allee (1942) the formation of a dominance order is at least in part related to the psychological principles of learning. Once such a relationship is formed and firmly established by habit, it may be extremely difficult to upset it by altering biological factors, as shown by Beeman and Allee (1945). Among the higher animals it is probable that all social relationships are affected by the psychological processes of problem solving (or adaptation) and habit formation. Neglect of these factors in favor of an assumption of purely genetic or instinctive determination of behavior may lead to serious errors of interpretation (Lehrman 1953).

As with physiological factors, psychological processes tend to introduce specificity into social relationships. In a study of social organization of sheep it was found that any given lamb had a general leader-follower relationship toward all adults in its tendency to follow them, although this tendency was strongest with regard to the mother. Its care-dependency relationships, on the other hand, were extremely specific and developed only with its own mother (Scott 1945).

In any species which has the psychological capacity to discriminate between individuals, such specific relationships will be expected to occur. It likewise follows that unless the scientific observer develops a similar ability to identify individuals, specific social relationships will pass unnoticed, and with them a large part of social organization. There is a vast difference between the observation that hens tend to peck each other (a general relationship) and the knowledge that within each pair there is one which always pecks and one which always dodges (a peck order consisting of a group of specific relationships).

If social relationships were entirely determined by biological factors it would be expected that all female-female relationships in a given species would be the same except as affected by chance genetic variability. Such is obviously not the case in the peck-order studies, and it is probable that a similar specificity will be found in many other types of social relationships when studied in detail. The general analytic method is to identify all individuals in the social group and then bring them together in pairs in a situation which will elicit the kind of behavior being studied (agonistic, sexual, etc.). A well-designed experiment includes results on all possible combinations of pairs, observed in an order which controls factors such as fatigue, habit formation, etc. The total possible number of combinations in a group is given by the formula $n(n - 1)/2$ (Carpenter 1940), so that such a study becomes very lengthy if n (the total number of individuals in the group) is large. The study should be supplemented with observations on the whole group, as it is possible that pairs may react differently when in the presence of others.

Many models for this type of study may be found in the literature (Collias 1951), particularly those done with dominance-subordination relationships, and the methods need not be described in greater detail here. Guhl (1953) has written an excellent summary of methods used for the study of specific dominance and sexual relationships in the domestic fowl. As indicated above, there is a need for the extension of these methods to the study of other sorts of social relationships in order to obtain a more complete picture of social organization.

The importance of specificity in social relationships is likewise apparent when analysis is made from a developmental viewpoint, and this has led to the concept of socialization.

SOCIALIZATION

Experiments which modify the social environment have tended to bring out the general principles of socialization. Any highly social animal that has been so far studied has behavioral mechanisms whereby, early in development, an individual forms positive social relationships with its own kind and usually with particular individuals of its kind. At the same time, other behavioral mechanisms operate to prevent such relationships being formed with other species and, to a lesser extent, with other groups of its own kind. Raising an individual with any other species including human beings usually produces an individual which is socialized to the strange species. Essential patterns of social behavior remain unaltered and are given in response to the strange species to the extent that such behavior is compatible.

The process of socialization has been shown to take place within limited periods of time by Lorenz (1935) in birds and also in such mammals as the sheep (Collias 1953) and dog (Scott and Marston 1950). Lorenz has been chiefly concerned with the positive mechanisms to which he has given the general term "imprinting," but, in the case of the mammals mentioned, some information is also present regarding the negative mechanisms which normally prevent social attachment to other species. In the dog and wolf, for example, agonistic behavior may be elicited by strangers at a very early age, effectively preventing positive contact as the animal grows older (Scott 1953a).

These effects have led to the concept of critical periods in the process of socialization (Scott and Marston 1950). There are points in development where it is very easy to change the individuals to which an animal becomes socialized, and other points later or earlier in development when this is difficult or impossible. A study of the process of socialization thus forms an important part of the developmental analysis of social organization.

An excellent review of experiments on the general effects of modifying early experience has been made by Beach and Jaynes (1954). As applied to the problem of social organization the most useful techniques may be outlined as follows. The first step is a detailed descriptive study of development, paying particular attention to social behavior patterns and changes in sensory, motor and psychological capacities. We have attempted to set up a model outline for this type of study in the case of two species of mammals, the dog and mouse (Scott and Marston 1950; Williams and Scott 1953).

A developmental study may be supplemented by two sorts of simple experimental procedures. One is to take male and female individuals at birth or hatching and have them reared by another species, human or otherwise. This method has produced brilliant results in the hands of Lorenz (1935), and may be extended further to the rearing of individuals in semi-isolation (Thompson and Heron 1954). The other is to castrate male and female individuals as early as possible in development, which gives some indication of the importance of hormonal changes and sexual behavior in social development.

Observations on the time of development of various capacities and patterns of behavior require experimental verification. On the basis of present evidence, the development of many species falls into natural periods based on beginnings or changes of important social relationships. This gives a basis for the experimental analysis of the factor of time in early social experience. Modification of social experience may be begun at different points in development and continued for appropriate periods. Controls for physiological and structural changes, genetic differences, random environmental factors and the psychological factors of learning are important in the design of these experiments (King and Gurney 1954).

SOCIAL ORGANIZATION BETWEEN GROUPS

Most of the work on analysis of social organization has been done within groups, and correctly so. The most frequent aspects of social life in animals appear to be concerned with what are called by the human social psychologists "face-to-face contacts in small groups." However, some organization between groups apparently does exist, as reported in Carpenter's (1934, 1940) studies of howling monkeys and gibbons. Likewise, the territorial organization of passerine birds during the breeding season may be considered as organization between small family groups. Obviously, such organization is most likely to occur under natural conditions, and its existence is one of the possibilities which should be looked for in field studies.

The evidence for the existence of territoriality in small mammals has been summarized by Blair (1953), who finds that instances of defense of definite boundaries are relatively rare. As with birds, group territorial defense in mammals may be described simply in terms of a general dominance-subordination relationship, in which the group or individuals within the group tend to be dominant over the individual trespassing on the territory (Murie 1944; King 1955). However, in the case of howling monkeys Carpenter (1934) reports that groups maintain regular daily contacts with each other by howling at dawn, and this is possibly also the case in birds such as quail which vocalize regularly. The "wars" between colonies of ants appear to involve a general relationship in which all strange individuals are attacked.

The relationship between separate social groups is a problem of considerable theoretical interest and should be investigated whereever possible. Analysis should include the means by which new groups are formed, and the fate of isolated individuals as well as territoriality. King (1955) has found a definite group territorial system in prairie dogs, with a tendency for adults to move out and colonize new areas after raising the young, which are left to occupy the old territory. Carpenter's (1940, 1934) studies of the gibbon and howling monkey are excellent models for the analysis of this and other aspects of social organization.

CONCLUSION

It will be seen from the foregoing outline that the complete analysis of the social organization of even a single species is an enormous task. It is not likely that the job will ever be entirely completed, though such a point is being approached in such favorite objects of study as the chicken, mouse, stickleback, honeybee, army ant and termite. The task must be divided into sections, and emphasis placed upon important points of fact and theory.

Collecting observations on behavior patterns and their organization into basic biologically determined social relationships can often be done with a study of a year or two. Much material is already available in publications written for other purposes, particularly in natural history and ecological life history studies. A great deal of information on European species is contained in studies of comparative behavior patterns done by the "ethologists," although they have frequently concerned themselves with the nature of stimulation ("releasers") rather than social organization. The systematic classification of material from these sources often saves a great deal of time as well as providing confirmatory evidence for original study.

The analysis of socialization and specific social relationships is more complicated and time-consuming, and is difficult to do except in laboratory or semi-natural environments, although it has been shown that social dominance does exist under natural conditions (J. W. Scott 1942). Indeed, the more basic the analysis, the slower it becomes, and a division of labor among scientists is necessary when physiological and genetic factors are studied. This brings up the problem of coordination of effort.

The study of the social organization of behavior tends to unify knowledge. Behavior is usually defined as activity of an entire organism and thus is affected by factors customarily divided up in all the conventional subdivisions of zoology and psychology. When behavior is considered in relation to social organization the subject matter is widened still further to include certain aspects of general social science. It is obviously impossible for anyone to have a thorough and complete knowledge of all these fields, but the specialist in any one of them should at least have a general knowledge of the others and their relation to his own. The ecologist, as a last surviving type of general biologist, should have a particular advantage in this respect. Meetings such as this one, in which the speakers have training in such diverse fields as genetics, psychology, and ecology, can do much to promote the interchange of ideas and mutual comprehension.

A final word may be said concerning the necessity of maintaining a high standard of scientific work. As stated in the beginning of this article, we still have very few specific standardized techniques for the analysis of social organization, and to insist upon the enforcement of standards prematurely would do much to discourage new and creative lines of research. The harm that can be done by publishing inconclusive pilot experiments or generalizing from superficial descriptions based on study of a few individuals is equally great. We can and should insist on general standards of thoroughness and repeatability, on controls for the wide variety of genetic, physiological, developmental, psychological, ecological, and social factors known to affect behavior, and on the necessity for final experimental verification of any theory.

The resulting well-established facts and theories of social organization in animals have widespread significance. Such information has great practical importance in wildlife management and in the care of animals under domestication. For example, if it is planned to recolonize a vacant territory with social animals, the new individuals must have been socialized toward each other or otherwise the group will disintegrate and fail to survive.

A knowledge of social organization is an essential part of understanding the general ecology of the species. Populations of animals do not exist in nature as randomly distributed individuals but as socially organized groups. Enough has been said in the foregoing article to indicate that an immense amount of information is still to be gathered about the social organization of animals, and even some of our common and familiar species are far from completely understood.

Finally, the collection of knowledge regarding social organization in animals and the resulting generalizations which will be made should prove to be of great help in understanding certain human problems. A great many problems of human maladjustment can be attributed to interference with the process of socialization, whose study should be one of the primary concerns of child psychology. A more thorough knowledge of animal societies should contribute greatly to our understanding of the biological and psychological bases of human social organization.

SUMMARY

An attempt has been made in this article to present a systematic general outline for the analysis of social organization in animals.

Methods include systematic description of the important behavior patterns of the species based on studies of the daily and seasonal cycles of behavior and upon the development of behavior in the individual from birth until maturity and old age. These basic patterns of behavior determine to a large extent the general types of social relationships which are possible in the species.

Further analysis of specific social relationships depends upon identification of every individual in the social group and should be verified by experimental combinations of every possible pair.

Study of the process of socialization should include a systematic descriptive study of changes in the basic behavioral capacities: sensory, motor, psychological, and patterns of social behavior, with particular reference to relative timing and its consequences. Some remarks are made concerning general application of the method, and the significance of the results.

REFERENCES

Allee, W. C. 1927. Animal aggregations. Quart. Rev. Biol., **2**: 367-398.

———. 1931. Animal aggregations. A study in general sociology. Chicago: Univ. Chicago Press.

———. 1950. Extrapolation in comparative sociology. Scientia, **43**: 135-142.

———, M. N. Allee, F. Ritchey, and E. W. Castle. 1947. Leadership in a flock of White Pekin ducks. Ecology, **28**: 310-15.

Allen, A. A. 1911-14. The red-winged blackbird: a study in the ecology of a cat-tail marsh. Abs. Proc. Linnean Soc. N.Y., No. 24-25.

Armstrong, E. A. 1952. Behavior is contagious, too. Animal Kingdom, **55**: 88-91.

Beach, F. A., and J. Jaynes. 1954. Effects of early experience upon the behavior of animals. Psych. Bull., **51**: 239-263.

Beeman, E. A., and W. C. Allee. 1945. Some effects of thiamin on the winning of social contacts in mice. Physiol. Zool., **18**: 195-221.

Blair, W. F. 1953. Population dynamics of rodents and other small mammals. Rec. Ad. Genetics, **5**: 1-41.

Carpenter, C. R. 1934. A field study of the behavior and social relations of howling monkeys. Comp. Psych. Monogr. No. 48, **10**(2): 1-168.

———. 1940. A field study of the behavior and social relations of the gibbon (*Hylobates Lar*). Comp. Psych. Monogr. No. 84, **16**(5): 1-212.

Collias, N. 1943. Statistical analysis of factors which make for success in initial encounters between hens. Am. Nat., **77**: 519-538.

———. 1944. Aggressive behavior among vertebrate animals. Physiol. Zool., **17**: 83-123.

Collias, N. 1951. Social life and the individual among vertebrate animals. Ann. N.Y. Acad. Sci., **51**: 1074-1092.

———. 1953. Some factors in maternal rejection in sheep and goats. Bull. Ecol. Soc. Amer., **34**: 78.

Darling, F. F. 1937. A herd of red deer. London: Oxford Univ. Press.

Dean, B. 1896. The early development of Amia. Quart. J. Mic. Sci., **38**: 413-444.

Ginsburg, B. and W. C. Allee. 1942. Some effects of conditioning on social dominance and subordination in inbred strains of mice. Physiol. Zool., **15**: 485-506.

Guhl, A. M. 1953. Social behavior of the domestic fowl. Kansas State College Ag. Exp. Sta. Technical Bull. No. 73.

———, and D. C. Warren. 1946. Number of offspring sired by cockerels related to social dominance in chickens. Poultry Sci., **25**: 460-472.

Howard, H. E. 1920. Territory in bird life. London: Murray.

King, J. A. 1955. Social behavior, social organization and population dynamics in a black-tailed prairiedog town in the Black Hills of South Dakota. Contr. Lab. Vert. Biol., Univ. Mich., No. 67, 123 pp.

———, and N. L. Gurney. 1954. Effect of early social experience on adult aggressive behavior in C57BL/10 Mice. J. Comp. and Physiol. Psych., **47**: 326-330.

Lehrman, D. S. 1953. A critique of Konrad Lorentz's theory of instinctive behavior. Quart. Rev. Biol., **28**: 337-363.

Lorenz, K. 1935. Der Kumpan in der Umwelt des Vogels. Journal für Ornithologie, **83**: 137-213, 289-413. For English summary see: The companion in the bird's world. Auk, **54**: 245-273, 1937.

Murie, A. 1944. The wolves of Mt. McKinley, U.S.D.I. Fauna Series No. 5.

Nowlis, V. 1942. Sexual status and degree of hunger in chimpanzee competitive interaction. J. Comp. Psych., **34**: 185-194.

Schjelderup-Ebbe, T. 1922. Beiträge zur sozial-psychologie des Haushuhns. Zeit. Psych., **88**: 225-252.

Scott, J. P. 1945. Social behavior, organization and leadership in a small flock of domestic sheep. Comp. Psych. Monograph No. 96, **18**(4): 1-29.

———. 1945a. Group formation determined by social behavior; a comparative study of two mammalian societies. Sociometry, **8**: 42-52.

———. 1950 (ed.) Methodology and techniques for the study of animal societies. Ann. N. Y. Acad. Sci., **51**: 1001-1122.

———. 1950a. The social behavior of dogs and wolves: an illustration of sociobiological systematics. Ann. N.Y. Acad. Sci., **51**: 1009-1021.

———. 1953. Implications of infra-human social behavior for problems of human relations. *In*: Group Relations at the Crossroads, M. Sherif and W. A. Wilson, eds. New York: Harper.

Scott, J. P. 1953a. The process of socialization in higher animals. *In*: Interrelations between the social environment and psychiatric disorders. New York: Milbank Memorial Fund.

———, and M. Marston. 1950. Critical periods affecting the development of normal and mal-adjustive social behavior of puppies. Jour. Genet. Psych., **77**: 25-60.

———, and E. Fredericson. 1951. The causes of fighting in mice and rats. Physiol. Zool., **24**: 273-309.

Scott, J. W. 1942. Mating behavior of the sage grouse. Auk, 59: 477-498.

Thompson, W. R. and W. Heron. 1954. The effects of early restriction on activity in dogs. J. Comp. and Physiol. Psych., **47**: 77-82.

Tinbergen, N. 1953. Social behaviour in animals. New York: John Wiley.

Wheeler, W. M. 1923. Social life among the insects. New York: Harcourt, Brace.

Williams, E., and J. P. Scott. 1953. The development of social behavior patterns in the mouse, in relation to natural periods. Behaviour, **6**: 35-64.

The Development of Social Organisation in the Domestic Chick

A. M. GUHL

The social behaviour of adult chickens has been investigated extensively. Reviews of behaviour studies (Wood-Gush, 1955) and of social behaviour in particular (Guhl, 1953) of these birds have shown that little is known about the development of behaviour patterns in domestic chicks, especially agonistic behaviour and the establishment of the initial peck-order. Noble & Zitrin (1942) experimented with sex hormones to induce precocious sexual behaviour. Collias (1950b) with somewhat similar treatment observed both sexual behaviour and aggressiveness. Smith (1957) found evidence of social "learning" in domestic chicks. Observations on the early socialisation of chicks (Collias, 1952) were not carried to the stage of peck-order formation. Wood-Gush (1957) noted some stages in the development of agonistic behaviour in chicks prior to the establishment of what he called the ontogenetic peck-order. However, he was primarily interested in the probable correlation between levels of aggressiveness and sexual activity.

The objectives of the study required some initial observations and a series of subsequent experiments. Information was needed on the various behaviour patterns; the sequence in which these appeared; and the age at which the initial peck-order developed. Sex hormones are known to influence social behaviour patterns in adults (Allee, Collias & Lutherman, 1939; Allee & Collias, 1940) and in chicks (Collias, 1950b). Could exogenous androgen and oestrogen

From *Animal Behavior*, 1958, **6**, 92-111.

affect the sequence in which behaviour patterns develop or the age at which dominance relations become established? Would castration cause any deviations from the normal development of social behaviour and the organisation? Do these hormones have similar inductive effects in both sexes? Experiments were also devised to give some information on the psychological aspects of developing social behaviour. Organised pecking as evidenced by dominance-subordination relations involves learning or conditioning. Does rearing in partial isolation alter the age at which the social order may be established? Of interest here are the effects of early inter-individual contacts on the later establishment of peck-rights, and the effects of certain habits (as the reinforcement which constitutes social inertia) on the evocation of behaviour patterns and social organisation. Finally, the results presented an opportunity to relate them to certain ontogenetic phenomena and concepts of inherent behaviour.

METHODS

Chicks were obtained from the Department of Poultry Husbandry and from a commercial hatchery. The former were received on the day of hatching and the latter on the day after hatching. One set of chicks, White Rock males, was four weeks old when received. Experiments included two strains of White Leghorns; one strain of White Rocks; and commercial hybrids. Samples of these strains and/or breeds were small and the results may not be typical of their populations. Availability determined the various breeds or strains used.

All experiments were conducted in a basement laboratory in Fairchild Hall. Ventilation was provided by two exhaust fans. During brooding and to about five weeks of age the chicks received 24 hours of light daily, thereafter a period of 12 hours of light was regulated by a time switch. This laboratory was steam heated during the winter months. The experiments were conducted during various seasons and over several years.

The equipment used to rear the birds varied and no experiments were made to determine whether such differences influenced the development of behaviour. Attempts were made to keep physical factors (temperature, hours of light, and floor space per bird) similar for group-reared and isolated chicks within each experiment. Three methods of brooding were used. The order in which they are described is the same as that in the presentation of the results. The heterosexual flocks and the White Leghorn males were started in a large brooder measuring (inside dimensions) 66 x 33 x 9 inches; the heating compartment was 24 x 33 inches. The area was partitioned as needed for groups of chicks and isolated chicks (cell areas were 28 x 4 inches with six inches extending under the heating compartment). The White Leghorn females were brooded on the floor in pens and heated with infra-red lamps. This arrangement facilitated observations. The chicks in partial isolation were in a floor cage constructed of half-inch mesh screening with cells 24 x 11 x 10 inches, and 25-watt lamps in the cells to furnish heat and light. The hybrid chicks in the capon experiment were brooded in five small (20 x 18 x 6 inches) brooders with wire floors and heated with a 25-watt lamp. The time at which chicks were moved from brooders to floor pens varied from three to six weeks of age. The floor pens had an approximate area of 8 x 7 feet.

The partially isolated chicks used in the experiments concerned with the assembly of chicks at various ages were reared in cages composed of cells. Two sizes were used. The smaller cells used during brooding were 10-inch cubes. The half-inch mesh partitions were arranged to give each chick two neighbours, and were heated with a 25-watt lamp. As the birds grew they were moved to cages with cells measuring 15 x 13 x 15 inches, in a similar arrangement. The outer walls of this cage were made of 2 x 3 inch welded wire, and troughs for food and water were suspended on the outside of these cages. Attempts by chicks to peck each other through the screen were unusual. The isolated chicks were assembled by removing the partitions. The group-reared controls of these experiments were brooded in the large brooder described above and then placed into cages having a unit floor area per bird which equalled that of the isolated birds. The final experiment on social inertia used these cages with or without the partitions as needed.

Within each experiment the chicks were distributed among cages at random. Upon receipt each chick was wingbanded as it was taken from the shipping boxes, marked with a colour(s) for rapid identification, and placed into a brooder, cage, or cell for isolation.

The placements followed an order until there were equal numbers (usually ten) in each group. The dyes were dissolved in 70 per cent. alcohol, which gave fairly rapid drying, and painted on the down of backs or wings. Re-application of colours was necessary as the feathers developed. The individuals are indicated in the tables by letters representing the colour(s) used.

The androgen used in some of these tests was testosterone propionate (Oreton[1]), and injected daily into breast muscles with the alternation of right and left sides. The oestrogen was a suspension of diethyl-estradiol (Jen-Sol[2]) which was injected every other day. All birds which received exogenous gonadal hormones, and all the capons, were autopsied at the end of each experiment to verify the sex or, with capons, to determine macroscopically whether any portions of testes were present.

Observations were made by the author and four different students who varied much in their training and experience with chickens. To keep subjective differences in the interpretation of a peck or threat at a minimum, it was agreed to record delivered pecks and to consider undelivered pecks as threats. Variables, in addition to those of probable genetic origin, may have been introduced by subjective differences in recording. However, the results were in basic agreement within certain limits.

THE DEVELOPMENT OF SOME BEHAVIOR PATTERNS

The prehatching and posthatching behaviour of domestic chicks were reviewed by Wood-Gush (1955) and discussed by Collias (1952). This report is concerned particularly with the developmental sequence of certain behaviour patterns which lead to social organisation. Behaviour patterns may be considered as social if they are either "contagious" (or social facilitated behaviour, Armstrong, 1947) or lead to inter-individual activity. The order in which they tended to appear was: escape (fear) reactions, frolicking, sparring, aggressive pecking, avoidance and fighting.

[1] From Schering Corporation, Bloomfield, N.J.
[2] From Jensen-Salsbery Laboratory, Kansas City, Mo.

The escape reaction was common after the third day posthatch, and could be readily elicited by any object moving above the chicks. Some chicks responded sooner than others and all soon dashed about the brooder frantically. Such reactions appear at a much later age in birds which are fed in the nest, e.g. passerines (Nice, 1943, p. 52). During the first week of age chicks began to frolic, a spontaneous activity in which individuals ran briefly with wings raised. Such activity by one often induced others to frolic although not necessarily in the same direction. By the second week frolicking led to sparring. Two chicks, after frolicking, jumped up and down, as adults do when fighting, but the chicks failed to deliver any blows with their beaks. The activity waned readily and the partners pursued other activities. The earliest aggressive peck was noted late in the second week. However, this behaviour was quite unusual at this early age. Avoidance of another chick in response to aggressive action was indicated during the fifth week, although a given chick did not habitually avoid certain others at this time. A chick would move away when pecked but might at times return to peck its aggressor. Fighting was observed as early as the sixth week, but usually ended without any decision.

Dominance-subordination relationships, or peck-rights, developed later, presumably when aggressive attacks were more intense and when individuals could be recognised and thereby avoided as individuals. Attempts to determine the age at which recognition of penmates developed were unsuccessful. The peck-order is the best evidence for recognition of individuals (Guhl & Ortman, 1953). Tests made with strange chicks (not members of the same group) were not conclusive. The introduction of younger chicks however elicited threatening stances or pecks as early as 10 days of age, but such chicks were dissimilar in appearance, size, and probably in behaviour, from penmates. Smith (1957) has presented some evidence that Leghorns of ten days of age would discriminate partners of the same breed but from a different flock.

In the sequence of development there was much variability between individuals and groups with regard to the age at which these behaviour patterns became evident. There was also much overlapping in the sequence. Presumably there was variability in rates of development, but there were also indications that the intensity of stimuli (external and/or internal) varied. Frolicking, sparring, or fighting occurred more often subsequent to turning on room lights, or at feeding time, but soon subsided. The chicks appeared to be well adjusted to a given behaviour level in development, and data were slow in accumulation. New patterns appeared rather abruptly and soon subsided with readjustment. These observations suggest what Kortlandt (1955) called "ruptural behaviour."

DIFFERENCES BETWEEN MALE AND FEMALE CHICKS

The initial observations were made on groups of chicks, the sex of which remained unknown until sexual dimorphism developed. These White Leghorn chicks (Kansas State College strain) were divided at random into two groups of 18 and 19. Observations began on the day after hatching and continued, for some of them, for 21 weeks.

Aggressive approaches and delivered pecks were recorded separately during the early weeks and also as to which chick pecked and which received the peck. No aggressive action was seen during the first week. After it was possible to determine the sex of the individuals the data were summarised (end of six weeks) as to unisexual and heterosexual pecking. This was of interest because adult males usually do not peck the hens nor are they pecked by them. An effort was made to note the age at which a pecking dichotomy would appear.

The aggressive actions recorded during the first six weeks are summarised in Table I. The cockerels (males) were more aggressive than the pullets (females). A total of 118 pecks by males on both sexes were observed, whereas the pullets pecked only 13 times during the same length of time. Only 36 of the pecks by males were delivered, and only 4 by the females. The pecking at this age was infrequent and of low intensity. There were about twice as many aggressions observed in group 9C as in 9D (88 to 43). This variable was related to the sex ratio. Group 9C contained 10 males and 8 females, and the 9D group had 8 males and 11 females. Most of the aggressive actions were between males; of the 118 actions by cockerels, 82 were on males and 36 on pullets. The pullets pecked cockerels more often than they pecked females, but the data are too few to be taken seriously. One may conclude that these figures indicate a partial dichotomy in social organisation at the onset of agonistic behaviour.

The chicks were moved from the brooder to floor pens at the

Table I. Peck-like aggressive approaches and delivered pecks observed during the second and through the sixth week; no aggressions were noted during the first week of age.

Interactions	*Groups**	*Peck-like action*	*Delivered pecks*	*Total*
Male on male	9C	46	16	62
	9D	11	9	20
Male on female	9C	12	9	21
	9D	13	2	15
Total by males		82	36	118
Female on male	9C	2	2	4
	9D	4	1	5
Female on female	9C	0	1	1
	9D	3	0	3
Total by females		9	4	13

* Group 9C composed of 10 males and 8 females.
Group 9D composed of 8 males and 11 females.

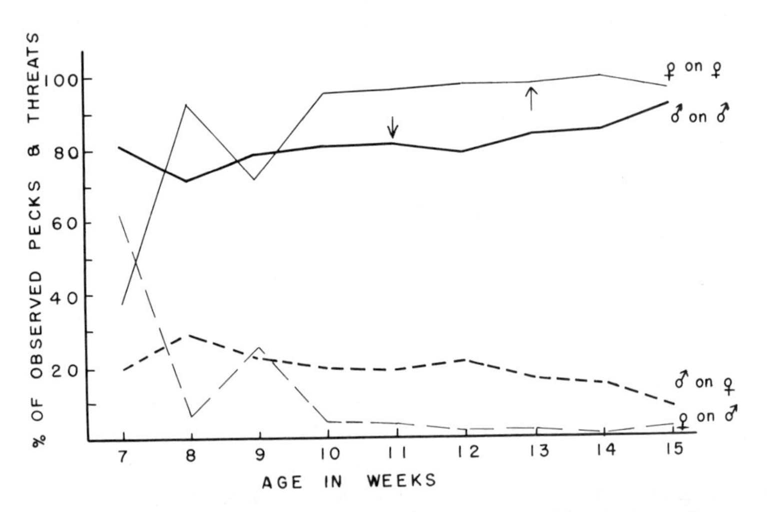

Fig. 1. The gradual development of unisexual pecking is shown by the percentage of unisexual and heterosexual pecking which occurred during the establishment and the maturation of peck-orders. Arrows indicate the time at which peck-orders were formed in group 9C.

end of the sixth week. Similar data for weeks 7 through 15 are given in Figure 1 as percentages of pecks delivered by members of each sex in group 9C. The periods of observation were not of uniform duration and rates of pecking could not be given. The curves in the figure are based on a total of 4,210 pecks, of which 3,585 were delivered by ten cockerels and 625 by eight pullets. Only 25 of the pullet's pecks were on males, but 637 were delivered by cockerels on the females. The figure shows that heterosexual pecking diminished gradually. The results from group 9D were quite similar, but with less heterosexual pecking during the seventh week.

The cockerels began to show sexual behaviour during the eighth week, but this behaviour did not become intense until the 15th week as did dominance behaviour. The pullets were definitely under social stress in both groups and had comparatively little opportunity to feed. Most of the cockerels were removed and observations on the pullets were continued to determine when they would develop sexually. The first sexual crouching by pullets was observed during the 18th week, and the first egg was laid during the 21st week.

A peck-order was not established until each individual formed definite dominance-subordination relationships (i.e. obtained the peck-rights over, or consistently avoided) with each of the penmates of its sex (see Guhl, 1953). Tabulations of pecks were made weekly and compared with those of the preceding week. When the pecking relationship between any two individuals became consistently uni-directional then dominance was considered as established for that pair. Tables II and III show the ages at which various peck-rights were established for each individual. The letters under the column "peck-order" represent the colour(s) used to identify each individual. In this column each chick pecked those listed below it unless an arrow shows a deviation from a straight-line peck-order.

On examination of Tables II and III it will be noted that the males began to establish dominance somewhat earlier than did the females, and that the cockerels also formed a peck-order earlier. A comparison of groups 9C and 9D shows that the 9C individuals began to set up peck-rights earlier than the 9D, and that the latter group formed a social organisation sooner. The mean ages at which the males established peck-rights were 7.58 and 8.03 weeks, and for the

Table II. Ages at which peck-rights were developed in the heterosexual group 9C of White Leghorn chicks.

		Weeks of age							
Number pecked	*Peck-order*	*6*	*7*	*8*	*9*	*10*	*11*	*12*	*13*
		Normal ♂♂							
8	RR	1	7						
8	BR		4	1	3				
7	RV	1	3	2	1				
7	Y		4	1	1		1		
5	RY		3	1	1				
4	BV	1	1		1	1			
3	B	2		1					
2	BG		1			1			
1	YY			1					
0	G								
45	Total	5	23	7	7	2			
		Normal ♀♀							
7	YV		1	1		3		1	1
6	BY		2	2	2				
5	R			1		3	1		
4	V			1	1		1		1
3	GV					1		2	
2	YG					1		1	
1	RG				1				
0	GG								
28	Total		3	5	4	8	2	4	2

females they were 9.75 and 9.33 weeks respectively. The males formed dominance relations 2.17 and 1.29 weeks earlier than did the females. Some of the variability probably was due to sampling error, because the chicks were under observation for comparatively short daily periods, and since the groups were very small samples of this strain of White Leghorns. Other variables to consider may be differences in sex ratios, the relative frequency at which any two birds met, and individual difference in rates of development.

There were some changes in the peck-order of the 9D females and the 9C males after an initial social order was formed. Although such reversals of dominance were expected, these changes raised the question of whether the original peck-order represented the relative

Table III. Ages at which peck-rights developed in the heterosexual group 9D of White Leghorn chicks.

		Weeks of age						
Number pecked	*Peck-order*	*6*	*7*	*8*	*9*	*10*	*11*	*12*
					Normal ♂♂			
7	BB		4	3				
6	BV			5	1			
5	R		1	3	1			
3	Y			3				
3	RR			2	1			
2	RY				1	1		
2	BR			2				
0	BG							
28	Total		5	18	4	1		
					Normal ♀♀			
10	BY				4	6		
9	G			5	3	1		
8	YG			1	6	1		
6	GV				1	5		
6	RV			1	3	2		
5	GG			1	3	1		
4	YY				1	2		1
3	RG				1	1	1	
3	YV				1	2		
1	V				1			
0	B							
55	Total			8	24	21	1	1

levels of aggressiveness of the individuals, or whether any individuals which developed more slowly might have their potential aggressiveness suppressed by low rank attained during the establishment of the order. At the age of 21 weeks the 11 females of 9D were isolated in a laying battery for about six weeks. The procedure permitted further development without stresses associated with the peck-order, and it caused the extinction of dominance relations between penmates (Collias, 1943; Guhl, 1953, present techniques used to measure aggressiveness). The pullets were then matched by pairs in initial encounters until each met each of the others to establish dominance in a neutral area. After one week these birds were paired again for another series of encounters. The pullets were then ranked according to the number of encounters won in each series.

Coefficients of correlation were determined between the number pecked in the original peck-order and the number of encounters won in each series. The results were as follows:

> Number pecked: Number of encounters won in first series, $r = +0.77$; $P = 0.01$.
> Number won in first series: Number won in second series, $r = +0.77$; $P = 0.01$.
> Number won in second series: Number pecked, $r = +0.61$; $P = 0.05$.

Although these correlations are significant there were changes in the number of individuals pecked as related to the number of encounters won. Four pullets had the same rank in the peck-order and in each of the two series of encounters, the other seven changed ranks from one to six steps between the original order and the second series of encounters, in about nine weeks. The lower coefficient of 0.61 (and barely significant) of this comparison probably indicates that some individuals developed at slower rates than others. Four pullets improved their status and three lost rank. Similar tests with other groups of chicks showed that changes in rank may or may not occur.

EFFECTS OF SEX HORMONES ON MALE CHICKS

With the background of information obtained from observations on heterosexual groups of chicks, experimentation was begun to determine some of the physiological and psychological factors influencing the development of social behaviour patterns and the establishment of a dominance order. Androgen and oestrogen were known to influence social behaviour in chickens (Allee, Collias & Lutherman, 1939; Allee & Collias, 1940) and other vertebrates (Beach, 1948).

Two sets of experiments were run with male chicks. The first was a test with androgen and the second with oestrogen. Each set used two groups of chicks; one of which served as a control or untreated group.

In the first set, White Leghorn (Kansas State College strain) chicks were divided at random into two groups of 9 and 10 chicks. The former group was used as a control, and each chick in the latter group received 0.5 mg. androgen daily from the third day after hatching to eight weeks of age. The development of dominance relations are shown in Table IV. There was no difference between the control and the treated cockerels in the span of weeks during which dominance relations were developed, but the injected birds established more peck-rights during the sixth and seventh weeks. The controls established peck-rights at a mean age of 7.75 weeks, the androgen treated males at 7.13 weeks, making a difference of only 0.62 week. It was of interest to note that androgen did not have as

Table IV. The effect of androgenic treatment on the development of peck-rights in a small group of White Leghorn male chicks.

		Weeks of age				
Number pecked	*Peck-order*	*6*	*7*	*8*	*9*	*10*
		Normal ♂♂				
8	GR	1	7			
7	V		2	4	1	
5	Y			4	1	
5	R		2		3	
4	G	1		2	1	
3	RR			2	1	
3	B		1	2		
1	VV			1		
0	VR					
36	Total	2	12	15	7	
		Androgen treated ♂♂, 3rd day–8 wks., 0.5 mg/day				
9	Gh	5	4			
8	Y	2	1	5		
7	RV	1	3	3		
6	RG	2	1	3		
5	RR	1	3	1		
4	V	1	2	1		
3	G		1	1	1	
2	Vh		1	1		
1	RY			1		
0	R					
45	Total	12	16	16	1	

marked an effect on domination as it did on other behaviour patterns such as crowing, which appeared a few days after injections were begun (see also Collias, 1950b).

The second experiment was run during the summer and because day-old chicks were not available some four-week old White Rock cockerels were received from a commercial source. In previous experiments no peck-rights developed before the normal male chicks were five weeks old. These chicks were divided at random into two groups, and those in one of these were injected every other day with 1.5 mg of diethyl-estradiol. Right and left sides of the breast were alternated as injection sites. Treatment started on the 28th day and was continued until the chicks were 59 days old.

Table V. The effects of œstrogenic treatment on the development of peck-rights in a small group of White Rock males.

		Weeks of age				
Number pecked	*Peck-order*	*5*	*6*	*7*	*8*	*9*
			Normal ♂♂			
9	Rh		7	2		
8	V	1	5	2		
7	Y	1	3	3		
5	R		2	1	2	
5	Yh		3	1	1	
4	Gh		2		2	
4	G		1	1	2	
2	VR		1	1		
1	Vh				1	
0	GR					
45	Total	2	24	11	8	
		Œstrogen treated ♂♂, 28th day–59th day, 1.5 mg/2 days				
9	VR	4	4	1		
7	V		4	3		
6	Y	2	1	3		
5	R	1	3	1		
5	Gh	3	1	1		
5	G		3	1	1	
4	Yh		2	1	1	
3	Vh	1	2			
1	Rh			1		
0	GR					
45	Total	11	20	12	2	

The results are given in Table V. The mean age at which the controls established peck-rights was 6.56 weeks and 6.11 for the œstrogen treated cockerels. The difference is only 0.45 week. Some peck-rights developed during the fifth week of age, or one week earlier than in the tests with White Leghorn cockerels treated with androgen. The peck-order also formed a week earlier, but these differences were not necessarily breed differences (see previous comments on size of sample and length of observation periods). No differences were noted which may be attributed to experience during the first four weeks, although it might have been a factor. These chicks came from a large group which are called "started chicks" in the poultry industry. The effects of œstrogen appeared to be similar to those of androgen treated chicks only in so far as there was a tendency to develop dominance relations earlier than among the controls of this test. There was a marked difference in behaviour patterns. Before the fifth week it was noted that the treated chicks failed to show any marked aggressiveness; more accurately stated they were rather phlegmatic. Although some pecking occurred, most of the dominance relations were determined on the basis of avoidance. Œstrogen treated chicks at this age were consistent in avoiding certain of their penmates, one of the criteria used to determine dominance status between any two individuals. The social order in this group of experimentals might be called an avoidance-order rather than a peck-order, if the emphasis is placed on negative reactions to specific penmates rather than on the aggressive actions.

EFFECTS OF SEX HORMONES ON FEMALE CHICKS

Two sets of experiments were run with female chicks of a commercial strain of White Leghorns which were received when two days old. Each experiment contained a control group and another of which the individuals were treated with a sex hormone. The chicks were taken at random from the shipping boxes and placed alternately into each of two floor pens.

Each group of the first set contained 10 chicks. The experimentals were injected with 0.5 mg of testosterone propionate daily from two days old through the eighth week. The results are given in Table VI. The treated pullets established more peck-rights

Table VI. The effects of androgenic treatment on the development of peck-rights in a small group of White Leghorn female chicks.

		Weeks of age				
Number pecked	*Peck-order*	*6*	*7*	*8*	*9*	*10*
		Normal ♀♀				
8	G	1		2	4	1
8	VR	1	2	5		
7	VV	1	1	4	1	
7	Rh		6	1		
5	V		2	2	1	
4	Gh		1	1	1	1
3	R					3
2	Yh				1	1
1	Y					1
0	Vh					
45	Total	3	12	15	8	7
		Androgen treated ♀♀, *2nd day–8 wks., 0.5 mg/day*				
9	VV	2	7			
7	GG	6	1			
6	Y		2	4		
6	G		2	4		
6	Vh		1	3	2	
5	Yh		1	4		
3	Rh		1	2		
2	Gh			1	1	
1	R				1	
0	V					
45	Total	8	15	18	4	

during the sixth and seventh weeks than did the controls; they also formed a peck-order about one week earlier. Mean ages for the formation of peck-rights were 8.09 and 7.40 weeks, with a difference of only 0.69 week, which is similar to the results of androgen injection into males.

The second set used for a test with œstrogen presented some problems. The chicks were chilled soon after they were placed on the floor and two died in each group of ten. Aggressive behaviour, when it did develop, was comparatively infrequent and the data were insufficient to ascertain the earliest established peck-rights. This is reflected in Table VII, since no dominance relations were known,

Table VII. The effects of œstrogenic treatment on the development of peck-rights in a small group of White Leghorn female chicks.

		Weeks of age				
Number pecked	*Peck-order*	*6*	*7*	*8*	*9*	*10*
				Normal ♀♀		
7	V				5	2
6	R				4	2
5	VV				3	2
4	RV				3	1
3	GR				2	1
2	Gh				1	1
1	Vh					1
0	Y					
28	Total				18	10
		Œstrogen treated ♀♀, 2nd day–10th wk., 1.5 mg/2 days				
7	VV*			7		
6	V				6	
5	R			1	4	
4	Y				4	
3	RV				2	1
2	VY				2	
1	RY				1	
0	GR					
28	Total			8	19	1

* Autopsy proved this chick to be a male.

with confidence, to be formed during the sixth and seventh weeks. Mean ages were 9.36 and 8.75 weeks for controls and experimentals respectively, with a difference between the means of 0.61 week. The pullets treated with 1.5 mg of diethyl-estradiol every other day however show a slight advance over their controls. This statement is qualified because autopsy revealed that the alpha bird (VV) was a male, and its early establishment of peck-rights must be disregarded in making comparisons. As with the males receiving œstrogen, consistency in avoiding specific individuals was more frequent than unidirectional pecking. The effects of œstrogenic treatment were an increase in submissive behaviour and a tendency toward an earlier establishment of a social order by means of avoiding reactions.

DEVELOPMENT OF PECK-RIGHTS IN CAPONS

Commercial hybrid males were divided into four groups at random. The cockerels of three of these groups were caponized. Each group contained 10 chicks at the start, but there was one death among the normal males and another in one group of capons. Chicks were castrated when nine days old by either Professor T. B. Avery of the Department of Poultry Husbandry or by Dr. E. H. Herrick of the Department of Zoology. It seemed advisable to attempt castration of these males prior to the onset of endogenous androgen. Willier (1952) states that gonadotropic activity is present with certainty by the fifth day after hatching, and that from this time on the gonadotropic activity gradually increases. Breneman & Mason (1951) in a critical study of pituitary-gonad relationship began their experiments with chicks 10 days old. It was therefore assumed that caponisation by the 10th day might preclude any conditioning of behaviour patterns by endogenous androgen.

Some comments need to be made here to account for the very high dosages of sex hormones used in this set of chicks. Breneman & Mason (1951) estimated that the physiological level of 40-day old White Leghorn cockerels was under 50 gamma (0.05 mg). Noble & Zitrin (1942) used 0.5 mg of testosterone propionate in cockerels beginning at the age of two days and of 15 days. Collias (1950b) varied the amount injected into two-day old cockerels from 0.1 to 0.7 mg per day and found that the frequency of certain behaviour patterns varied positively with the dosage. Both of these experiments were concerned with the early appearance of certain behaviour patterns. Noble & Zitrin used dead or anaesthetised pullet chicks to act as stimuli for the treated cockerels; they also paired cockerels and pullets during experimentation. Collias did not give details of his procedures. He stated that the birds tended to become refractory with continued treatment. A probably similar change was noted by Noble & Zitrin as they found that the copulatory response to a dead or anaesthetised chick was not elicited as frequently after treated males were paired with œstrogen treated females. The question arose as to whether this change to a higher threshold for response was mediated through essentially physiological or psychological factors, and if the latter, could it be bridged by still higher dosages of androgen.

Certain observations have indicated that psychological factors (learned behaviour) may be very important in determining whether a particular behaviour pattern is evoked. It was previously stated that new behaviour patterns appeared and waned in frequency with behavioural readjustment in normal chicks. Peck-orders are evidence of adjustment to aggressive behaviour, and further adjustments have been shown by the relation between sexual activity and position in a social order (Guhl & Warren, 1944; Guhl, 1950). Other instances of the dominance of psychological factors over physiological state were given by Guhl, Collias & Allee (1945); a hen treated with an androgen showed her increased aggressiveness in a discrimination cage long before it became evident in the social interactions of her "home" flock. Similarly, two cocks failed to show mating behaviour in their "home" flock (due to social suppression) but mated readily with hens in another pen. There is further evidence of social inertia in tests with androgen treated hens by the fact that once higher social status was attained it persisted after the exogenous hormone was withdrawn (Allee, Collias & Lutherman, 1939).

The test presented here differed from those referred to above. Attention was focussed on the establishment of peck-rights (social adjustments) and not on the earliest appearance of social behaviour patterns. Therefore the birds were not presented special stimuli but were disturbed as little as possible even when fed and injected. In an effort to counteract the social inertia caused by adjustments in behaviour, which formed early in the life of the chicks, very high levels of androgen were used.

The results of this set of experiments are given in Table VIII. It will be noted that the normal cockerels began to form peck-rights about as early as the cockerels of other genetic backgrounds, but there was a greater span of weeks before all dominance relations were established and the mean age was 9.92 weeks. Capons treated with testosterone propionate (from the 10th day of age) began to develop peck-rights a week earlier. The mean age of 7.82 weeks was 2.10 weeks earlier. These capons received injections of 0.5 mg per day at the start, and the amount was increased by 0.5 mg weekly until four weeks old, and kept at that level until nine weeks old. As expected, this treatment suppressed growth (the average body weight was 564 grammes as compared with 905 grammes for the normal males) and injections were stopped although the capons appeared to be in good

Table VIII. The effect of androgenic treatment on the development of peck-rights in caponized chicks as compared with normal cockerels and capons of the same age.

Number pecked	*Peck-order*	*Weeks of age* 5	6	7	8	9	10	11	12	13	14	15	16	17
		Normal males												
8	GV				1	3	3	1						
7	GY		1		3	2		1						
6	VY			2	1			1	1	1				
5	V							2	2	1				
3	R						1			2				
3	VV					1		1		1				
3	RY			1	1					1				
1	YY				1									
0	BB													
36	Total		1	3	7	6	4	6	3	6				
		Androgen treated capons, 10th day–63rd day												
9	GB	3	2	1	2			1						
8	GV	5		1	1		1							
7	B		2	1	2		2							
5	R	2		1	1	1								
5	VB		1		2		1		1					
4	Y			1	1	1	1							
4	BB					1		2	1					
2	V						1	1						
1	GR						1							
0	VY													
45	Total	10	5	5	9	3	7	4	2					
		Androgen treated capons, 35th day–84th day												
9	GV		2	1	3	1	1		1					
7	G		2	1	1	2	1							
6	GB			1	3		1		1					
6	VB		1	2		1	1		1					
5	RR			1	3			1						
5	GY			1	2		2							
3	B					1	1	1						
2	VY				1		1							
1	GR				1									
1	BB						1							
45	Total		5	7	14	5	9	2	3					

Number pecked	*Peck-order*	*Weeks of age* 5	6	7	8	9	10	11	12	13	14	15	16	17
							Capons							
8	R									2	1	4	1	
7	GV			1	1		1	2		2				
6	GY				1			1	1	2				1
4	GR							1	1	1				1
4	B								1				1	2
4	VY											1		3
2	GB											1		1
1	GG													1
0	G													
36	Total			1	2	0	1	4	3	7	1	6	2	9

health. During the next three weeks they continued to establish peck-rights and formed a peck-order about one week earlier than the normal cockerels.

The second group of capons received 2.0 mg daily from the 35th to the 84th day of age. The mean age of peck-right establishment was 8.53 weeks, which was 1.39 weeks earlier than that of the normal males and 0.71 week later than that of the capons injected from the 10th day. The response was immediate as shown by the formation of peck-rights during the sixth week. The delayed injection showed that the immediate response to a suitable hormone must be associated with the level of development. This point is further substantiated by the fact that androgen administrated soon after hatching (in intact males as well as in capons) did not markedly augment the establishment of peck-rights although certain behaviour patterns could be augmented, such as crowing and pecking. Apparently nervous mechanisms associated with individual recognition and ability to form associations between experiences may have not developed sufficiently, or the characteristics serving as the basis for individual recognition were not present (e.g. features of the combs, Guhl & Ortman, 1953).

Turning to the untreated capons of this set, Table VIII, peck-rights began to form a week later than among normal cockerels, but the peck-order was not completed until the 17th week. The mean age was 13.69 weeks and 4.02 weeks later than that of the normal males. Apparently androgen level is not the only factor involved in the establishment of dominance relations. These results indicate that the development of pecking and of peck-rights are basically mechanisms within the nervous system. It is generally known that androgen lowers the threshold for aggressive action (Beach, 1948). The results given here suggest that this hormone has little direct effect on the early development of dominance relations. The greater spread of time during which peck-rights developed in these capons might be related to the low intensity and frequency of pecking among capons (i.e. a high threshold for aggressive behaviour) Scott & Fredericson (1951) found that pain was an important factor in causing non-competitive fighting. The lower frequency of pecking would result in less reinforcement. The ability to make the associations required for the establishment of dominance relations appeared to develop at about the fifth or sixth week of age (see controls in previous tables) under the conditions of these experiments. With stronger or more appropriate stimulation one may assume somewhat different results. This point will be considered later.

There still remains the question of whether these capons were devoid of endogenous androgen. Breneman (1951) considered the probability of the adrenals as a source of androgen in chicks but his experiments gave no such evidence. A number of capons had a portion of a testis remaining, which was noted macroscopically at autopsy. Among the 20 capons injected with androgen, 11 had a portion of a testis (the largest was less than one third of the size of a normal testis). Although a "slip" ranked highest in each of these two groups, these two had the smallest remnant in their group. There appeared to be no relationship between the size of testis material, or lack of it, and social rank. Among the untreated capons, 4 of the 9 retained a remnant and they ranked 2, 6, 7, and 9 in the original peck-order. A "complete" capon was the alpha bird and the "slip" with the largest fragment of testis was in the omega rank. The "incomplete" capons, or "slips," were detected by, or before, the 17th week as the combs were somewhat larger and of a deeper red than those of the other capons.

A test was devised to determine the probable influence of the presence of some testicular tissue on the relative aggressiveness of the individuals in the group of 9 untreated capons. After the 17th week the individuals were isolated in a laying battery for about 4 weeks to extinguish dominance relationships and to allow for further development of gonadal activity. Each bird was then paired with each of the others in a neutral area to establish dominance. The birds were then rated in accord with the number of contests won. This method gave an estimate of the relative aggressiveness of the individuals in this group.

Of the 36 possible dominance relationships in this group of nine capons, the "complete" capons had 23 peck-rights in the original peck-order. The results of the initial encounters gave these capons 17 wins to 19 for the "slips." There were 10 changes in dominance rating; 4 were capons over capons, and 6 were "slips" over capons. This suggested a gain by birds which had some remnants of a testis, as was expected because the birds were now 22 weeks old and testes are usually well developed at this age. However, the changes were not as striking as it appeared at first consideration. The "slip" with the largest remnant was still at the bottom of the rating based on initial encounters. The correlation coefficient between the number of individuals pecked in the original peck-order and the number of contests won was 0.69 (P less than 0.05). Similar tests made with normal cockerels and pullets (Guhl, 1953) also showed shifts in dominance, and the coefficients of correlation varied from less than 0.50 to 0.88. These comparisons do not preclude the possible influence of androgen in the "slips," but raise some doubt as to whether the concentration of endogenous androgen was sufficient to question seriously the results obtained in these sets of capons.

At this point in the investigation an inspection of the Tables II through VIII suggested that individuals ranking high in the peck-order might establish peck-rights earlier than low ranking chicks. Coefficients of correlation between the number of individuals pecked in the original peck-order and the mean age at which peck-rights were established by each individual were calculated for the 16 flocks. All correlations were negative and the coefficients ranged from 0.09 to 0.65, of which 8 of the 16 were statistically significant. This suggests that individuals which mature earliest may assume high rank, which they may retain by reinforcement through pecking activity. If the rates of development are approximately equal between any two chicks, the characteristic level of aggressiveness may determine dominance relations. Several other factors (Allee, Collias & Lutherman, 1939) might influence the outcome of initial pair contests. Birds which develop more slowly, but otherwise are relatively aggressive, may revolt and alter their status as incidences leading to back-pecking arise. Some changes in dominance status were noted after an original peck-order was determined. The results of initial encounters conducted with the White Leghorn pullets in 9D also show shifts in dominance. The relatively low coefficients are indicative of a multifactor situation but definite trends are in evidence.

EFFECTS OF REARING IN PARTIAL ISOLATION

In four of the above sets of experiments some chicks were placed into partial isolation when received, and taken at random as were those composing the afore-mentioned groups. The object of this test was to determine whether the lack of early experience with other chicks influenced the time at which chicks learned to form a peck-order. That is, could chicks reared without the early social experiences associated with the development of frolicking, pecking, fighting, and other social patterns, form a peck-order at the age when the control group became organised.

The isolated chicks were assembled when their respective control group established a peck-order. Six isolated White Leghorn cockerels from the same hatch as those listed in Table IV were assembled when nine weeks old. Observations made during the next 48 hours gave good indications of a peck-order. Although the White Rock cockerels (Table V) were four weeks old when received, 10 individuals were placed into isolation until eight weeks old. These males formed a peck-order within 48 hours. There was no suggestion that the experience of the first four weeks facilitated the formation of a social organisation. Two sets of pullets were also assembled. These were from the hatches listed in Tables VI and VII. There were 7 in the former and 8 in the latter group, and the pullets were 10 weeks old when assembled. The first group was organised after three hours, and the second after eight hours. Short observation periods were made on the male chicks but both pullet groups were observed continuously for four hours after assembly. Males may not establish dominance as readily as females, as suggested here, but the difference may be due, in part, to the difference in the time spent on post-assembly observations.

The size of the group may be a factor in the time required to form a peck-order. The 6 White Leghorn males had only 15 possible peck-rights, whereas the 10 White Rock males had 45. The pullet groups had 21 and 28 possible dominance relationships. It would be of interest to vary the size of groups formed by chicks reared in isolation to get a measure of the extent to which chicks are able to make associations among individuals. However, individual variations in such development appeared to be great, as may be noted in the span of weeks during which dominance developed in the various groups reared together (Tables II to VIII).

The results of these tests show that chicks reared without the early social experience of frolicking, pecking, and fighting as free bodily contacts, could establish a social order in a comparatively short time. Presumably the stimuli which evoke agonistic behaviour patterns may have been present to some degree in partial isolation, as the chicks could hear and see neighbours. It did not require 5 to 10 weeks of experience, such as inter-individual bodily contacts, to establish peck-rights. Nor can it be concluded from these results that the ability to recognise individuals developed only at these ages. The establishment of peck-rights between any two chicks in group-reared chicks might be augmented or retarded by the persistence of existing behaviour patterns through reinforcement. The question arises as to whether the time of peck-right formation might have as its primary basis the maturation of the nervous and/or endocrine systems. Could chicks reared in partial isolation form a social order when assembled at ages earlier than those at which the group-reared chicks became organised?

INFLUENCE OF SOCIAL ADJUSTMENTS AND SEX HORMONES ON THE DEVELOPMENT OF DOMINANCE RELATIONS

Two tests were made to determine whether chicks reared in isolation could form a dominance order earlier than chicks reared as a group. This appeared to be probable because the control groups, in previous tests, exhibited adjustments to behaviour patterns existing at a particular age, and new patterns seemed to appear rather abruptly. Chicks reared in partial isolation should not possess such social inertia. The assembly of isolated chicks also introduced a stimulus for aggressive action because the birds would meet as strangers. Both of these tests were with commercial hybrids; one with cockerels and the second with pullets.

The cockerels were divided at random into five groups; a group of 11 untreated controls reared together; a group of 11 androgen treated controls also reared together; and three groups of 10 each reared in isolation which were treated with testosterone propionate (0.5 mg beginning on the 15th day). Androgen was used with the expectation that each individual would have nearly the same concentration of the hormone in its blood stream, and thereby reducing individual variation except for any probable basic differences in thresholds of response to this hormone or of reaction thresholds.

The schedule for assembling the isolated cockerels was somewhat arbitrary. The first group was to be assembled about the time that the similarly injected controls began to show indications of setting up peck-rights, and before the normal controls began to establish any dominance relations. One group was assembled when 31 days old. Ten days later another group of isolated birds assembled, and the third group when 51 days old. Each group of isolates was observed for a week following assembly. The two control groups were observed from the beginning of this experiment until 56 days old, when the test was terminated. In previous experiments many of the males treated with androgen had established some peck-rights at this age.

The results are given in Fig. 2 which shows the total number of peck-rights established in each of the five groups at various ages. The ratios at each curve indicate the number of peck-rights established at that point in relation to the possible number of unidirectional dominance relations in the flock. As expected from previous tests the injected controls established peck-rights earlier than did the normal cockerels, and nearly completed the development of a peck-order at 56 days of age (53 out of a possible 55). The first group of isolates nearly completed a social order (42 out of 45) when 37 days old and exceeded the treated males reared as a group. From this result one may conclude that the inertia associated with inter-individual adjustments in group-reared chicks may have an inhibitory effect on new behaviour patterns even when under the influence of exogenous androgen. On this basis one would anticipate

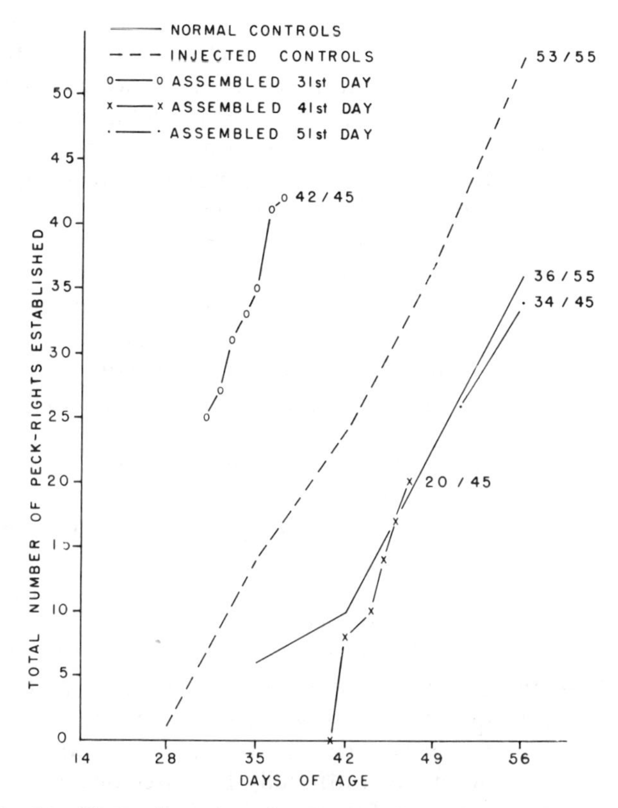

Fig. 2. The total number of peck-rights established at various ages among cockerels reared as a group and others reared in partial isolation and assembled at different ages. The caged isolates and one group, reared together, were injected with an androgen.

a more rapid development of a social order in the two groups of similar isolates when assembled at a later age. However the results were strikingly different.

The second group failed to establish any peck-rights during the first day after assembly and formed only 20 out of 45 peck-rights by the end of a week. The third group performed somewhat better. The data (and motion pictures taken during the first hour or longer after assembly) show that these three groups differed in their reactions. The first group began to peck and fight after a few minutes of adjustment to the new situation. Some peck-rights were formed within one hour. Sexual behaviour, such as attempts to mount, occurred early in the week during which they were observed. The initial reactions of the second group, after a brief adjustment period, were almost entirely sexual. Attempts to mount were very frequent. The males responded with a strong negative reaction to such behaviour, and they soon collected at one end of the cage. Under such conditions the aggressive drive appeared to be suppressed for there was no fighting, and no peck-rights were established during the first day. By the second day some fighting developed, and attempts to mount were less frequent. The typical adjustment in this group was to collect in a group and to remain standing (the resting position stimulated mounting behaviour). This was the usual situation for the rest of the week.

The group assembled at 51 days of age started to fight immediately and some peck-rights were established within two hours. Attempts to mount were observed but they were not as frequent as in the second group. By the end of a week only 34 of a possible 45 peck-rights were formed, which was similar to the situation among the normal controls at the same age.

No adequate explanation can be given for the differences between these three experimental groups. The first and third were assembled early in the afternoon whereas the second was assembled early in the evening. It was necessary to choose an hour after which the birds could be observed continually for three or more hours, and there was no known reason for expecting differences due to time of day for birds reared indoors under artificial light. However, a theoretical explanation is possible although it has several questionable aspects.

The level of androgen in the blood stream influences both aggressiveness and sexual behaviour. Although the injected birds received the same amount of androgen daily, the dosage, when related to body weight of growing birds, actually decreased with time. On the 51st day the mean body weights were about twice that at 31 days of age. However, the injected controls continued to establish peck-rights at a fairly uniform rate, whereas the second and third groups approached the rate of the normal controls.

The various behaviour patterns, and/or their thresholds, tend to develop in some order and certainly not all at the same time. This is shown by the fact that high levels of exogenous androgen at an early age did not produce the full repertory of all the adult behaviour patterns. Although aggressive behaviour and sexual behaviour are both mediated by androgen the observations in the experiments reported here suggest that the former appear earlier than do the latter, with some overlapping (certain components or motor outlets occur in both chains of these two behaviour patterns). Such a sequence is common among feral birds that are seasonal in their breeding. No qualitative study was made which measured intensities of reactions nor were the stimuli evaluated. It may be assumed that at 31 days of age the mechanism(s) for patterns of aggressive behaviour had progressed further in development than those for sexual behaviour, whereas at 41 days the latter had emerged and the birds were assembled before much, if any, extinction had occurred. At 51 days of age and with somewhat lower dosage (per gramme of body weight) a balance between the two drives was being established. Such a conflict between these two drives has been demonstrated by Hinde (1953) in the Chaffinch.

If these interpretations of the results are acceptable at present, then one may conclude that the ability to make associations between individuals (as in peck-orders) in small groups of chicks developed during the fifth week of age. Larger groups would place a strain on this learning process. If more than one behaviour pattern should develop at about the same time (as shown by injections appearing to compress, in time, the sequence in which various patterns matured) then the complexity of adjustments would be compounded; such may have been the situation with the second and third groups when assembled. To this confusion could be added the variability in the development of individuals.

A similar, but simpler, situation was devised with the pullets. In this test there was no complication with sex drive (pullets do not display the receptive crouch until late in development) and no sex hormones were injected. The pullets were divided at random into four groups when received. There were three groups of 10 each which were reared in partial isolation, and 6 controls reared together. The isolated chicks were assembled at 45, 52, and 66 days of age, which was later than with the males since females are less aggressive than cockerels and because there was no androgenic treatment.

In a group composed of 10 individuals there are 45 possible

peck-rights. The chicks assembled at 45 days of age established 19 of these during the first day after assembly; and those assembled at 52 and 66 days established 21 of a possible 45 peck-rights each during their first days. The six controls established 12 of a possible 15 peck-rights by the age of 49 days and did not complete a peck-order until 63 days old. Except for the first group of isolates, observations were not continued beyond the first day after assembly. Social inertia among the controls was not obvious under these limited comparisons, in part, because there were fewer individuals (i.e. less social stress) and therefore only one third as many peck-rights as among the experimental chicks. However, by comparison, the isolates assembled on the 45th day showed marked progress as they established 35 out of 45 possible peck-rights by the end of the second day.

The comparisons between the data (Fig. 2) on the group-reared cockerels and the assembled isolates present some other difficulties in explanation. Some sexual behaviour was observed early among the injected controls and somewhat later among the normal controls. The relative infrequency of sexual behaviour among the injected controls, as compared with the treated isolates when assembled, probably was in relation to the gradual adjustments possible in the group and/or to social inertia. Those assembled at 31 days did not display these restraints nor an intense sexual drive at that age. The chicks in this group demonstrated, as did the pullets, that they were capable of making some inter-individual associations, and that at a higher rate than either of the group-reared chicks.

These experiments with cockerels and pullets reared in partial isolation showed that some individuals could establish peck-rights at an early age without the experience of previous bodily contacts. Much individual variation occurred in the development of agonistic behaviour patterns.

SOCIAL INERTIA AND THE DISPLAY OF AGONISTIC BEHAVIOUR

The previous tests showed that chicks reared in groups became adjusted to each other and developed social inertia, and that chicks reared in partial isolation may, after short periods of adjustments, stimulate each other agonistically or sexually when assembled. The problem in such experimentation is to recognise the stimuli which evoke the agonistic behaviour pattern. One cannot, with confidence, state that the chicks did not have the ability to respond just because the behaviour patterns were not observed. It may be that adequate stimulation was lacking or that social inertia caused suppression or extinction. The tests using chicks reared in isolation and assembled at various ages were designed to provide stimulation, for adults are known to show agonistic behaviour when they meet as strangers. Another attempt was made to induce agonistic behaviour at early ages, using the techniques of shifting flock membership (see Guhl & Allee, 1944).

Forty newly hatched hybrid cockerels were placed at random into four cages of the same floor area. One of these cages was divided into 10 isolation cells, as described earlier. The 10 chicks in the other three cages formed groups. Two types of rotating group membership were started on the third day. A chick from isolation was placed into one of the groups and one from the group was placed into isolation. Shifting followed a schedule of rotation between isolation and this group with replacements made every other day. A similar shifting of individuals was made between the groups in the other two cages. This method required 20 days for a complete round. The experiences of chicks in each of these two plans of rotation differed in that isolated chicks had 20 days during which any adjustments such as individual recognition, if any, or any habits which contribute to social inertia could be extinguished (adults after separation for 21 days meet former penmates as strangers, Guhl & Allee, 1944).

The chicks were observed for only 15 minutes daily per group until eight weeks old, or up to the age at which dominance relations may be established in normal group rearing. The data included sparring, pecking, fighting, and avoiding reactions. The results are given in Fig. 3 for each of the three groups with shifting membership. The group of cockerels shifted from isolation showed a markedly higher frequency of agonistic behaviour than did those of the groups in which there was an intergroup transfer. This difference appeared to be due to the greater stimulus provided by the chick taken from isolation and to social inertia in the other two groups. Although there was much variation among individual chicks in both sets of tests, those admitted from isolation were most involved in

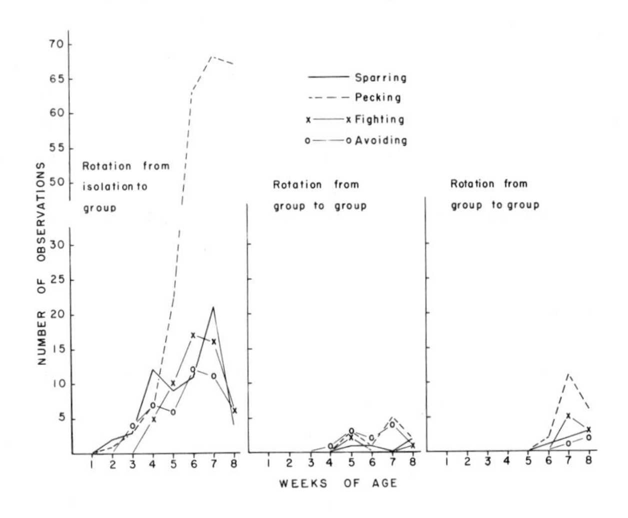

Fig. 3. Differences in the frequency of some behaviour patterns of cockerels rotated between isolation and a group, and those rotated from group to group. The latter show social inertia.

interactions. The isolate often appeared very alert, with tail and head held erect or, if a relatively unaggressive individual, it showed marked escape tendencies which stimulated pursuit. Some were inactive in these respects and evoked little reaction when placed into the group. The chicks entering a group from a group typically did not display the stance associated with alertness or strangeness. They often preened, fed, joined or avoided the others in the cage. It appeared that habits of behaviour were carried over from group to group as a form of social inertia. A chick shifted from isolation into a group probably lost such habits after 20 days of separation, and in addition it entered a spacious cage. These factors may have augmented any strangeness which it may have sensed.

In addition to the more frequent display of these behaviour patterns the chicks taken from isolation also showed these patterns of behaviour earlier than did the intergroup shifting individuals. The order of emergence varied somewhat from that mentioned previously, but least so in the group shifted from isolation. Under such changing situations one might expect the avoiding or escape reactions to be evoked more readily, and except for avoidance, the order in this group was essentially as anticipated from previous observations. There is also a suggestion that under high stimulation psychologically, as under highly altered physiological conditions with injected androgen, that the ages at which these behaviour patterns appeared initially were not only earlier but spread less in time.

This test demonstrated social inertia in group-reared chicks, and also showed that agonistic behaviour patterns may appear earlier under certain experimental situations than under what might be considered a more normal developmental situation for these domestic birds.

DISCUSSION

In developmental studies of behaviour one is impressed by variability and adaptability. Variations occur not only among individuals but also in time, and the individuals must adjust to both in order to maintain themselves and the group. The history of development is one of change and adequate adaptation.

Individual variation in agonistic behaviour is evident in the peck-order of adults as a gradient in levels of aggressiveness and/or submissiveness. Intragroup variations reported here in the development of behaviour patterns were anticipated, although some may be due to sampling errors. It is not to be assumed that they suggest the limits of variability for the strains or breeds used. Changes in individuals showed differences when viewed as rates of development, whether in behaviour patterns as given here or in body weights or comb sizes which have not been included in this report.

Each individual must adapt itself to developmental changes within itself, particularly such as influence its behaviour, but also to alterations in the behaviour and appearance (as familiar objects) of its penmates. The growth of feathers, comb and wattles result in marked modification of contour, colour, and facial patterns, which would require constant learning if individual recognition were critical at these developmental stages. It might be assumed that social adjustments are simplified during the early weeks by the importance of vocalisations in hen-chicks and chick-chick relationships (Bruckner, 1933; Collias, 1952; Collias & Joos, 1953).

There is relatively little information on physiological developments during the post-hatch life of the chicks, especially such as may influence behaviour patterns. Willier (1952) has reviewed some interesting pituitary-gonadal relationships and summarised them in a chart giving changes occurring over certain spans of time during incubation and post-hatch. Breneman & Mason (1951) have shown that there is a marked increase in the secretion of androgen in the male chick at about 30 days post-hatch. This is about the age at which cockerels began to establish peck-rights (e.g. normal males, Fig. 2).

Other physiological developments which may be worthy of note were summarised by Sturkie (1954). Erythrocyte number and hematocrit increased in relation to androgen. Hemoglobin values increased and thrombocyte number decreased during the same time. Body temperature of day-old chicks is about 3°F below that of the adult but at 10 days is about the same as the adult. Temperature control develops from seven days to three weeks of age, around the time of juvenile plumage. The greatest increase in the secretion rate of thyroxine in White Leghorn cockerels is during 4-12 weeks, which is the period of greatest growth and also the time of peck-right establishment. Adrenal size, in proportion to body weight, decreases during early weeks of life. These items are of interest as they reflect, in part, a stress syndrome during early days or weeks. Garren & Shaffner (1956) found that periods of exposure to cold caused an adrenal hypertrophy. Adjustments to the inadequacy of temperature control are also reflected in early social behaviour. Recently hatched chicks do not approach one another until after experiencing some minutes of bodily contact (Collias, 1950a). Warmth from other chicks (or a hen), as well as vocalisations (Collias, 1950b) form the primary family bonds and facilitate aggregation and socialisation. Centripetal social forces are established long before centrifugal forces caused by the development of agonistic behaviour, which is the subject of this report. Apparently these early adaptations have a permanency similar to imprinting (Lorenz, 1935).

There was some indication that certain behaviour patterns tended to appear in a sequence but with much overlapping. These observations were not under critical study and the order of emergence cannot be given as definite for several reasons. Although the chicks of each set were from the same hatch, they were not necessarily of the same age in terms of hours. In large hatches the chicks are not removed as they hatch, and some may be as much as 24 hours older than others. Behaviour patterns, such as pecking, fighting, and sexual behaviour, which appear later than others, at least in frequency and intensity, may be influenced less by hourly differences in age. Some experiments, such as those of Noble & Zitrin (1942), Collias (1950b), and certain sets of this experiment have shown that exogenous gonadal hormones may cause some precocious development of certain of these behaviour patterns, particularly agonistic and sexual behaviour. Differences in the results as recorded according to the earliest appearance may be due to a number of factors, such as size of sample, dosage of hormone, and the stimulus situation.

Wood-Gush (1957) reported indications of such a sequence in chickens but was chiefly concerned about the order in which aggressiveness and sexual behaviour emerged. He postulated that aggressiveness may respond to a lower level of testicular hormone than does sexual behaviour, or that either drive might depend on the interaction of this hormone with one or more other specific substance(s). As shown by the results given in Fig. 3, more attention might be given to stimuli which evoke these behaviour patterns. One might also assume that differences in sensitivity to certain stimuli (possible releasers) may occur at various ages, as Beach (1955) has suggested. That is, development is dependent upon various inherent characteristics, including its sensitivity to external influences. This capacity for response is not constant or stable, but tends to rise and then decrease so that critical extrinsic factors can exert their normal effects only if present when responsivity is high. Certainly there is a similarity between certain behaviour pattern sequences in ontogeny and similar ones in the development of reproductive behaviour in cyclical feral birds (e.g., Collias & Taber, 1951; Petersen, 1955). The study of this aspect of behaviour in chicks could be facilitated if there were better information on the specific stimuli which evoke specific patterns of behaviour, and if one could standardise these stimuli as attempted by Fisher & Hale (1957) for adult cocks.

For some years the writer has questioned what Kortlandt (1955) has called the "preformationist doctrine" of instinct, and was attracted by his statement that "hierarchy of instincts serves to shape non-instinctive behaviour patterns during ontogenetical development." That is, that there is no dichotomy of innate behaviour and experience any more than that anatomy and physiology can be considered independently in any final analysis. About 15 years ago we acquired a cock which had been reared by children who obtained it as an Easter gift. This bird had never seen a chicken after it was separated from other chicks of its hatch. When fully mature, in the following fall, it was placed with adult hens which it avoided immediately and flew to roost. Sexual approaches were made toward the observer. After some days it tried to mount a hen, and in its first attempt it mounted backwards; instead of treading it stood on the crouching hen and crowed. Although the behaviour patterns improved in orientation, it did not become very efficient during the several weeks it was observed. As a result of this observation the isolated chicks of the present experiment were permitted to see and hear each other, to come into close proximity of each other, and limited only in their ability to peck each other, thereby reducing any abnormal behaviour to a minimum. Aberrant behaviour was reported by Fisher & Hale (1957) in cockerels reared in visual and spacial isolation.

Leherman's (1953) clear statements are worthy of inclusion here. "It has become customary, in recent discussions of the 'heredity-environment' problem, to state that the 'hereditary' and 'environment' contributions are both essential to the development of the organism; that the organism could not develop in the absence of either; and that the dichotomy is more or less artificial." . . . "The problem of development is the problem of the development of new structure and patterns, within the organism and its internal environment, and between the organism and its outer environment. At any stage of development, the new features emerge from the interactions within the current state and between the current stage and the environment. The interaction out of which the organism develops is not one, as is so often said, between heredity and environment. It is between organism and environment! And the organism is different at each different stage in its development."

Although the emergence and interrelationships of behaviour

patterns need more critical study than that made during the observations given here, some further discussion might be of value. Frolicking is a rather simple spontaneous behaviour which appeared quite early and most often during the stimulation caused by disturbances such as filling feed troughs and turning on the room lights. When two frolicking chicks ran together, they would jump up and down making head thrusts toward each other. This was called sparring and no pecks were delivered. The stimulus for sparring seemed to be a contact with another chick when both showed excitability during frolicking. Pecking occurred quite early and infrequently, but later became associated with sparring and thereby became fighting, which often ended without a decision during the early stages. Pecking and avoidance during the early weeks was bidirectional and later became unidirectional, and peck-rights were established, indicating that an association of aggressive behaviour with a particular individual appeared later. The point of interest is a suggestion of what Kortlandt (1955) called the pathfinding function of instincts in which the innate patterns act as organisers during development of non-instinctive behaviour. That is, owing to ascending maturation and integration "the characteristics of the objects toward which the bottom-level instincts have become conditioned are subsequently taken over by the next-higher-level instincts and largely constitute the characteristics of the objects toward which these instincts appear directed as soon as they mature." However, it is not clear just how this integration occurs. The mechanisms by which innate and acquired behaviours are integrated appear to be hypothetical but the importance of the interplay between extrinsic and intrinsic factors is recognised (Beach, 1955).

Evidences of learning in chicks have been summarised by Wood-Gush (1955) and Thorpe (1956). Whether or not the integration of behaviour patterns mentioned above are accomplished by some type of learning or by some neurophysiological changes implied by Kortlandt's concept of priming, or both, cannot be determined by the data presented here. The injection of exogenous gonadal hormones is followed by precocious behaviour, but such treatment does not produce the full repertory of adult behaviour patterns with the same number of daily injections, Crowing occurs early whereas pecking is less frequent, and both increase in frequency with high dosages of androgen (Collias, 1950b); and mating behaviour appears to have a higher threshold but may occur if adequate stimulation is provided (Noble & Zitrin, 1942). Learning is most evident during and following the establishment of the peck-order.

Some aspects of learning are evident during the formation of a peck-order among adult chickens of either sex. When unacquainted birds are placed together they soon engage in pair-contests, the outcome of which settles dominance-subordination or peck-right relationships. These encounters may vary considerably in intensity, from passive submission by one of the contestants to strenuous fighting which at times is repeated. The stimuli which may evoke either aggressive or submissive acts are yet to be analysed. Fisher & Hale (1957) have made some progress in this direction; Foreman & Allee (1954) have noted that postural stance influences the outcome of such initial contests. The lack of individual recognition (Guhl & Ortman, 1953) appears to evoke non-competitive aggressive behaviour whereas posturing may determine the type and intensity of agonistic behaviour which ensues.

The winner of these contests thereafter asserts its dominance by repeated pecking or threatening while the loser submits or avoids the dominant, thus reinforcing the decision reached at the first meeting. Hard fought encounters may be followed by more intense reinforcement activity. Habits of either attack or escape are formed between all pair combinations in the flock, and these constitute the peck-order. As the recognition of individuals improves and appropriate reactions are facilitated, reinforcement wanes to the point of extinction in very small flocks, or to the level of symbolic threatening. The result is the social inertia which well acquainted flocks show as toleration (Guhl & Allee, 1944). Deviations from such behaviour, as back-pecks, are rare and, if they do occur, are followed by the reactivation (reinforcement) of delivered pecks or, failing that, in a reversal of dominance.

Returning to the behaviour of chicks which were shifted regularly between groups and from isolation into a group (Fig. 3), it was noted that the level of agonistic activity was lower among group-reared chicks. This difference may be attributed to some type of learning or adaptation to group living (i.e. social inertia) which was carried from group to group, whereas chicks in isolation lost appropriate adjustments. It was mentioned that chicks entering a group from isolation reacted to the new situation and that their stance stimulated residents to react. Apparently the ability to recognise individuals was not developed during much of this test since chicks transferred from group to group did now show the typical reaction that adults do under similar situations (Guhl & Allee, 1944). Differences between these groups of changing membership began to appear prior to the age at which chicks typically began to form peck-rights, indicating individual recognition. One might also consider the possibility that chicks coming from isolation had not learned (or extinction had occurred) that to assume a certain stance might provoke an attack. The indications are that some type of social adjustment or learning may occur prior to the age at which peck-rights are developed. Smith (1957) found that chicks at 10 days could discriminate partners of the same breed but from a different flock.

The kind of social organisation found in a species is determined by the behaviour patterns characteristic of the species. All breeds and/or strains of chickens which have been studied (Potter, 1949; Holabird, 1955; Banks, 1956) have shown very similar organisation, but differences between breeds have been suggested in the intensities of agonistic behaviour (Allee, Foreman & Banks, 1955; Hale, 1954). Studies are now underway at our experimental station, and at others, on mixed flocks. Information on the comparative development of behaviour is needed to determine the relative compatibility of several breeds or strains in such mixed flocks, and to learn whether early experience might influence adult behaviour or the ranks of breeds in the peck-order. Experiments on the inheritance of aggressiveness have been conducted during the same years as the observations on the development of social behaviour in chicks; and the results will be published elsewhere.

SUMMARY

1. Certain behaviour patterns tended to appear in a sequence as escape reactions, frolicking, sparring, aggressive pecking, avoiding re-actions, and fighting.

2. In heterosexual groups of chicks pecking occurred between the sexes with males pecking more often on all chicks and more frequently on the males. The limitation of agonistic behaviour between members of the same sex developed gradually.

3. Males established dominance-subordination relationships, peck-rights, and a peck-order earlier than females.

4. Both males and female chicks treated with gonadal hormones formed peck-rights and a peck-order somewhat earlier than did untreated chicks of the same hatch. Androgenic treatment caused an increase in aggressiveness, whereas œstrogen treated chicks were more submissive than their controls and showed more instances of submission than domination.

5. Capons showed much variability as to the age at which peck-rights were established. Many were formed long after their normal controls developed a peck-order. Androgenic treatment of capons reduced the age at which dominance relations were established.

6. Chicks of either sex reared in partial isolation (non-contactual) established a dominance order in a matter of hours when assembled at the age at which group-reared controls formed a peck-order. These results suggest that the age at which peck-rights form is determined essentially by processes of maturation rather than of learning only. The indications are that the development of nervous mechanisms was involved.

7. Androgen treated cockerels reared in partial isolation were assembled at various ages during which group-reared controls were establishing their peck-rights. Isolated cockerels assembled at 31 days of age nearly established a social order within 6 days and much earlier than the controls. Two groups assembled at 41 and 51 days failed to show much advance over group-reared normal cockerels. The indications were that at these ages there was a conflict between aggressive behaviour and newly developed sexual drive which required more time for social adjustments. The sex drive in pullets appears much later than in cockerels and a similar test with normal pullets (untreated) did not show this conflict resulting from an overlapping in the development of aggressive and sexual behaviour patterns.

8. Social inertia was demonstrated by shifting chicks regularly between partial isolation and a group, and also shifting chicks between two groups. Chicks shifted from group to group carried with them certain behaviour patterns whereas chicks from isolation evoked agonistic behaviour.

REFERENCES

Allee, W. C. & Collias, N. E. (1940). The influence of œstradiol on the social organisation of hens. *Endocrinology,* **27**, 87-94.

Allee, W. C., Collias, N. E. & Lutherman, C. Z. (1939). Modification of the social order in flocks of hens by the injection of testosterone propionate. *Physiol. Zool.,* **12**, 412-440.

Allee, W. C., Foreman, D. & Banks, E. M. (1955). Effects of an androgen on dominance and subordinance in six common breeds of *Gallus gallus. Physiol. Zool.,* **38**, 89-115.

Armstrong, E. A. (1947). *Bird display and behaviour.* London: Lindsay Drummond.

Banks, E. M. (1956). Social organisation in red jungle fowl hens (*Gallus gallus* subsp.). *Ecology,* **37**, 239-248.

Beach, F. A. (1948). *Hormones and behaviour.* New York: Paul B. Hoeber.

Beach, F. A. (1955). Ontogeny and living systems. In *Group Processes, Trans. First Conference,* **1954.** New York: Josiah Macy, Jr. Foundation.

Breneman, W. R. (1951). A factorial analysis of pituitary-gonad-comb relationships in the chick. *Poult. Sci.,* **30**, 231-239.

Breneman, W. R. & Mason, R. C. (1951). Androgen influence on pituitary-gonad interrelationship. *Endocrinology,* **48**, 752-762.

Bruckner, G. H. (1933). Untersuchungen zur Tiersoziologie, inbesondere zur Ausflörsing der. Familie. *Z. Psychol.,* **128**, 1-105.

Collias, N. E. (1943). Statistical analysis of factors which make for success in initial encounters between hens. *Amer. Nat.,* **77**, 519-538.

Collias, N. E. (1950a). The socialisation of chicks. *Anat. Rec.,* **108**, 65.

Collias, N. E. (1950b). Hormones and behaviour with special reference to birds and the mechanisms of hormone action. In *A symposium on steroid hormones*, 277-329. Madison: University of Wisconsin Press.

Collias, N. E. (1952). The development of social behaviour in birds. *Auk,* **69**, 127-159.

Collias, N. E. & Joos, M. (1953). The spectrographic analysis of sound signals of the domestic fowl. *Behaviour,* **5**, 175-187.

Collias, N. E. & Taber, R. D. (1951). A field study of some grouping and dominance relations in Ring-necked Pheasants. *Condor*, **53**, 265-275.

Fisher, A. E. & Hale, E. B. (1956-57). Stimulus determinants of sexual and aggressive behaviour in male domestic fowl. *Behaviour,* **10**, 309-323.

Foreman, D. & Allee, W. C. (1954). A correlation between posture stance and outcome in paired contests of domestic hens. *Bull. ecol. Soc. Amer.,* **35**, 68.

Garren, H. W. & Shaffner, C. S. (1956). How the period of exposure to different stress stimuli affects endocrine and lymphatic gland weights of young chickens. *Poult. Sci.,* **35**, 266-272.

Guhl, A. M. (1950). Social dominance and receptivity in the domestic fowl. *Physiol. Zool.,* **23**, 361-366.

Guhl, A. M. (1953). Social behaviour of the domestic fowl. *Tech. Bull.,* **73**, *Kansas Agricultural Experiment Station.* Manhattan.

Guhl, A. M. & Allee, W. C. (1944). Some measurable effects of social organisation in flocks of hens. *Physiol. Zool.,* **17**, 320-347.

Guhl, A. M. & Ortman, L. L. (1953). Visual patterns in the recognition of individuals among chickens. *Condor,* **55**, 287-298;

Guhl, A. M. & Warren, D. C. (1946). Number of offspring sired by cockerels related to social dominance in chickens. *Poult. Sci.,* **25**, 460-472.

Hale, E. B. (1954). Androgen levels and breed differences in the fighting behaviour of cocks. *Bull. ecol. Soc. Amer.,* **35**, 71.

Hinde, R. A. (1953). The conflict between drives in the courtship and copulation of the Chaffinch. *Behaviour,* **5**, 1-31.

Holabird, C. (1955). Social organisation in flocks of Light Brahma hens with comparisons to other breeds of the common domestic hens. *Physiol. Zool.,* **28**, 239-255.

Kortlandt, A. (1955). Aspects and prospects of the concept of instinct. *Arch. neerl. Zool.,* **11**, 155-284.

Lehrman, D. S. (1953). A critique of Konrad Lorenz's theory of instinctive behaviour. *Quart. Rev. Biol.,* **28**, 337-363.

Lorenz, K. (1935). Der Kumpan in der Umwelt des Vogels. *J. Orn. Lpz.,* **83**, 137-213; 289-413.

Nice, M. (1943). Studies in the life history of the Song Sparrow. II. The behaviour of the Song Sparrow and other passerines. *Trans. Linn. Soc. N.Y.,* **6**, 1-328.

Noble, G. K. & Zitrin, A. (1942). Induction of mating behaviour in male and female chicks following injection of sex hormones. *Endocrinology,* **30**, 327-334.

Petersen, A. J. (1955). The breeding cycle of the Bank Swallow. *Wilson Bull.,* **67**, 235-286.

Potter, J. H. (1949). Dominance relations between different breeds of domestic hens. *Physiol. Zool.,* **22**, 261-280.

Schjelderup-Ebbe, T. (1935). Social behaviour in birds. In *Murchison's handbook of social psychology*, 947-972. Worcester: Clark Univ. Press.

Scott, J. P. & Fredericson, E. (1951). The causes of fighting in mice and rats. *Physiol. Zool.,* **23**, 273-309.

Smith, W. (1957). Social "learning" in domestic chicks. *Behaviour,* **11**, 40-55.

Sturkie, P. D. (1954). *Avian physiology.* Ithaca: Comstock.

Thorpe, W. H. (1956). *Learning and instinct in animals.* London: Methuen.

Willier, B. H. (1952). Development of sex-hormone activity of the avian gonad. *Ann. N.Y. Acad. Sci.,* **55**, 159-171.

Wood-Gush, D. G. M. (1955). The behaviour of the domestic chicken: A review of the literature. *Brit. J. anim. Behav.*, **3**, 81-110.

Wood-Gush, D. G. M. (1957). Aggression and sexual activity in the Brown Leghorn cock. *Brit. J. anim. Behav.*, **5**, 1-6.

Behaviour and Life History of the Wildebeest

RICHARD D. ESTES

The migratory habits and population dynamics of the wildebeest (or gnu), a dominant herbivore in eastern-Africa steppe-savanna, have been studied in considerable detail by Grzimek and Grzimek,[1] Talbot and Talbot,[2] and Watson,[3] on the Serengeti Plains. From November 1962 until June 1965, I studied the behaviour of a resident population of 14,000 wildebeest in Ngorongoro Crater, Tanzania, a caldera enclosing 104 square miles of mostly treeless grassland. Other resident and migratory populations in East, Central and South Africa were also observed in order to validate results for the species as a whole. Some of the findings, to be published as a book on the behaviour and life history of the wildebeest, are summarized in the present article.

THE SOCIAL SYSTEM

As with most gregarious ungulates, wildebeest society is divided into two main classes: (1) nursery herds of females and young of the year, generally the most numerous and cohesive class; (2) bachelor herds, comparatively loose-knit associations of yearling and older males. A small class of territorial males more or less distinct from (2) depending on the environment and season, is typical of many antelope societies.

From *Nature*, 1966, **212**, 999-1000.

Large aggregations are characteristic of wildebeest, especially of migratory populations like that of the Serengeti. Most of the Ngorongoro gnus stayed in gatherings of fifty to more than a thousand throughout the year; only 20-30 per cent were found in separate small herds, averaging ten females, yearlings and calves, and scattered across the crater floor within a network of territorial males. Some striking behavioural differences, summarized here, suggest that small herds and aggregations are adapted to different environmental conditions.

Small herds appear to be semi-exclusive and enduring associations derived from the tendency of females with young calves to band together, and probably also from continuing bonds between cows and their female calves. Strangers attempting to join the herd are generally rejected. Each herd acts largely independently and remains within a restricted home range, often less than one square mile, during the rainy half of the year (November-May). The herds from a given locale aggregate on the best available pasture in the dry season, but the aggregations usually disperse at the end of the day as each herd returns to its accustomed ground.

"Permanent" aggregations contain more or less distinct herdlike groupings, the exact nature of which remains to be determined. They are fluid and highly mobile, concentrating for up to a month or two at a time wherever the grazing is best, and make regular daily movements to and from pasture, in the long files characteristic of trekking wildebeest. The evening movement brings together many aggregations on the central plain of the crater, where they customarily spend the night on short grass. Instead of dispersing, aggregations mass in dense columns at dusk and when ruminating at night lie in linear bedding formations, no more than ten animals deep, which are able to disperse instantly when alarmed. Herdlike groupings were not discerned in these bedding formations.

The behaviour of the Ngorongoro aggregations is essentially that of a migratory population, while small herds and an established territorial network are typical of a sedentary population. The co-existence of two systems adapted to different environments can be explained by the unusual nature of the ecosystem of the crater: it provides enough space for only a limited resident population of the usual type, but a productivity, stemming from comparatively abundant rainfall and fertile volcanic soil, adequate to carry a much greater density. Perhaps the real key to its carrying capacity of around 25,000 large herbivores is the extensive marshes created by perennial springs and run-off from the surrounding highlands; up to 80 per cent of the game concentrates on the lush pastures the marshes provide through the long dry season. Thus the wildebeest population of the crater is divided up into a small number displaying the sedentary habits typical in habitats that provide permanent water and grazing, and a much greater number which lead a migratory existence within a very small ecosystem. A small number do leave the crater: an estimated 10-20 per cent left in November between 1962 and 1965, migrated 7 miles to a valley separating the Crater Highlands from the Serengeti Plains, and returned the following May when the rainwater pans went dry.

Evidence of a similar dichotomy in a related species has been found in Queen Elizabeth National Park, Uganda, among a population of topi (*Damaliscus korrigum*). In one area only small herds with territorial males were observed. Less than 3 miles away, separated by a small river, the main population of more than a thousand formed a single, highly mobile aggregation that included all males. These examples suggest there are no inherent differences between migratory and resident populations. On the other hand, habit and experience may be so important that sedentary animals could not readily adopt migratory habits, while migrants would be restricted to their traditional range. If a severe drought should cause the marshland grazing and main water supplies of the crater to fail, it would be most interesting to see what proportion of the wildebeest population would migrate right out of the area.

TERRITORIAL BEHAVIOUR

Territorial behaviour throughout the year in the wildebeest is an interesting phenomenon, considering that it is one of the few mammals in equatorial Africa with a strongly seasonal reproductive cycle. Presumably the basic reproductive function would be adequately served if males were only territorial around the month of peak rutting when at least 80 per cent of all mature females copulate. Territorial behaviour is actually greatly attenuated in migratory populations, although temporary territories are established whenever an aggregation settles down, no matter how briefly. A sample of thirty-five known Ngorongoro males kept under observation for a full year, of which twenty-five kept the same territory, suggests that at least 70 per cent of all territorial males occupy their grounds for more than a year in resident populations. Eleven of nineteen were known to remain on territory for more than 2 years and it seems quite likely that established males continue to defend the same ground throughout their prime (10 years or more), if not prevented by accident, sickness, competition or changed environment.

The basis for permanent territories is probably keen competition for a limited number of desirable grounds, coupled with the potential opportunity to mate with the females that come into oestrus for another 5 months after the rutting peak. Males are almost certainly capable of reproducing all through the year. The sense of ownership gives established males a distinct psychological advantage over those trying to stake out grounds within the network. Permanently established males have a better chance of having and holding a territory during the rigorous competition of the rut and therefore of reproducing, because only holders of territories have the opportunity to breed. All others are relegated to bachelor herds, wherein a percentage of perfectly fit looking adults may usually be found. A few males are able to participate in the rut at 28 months, but most only after another year; this contrasts with a breeding age of 15 months for 75 per cent of all females.

Once established, males maintain the territorial *status quo* through ritualized encounters performed daily with each neighbour, in which largely symbolic fighting is only one of some twenty possible steps involved in the ritual. The ritual seems also to fill a need for social contact; with no herd in his territory 80 per cent of the time, the average male would otherwise lead a largely solitary existence. Spacing between males averages about 60 yards in areas frequented by small herds, but varies from more than half a mile in marginal habitat to less than 30 yards in the middle of large aggregations.

The entire wildebeest habitat is included in the territorial network, and therefore a herd is always in the territory of some male. When an aggregation moves on to unoccupied ground, males move with it and immediately set up territories. Thus a small class of the population (10-15 per cent) largely dominates the lives of all the rest through its herding, chasing and generally more aggressive behaviour.

The effects of territorial activity may strike the observer as mainly disruptive: large aggregations are fragmented and kept in continual flux by herding and chasing males; herds attempting to move from point *A* to point *B* are forced to run a gauntlet of pursuing males, and the separation of females and young that may result undoubtedly contributes to a high post-natal mortality. But other, less conspicuous results are undoubtedly beneficial to the species. Bachelor herds are driven into the least desirable parts of the habitat and thus largely removed from food competition with small nursery herds. They are tolerated in large aggregations, however, within which some succeed in setting up temporary territories, between resident males. Bulls accomplish the separation of yearling males from their herds, often against the vigorous defence of their mothers. The initial stimulus comes, not from sexual antagonism, but from the hostility females with young calves display toward yearlings. It seems that any animal which behaves conspicuously arouses aggression in the territorial male; thus individuals of either sex which are unwelcome in a herd are persistently chased out.

Bulls provide some slight protection to nursery herds by occasionally attacking prowling spotted hyenas (*Crocuta crocuta*). Much more important, members of the territorial network function as sentinels that warn of approaching danger, and bear the brunt of predation by lions, which prey chiefly on wildebeest where the two species are sympatric and apparently largely on territorial males. Considering the comparatively great vulnerability of a territorial existence, the selection pressure for a territorial existence all through the year must indeed be strong.

ADAPTIVE FEATURES OF THE REPRODUCTIVE SYSTEM

The reproductive cycle is characterized by sharp mating and birth peaks. The former occurs at about the middle of the long rains, the latter 8-8.5 months later about a month before the start of the long rains. Peak calving begins abruptly, continues at a fairly constant rate for 2-3 weeks, then declines more gradually, with up to 20 per cent of births spread over the following 4-5 months. Most births occur in the forenoon, in large aggregations on calving grounds preferentially located on short grass. Females tend to divide into pregnant, parturient and post-parturient groups, particularly the last. Labour can be voluntarily interrupted and delivery delayed indefinitely until the calf's head emerges. Calves are able to stand and run within an average of 7 min. after birth. Their light fawn colour contrasts with the dark brown of older animals. The following response is highly developed but initially unselective; recognition of the parent probably begins with the first successful suckling; it is facilitated by the active rejection of strange calves by other females. The afterbirth is not dropped for at least 3 hours after parturition, and is generally appropriated by vultures and jackals before the mother has a chance to eat it. There is no concerted defence of the young in wildebeest; the mother will defend its calf, but only after being overtaken in flight.

Considered as an adaptation to life on the steppe-savanna, this system, which is common to the Alcelaphine antelopes, is less typical than one represented by the sympatric gazelles. The latter have no well-defined breeding season; females withdraw from their herds before parturition, and the cryptically coloured young are concealed for the first week or two.

While the reproductive cycle of the wildebeest is undoubtedly geared to the climatic regime (and can be thrown out of phase by drastic climatic change), seasonal breeding in equatorial Africa is obviously not dictated by climate. This and all the other major features of the system have probably been shaped by predation, quite possibly by the one ranking predator on the young, the spotted hyena. Observations of hyena hunting behaviour and kills indicate that it selects new calves and mainly ignores those more than a few days old, which are far harder to catch, unless they are separated from a herd. When pursued, a female with calf invariably runs into the nearest herd. Survival chances for new calves are best where there are numerous slightly older ones that make it hard for a hyena to single out and keep a particular quarry in sight. By selecting against calves born outside the season, particularly ahead of time, hyena predation thus acts to maintain a sharp peak; by the same token, mortality is far more severe in small herds than in large aggregations. Indeed, the consistently much higher percentage of calves found in concentrations throughout the year is one of the most significant observed differences between aggregations and small herds. It may help to explain the extraordinary success of migratory wildebeest populations under the generally rigorous environmental conditions of the African steppe-savanna.

This work was supported by grants from the National Geographic Society, the New York Explorers Club and the Tanzania Ministry of Agriculture, Forests and Wildlife.

REFERENCES

[1] Grzimek, M., and Grzimek, B., *Z. für Säugerierkunde,* **25**, i (1960).
[2] Talbot, L. M., and Talbot, M. H., *Wildlife Monographs,* **12**, 8 (1963).
[3] Watson, M., and Kerfoot, O., *Z für Säugerierkunde,* **29**, 320 (1964).

Endocrines, Behavior, and Population

JOHN J. CHRISTIAN

DAVID E. DAVIS

For several decades the spectacular increase and decrease of certain arctic mammals has stimulated research on populations. The crashes of rabbits were dramatized by Seton (*1*), and the suicidal movements of lemmings were publicized by many authors. However, as is so often the case, the conspicuous features turn out to be merely an extreme case of a very general phenomenon—namely, the fluctuations of a population. Investigators first sought an explanation for the "crash," but now most of them search for a description and understanding of the interaction and relative importance of the many factors that influence the ups and downs of populations.

In this article we describe the current status of our understanding of population fluctuations, emphasizing the regulatory features that prevent populations from destroying the habitat. The research discussed is limited to work with mammals, since the mechanisms are best known for that class. It is assumed that the reader has knowledge of ecological principles such as density dependence and limiting factors.

For many years it was assumed that epizootics, famine, and climatic factors terminated the explosive rises in population size and precipitated the often spectacular crashes (*2*). However, by the early 1940's it had become apparent that none of these mechanisms explained some of the observed declines in population, and it was suggested that factors intrinsic to the population were involved in its

From *Science,* Vol. 146, pp. 1550-1560, 18 December 1964.

regulation (*3*). The skepticism toward earlier explanations was reflected further in a review by Clarke in 1949 (*4*), as well as in Elton's classic earlier work (*5*). Probably the greatest shift in emphasis has occurred since 1949; there has been an upsurge of investigations in which density-dependent changes in the animals themselves have been explored, and of theories in which the observed phenomena of population growth and decline (*6-9*) are explained in terms of biological mechanisms intrinsic in the populations and not only as results of the action of external factors. It is clear that food, climatic factors, and disease may cause population change. Indeed, it would be foolish to state that these factors do not, under certain circumstances, limit population growth or produce spectacular decline. The early investigations of Emlen, Davis, and their co-workers (*8*) on populations of Norway rats demonstrated clearly that environmental factors can reduce a population. For example, a drought followed by excessive rain resulted in a notable decline in rats in Baltimore (*8*). However, as early as 1946 spectacular declines in rat populations were found to be coincident with social disturbances rather than with environmental changes.

The suspicion that social phenomena were involved prompted a search for mechanisms that could regulate the growth of populations in a density-dependent manner. No longer is attention focused exclusively on spectacular crashes and the causes of death. Instead, an attempt is made to integrate the social actions and the well-known habitat factors into a scheme that will explain the changes in populations. Since social or behavioral features are density-dependent, they become evident only at high population levels. Nevertheless, such features are present in low populations, but inconspicuous. Purely ecological factors, such as food and climatic conditions, also affect populations and, indeed, may prevent a population from attaining a level where social forces can become important. Hence, examination was begun of a theory which states that, within broad limits set by the environment, density-dependent mechanisms have evolved within the animals themselves to regulate population growth and curtail it short of the point of suicidal destruction of the environment (*6, 10-13*). Milne (*12*) has summarized this point of view as follows: "The *ultimate* capacity of a place for a species is the maximum number of individuals that the place could carry without being rendered totally uninhabitable by utter exhaustion or destruction of resources. . . . The environmental capacity cannot be greater than ultimate capacity; it could conceivably be equal to ultimate capacity but . . . is usually somewhat smaller." We would modify the "somewhat" to "considerably," in view of the situation most often observed for mammals (here we are talking primarily of herbivores and rodents). Milne goes on to say that "the one and only perfectly density-dependent factor [is] intraspecific competition."

While some investigators ascribe all regulation and limitation of populations to direct effects of environmental factors, others recognize that a feedback control of population growth exists. However, there is not complete agreement on the mechanisms by which these results are achieved. In the rest of this article we review the more recent results of experiments made to test the hypothesis that a behavioral-physiological mechanism operates to control population growth in mammals, and we consider criticisms of this view in the light of the evidence on which they are based. The acceptability of the hypothesis should be considered from the viewpoint of what would constitute disproof. To prove that behavioral mechanisms *never* affect population growth is of course impossible. To cite one or more cases in which some habitat factor controlled the population is merely an elaboration of the obvious. Thus, proof or disproof of the hypothesis reduces to the problem of finding how frequently and under what circumstances the behavioral mechanism does operate. The discovery of other physiological mechanisms [for example, pregnancy block caused by the proximity of strange males (*14*) or direct block of reproduction organs in *Peromyscus* (*15*)] does not alter the situation. Similarly, the absence of the mechanism in certain mammals would not prove its absence in rodents. The problem, then, is not that of proving the existence of a behavioral-physiological mechanism but that of proving the importance of such a mechanism in the regulation of populations.

PHYSIOLOGICAL MECHANISMS

On the basis of the knowledge of pituitary-adrenocortical physiology available prior to 1950, it was proposed (*16*) that stimulation of pituitary-adrenocortical activity and inhibition of reproductive function would occur with increased population density. It was suggested, further, that increased adrenocortical secretion would increase mortality indirectly through lowering the resistance to disease, through parasitism or adverse environmental conditions, or, more directly, through "shock disease," although it soon became evident that unwarranted emphasis was being placed on "shock disease." Implicit in this theory and in the design of experiments to test it was the theory that behavioral factors (aggressive competition, for example) comprised the only stimulus to the endocrine responses which would invariably be present in every population. Experiments to test the theory were conducted on animals which were provided with (or known to have) more food, cover, and other environmental assets than they could utilize, and were thus in populations either totally free of predation or having a minimum degree of predation (*17-19*).

The endocrine responses were first assessed through measurement of changes in the weights of the adrenals, the thymus, the reproductive organs, and certain other organs. Interpretations of adrenal weights are reliable and simple in species that have been adequately studied in the laboratory – for example, in rats and mice, whose adrenal physiology and morphology have been examined in detail under a variety of circumstances. In particular, the immature zonation (X-zone) of mice and its changes with respect to age and sex had been thoroughly explored (*20*). An important point was the lack of evidence of function for this zone. Where adrenal weight could be reliably interpreted in terms of function, it seemed better, in the study of populations, to use an indicator of long-term conditions, rather than indicators highly sensitive to acute stimuli. For example, concentrations of ascorbic acid in the adrenal gland and concentrations of corticosteroid in plasma respond very rapidly to acute stimuli. Furthermore, the interpretation of changes in adrenal weight was supported by other morphological criteria of increased corticosteroid secretion, such as involution of the thymus, though the possible role of other factors in the alteration of these other organs was not overlooked. Nevertheless, even in rats and mice, changes in adrenal weight can only be considered strong presumptive evidence of changes in adrenocortical function until validation is obtained by direct functional studies.

Adrenal weights are not valid indices of function unless

certain precautions are observed. The presence of immature zones (X-zones) complicates the use of adrenal weights as indices of function, since evidence that such zones contribute to cortical function is lacking. Another complication is the possibility of weight loss with sudden or excessive stimulation. Moreover, there may be a misleading increase in adrenal weight due to accumulation of lipids with cessation of adrenocorticotropic hormone (ACTH) stimulation. Also misleading is the hypertrophy of the adrenal medulla which occurs in some instances, but this usually is not important (*21*). In addition, qualitative changes in the corticosteroids secreted may require modification of interpretations based on adrenal weight. Finally, sexual maturation or activity may alter cortical function and adrenal weight. Androgens involute the X-zone or decrease adrenal weight in adult animals, whereas estrogens commonly increase adrenal weight. It is axiomatic that, in comparing changes in adrenal weight with changes in population, one must consider adrenal changes due to reproductive condition, and that only adrenals from animals of similar reproductive status can properly be compared.

In addition to these physiological considerations, there is the problem of obtaining adequate samples. Since there are two sexes and at least two age groups, the sample must contain enough animals in each of four categories for appropriate analysis. This requirement may seem obvious, but it often has been neglected.

The foregoing principles regarding the interpretation of adrenal weights have been presented because in many studies one or more of these principles has been neglected. Earlier work on physiological responses to changes in populations has been reviewed elsewhere (*6, 17-19*) and is only summarized here. In experiments with mice in the laboratory, progressive adrenocortical hypertrophy and thymic involution were observed to occur with increasing size of population. Somatic growth was suppressed and reproductive function was curtailed in both sexes. Sexual maturation was delayed or, at higher population densities, totally inhibited. Spermatogenesis was delayed, and the weights of the accessory sex organs declined with increasing population density. In mature females, estrous cycles were prolonged and ovulation and implantation were diminished; intrauterine mortality of the fetuses increased. Recent results in rabbits show an increase in intrauterine mortality in association with increased population density, especially in the fetuses of socially subordinate females (*22*). In another study a similar increase in intrauterine mortality was noted, but no difference in rate of resorption of embryos relative to social rank was observed (*23*). Increased resorption of embryos also followed grouping of *Peromyscus* (*24*). However, in mice, the importance of resorption of embryos in regulating birthrates may vary considerably from population to population (*17*). Also, increased population density resulted in inadequate lactation in mice, so that nurslings were stunted at weaning. This effect was seen again, though to a lesser degree, in animals of the next generation not subjected to additional crowding (*25*). It has since been found that crowding of female mice prior to pregnancy results in permanent behavioral disturbances in subsequently conceived young (*26*). Particularly interesting in this regard is the observation that increased concentrations of corticosterone may permanently affect the development of the brain in mice (*27*). Increased population size also delayed or totally inhibited maturation in females, as well as in males, so that in some populations no females reached normal sexual maturity. The combination of these responses, believed to result from inhibition of gonadotrophin secretion, resulted in a decrease in birthrate, or an increase in infant mortality, or both, as populations increased, until increase of the population through the production of young ceased. Concentrations of gonadrotrophins in relation to changes in population size have not been measured. However, increase in the number of rats per cage was found to alter responses to injected gonadotrophins, even when the area per rat was kept constant (*28*).

Increased population density may affect reproductive function in male and female house mice differently in different populations. The growth of one population was slowed and eventually stopped mainly by a decline in birthrate due to (i) failure of the young to mature and (ii) decrease in the reproductivity of mature animals (*17*). Infant mortality was a negligible factor in this population. In several others a decline in the survival of nurslings was largely responsible for a slowing and stopping of population growth, although a lowering of the birthrate also occurred (*17, 19*). In most populations both a decrease in birthrate and a decrease in the survival of nurslings contributed importantly to slowing of the rate of population growth and limitation of numbers, but, as one might expect, the relative importance of these two factors varied among populations. In populations in which a change in birthrate was the main regulating factor, other measurements indicated that it was the males which were primarily affected by increased population density, the effect on females being slight. When increasing mortality of nurslings was the main regulating factor, the females were severely affected and the males were relatively less affected than in other populations (*17*). These results imply that effects on the male may be important in producing declining birthrates, although failure of females to mature also would contribute to a decline in birthrate in any population and cannot be excluded. Final conclusions regarding this problem must await further investigation.

For many years it has been known that disease sometimes becomes rampant when populations reach peak levels (*5*). However, the belief that disease usually is a primary cause in the reduction of populations has not been supported (*5, 11*). A change in host resistance has been suggested as an underlying condition leading to increased mortality from epizootics (*6, 11, 17*). It is well known that glucocorticoids reduce resistance to infectious disease by inhibiting the normal defense reactions. They may also be involved to some extent in the pathogenesis of other disease, such as glomerulonephritis as seen in woodchucks (*17*). Furthermore, grouping, presumably through adrenal stimulation, augments adrenal-regeneration hypertension in rats (*29*). Experiments have shown that, with increased population density, there is a marked depression of inflammatory responses, of formation of antibodies, and of other related defenses, with a resultant increase in susceptibility to infection or parasitism. For example, in a confined population of rabbits a highly lethal epidemic of myxomatosis occurred coincident with attainment of a high density (*22*). During this epidemic dominant animals and their descendants had the highest survival rate, implying a breakdown in host resistance following increased social competition. Similar results were observed in a population of deer, associated with high densities and subsequent decline in population (*30*). Increased density also enhances mortality from other causes – for example, radiation, amphetamine toxicity, and toxicity due to other pharmacologic agents (*31*). Decreased resistance to amphetamine following grouping is probably due to increased secretion of epinephrine and not to increased secretion of corticosteroids (*32*). Emotional stress also enhances mortality from disease, probably through the same endocrine mechanisms (*33*). These results suggest that at high population densities an epidemic occurs in part because resistance is lowered. Thus, disease is a consequence of high population rather than a primary cause of a decline in population.

BEHAVIORAL ASPECTS

What basic behavioral factors result in these profound effects? It seemed to us that any density-dependent effects would be related to social rank. Experiments made to test this hypothesis showed that adrenal weight and somatic growth were related to social rank (*18, 34*). Other experiments, in which adrenocortical function was assessed from counts of circulatory eosinophils (*36*), confirmed these results. Adrenal cortical activity is similarly related to social rank in rats and dogs, as determined by lipid and cholesterol concentrations in the adrenals of rats and by hydrocortisone secretion in dogs (*36*). In several somewhat related experiments it has been shown that the degree of response to changes in population size is dependent on the behavioral aggressiveness of the strain or species involved (*19, 37*). In the highly aggressive house mouse (*Mus musculus*), changes in adrenal weight, ascorbic acid content, and cholesterol content demonstrated the important role of behavioral factors in the responses to changes in population density. In contrast, deer mice (*Peromyscus maniculatus bairdii*) failed to respond, due to behavioral characteristics and not to an inherently unresponsive endocrine system (*37*). The two species responded equally when exposed to trained fighters of their own species or when subjected to cold.

In most studies of social rank an indirect measure of adrenocortical function was used, such as the weights of adrenal and thymus, cholesterol and ascorbic acid content of the adrenal, and numbers of circulating eosinophils. Recently, a number of investigators have observed increases in adrenocortical function with increases in population density. There is an appreciably greater in vitro production of corticosteroids by adrenals in grouped mice than in singly caged mice (*38*). Albino laboratory rats show an increase in plasma corticosterone concentrations from 6.7 to 22 micrograms per 100 milliliters when they are maintained in colonies rather than in groups of four to a cage (*39*). There was also a fivefold increase in the in vitro production of corticosteroids by the adrenals of the colony-maintained rats. Barrett and Stockham (*40*) reported a 73-percent increase in plasma corticosterone concentrations, as measured fluorometrically, in albino rats kept in groups of 20 as compared with concentrations in singly caged animals. Pearson (*41*) found that, in general, plasma corticosterone levels increased with increasing density in freely growing populations of mice, although there was considerable scatter in the results, possibly because of capture and handling procedures. Thus, direct measurement of corticosteroid levels confirms conclusions from experiments in which morphological criteria were used to assess adrenocortical function in Norway rats and house mice.

Increases in the weight of the spleen in response to increased population density have been reported in mice and voles (*6, 42, 43*). In house mice the increase in splenic weight is due to increased hematopoiesis involving all blood-forming elements, and not solely to erthyropoiesis, as in voles (*43*). The increase probably is related to social rank (*44*), although a response to injuries from fighting could not be ruled out.

The problem of the role of food invariably arises in discussion of changes in population. A shortage of food might have the direct effect of causing starvation or an indirect effect by increasing competition among animals. Contrary to a widely held belief, chronic inanition per se (as opposed to acute starvation) appears not to result in increased adrenal weight or increased cortical function in rats, mice, and men (*45, 46*). Experiments with mice showed that chronic inanition had no effect on adrenal weight, either directly or indirectly (*46*). However, inanition curtailed reproductive function independently of its effects on the pituitary-adrenocortical system. In some species, limitation of the food supply apparently increases competition (*22, 47, 48*), and thus subordinate animals are more affected by the shortage than dominant ones. Resistance to starvation (and thus survival) is greater in dominant or older animals than in subordinate or younger animals (*22*). Also, the decreased need for protein seen in deer during winter and early spring is frequently overlooked (*49*). It is possible that some microtines or other rodents also have mechanisms for taking advantage of bacterial protein synthesis during periods when proteins and natural plant foods are scarce. On the basis of existing evidence (*11, 50*), the direct effect of food shortages cannot be considered a common denominator in the regulation and limitation of growth of populations of herbivorous mammals. Studies of populations of *Clethrionomys* (*51, 52*), lemmings (*53*), voles (*11, 19*), woodchucks (*54*), *Apodemus* (*52*), and other mammals have shown that a deficiency of food either was not a factor in population decrease or else had an effect complementary to behavioral changes associated with changes in population density (*47*). From evidence currently available it appears that the effects of restricting water intake over a long period can be regarded in the same fashion as the effects of chronic inanition. In a thorough study of food requirements and availability of food in relation to populations of small mammals, it was shown that food was not a limiting factor in the area studied (*50*). More critical studies of this sort are needed before a final evaluation can be made of the relative importance of food shortages in limiting population growth and of the degree to which such limitation, when it does occur, is associated with increasing competition within existing hierarchical structures.

The important point, in assessing the effects of behavioral factors on adrenal function, is the number of interactions between individuals rather than density of population per se. Thus, age, sex, previous experience, local distribution, and other factors may be critical in producing effects (*6, 17-19, 55*). The development of the adrenal responses may be produced by very brief encounters with other animals. Experiments showed that 1-minute exposure to trained fighter mice 1, 2, 4, and 8 times a day for 7 days produced increases in adrenal weight and increases in adrenal and plasma concentrations of corticosterone (*56*). As few as two 1-minute exposures per day resulted in a 14-percent increase in adrenal weight, and eight exposures daily resulted in a 29-percent increase. Plasma corticosterone increased by 67 percent. Adrenal levels of corticosterone increased in proportion to adrenal weight, so corticosterone concentrations per gram of adrenal tissue remained constant. These results validate, for mature male house mice, the use of adrenal weight as an index of cortical function. Thus, a few short daily exposures to aggressive mice produced a greater increase in adrenal weight than caging male mice of the same strain together in groups of eight continuously for a week (*37, 56*). These results should serve as an answer to the criticism that laboratory experiments on populations are not realistic because of artificially high densities.

Differences in basic aggressiveness of the strain or species must be considered in a comparison of relative population densities. For example, albino mice are extremely docile in contrast to some strains maintained in the laboratory (*57*). *Peromyscus maniculatus bairdii* also is nonaggressive – even more so than albino *Mus* (*37*). Recently Southwick has demonstrated the importance of behavioral factors in eliciting an adrenocortical response in *P. leucopus* by showing that grouped animals had no adrenal response when they were "compatible" but did if they were "incompatible" (*58*). Thus, to compare absolute densities in the laboratory with those of feral populations is not a justifiable procedure.

It is often said that fighting per se, or injury from fighting, produces the endocrine changes that occur with change in rank and number (*59*). However, data from a large number of populations of mice demonstrate that the endocrine responses to grouping are identical whether or not there is fighting or injury (*6*). Fighting is another symptom of social competition. It seems clear that the basic stimulus to the endocrine changes are sociopsychological, or "emotional." and not physical in nature. Pearson has made the interesting observation that in freely growing populations a few excessively submissive, thoroughly beaten-up, badly scarred mice have low plasma concentrations of corticosterone (*41*). This result agrees with our observations that mice that sink to this level are so abjectly submissive that the more dominant animals no longer pay any attention to them. Because they no longer interact with other members of the population, they cease to be part of it. Also, their continuing existence is probably the result of an artificial situation created by confinement, as in natural populations such animals would doubtless have been forced to move continually; hence most of them would have become mortality statistics. Such submissive animals have been observed and repeatedly captured in a population of woodchucks.

CRITICISMS OF THEORY

The criticism has been made as stated earlier, that results from studies on populations in the laboratory cannot be extrapolated to natural populations because of the excessive densities in the laboratory (*11, 60-62*). The work cited above (*56*) showed that mice exposed to crowding for very short periods each day had an increase in adrenal function. In addition, data on density for most natural populations are often misleading, as many species of rodents, especially rats, voles, and mice, often occur in local "colonies" that may be rather crowded even though areas around them may be very sparsely inhabited. Localized groups of rats in natural populations apparently behave like independent populations, with different degrees of crowding, until the numbers and movement increase sufficiently to fill the general area, at which time the colonies lose their identity and become part of a larger population (*6*). Furthermore, comparable endocrine changes have been observed in natural

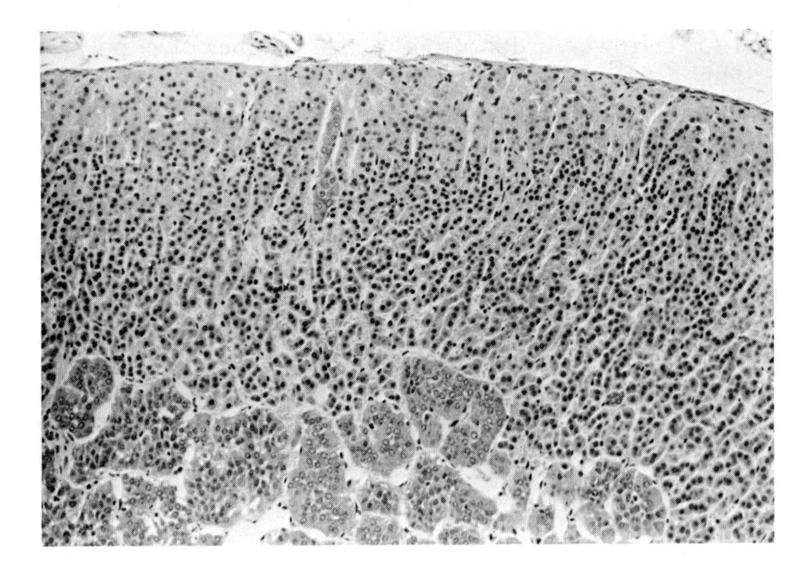

Fig. 1. Adrenal of an immature 15-gram male *Microtus pennsylvanicus*, trapped 15 June, illustrating zonation of the cortex. The cortical zone next to the medulla is composed of compact, lipid-free cells with moderately hyperchromatic nuclei. Between this zone and the typical fasciculata is a zone of small cells containing some lipid (its distinctiveness is more clearly apparent in the original sections than in black and white photomicrographs). These two zones appear to differ morphologically from the X-zone of *Mus*, although both involute with attainment of sexual maturity. Spermatogenesis had nowhere advanced beyond primary spermatocytes in the testes of this vole. The seminal vesicles and coagulating glands together weighed 2.3 milligrams. (Five-micron section stained with hematoxylin and eosin; x 143)

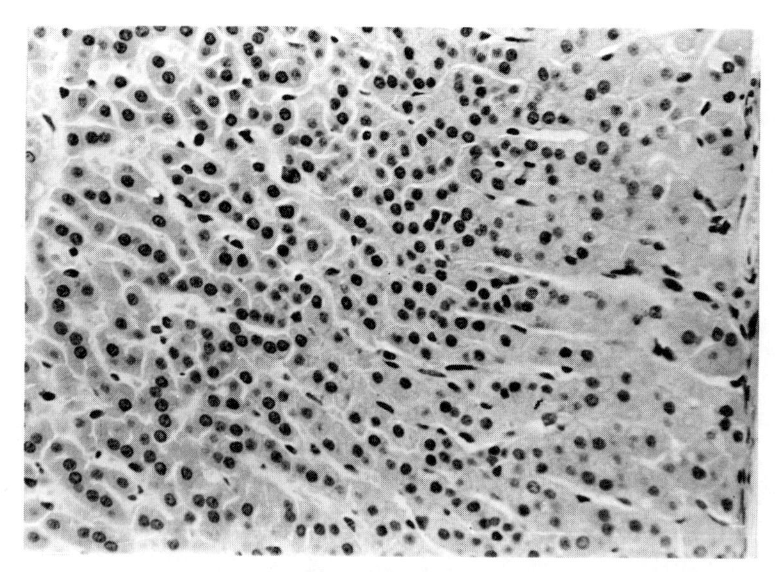

Fig. 2. Same adrenal as Fig. 1 at higher magnification, showing cellular details more clearly. Outer cortex at the right. (x 358)

populations of a number of other species–voles, rats, Japanese deer (sika), woodchucks, and rabbits (*30, 53, 63-65*). Increased social strife produced by the introduction of aliens into a population of rats will induce movements, increase mortality, and, if the original population was high, cause a striking decline from original densities (*18, 66*). Conversely, artificial reduction of a population or alteration of its social structure in a way that reduces competition will reduce adrenal weight and incidence of disease accordingly (*17, 22, 67*). This reduction has been observed in rats, deer, and woodchucks (*30, 65, 67*).

In some situations no correlation has been shown between adrenocortical function and changes in population, but so far the cases fall into two categories. The first is that where the sample is too small to demonstrate any correlation. For instance, Negus (see *61*, Table 4) studied only 98 animals over a 2-year period, of all ages and both sexes (*61*). A second cause of lack of correlation is inaccuracy of population measurement, primarily because currently available census methods are notoriously poor and confidence limits of the estimates have been disregarded (*61*).

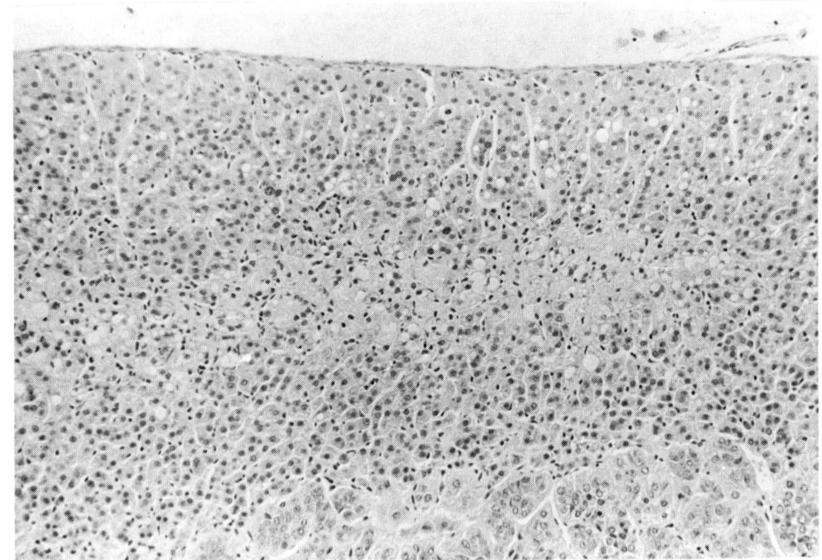

Fig. 3. Adrenal of a more mature male *Microtus pennsylvanicus* than that of Fig. 1. Two distinct cortical zones of degeneration may be seen, one juxtamedullary and the other midcortical. The midcortical zone results from involution of the central cortical zone shown in Figs. 1 and 2, while the juxtamedullary involution arises from involution of the innermost zone. This involution occurs when spermatogenesis is complete, with sperm in the epididymis, but before the seminal vesicles have attained mature size. The seminal vesicles and coagulating glands together weighed 434 milligrams. (Five-micron section stained with hematoxylin and eosin; x 143)

Since changes in adrenal weight occur with reproductive activity, several authors have concluded that adrenal weight cannot be used as an index of adrenocortical function in the study of populations (*68, 69*). It was implied in these accounts that these changes in adrenal weight with changes in reproductive status were overlooked when conclusions concerning population were drawn from changes in adrenal weight in earlier studies of house mice or other species (*62, 68, 70, 71*). Our published data show that these factors were taken into consideration in our studies (*64, 72*). On the other hand, a number of workers may have failed to find a correlation between population status and adrenal weight because changes with sexual function were disregarded. It is well known that

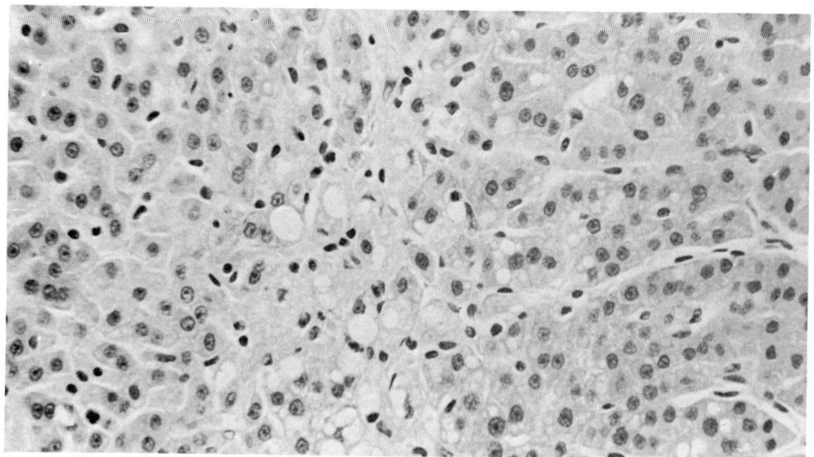

Fig. 4. Same adrenal as in Fig. 3, showing more clearly the unique mid-cortical zone of degeneration which closely resembles the fatty type of degeneration of the X-zone often seen in female *Mus*. Outer cortex at the right. (x 358)

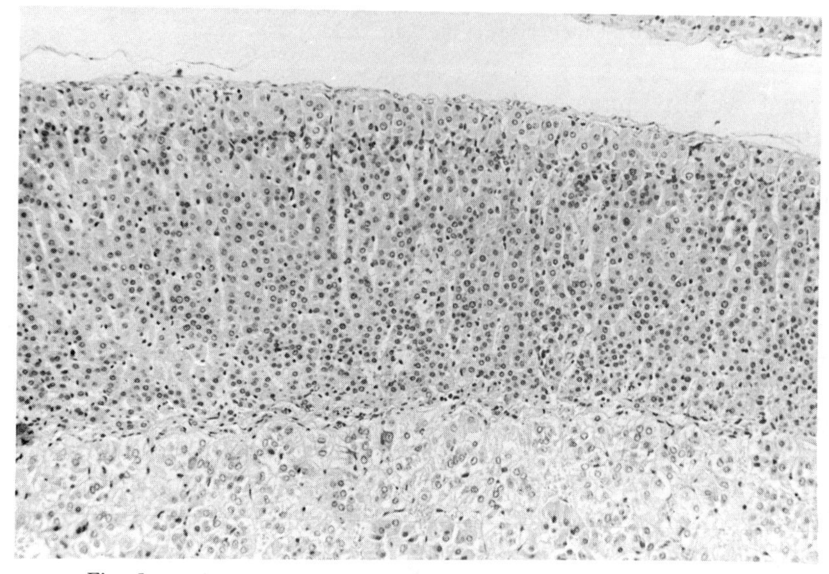

Fig. 5. Adrenal of a fully mature male *Microtus pennsylvanicus* captured on 15 June, typical of a mature adrenal cortex in males of this species, having a conspicuous zona glomerulosa and zona fasciculata and a central, rather thin zona reticularis. The seminal vesicles and coagulating glands together weighed 1479 milligrams. (Five-micron section, stained with hematoxylin and eosin; x 143)

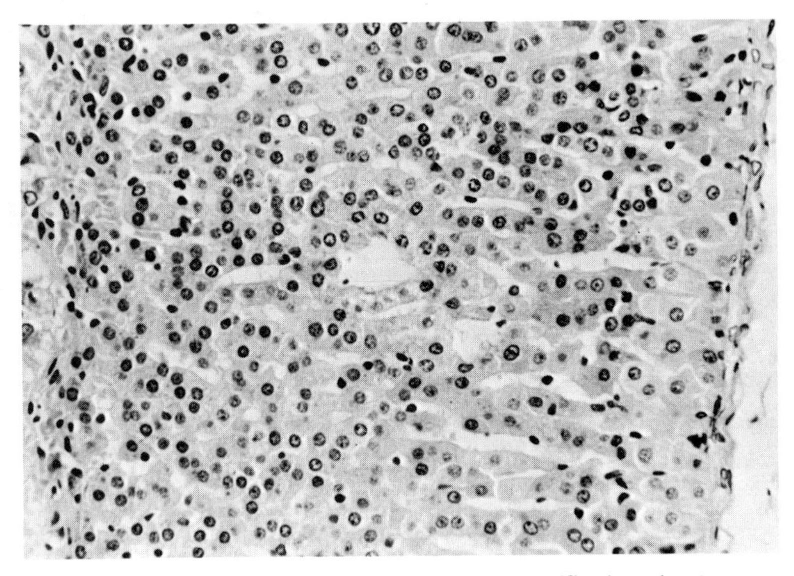

Fig. 6. Same adrenal as in Fig. 5 at higher magnification, showing more clearly the details of zonation of the mature cortex of *Microtus pennsylvanicus*. Outer cortex at the right. (x 358)

adrenal weight increases during pregnancy or with estrogen stimulation in some species, but it is not always remembered that changes in adrenal weight due to population changes can be superimposed on these increases (*19, 64, 65, 70*). Changes in adrenal weight with change in reproductive status fall into two categories: (i) change in weight when there is immature zonation which later disappears, and (ii) change in weight in fully mature animals which is associated with reproductive activity. Obviously, only changes in adrenal weight or function in animals in the same reproductive condition can be properly compared or correlated with changes in population. Chitty and Clarke (*71*) have claimed that a marked increase in the size of the adrenal in female voles (*Microtus agrestis*) is restricted to pregnant animals. However, McKeever reported similar increases in nonpregnant, nulliparous, but sexually mature, females of *M. montanus* (*69*). Our results with *M. pennsylvanicus* are similar, although mature nonpregnant, nulliparous females are scarce, as one would expect. It appears, at least in the North American voles, that the striking increase in the size of the adrenal is associated with

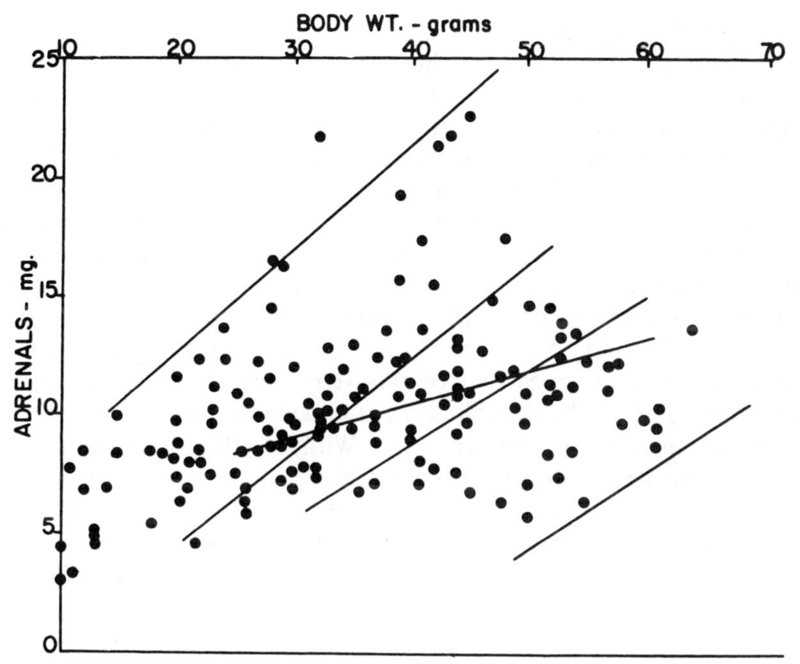

Fig. 7. A plot of adrenal weights (in milligrams) against body weights (in grams) for male *Microtus pennsylvanicus.* The lines were not fitted but were drawn in approximately as follows. The two parallel lines at upper left enclose points for immature animals whose adrenals showed typical immature zonation, as shown in Figs. 1 and 2. The two parallel lines at lower right enclose points for fully mature animals resembling those of Figs. 5 and 6. The points between (and inevitably to some extent some points enclosed by the parallel lines) are for animals in the process of maturing. The single line corresponds roughly to the mean adrenal weights of maturing animals; however, this is not a fitted line and only suggests the direction of transition. It was found impossible to fit regressions of adrenal weight relative to body weight (or body length) for these data in defining starting or end points of zonal involution.

maturation and estrogen secretion and is not limited to pregnancy. However, we have long been aware that adrenal size increases during pregnancy in many species and that this must be considered in using adrenal weights as indices of adrenal function. In other cases, a change in adrenal weight is related to seasonal behavioral changes (*64*), as originally suggested for muskrats (*73*) and later for *Microtus* (*70*).

Further criticism of the theory that behavioral-endocrine mechanisms are operative in the control of population growth is based on recent reports of a lack of correlation between adrenal weight and changes in population size, from which it has been concluded that endocrine mechanisms do not affect population growth (*61, 68, 69*). In another report it was stated that there is no evidence of a "stress mechanism" in a collapse of a lemming population, as no related changes in adrenal weight were found (*74*). First, it must be noted that failure to demonstrate a correlation, without consideration of pertinent relationships, is not disproof of a correlation. Second, these criticisms have been based on observed adrenal weights in voles or rice rats (*Oryzomys*), primarily in the former, without critical evaluation and validation, microscopic or otherwise, of the weight changes. While such conclusions may eventually prove correct in some instances, the inappropriate use, in the studies reported, of adrenal weight as an index of adrenocortical function in these rodents invalidates the conclusions. A basic error in the studies was failure to recognize that many rodents have zones in the adrenal cortex which in many ways resemble the X-zone in house mice, and that these zones are without known function. The use, as indices of function, of the weights of adrenals which include these zones is not appropriate. Delost has published numerous reports on the existence of an "X-zone" in the adrenals of voles (*Clethrionomys, Pitymys,* and *Microtus*) which involutes at maturity in males and regenerates during sexual quiescence (see *6*). Chitty and Clarke (*71*) have further explored this problem in *M. agrestis.* On morphological grounds and because we have observed two immature zones in male *M. pennsylvanicus*, we do not entirely agree with Delost that these should be called X-zones, but the basic observation that in immature voles there are zones which later involute, spontaneously or on administration of testosterone, remains valid. Male *M. pennsylvanicus* appears to have two distinct zones which involute at maturity (Figs. 1-6), neither one of which appears to be entirely comparable morphologically to the X-zone of house mice. The male *Pitymys, Synaptomys*, and *Clethrionomys* that we have examined, and possibly other voles, have similar zonation, although the probability of differences between species or genera must be kept in mind. These zones persist with inhibition of maturation, so that in such voles adrenal weight is relatively much greater in immature than in mature males (Fig. 7). The converse is true for the adrenals of female voles (Figs. 8-10), which undergo a striking hypertrophy at maturity, probably as an exaggerated effect of estrogens, as described for many species, although this has not been tested as yet (*74a*). McKeever (*69*) has demonstrated changes in adrenal weight with age and maturation in *Microtus*, illustrating changes occurring with maturation, but he failed to recognize the zonal changes and probably typical, but enhanced, responses to estrogen, and so arrived at unjustified conclusions. In addition, the picture is confounded by the fact that all gradations between the immature and the fully mature condition of the adrenals occur, as shown in Figs. 8 to 11.

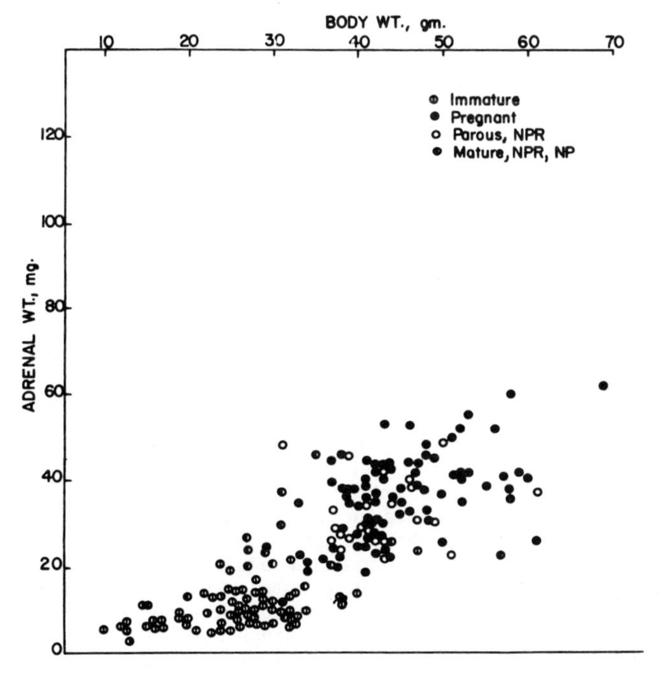

Fig. 8. A plot of adrenal weights (in milligrams) against body weights (in grams) for female *Microtus pennsylvanicus* captured at all seasons of the year. Reproductive status is indicated as shown (NPR, nonpregnant; NP, nulliparous). It may be seen that adrenal weight increases sharply with sexual maturation whether or not the animal is pregnant or parous, although most were pregnant. As may be seen in Fig. 9, most of the immature animals were captured in the late fall and early winter and mainly represent suppressed maturation in young of the preceding breeding season.

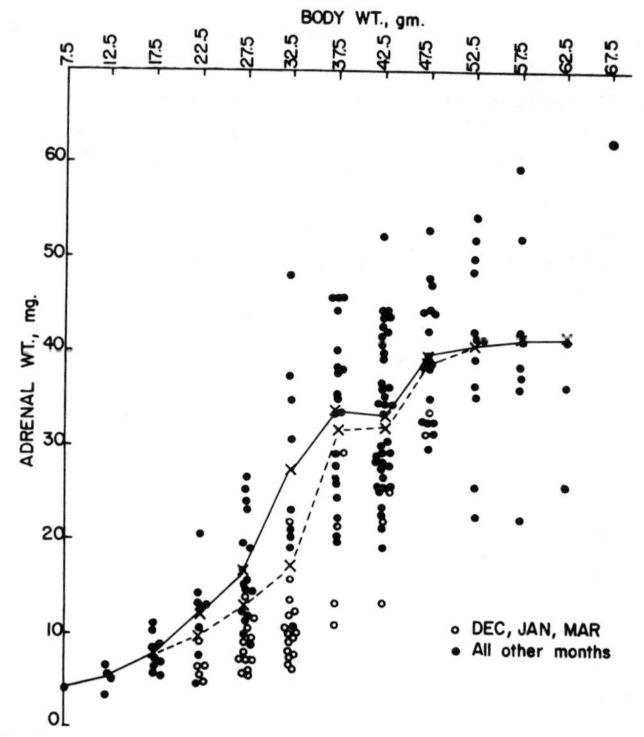

Fig. 9. Weights of adrenals from the animals of Fig. 8 plotted against body weights, with season of capture indicated. A large number of the adrenal weights for immature females are for animals captured between December and March, as indicated in Fig. 8. (Solid line) Mean adrenal weight for animals captured in any month other than December, January, and March; (dotted line) mean adrenal weight for all animals. Figures 8 and 9 show that only the weights of adrenals from mature animals can properly be used for comparing changes in weight with changes in population; in the main, this means that only the weights of adrenals of animals weighing more than 35 grams can be used, but in the winter one finds a few immature females even in this weight range. For this reason the values for mean adrenal weight that we previously published (*18*) for female *Microtus montanus* captured in winter are probably too low, although we used only weights of the adrenals of animals weighing 37.5 grams or more in the study, thus largely, but not entirely, avoiding this pitfall.

Further complicating the picture is the fact that most small mammals born in the fall, and probably even those born at the end of the spring and in the early summer breeding season in a period of relatively high population density, overwinter in the immature condition (*17, 19, 75, 76*), so that a persistence of immature

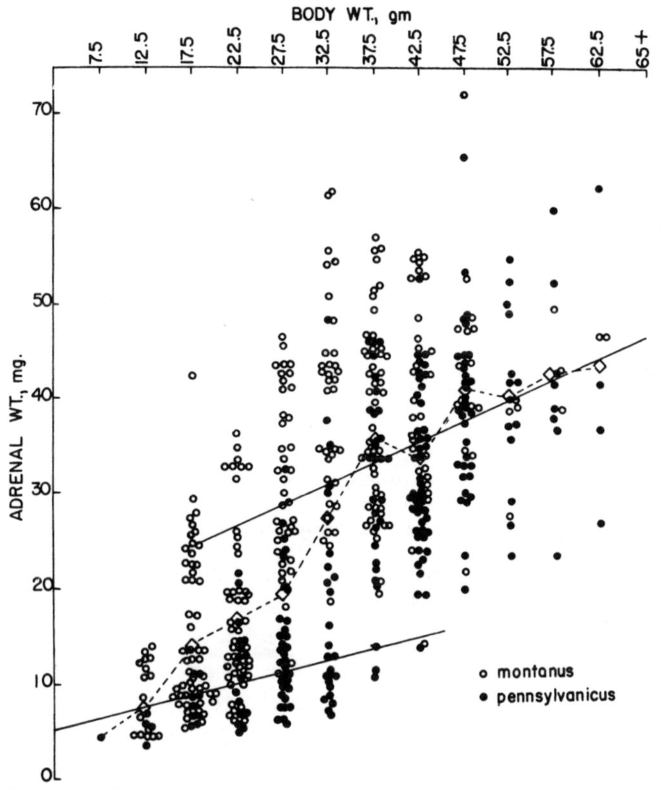

Fig. 10. Plot of adrenal weights against body weights for female *Microtus pennsylvanicus* and *M. montanus*. Regression curves were fitted to points for fully mature females (upper curve) and to points for immature females (lower curve). Weights of adrenals from maturing females form a continuum between these end stages. This plot again illustrates the problems one encounters in using adrenal weight of voles to assess adrenocortical function in relation to population changes unless one uses only fully mature animals. It appears from this diagram that female *M. montanus* mature somewhat earlier than female *M. pennsylvanicus*, but a number of other factors, including differences in populations, confound the data and make it impossible to draw a definite conclusion.

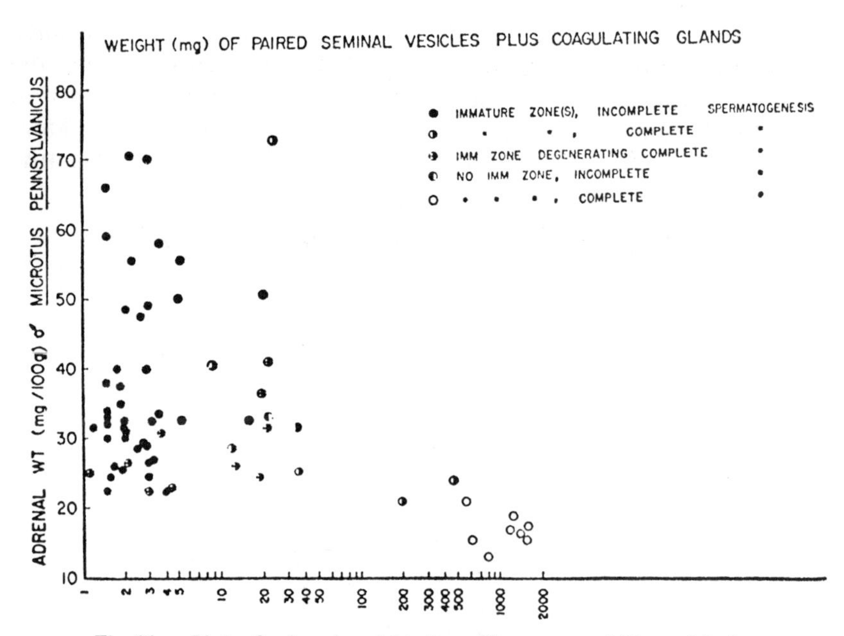

Fig. 11. Plot of adrenal weight (in milligrams per 100 g of body weight) for male *Microtus pennsylvanicus* against the logarithms of values for combined weights (in milligrams) of seminal vesicles and coagulating glands. The state of sexual maturity is indicated in the key. This plot depicts the difficulties encountered in using adrenal weight to assess adrenocortical function in male microtines because of the presence of immature cortical zones.

zonation in males and, in females, the small size of the adrenals unstimulated by estrogen (or whatever factors stimulate the hypertrophy associated with maturation) would be expected (Figs. 8 and 9). The basic error in the conclusions of several investigators was the assumption that adrenal weight is always synonymous with cortical function. In addition, nothing is yet known about the steroids secreted by these species or the possible relation of steroid secretory patterns to changes in zonation. Obviously, if adrenal weight is to be used as an index of adrenocortical function in these species, comparisons can be made only between animals in the same state of reproductive function and with the same degree of involution of immature adrenal zones. Thus, for practical purposes, comparisons are limited to fully mature, sexually active animals. This means, in our experience, that in *Microtus* (*pennsylvanicus* or *montanus*) one usually is limited to the use of animals weighing 35 to 40 grams or more and having uninhibited reproductive function. The relationship between adrenal weight and reproductive function in terms of the weight of seminal vesicles in *M. pennsylvanicus* is shown in Fig. 11. These data illustrate problems one encounters in attempting to make comparisons of adrenal weight for other than fully mature, sexually active males (Figs. 7 and 11).

Another cause of failure to demonstrate a correlation between adrenal weight and population density is failure to consider the social rank of individuals in the samples examined. Since high-ranking individuals generally do not have enlarged adrenals, comparisons of high-ranking individuals at low and high population densities will reveal no changes in adrenal weight or function. McKeever may have made this error when he divided animals into sexually nonactive and active categories (*69*). At high population densities maturation of subordinate animals would be delayed, and these animals would be called nonactive. McKeever's Table 2 (*69*) may simply show that high-ranking animals have similar adrenal weights at low and high population densities, and that low-ranking animals do also. However, comparisons between sexually inactive animals in this case are very probably invalid because of the persistence of immature zonation. Another example of failure to consider social rank is Rudd and Mullen's consideration of only the survivors from groups of pocket gophers (*77*).

In most instances, failure to find a correlation between adrenal weight and population density is due to inclusion of immature animals in samples in progressively larger numbers with seasonal progression. Seasonal or maturational changes in the adrenals do not invalidate the use of adrenal weights as indicators of adrenocortical function if the weights are used critically, but comparisons must be made between comparable animals at comparable times. For example, it has been possible to show a significant decrease in the size of adrenals of woodchucks with alteration of social structure and diminution of competition during the time of rapid increase in adrenal weight by making the appropriate adjustments (*64, 65*); however, there is no complicating zonation in this mammal.

So far we have discussed primarily the restriction of increases of populations due to the effects of high densities. In addition, this explanation should provide some understanding of the increased mortality of young that occurs in subsequent generations. One of the striking aspects of both a natural and a confined population is the observation that young animals have a higher mortality than adults coincident with high population and, in natural populations, also after population density has fallen to relatively low levels (*7*). Chitty (*7*) explained these losses of young in two ways: losses in the year of peak population he attributed to attacks by adults, and losses in the following spring he attributed to some unknown congenital condition acquired *in utero.* Evidence consistent with this view was presented by Godfrey (*78*). Body weights that were low as compared with those in the peak year have been reported in these studies (*79*), and we have observed a similar nonoccurrence of large animals following a peak in population (*19*).

Chitty (*79, 80*) invoked genetic selection to explain how later generations might be influenced by conditions existing before they were born. Therefore, he postulates an effect of social behaviour different from that proposed by us (*17, 19*). Thus, he and his colleagues–for example, Krebs (*74*) and H. Chitty (*70*)–differ from us on the *kind* of physiological and behavioral changes they postulate, but not on the question of whether behavioral changes play an essential part in the regulation of numbers. We find Chitty's explanation for the events in natural populations difficult to accept because it requires genetic selection acting rapidly for a year or two with a subsequent return to, or close to, the original genetic status. In contrast, we believe there is ample evidence of endocrine mechanisms which have the prolonged effects necessary to account for the increased mortality of young during, and for a considerable time after, episodes of maximum density. We have mentioned some of these effects, but we should also call attention to the life-long effects on reproductive function of single injections of androgens into mice or rats less than 10 days old (see *81*); the behavioral effects produced *in utero* reported by Keeley (*26*); the effects of the injection of corticosteroids or other hormones during pregnancy on later behavior (*82*); and the effects of corticosteroids on brain development (*27*). Undernutrition during nursing also has profound and permanent effects on offspring (*83*), which are consistent with the observed reduced growth at high population levels. Actually neither the endocrine nor the genetic selection explanations have been adequately tested, but there appears to be more evidence in support of the former. However, selection must play a long-range role, if not a short-term one (*19*). Whatever the mechanisms accounting for the observed increased mortality of young during and following episodes of high density, it seems evident that the altered status, which we believe to be physiological, will increase susceptibility to adverse environmental conditions, and that behavioral factors are of primary importance in the genesis of the altered status. It is clear that, in a general way, we arrive at the same ultimate conclusions as Chitty, but we place more emphasis on decreased productivity than on increased mortality, although one would anticipate various combinations of these two factors to occur in different populations and under different circumstances. One would expect altered reproductive function to be of greater importance in mammals with a high reproductive rate than in those with a much lower reproductive rate, such as woodchucks. Woodchucks exhibit decreased reproductive function with increased social pressure, brought about by an increased failure to mature in their first year, and increased intrauterine mortality (*84*; *85*), but this is less important in regulating their population than movement of young or mortality (*17*, *84*). Of interest in this regard is the finding that young woodchucks become more seriously affected by renal disease at high population densities, and that this probably results in appreciable mortality (*17*).

These comments lead to consideration of another recent discovery of direct pertinence to the question of the greater effects of high population density on young than on adult mice. First, we repeat that the young in general are subordinate animals and thus, other things being equal, more seriously affected by crowding. However, immature house mice secrete appreciable quantities of 17-hydroxycorticoids, especially hydrocortisone, and, when they are grouped, not only does the total adrenal corticosteroid production increase but the hydrocortisone-corticosterone ratio increases as well (*38*, *86*). With sexual maturation of male mice, the ability to produce hydrocortisone is greatly reduced. Also, if there is delayed maturation accompanying increase in numbers, the secretion of appreciable amounts of hydrocortisone is prolonged. The importance of this finding is that hydrocortisone is a much more potent glucocorticoid than corticosterone, which is the principal compound secreted by adult mice, adult rats, and probably a number of other adult rodents (see *6*). Therefore similar degrees of stimulation of the adrenals of immature and adult mice should result in more profound effects in the immature animals even if there were no difference in social rank. This difference has been observed biologically in the much greater degree of thymic involution and growth suppression produced in immature mice either by ACTH or by grouping than can be produced in adults by similar treatment or by the injection of relatively high amounts of corticosterone (*18, 19, 87, 88*). Similarly, gonadotrophin secretion is suppressed by much smaller doses of steroids in immature than in mature mice and rats (*89*), so that inhibition of maturation of the young in experimental and natural populations may be explained on this basis.

In attempting to explain the mechanisms of the progressive inhibition of reproductive function with increasing population density we postulated that increased secretion of adrenal androgens in response to increased secretion of ACTH might be sufficient to inhibit gonadotrophin secretion, especially in immature mice, and thus explain the observed declines in reproductive function (*6, 90*). Indeed, the injection of adrenal androgens at nonvirilizing physiological concentrations suppresses gonadotrophin secretion and inhibits normal maturation in immature female mice (*91*). Injection of ACTH in intact immature mice also totally inhibits normal maturation (*87*). Surprisingly, ACTH has a similar effect in adrenalectomized mice maintained on hydrocortisone (*88, 92*); thus it appears that ACTH has a direct suppressive effect on reproductive function and therefore on maturation (the site of action is as yet unknown) of immature female mice. Consequently there are at least two distinct mechanisms capable of inhibiting maturation, whose relative importance in the intact animal is unknown. There also remains the distinct possibility that the central nervous system, in response to emotional stimuli, may inhibit gonadotrophin secretion even more directly. In any event, there is ample explanation, including both behavioral and physiological mechanisms, for the differences in the effects of high population levels or increased competition on reproduction, growth, and mortality of the young in contrast to adult animals.

CONCLUSIONS

The experimental results suggest that there are mechanisms for the regulation of many populations of mammals within the limits imposed by the environment, including food. We subscribe to the view that density-dependent mechanisms have evolved in many forms, and probably in most mammals (*11-13, 19, 93*). Thus, mammals avoid the hazard of destroying their environment, and thus the hazard of their own extinction. We believe that the evidence, as summarized here, supports the existence of endocrine feedback mechanisms which can regulate and limit population growth in response to increases in overall "social pressure," and which in turn are a function of increased numbers and aggressiveness behavior. Neither increased numbers nor increased aggressiveness can operate wholly independently. Furthermore, we believe that environmental factors in most instances probably act through these mechanisms by increasing competition. A good example of this would be the situation described by Errington for muskrats (*94*). A drought causes the animals to concentrate in areas of remaining water, with the result that competition and social strife are greatly increased. It follows that increased strife, with increased movement, will also increase losses through predation, another way of increasing mortality of subordinate animals (*22, 47, 94*).

Finally, we might paraphrase Milne's statements (*12*) regarding density-dependent regulation of population growth as follows: Environmental factors (food, predation, disease, physical factors) may limit population growth, but if they do not, as appears more often than not to be the case in mammals, the physiologic mechanisms outlined above will. And finally, the action of these mechanisms is always proportional to changes that depend on changes in population density, behavior, or both. The fact that a sigmoid growth form requires the operation of such a "density-dependent damping factor" supports this conclusion, whereas external limiting factors, unless they operate through the density-dependent damping mechanism, will characteristically truncate a growth curve. Truncation is seldom seen, but the best example of such a curve for mammals that we have seen is that given by Strecker and Emlen (*95*).

In summary, we believe that the behavioral-endocrine feedback system is important in the regulation of populations of rodents, lagomorphs, deer, and possibly other mammals. One would expect other factors to occasionally limit population growth, but, when these fail to do so, the feedback mechanism acts as a safety device, preventing utter destruction of the environment and consequent extinction. Because of time-lag effects, this feedback system should not be expected to work perfectly in every situation.

REFERENCES

1. E. T. Seton, *The Artic Prairies* (Scribner, New York, 1911).
2. J. R. Dymond, *Trans. Roy. Soc. Can. Sect. 5* **41**, 1 (1947).
3. P. H. Leslie and R. M. Ransom, *J. Animal Ecol.* **9**, 27 (1940).
4. C. H. D. Clarke, *J. Mammal,* **30**, 21 (1949).
5. C. Elton, *Voles, Mice and Lemmings* (Clarendon, Oxford, 1942).
6. J. J. Christian, in *Physiological Mammalogy*, W. V. Mayer and R. G. Van Gelder, Eds. (Academic Press, New York, 1963).
7. D. Chitty, *Trans. Roy. Soc. London* **B236**, 505 (1952).
8. D. E. Davis, *Quart. Rev. Biol.* **28**, 373 (1953).
9. P. L. Errington, *Am. Naturalist* **85**, 273 (1951).
10. A. J. Nicholson, *Ann. Rev. Entomol.* **3**, 107 (1958).
11. D. Chitty, *Can. J. Zool.* **38**, 99 (1960).
12. A. Milne, *J. Theoret. Biol.* **3**, 19 (1962).
13. V. C. Wynne-Edwards, *Ibis* **101**, 436 (1959).
14. H. M. Bruce, *J. Reprod. Fertil.* **1**, 96 (1960).
15. C. R. Terman, *Ecol. Bull.* **44**, 123 (1964).
16. J. J. Christian, *J. Mammal.* **31**, 247 (1950).
17. ———, *Military Med.* **128**, 571 (1963).
18. ———, *Proc. Columbia Univ. Symp. Comp. Endocrinol.*, A. Gorbman, Ed. (Wiley, New York, 1959), p. 31.
19. ———, *Proc. Natl. Acad. Sci. U.S.* **47**, 428 (1961).
20. I. C. Jones, *The Adrenal Cortex* (Cambridge Univ. Press, Cambridge, 1957).
21. P. V. Rogers and C. P. Richter, *Endocrinology* **42**, 46 (1948).
22. R. Myktowycz, *Australia Commonwealth Sci. Ind. Res. Organ. Wildlife Res.* **6**, 142 (1961).
23. K. Myers and W. E. Poole, *Australian J. Zool.* **10**, 225 (1962).
24. R. L. Helmreich, *Science* **132**, 417 (1960).
25. J. J. Christian and C. D. LeMunyan, *Endocrinology* **63**, 517 (1958).

26. K. Keeley, *Science* **135**, 44 (1962).
27. E. Howard, *Federation Proc.* **22**, 270 (abstr.) (1963).
28. M. R. A. Chance, *Nature* **177**, 228 (1956).
29. L. L. Bernardis and F. R. Skelton, *Proc. Soc. Exptl. Biol. Med.* **113**, 952 (1963).
30. J. J. Christian, V. Flyger, D. E. Davis, *Chesapeake Sci.* **1**, 79 (1960).
31. J. A. Gunn and M. R. Gurd, *J. Physiol. London* **97**, 453 (1940); M. R. A. Chance, *J. Pharmacol. Exptl. Therap.* **87**, 214 (1946); ———, *ibid.* **89**, 289 (1947); E. A. Swinyard, L. D. Clark, J. T. Miyahara, H. H. Wolf, *ibid.* **132**, 97 (1961); G. B. Fink and R. E. Larson, *ibid.* **137**, 361 (1962); R. Ader, A. Kreutner, Jr., H. L. Jacobs, *Psychosomat. Med.* **25**, 60 (1963).
32. E. A. Swinyard, N. Radhakrishnan, L. S. Goodman. *J. Pharmacol. Exptl. Therap.* **138**, 337 (1962); B. Weiss, V. G. Laties, F. L. Blanton, *ibid.* **132**, 366 (1961).
33. J. T. Marsh and A. F. Rasmussen, Jr., *Proc. Soc. Exptl. Biol. Med.* **104**, 180 (1960).
34. D. E. Davis and J. J. Christian, *ibid.* **94**, 728 (1957).
35. J. G. Vandenbergh, *Animal Behavior* **8**, 13 (1960).
36. S. A. Barnett, *Nature* **175**, 126 (1955); K. Eik-Nes, *Record Progr. Hormone Res.* **15**, 380 (1959).
37. F. H. Bronson and B. E. Eleftheriou, *Physiol. Zool.* **36**, 161 (1963).
38. H. H. Varon, J. C. Touchstone, J. J. Christian, *Endocrinology*, in press.
39. W. Eechaute, G. Demeester, E. LaCroix, I. Leusen, *Arch. Intern. Pharmacodyn.* **136**, 161 (1962).
40. A. M. Barrett and M. A. Stockham, *J. Endocrinol.* **26**, 97 (1963).
41. P. G. Pearson, *Bull. Ecol. Soc. Am.* **43**, 134 (abstr.) (1962).
42. J. R. Clarke, *J. Endocrinol.* **9**, 114 (1953).
43. J. Dawson, *Nature* **178**, 1183 (1956).
44. J. P. Rapp and J. J. Christian, *Proc. Soc. Exptl. Biol. Med.* **114**, 26 (1963).
45. R. A. Huseby, F. C. Reed, T. E. Smith, *J. Appl. Physiol.* **14**, 31 (1959); K. A. Khaleque, M. G. Muazzam, R. I. Choadhury, *J. Trop. Med. Hyg.* **64**, 277 (1961); G. G. Slater, R. F. Doctor, E. G. Kollar, paper presented at the 44th meeting of the Endocrine Society (1962).
46. J. J. Christian, *Endocrinology* **65**, 189 (1959).
47. R. M. Lockley, *J. Animal Ecol.* **30**, 385 (1961).
48. C. Kabat, N. E. Collias, R. C. Guettinger, *Wis. Tech. Wildlife Bull. No. 7* (1953).
49. L. C. McEwan, C. E. French, N. D. Magruder, R. W. Swift, R. H. Ingram, *Trans. North Am. Wildlife Conf.* **22**, 119 (1957); H. Silver and N. F. Colovos, *Proc. Northeast. Wildlife Conf., Portland, Me.* (1963).
50. W. Grodzinski, *Proc. Intern. Congr. Zool., 16th* (1963), vol. 1, p. 257.
51. O. Kalela, *Ann. Acad. Sci. Fennicae* **A-IV**, No. 34 (1957).
52. A. Gorecki and Z. Gebcaynska, *Acta Theriol.* **6**, 275 (1962).

53. K. Curry-Lindahl, *J. Mammal.* **43**, 171 (1962).
54. J. A. Lloyd and J. J. Christian, *Proc. Intern. Conf. Wildlife Distr., 1st* (1963).
55. B. Welch, *Proc. Intern. Congr. Zool., 16th* (1963), vol. 1, p. 269.
56. F. H. Bronson and B. E. Eleftheriou, *Gen. Comp. Endocrinol.* **4**, 9 (1964).
57. J. J. Christian, *Am. J. Physiol.* **182**, 292 (1955).
58. C. H. Southwick, *Science* **143**, 55 (1964).
59. ——— and V. P. Bland, *Am. J. Physiol.* **197**, 111 (1959).
60. P. Crowcroft and F. P. Rowe, *Proc. Roy. Zool. Soc. London* **131**, 357 (1958).
61. N. C. Negus, E. Gould, R. I. Chipman, *Tulane Studies Zool.* **8**, 95 (1961).
62. R. Tanaka, *Bull. Kochi Women's Univ.* **10**, 7 (1962).
63. B. L. Welch, *Proc. Natl. Deer Distr. Symp., 1st* (Univ. of Georgia Press, Athens, 1962); K. Wodzicki and H. S. Roberts, *New Zealand J. Sci.* **3**, 103 (1960); E. F. Patric, *J. Mammal.* **43**, 200 (1962).
64. J. J. Christian, *Endocrinology* **71**, 431 (1962).
65. J. A. Lloyd, J. J. Christian, D. E. Davis, F. H. Bronson, *Gen. Comp. Endocrinol.* **4**, 271 (1964).
66. D. E. Davis, *Trans. North Am. Wildlife Conf., 14th* (1949), p. 225.
67. J. J. Christian and D. E. Davis, *Trans. North Am. Wildlife Conf., 20th* (1955), p. 177.
68. D. A. Mullen, *J. Mammal.* **41**, 129 (1960).
69. S. McKeever, *Anat. Record* **135**, 1 (1959).
70. H. Chitty, *J. Endocrinol.* **22**, 387 (1961).
71. ——— and J. R. Clarke, *Can. J. Zool.* **41**, 1025 (1963).
72. J. J. Christian, *Ecology* **37**, 258 (1956).
73. J. R. Beer and R. K. Meyer, *J. Mammal.* **32**, 173 (1951).
74. C. J. Krebs, *Science* **140**, 674 (1963).
75*a* *Note added in proof*: Results from a recent study of the relationships between sexual maturity, the adrenal glands, and population density in female *M. pennsylvanicus* from a natural population suggest that *female* voles of this species have no X-zone as it is defined for house mice (*20*). Apparently it is a hypertrophic reticularis and inner fasciculata [resembling the adrenals of woodchucks in this respect (*54, 64*)] which have been labeled an X-zone. There is no involution at pregnancy. The cells contain lipids, and the hyperplasia occurs with maturation, as pointed out by Chitty and Clarke (*71*). Adrenal weight relative to body weight is a discontinuous function in these animals as a result of the sudden increase at maturation. Therefore, regressions of adrenal weight relative to body weight or body length are invalid if the data come from both immature and mature females. When these facts are taken into account it is clear that there is no change in adrenal weight relative to body weight with reproductive status in mature females, and that there is a remarkable

parallelism between mean adrenal weight of mature females and population size.

75. A. van Wijngaarden, *Verslag Landbouwk. Onderzoek No. 66.22* (1960), pp. 1-68.
76. D. A. Spencer "The Oregon Meadow Mouse Irruption of 1957-58," *Fed. Coop. Expt. Serv., Corvallis, Publ.* (1959), p. 15; K. A. Adamczewska, *Acta Theriol.* **5**, 1 (1961); W. Sheppe, *J. Mammal.* **44**, 180 (1963); D. R. Breakey, *ibid.*, p. 153.
77. R. L. Rudd and D. A. Mullen, *J. Mammal.* **44**, 451 (1963).
78. G. R. Godfrey, *ibid.* **36**, 209 (1955).
79. D. Chitty, *Cold Spring Harbor Symp. Quant. Biol.* **22**, 277 (1958).
80. H. Chitty and D. Chitty, *Symp. Theriol., Prague* (Czechoslovak Academy of Science, Prague, 1962), p. 77.
81. R. A. Gorski and C. A. Barraclough, *Endocrinology* **73**, 210 (1963).
82. M. W. Lieberman, *Science* **141**, 824 (1963).
83. E. M. Widdowson and G. C. Kennedy, *Proc. Roy. Soc. London* **B156**, 96 (1962); E. M. Widdowson and R. A. McCance, *ibid.* **B158** 32 (1963).
84. D. E. Davis, *J. Wildlife Management* **26**, 144 (1962).
85. R. L. Snyder, *Ecology* **43**, 506 (1962).
86. H. H. Varon, J. C. Touchstone, J. J. Christian, *Federation Proc.* **22**, 164 (abstr.) (1963).
87. J. J. Christian, *Endocrinology*, **74**, 669 (1964).
88. ———, *ibid.* **75** 653 (1964).
89. W. W. Byrnes and R. K. Meyer, *ibid.* **48**, 133 (1951); W. W. Byrnes and E. G. Shipley, *Proc. Soc. Exptl. Biol. Med.* **74**, 308 (1950); D. Ramirez and S. M. McCann, *Endocrinology* **72**, 452 (1963).
90. J. J. Christian, *Proc. Soc. Exptl. Biol. Med.* **104**, 330 (1960).
91. H. H. Varon and J. J. Christian, *Endocrinology* **72**, 210 (1963); G. E. Duckett, H. H. Varon, J. J. Christian, *ibid.*, p. 403.
92. J. J. Christian, *Federation Proc.* **22**, 507 (abstr.) (1963).
93. F. A. Pitelka, *Cold Spring Harbor Symp. Quant. Biol.* **22**, 237 (1958).
94. P. L. Errington, *Agr. Expt. Sta. Iowa State Coll., Ames, Res. Bull. 320* (1943).
95. R. L. Strecker and J. T. Emlen, *Ecology* **35**, 249 (1953).

Ritualization of Animal Activities in Relation to Phylogeny, Speciation and Ecology

J. M. CULLEN

Zoologists studying the social communication of animals have used the word 'ritualization' broadly speaking to describe changes in the signalling system during the course of evolution which have come about to make the signals more effective in evoking appropriate behaviour in a partner. (Critiques of different uses of the term in animals studies may be found in Blest (1961) and Wickler (1961).) Usually such signals operate within a species but some symbiotic relationships between different species also involve signals for which the word may reasonably be used (Baerends 1950). The chief emphasis in discussions of ritualization has been laid on evolutionary changes in form such as exaggerated amplitude of movement, alterations in frequency, increased regularity of rhythm, stereotyping of orientation, etc., besides the acquisition of morphological characters such as colours, sound-producing structures, to enhance the effectiveness of the signals. For signals to work the responding partner must of course be suitably tuned to them, but relatively little is known how well signal and responsiveness are matched (Marler 1961). Moreover, some ritualized signals may work, at least partly, through their general attention-catching properties rather than as the result of specifically evolved responsiveness, e.g. the red spot on the beak of an adult Herring Gull (*Larus argentatus*) makes the young peck at it for food partly through its mere contrast with the yellow beak (Tinbergen & Perdeck 1951). In addition, learning may play some role in the tuning of responsiveness to signals in natural situations, as can be seen in the development of inter-specific responses of species which consort (Bergman 1957). In spite of these uncertainties there is no doubt that with the evolution of much ritualized behaviour changes in responsiveness of the recipient have also evolved.

From *Philosophical Transactions of the Royal Society of London*, B, **251**, 363-374, 1966.

Ritualization has not merely produced signals which are conspicuous but, more important, it has lessened their ambiguity and made them more distinguishable from signals carrying a different message. Two examples may be cited to show what happens when this ambiguity arises. In her pre-copulatory invitation posture the female Shag (*Phalacrocorax aristotelis*) tilts her body forward, raises her tail and then bows her head abruptly forwards to nibble at the nest material (Snow 1963, fig. 1 *g*). In response to the display the male often mounts her. When preparing to defecate a Shag tilts its body and raises its tail in much the same way, though tending to orientate with the tail outwards from the nest. These preliminaries by a female occasionally provoke her mate to mount, though mating is not consummated and when the male dismounts or is thrown off, the female completes her defecation (personal observation). Such mistakes are not serious and the ambiguity of the female's posture has presumably not been worth eliminating.

The second example of the ambiguity of signals concerns Honey-bees performing the dance which conveys to their fellows the distance and direction of food they have located. Distance is coded in some measure of the number of dances per unit time, probably the mean duration of the central run (von Frisch & Jander 1957) or perhaps a sound closely correlated with this (Wenner 1962). Schweiger (1958) showed that there were distinct differences in individual coding: for food at a particular distance some bees danced more slowly than others. There was also a surprisingly large scatter. One third of the dances of a particular stock of bees indicating food at 200 m were more than 90 m out according to the 'average' coding. (These observations were only made under standard wind conditions as changes in wind are known to affect the dance code.) One source of individual variation was found to be age; with food at 200 m there was a smooth decline in dance rate from the first day of foraging to the 24th, and this decrease was such that the code of old bees indicated that the food was about 150 m farther away than the young ones. Schweiger also showed that errors in dancing led to the foragers recruited by the dance making errors in searching for the food. Fast dancers made the recruits search for food at a shorter distance. That differences in dance rates affect the searching distance of recruits had been found earlier by Boch (1957) studying different races of Honey-bees, which differ slightly in their coding of dance rate and distance. If bees of two races were mixed in a hive, each would correctly code and decode the dances of her own race, but would make mistakes when decoding the dances of the other. It is not surprising that differences exist in the coding pattern of different races of bees since, except under experimental conditions, they will seldom decode each other's dances, but the variation within members of a single hive is a more serious defect. It should be remembered, however, that the importance of visual and olfactory cues given off by flowers increases the 'target area' of the natural food.

When considering animal signalling systems it would seem natural to try and make use of the formal analyses of communication channels developed in information theory (e.g. Shannon & Weaver 1949). In any real information channel it can be shown that there will inevitably be errors made by the receiver in reading signals and it is possible to give a precise method of measuring this ambiguity or 'equivocation' as Shannon calls it. However, in our present state of knowledge about animal communication it is not possible to apply this approach except in a very few cases. Moles (1963) has pointed out some of the pre-requisites for doing so, such as determining the minimum discriminable unit in the sensory dimension involved, and the corresponding 'time quantum' necessary for the animal to perceive such units. There seem to have been only two attempts to measure the information content of animal signals, one by Haldane & Spurway (1954) for the bee-dance, the other by Wilson (1962) for a chemical signal, an odour trail indicating distance and direction of food, in the Fire-ant (*Solenopsis saevissima*). Perhaps one of the main values of such exercises is to show the kind of facts which are necessary and to make explicit the assumptions on which such calculations are based. Such data are at present regrettably rare in studies of animal signalling, and no attempt will therefore be made to estimate ambiguity quantitatively for the signals to be considered in the remainder of this paper.

SELECTION PRESSURES FOR THE ELIMINATION OF AMBIGUITY

The ambiguity inherent in any communication channel is aggravated in animal communication because of the nature of the historical development of the signals themselves. Comparative studies on a number of species, mainly arthropods and vertebrates, have shown that it is possible in many cases to trace the evolutionary history of signals, and this has frequently indicated that two signals in the same species or a signal in two different species have a common evolutionary origin (e.g. Lorenz 1941; Tinbergen 1960; Alexander 1962). As has often been pointed out, this process is exactly comparable to the cultural evolution of language with diversification of words from a common origin. Signals which have a common origin in time are intrinsically likely to be similar and give rise to ambiguity if they need to be distinguished from the 'parental' or from the 'sister' form. The reduction of this ambiguity has been due to a number of different selection pressures: for distinguishing members of different species, members of the two sexes or other subgroups within a species, between individuals in different physiological states and even between individuals themselves.

The best known of these selection pressures are those responsible for reproductive isolation between species, preventing hybridization. Differences in ritualized courtship signals, visual and auditory are widespread in sympatric species (Lanyon & Tavolga 1960; Blair 1961; Mayr 1963; Busnel 1963 *a*). In species which overlap in parts of their breeding range the differences are sometimes enhanced in the area of overlap (Blair 1964). Courtship usually consists of a loosely knit chain of reactions involving distinct signals by both partners. Reproductive isolation is achieved by differences in signals and the response to them at one or more stages in the chain. It has been found in several groups that the signals which come early in the courtship sequences show more variation from one species to another than do the actions immediately preceding copulation (Hinde 1959; Alexander 1962). Selection has acted to prevent mistakes as early as possible. However, double-assurance mechanisms are also well known, reducing still further the chance of a hybrid mating.

Until recently the evidence for the function of ritualized signals in reproductive isolation was mainly circumstantial, but it has now been possible to demonstrate this experimentally. The male *Scleropus* lizard nods his head on encountering another individual on his territory. The temporal patterning of nods varies from species to species, and with a cam suitably shaped Hunsaker (1962) was able to make a model simulate the nodding patterns of the different species, and show that the females responded to the pattern of their own species. On the whole sound signals are easier to manipulate than visual ones, and many workers have studied species recognition of songs and calls. Sometimes it has been possible to investigate female choice (e.g. Perdeck 1958; Blair & Littlejohn 1960) but often the test of 'species recognition' has been whether or not males show aggressive behaviour or counter-sing, which they normally do only in reply to songs of their own species. For instance, Dilger (1956) tested the response of five species of thrushes when a song was played from near a stuffed specimen of one of the five species placed in a male's territory. The songs of the species are more different than their appearances, and it depended on the species of song alone whether or not the mounted thrush would be attacked.

The experimental investigation of signals makes it possible to analyse what features of a signal are carrying the essential message, by progressively eliminating one or other of the potentially relevant parameters and testing the animal's response to the altered signal. A promising start has been made for some of the calls of Orthoptera and birds and shown clearly that some aspects of song are of little importance while others greatly affect the response. For example, Falls (1963) studied the monotonous song of the Ovenbird (*Seiurus aurocapillus*), which consists of a series of trisyllabic phrases, and found that elimination of the first syllable did not affect the response of other males to the song. The presence of the other two syllables was important and so was their order–reversed songs evoked a reduced response.

The full exploitation of this type of analysis depends not only on testing the responses to natural calls which have been altered, but to synthetic sound signals of any desired frequency and amplitude pattern. This poses considerable technical problems, but some first steps have been taken in work with Orthoptera (Busnel 1963 *b*). Capranica (1965) has made an elegant analysis of the part of the mating call of the male Bullfrog (*Rana catesbiana*) necessary for evoking the song of other conspecific males in reply. By using POVO, an electric analog sound generator developed by the Massachusetts Institute of Technology in connexion with speech research, he was able to show that the message resided in the frequency structure within the individual croaks, and depended upon a complicated balance between the relative sound energies in three neighbouring frequency regions.

Species recognition has sometimes played a part in the evolution of signals in another way. (The following argument has been modified slightly from that of Hamilton (1962).) When closely related species occur in the same habitat but differ in ecology, e.g. in food, they need to develop isolating mechanisms to avoid wasting time by provoking each other's aggression, and possibly being injured in fights. Thus they will tend to diverge in threat signals and response to threat signals. In Britain four species of Paridae with different food habits, breed within a habitat with overlapping territories with little inter-specific aggression between them. On the other hand, in North America the Paridae are ecologically more similar and rarely coexist within the same habitat without territorial exclusion. The crucial point seems to be whether by fighting with the other species they are driving away a competitor for some limited commodity. In colonial nesting gulls the function of territory is to secure a place around the nest in which the young can space themselves out as they hide from predators (Tinbergen 1956). In this area a member of a closely related species is as dangerous as a member of ones own, and correspondingly where *Larus argentatus* and *L. fuscus* form mixed colonies their territories form non-overlapping mosaics.

Among coral reef fishes in which the sexes are alike there are often striking differences in the gaudy patterns of related species, e.g. Chaetodontidae. These differences are thought to be due to the need for avoiding aggression towards species which are not ecological competitors (Lorenz 1964 *b*; Zumpe 1965).

SEPARATION WITHIN A SPECIES

Within a species there is often considerable differentiation in the social role of members differing in age, sex, etc., and there are many differences in the structure, appearance and behaviour of such groups which enable them to be recognized. Two examples will be described, in which the role of the signals has been experimentally verified.

In the Zebra Finch (*Taeniopygia castanotis*) flocks consist of pairs, which spend much of their time sitting together, and juveniles, which clump side by side in larger groups. Young and adults differ in plumage and beak colour. When the young moult out of their first plumage and their beak changes at the same time from the juvenile black to the adult red, they lose their readiness to clump and begin to search for a mate. These changes in appearance, which are typical of many vertebrates, have been shown by Immelmann (1959) to act as signals affecting the behaviour of young and adult to each other. Beak colour was particularly important: a male would start to court one of his own fledged young if its beak were artificially coloured red, though only intermittently. Conversely, young would cease to beg from one of their parents whose beak was coloured black. There are also differences in plumage between the sexes and a slight but distinct difference in the shade of red of the beaks. By altering the appearance of normal birds of either sex and of three types of mutants and by presenting models, Immelmann showed the role of these differences in sex recognition. Immelman's results by no means exclude the role of behaviour in recognition. Coloration was often found to determine the initial response of one bird to another, but its effect would wane, particularly in females selecting males, if the behaviour of the partner was inappropriate.

The break-down of sex recognition can be more serious in spiders where the female may treat a courting male as food. Crane (1949) described the courtship of fifteen species of jumping spiders (Salticidae) showing how the strikingly marked first legs, palps or chelicerae of the male are displayed. *Epiblemum scenicum* holds its black-and-white banded legs out sideways and waves them up and down as it approaches the female. A female will hunt and attack a wide range of moving objects (Drees 1952). If a small disk with a wire projecting on either side, a 'male model', is presented she will stalk and jump on this too. But by making the wires move like the courting male's first legs (by switching on and off an electromagnet beneath the experimental table), Drees showed that the female's attack could be stopped and she would permit the male model to come right up to her.

Intraspecific signals play a role in many situations, and need to be distinct from each other. This is the Principle of Antithesis recognized by Darwin (1873). Many animals 'walk tall' when confidently threatening, but 'fold up' when beaten. When aggressive the offensive weapons are directed towards the opponent, when submissive they are turned away (Tinbergen 1959). The same principle can apply to sounds. Alexander (1962) concluded that the structure of the evolutionarily more primitive 'calling song', which is the most important signal possessed by field crickets, seems largely to have determined the methods by which the species could evolve distinctive sounds operating unambiguously in other situations.

Selection pressures so far considered have favoured unambiguous recognition, the evolution of a signal which is as distinct as possible from, say, other signals within the species with which it might be confused. Such signals may be called 'disjunctive'. But there is an important type of signal, which will be considered next, where 'conjunctiveness' has advantages where variability is beneficial when it expresses the fluctuating state of the displaying animal and therefore predicts what it is likely to do in the near future. Such signals are widespread in the courtship and threat of vertebrates, where it can be shown that the animals are simultaneously aroused to behave in different ways—to attack and flee in the case of threat, to attack, flee and mate in the case of courtship (Tinbergen 1952; Morris 1956; Hinde 1959; Wiepkema 1961). As the relative strengths of the arousal of these different tendencies are continually changing, this is reflected in the form of the display. Thus Stokes (1962), quantifying the components of the threat display of the Blue Tit (*Parus caeruleus*), found that if the body is horizontal and orientated towards the opponent with the wings raised and tail fanned, the display is likely to be followed by an attack; but if these features are lacking and instead the feathers are fluffed and the crest raised, the displaying bird is more likely to flee. Should the bird have its nape feathers raised and open its beak, this means that it is unlikely to attack or flee, but will defend the spot where it is (usually at food).

The importance of this variability of form is that it can be read by the observer, and doubtless by a fellow member of the species, as indicating future behaviour, and appropriate action can be taken in advance. During the highly ritualized fighting of many Cichlid fish such as *Aequidens latifrons* there is a gradual escalation of threat which allows either contestant to withdraw if it is not prepared, as it were, to raise its stakes (Oehlert 1958; Ohm 1958-59).

The development of ritualized fighting in highly social animals, with its diminished risk of injury for the individual, both winner and loser, has been reiterated by Lorenz (e.g. 1964 *a*). Within a taxonomic family one can see this trend for species with smaller territories to have more ritualized threat displays and/or conspicuous signal structures demonstrated in threat. Dr. Bryan Nelson has drawn my attention to it in the Sulidae, and it can be seen in other birds: Sterninae (Cullen 1956), Ploceinae (Crook 1964). From Oehlert's (1958) descriptions it appears to hold in some genera of Cichlids. Presumably in dense territories with steep attack-flee gradients, misunderstanding a signal is quickly penalized by an attack, so that displays have become more ritualized to reduce this danger.

Sometimes the transitions in motivation from fleeing to attacking or mating can be read in a smooth transition in the form of the display, but Morris (1957) has pointed out the important principle that many displays develop 'typical intensity' or 'typical compromise'.[1] Instead of reflecting the minor changes in motivation, the form of the display has become stabilised. For instance the S-posture threat display of the Poecilid fish *Xiphophorus helleri* and *montezumae* has become fixed with the rivals side by side, parallel or anti-parallel, each with its swordtail bent slightly towards the other and its head away, and they maintain this 'typical form' until one attacks or the other flees (Franck 1964; contrast Morris 1957). In other species, X. *pygmaeus, maculatus* and *xiphidium*, the S-posture has not developed a 'typical form', or not to the same extent. Their threat displays, though basically similar to the S-posture of the first two species, are more variable and express in the head orientation and general positioning of the body the momentary attack-flee balance.

This evolution of 'typical form' is a trend away from the conjunctive signal code to a disjunctive one. As Morris points out this implies that the reduction in information provided about the state of the signaller is more than compensated by the elimination of signal ambiguity. Moreover, he adds, the state of the signaller can still be represented in other parameters of the display such as its frequency. It is not clear why some species have evolved 'typical form' signals while others have not. A stimulating discussion of what is essentially the same problem is to be found in Alexander (1962) where he discusses the evolution and diversification of the four main types of cricket calls, occurring in the situations of advertisement, courtship, aggression and after copulation.

[1] 'Typical form' (Tinbergen 1964) seems a better general name, which would include both the others.

INDIVIDUAL DIFFERENCES

The existence of individual differences in a signalling code can seriously impair its accuracy, as has been shown in the experiments of Schweiger (1958) already discussed. But Marler (1961) has pointed out that a call can encode both the individuality of the caller and the main message provided that different parts of the signal are utilized. From sound-spectrograph analyses this seems to be the case for the songs of *Pipilo fuscus*, a species with considerable individual variation (Marler & Isaac 1960 *a,b*). In other species an individual may have a variety of songs, many of them peculiar to himself, all sharing broad species-specific or population-specific characteristics (Marler & Tamura 1962; Mulligan 1963).

In birds the identity of the caller is often an important piece of information. Precise evidence that individuals can recognize one another by voice is not abundant (Marler 1956; Thorpe 1961; Tschanz 1964), but there is much circumstantial evidence that at least in those species with a lasting pair bond, the mates recognize one another in this way. Male-male recognition may also be important in stabilizing the territorial structure of a neighbourhood, and Weeden & Falls (1959) showed that Ovenbirds distinguished between played-back songs of their neighbours and more distant males, being more likely to ignore a neighbour's song.

LIMITS TO DIVERSITY: DIRECTION OF SIGNAL EVOLUTION

The diversification of ritualized signals has been encouraged by the selection pressures outlined above, but it has been restricted to some extent by the signal-generating structures and sense organs available to a species. The vocal apparatus of fish and Amphibia limits most of their utterances to croaks and grunts (Moulton 1963; Bogert 1960), while the more specialized syrinx and larynx of birds and mammals allow elaborate frequency-modulated whistles and howls (Thorpe 1961; Kelemen 1963; Tembrock 1963). Correspondingly, while the ears of birds and mammals are very sensitive to frequency changes, the sound-detectors of insects are not, and respond chiefly to amplitude modulation (Autrum 1963). The tympanal organs of Orthoptera, the insect group most specialized for sound signalling, are particularly sensitive to rapid changes in amplitude and can distinguish between differences in such transients, so that the messages can be coded in the rhythm of the song, the steepness of the transients and the duration of individual sound pulses (Autrum 1963). Differences in temporal resolution, the ability to separate successive stimuli so that they are perceived as distinct rather than continuous, may account for differences in signals between birds and mammals. Pumphrey (1961) estimated that a bird song would need to be slowed up at least ten times before the human ear could fully resolve the detail a young Chaffinch (*Fringilla coelebs*) hears and reproduces.

Since many visual displays have apparently originated from 'intention movements' of locomotion (Daanje 1950), this might be expected to have restricted diversification. Very similar displays seem indeed to have evolved independently. For instance, in birds the upward stretched posture with beak pointing vertically is found widely in passerines, herons, terns and gannets (Andrew 1961; Meyerriecks 1960; Moynihan 1955; Dorward 1962) and seems to have originated in each group from a flying-up movement. However, in cases where diversification of signals is at a premium, as in reproductive isolation between related species, a great variety of modifications can be achieved on the same basic patterns (e.g. in surface-feeding ducks–Lorenz (1941)).

Much of this variety appears arbitrary, with no indication of why one species should ritualize its behaviour in this way, and another in that, but some general trends can be recognized. (For further examples see Wickler (1961).) Habitat and general habits play an important part. Within a family of birds the smaller species are usually more agile on the wing, and these are the ones which have the most elaborate aerial displays (Moynihan 1955; Meyerriecks 1960). Passerine species living in open country with few bushes and trees for song-posts have song-flights instead (Howard 1920). Fish living in rapidly flowing streams have, in different families, developed a parallel-swimming threat display, sometimes with their bodies in contact along their length and with tail beats precisely synchronized

(Wickler 1959). This parallel orientation is doubtless connected with the way these fish have to head into the current to maintain position. The calling songs of male crickets, by which females are attracted, are much louder in the relatively solitary desert species than in those which aggregate in leaf litter (Alexander 1962). In the mating calls of frogs, the dominant frequency and pulse rate vary widely from species to species, but show a negative correlation with body size (Blair 1964).

By their very nature signals will make an animal not only more conspicuous to its own species but also to predators, so that signals which have evolved must be considered a compromise between conspicuousness and concealment. An interesting example concerns the hawk-alarm-call of a number of bird species, which warns other members of the flock but must also to some extent endanger the individual which calls. This call is surprisingly similar in different taxonomic families, and Marler (1956) has shown that its amplitude and frequency structure are precisely those which make it difficult for a vertebrate predator to pinpoint, using the three known methods of sound localization which would be available to it.

Species which are less vulnerable from predators may in consequence be able to afford more conspicuous signals. Hoogland, Morris & Tinbergen (1956-57) proved that the stout spines of the Stickleback (*Gasterosteus aculeatus*) help to protect it against fish predators, and that the weaker spines of the related *Pygosteus pungitius* are less effective. *Gasterosteus* also differs from *Pygosteus* in being less timid, in nesting in the open instead of in weed and in being more conspicuous in breeding coloration. Hoogland *et al.* suggested that this was because the strong spines permitted a more exposed way of life. Work in progress (K. Wilz, personal communication) indicates that some of the differences in the courtship of the two species can also be ascribed to the change which lead to the greater aggressiveness of *Gasterosteus*. Shifts in the balance of attacking, fleeing and mating tendencies account for many differences in the courtship displays of related species, e.g. Fringillid finches (Hinde 1955-56, 1959) and Cichlid fish (Baerends & Blockzijl 1963).

The behaviour of the cliff-nesting Kittiwake Gull (*Rissa tridactyla*) in contrast to its more typical ground nesting relatives illustrates how a hierarchy of adaptive modifications may be brought about by a single major change (E. Cullen 1957). The shift to the new nesting habitat safe from predators led to over thirty changes, including alteration of fighting technique, threat and appeasement displays, male advertisement, food begging posture and calls, and the development of an appeasement posture by the young with a special black band on the nape to reinforce its effect. In the related group of terns a somewhat similar aberrant cliff- and tree-nesting species was found to have undergone some of the same modifications as the Kittiwake (Cullen & Ashmole 1963).

The interaction of different behaviour systems is shown on a grander scale in a long series of papers by Crook, culminating in 1964, on fifty species of weaver birds, showing the correlation between food, habitat and social structure. Differences in the advertisement displays of the males were linked with nests of different structures and these in turn were associated with a particular type of breeding social organization.

Sometimes correlated differences may be difficult to interpret. Crane (1957) reported that in two taxonomic groups of fiddler crabs (*Uca*) the displays were particularly elaborate in species living on the shores of bays protected from waves, but only when salinity was high. This puzzling pattern was repeated in two geographical areas. Alexander (1962), with data from about 100 species of crickets, found particularly structural types of calls had arisen independently in different groups, and tentatively attributes this to the way the crickets auditory system functions in making certain kinds of sounds more easily decoded than others. Whether or not this view is correct, this kind of correlation analysis, combined with a detailed knowledge of the animal's ecology and sensory physiology, offers the best hope for understanding the diversification of such complicated signals.

In the past, with a few exceptions, comparative studies of ritualized behaviour were made either on many species in captive or semi-wild conditions where their ecology was more or less distorted, or else under natural conditions but with far fewer species. It is now clear that the evolutionary processes which have shaped and are shaping the behaviour we see today can only be properly assessed when an animal's behaviour in its normal surroundings are thoroughly known, together with the capabilities of its sensory systems and signal-generating organs. Moreover, since the only way we can trace the evolution of behaviour is by comparing existing species, we need to have this information for related species living in different habitats, and unrelated species living in the same habitat. In view of our virtual ignorance of many of these facts, it is small wonder that there are still many unsolved puzzles about ritualized behaviour.

ABSTRACT

Ritualization consists of the evolution of increased conspicuousness of signals and decreased ambiguity. Errors of signalling occur, even in that most remarkable of known animal signalling systems, the bee dance. Selection pressures moulding the reduction of ambiguity;

(1) Between species: reproductive isolation to prevent hybridization, and isolation to reduce aggressive encounters between closely related, ecologically non-competing species.

(2) Within species: Darwin's principle of antithesis leads to displays with the opposite meaning looking as different as possible. The ritualization of fighting is widespread, especially in densely territorial species. 'Disjunctive' and 'conjunctive' signals are distinguished, the former being relatively distinct from each other, the latter intergrading. Displays signalling an individual's precise motivational state at a certain moment make use of conjunctive systems, though these may break into disjunctive 'typical forms'.

(3) Individual differences, if not introducing ambiguity in signalling, can be important, as the identity of the signaller is often a relevant piece of information in higher vertebrates with developed personal relationships.

The nature of the sense organs and potential signal-generator organs of the species limit the types of signal produced and the way the message is coded in them. In spite of the apparent arbitrariness of many of the signals used by different species, detailed examination of some has shown that it is sometimes possible to identify the selection pressures which shaped them.

REFERENCES

Alexander, R. D. 1962 Evolutionary changes in cricket acoustical communication. *Evolution* **16**, 443-467.

Andrew, R. J. 1961 The displays given by passerines in courtship and reproductive fighting: a review. *Ibis* **103***a*, 315-348, 549-579.

Autrum, H. 1963 Anatomy and physiology of sound receptors in invertebrates. In *Acoustic behaviour of animals* (ed. Busnel, R. G.). Amsterdam: Elsevier.

Baerends, G. P. 1950 Specialization in organs and movements with a releasing function. *Symp. Soc. Exp. Biol.* **4**, 337-360.

Baerends, G. P. & Blokzijl, G. J. 1963 Gedanken über das Entstehen von Formdivergenzen zwischen homologen Signalhandlungen verwandter Arten. *Z. Tierpsychol.* **20**, 517-528.

Bergman, G. 1957 Zum Problem der gemischten Kolonien. *Vogelwarte* **19**, 15-25.

Blair, W. F. (ed.) 1961 *Vertebrate speciation.* Austin: University Texas Press.

Blair, W. F. 1964 Isolating mechanisms and interspecies interactions in anuran amphibians. *Quart. Rev. Biol.* **39**, 334-344.

Blair, W. F. & Littlejohn, M. J. 1960 Stage of speciation of two allopatric populations of chorus frogs (*Pseudacris*). *Evolution* **14**, 82-87.

Blest, A. D. 1961 The concept of ritualization. In *Current problems in animal behaviour* (eds. Thorpe, W. H. and Zangwill, O. L.). Cambridge University Press.

Boch, R. 1957 Rassenmässige Unterschiede bei den Tänzen der Honigbiene (*Apis mellifica* L.). *Z. vergl. Physiol.* **40**, 289-320.

Bogert, C. M. 1960 The influence of sounds on the behavior of amphibians and reptiles. In *Animal sounds and communication* (eds. Lanyon, W. E. and Tavolga, W. N.). Washington: American Inst. Biol. Sci.

Busnel, R. G. (ed.) 1963*a* *Acoustic behaviour of animals.* Amsterdam: Elsevier.

Busnel, R. G. 1963*b* On certain aspects of animal acoustic signals. In *Acoustic behaviour of animals* (ed. Busnel, R. G.). Amsterdam: Elsevier.

Capranica, R. R. 1965 The evoked vocal response of the bullfrog. *M.I.T. Research Monograph.* No. 33.

Crane, J. 1949 Comparative biology of salticid spiders at Rancho Grande, Venezuela. Part IV. An analysis of display. *Zoologica, N.Y.* **34**, 159-214.

Crane, J. 1957 Basic patterns of display in fiddler crabs (Ocypodidae, Genus *Uca*). *Zoologica, N.Y.* **42**, 69-82.

Crook, J. H. 1964 The evolution of social organization and visual communication in the weaver birds (*Ploceinae*). *Behaviour* (Suppl., no. 10).

Cullen, E. 1957 Adaptations in the Kittiwake to cliff-nesting. *Ibis* **99**, 275-302.

Cullen, J. M. 1956 A study of the behaviour of the Arctic Tern. D.Phil. thesis, Oxford University.

Cullen, J. M. & Ashmole, N. P. 1963 The Black Noddy *Anous tenuirostris* on Ascension Island. Part 2. Behaviour. *Ibis* **103** *b*, 423-446.

Daanje, A. 1950 On locomotory movements in birds and the intention movements derived from them. *Behaviour* **3**, 48-98.

Darwin, C. 1873 *The expression of the emotions in man and animals.* London: Murray.
Dilger, W. C. 1956 Hostile behavior and reproductive isolating mechanisms in the avian genera *Catharus* and *Hylocichla. Auk* **73**, 313-353.
Dorward, D. F. 1962 Behaviour of boobies *Sula* spp. *Ibis* **103** *b*, 174-220.
Drees, O. 1952 Untersuchungen über die angeborenen Verhaltensweisen bei Springspinnen (Salticidac). *Z. Tierpsychol.* **9**, 169-207.
Falls, J. B. 1963 Properties of bird song eliciting responses from territorial males. *Proc. 13th Int. Orn. Congr., Ithaca*, pp. 259-271.
Frisch, K. von & Jander, R. 1957 Über den Schwänzeltanz der Bienen. *Z. vergl. Physiol.* **40**, 239-263.
Franck, D. 1964 Vergleichende Verhaltensstudien an lebendgebärenden Zahnkarpfen der Gattung *Xiphophorus. Zool. Jb. Physio.* **71**, 117-170.
Haldane, J. B. S. & Spurway, H. 1954 A statistical analysis of communication in *Apis mellifera* and a comparison with communication in other animals. *Insectes Sociaux* **1**, 247-283.
Hamilton, T. H. 1962 Species relationships and adaptations for sympatry in the avian genus *Vireo. Condor* **64**, 40-68.
Hinde, R. A. 1955-56 A comparative study of the courtship of certain finches (Fringillidae). *Ibis* **97**, 706-745; **98**, 1-23.
Hinde, R. A. 1959 Behaviour and speciation in birds and lower vertebrates. *Biol. Rev.* **34**, 85-128.
Hoogland, R., Morris, D. & Tinbergen, N. 1956-57 The spines of sticklebacks (*Gasterosteus* and *Pygosteus*) as a means of defence against predators (*Perca* and *Esox*). *Behaviour,* **10**, 205-236.
Howard, E. 1920 *Territory in bird life.* London: Murray.
Hunsaker, D. 1962 Ethological isolating mechanisms in the *Scleropus torquatus* group of lizards. *Evolution* **16**, 62-74.
Immelmann, K. 1959 Experimentelle Untersuchungen über die biologische Bedeutung artspezifischer Merkmale beim Zebrafinken (*Taeniopygia castanotis* Gould). *Zool. Jb. Syst.* **86**, 437-592.
Kelemen, G. 1963 Comparative anatomy and performance of the vocal organ in vertebrates. In *Acoustic behaviour of animals* (ed. Busnel, R. G.). Amsterdam: Elsevier.
Lanyon, W. E. & Tavolga, W. N. 1960 *Animals sounds and communication.* Washington: Amer. Inst. Biol. Sci.
Lorenz, K. Z. 1941 Vergleichende Bewegunsstudien an Anatinen. *J. Orn.* **89**, 194-294.
Lorenz, K. Z. 1964 *a* Ritualised fighting. In *The natural history of aggression* (eds. Carthy, J. D. and Ebling, F. J.). London: Academic Press.
Lorenz, K. Z. 1964 *b* *Das Sogenannte Böse.* Vienne: Borotha-Schoeler Verlag.
Marler, P. 1956 The voice of the Chaffinch and its function as language. *Ibis* **98**, 231-261.

Marler, P. 1961 The filtering of external stimuli during instinctive behaviour. In *Current problems in animal behaviour* (eds. Thorpe, W. H. and Zangwill, O. L.). Cambridge University Press.

Marler, P. & Isaac, D. 1960 *a* Analysis of syllable structure in songs of the Brown Towhee. *Auk* **62**, 433-444.

Marler, P. & Isaac, D. 1960 *b* Song variation in a population of Brown Towhees. *Condor* **62**, 272-283.

Marler, P. & Tamura, M. 1962 Song 'dialects' in three populations of White-crowned Sparrows. *Condor* **64**, 368-377.

Mayr, E. 1963 *Animal species and evolution.* Harvard University Press.

Meyerriecks, A. J. 1960 Comparative breeding behaviour of four species of North American herons. *Publ. Nutall Onr. Cl.* **2**, 1-158.

Moles, A. 1963 Animal language and information theory. In *Acoustic behaviour of animals* (ed. Busnel, R. G.). Amsterdam: Elsevier.

Morris, D. 1956 The function and causation of courtship ceremonies. In *L'Instinct dans le Comportement des Animaux et de l'Homme.* Paris: Fondation Singer-Polignac.

Morris, D. 1957 'Typical Intensity' and its relation to the problem of ritualization. *Behaviour* **11**, 1-12.

Moulton, J. M. 1963 Acoustic behaviour of fishes. In *Acoustic behaviour of animals* (ed. Busnel, R. G.). Amsterdam: Elsevier.

Moynihan, M. 1955 Some aspects of reproductive behaviour in the Black-headed Gull (*Larus ridibundus* L.) and related species. *Behaviour* (Suppl.), no. 4.

Mulligan, J. A. 1963 A description of Song Sparrow song based on an instrumental analysis. *Proc.* 13*th Int. Orn. Congr., Ithaca,* pp. 272-284.

Oehlert, B. 1958 Kampf und Paarbildung einiger Cichliden. *Z. Tierpsychol.* **15**, 141-174.

Ohm, D. 1958-9 Vergleichende Beobachtungen am Kampfverhalten von *Aequidens* (Cichlidae). *Wissensch. Z. Humboldt-Univ. Berlin* **8**, 1-48.

Perdeck, A. C. 1958 The isolating value of specific song patterns in two sibling species of grasshoppers (*Chorthippus brunneus* Thunb. and *C. biguttulus* L.). *Behaviour* **12**, 1-75.

Pumphrey, R. J. 1961. Sensory organs: hearing. In *Biology and comparative physiology of birds*, Vol. 2. (ed. Marshall, A. J.). New York: Academic Press.

Schweiger, E. M. 1958 Über individuelle Unterschiede in der Entfernungs- und Richtungsangabe bei den Tänzen der Bienen. *Z. vergl. Physiol.* **41**, 272-299.

Shannon, C. E. & Weaver, W. 1949 *The mathematical theory of communication.* Urbana: University Illinois Press.

Snow, B. 1963 The behaviour of the Shag. *Brit. Birds* **56**, 77-103, 164-186.

Stokes, A. W. 1962 The comparative ethology of Great, Blue, Marsh and Coal Tits at a winter feeding station. *Behaviour* **19**, 208-218.

Tembrock, G. 1963 Acoustic behaviour of mammals. In *Acoustic behaviour of animals.* (ed. Busnel, R. G.). Amsterdam: Elsevier.

Thorpe, W. H. 1961 *Bird-song.* Cambridge University Press.

Tinbergen, N. 1952 'Derived' activities; their causation, biological significance, origin, and emancipation during evolution. *Quart. Rev. Biol.* **27**, 1-32.

Tinbergen, N. 1956 On the functions of territory in gulls. *Ibis* **98**, 401-411.

Tinbergen, N. 1959 Einige Gedanken über Beschwichtigungsgebärden. *Z. Tierpsychol.* **16**, 651-665.

Tinbergen, N. 1960 Comparative studies of the behaviour of gulls (Laridae): a progress report. *Behaviour*, **15**, 1-70.

Tinbergen, N. 1964 The evolution of signalling devices. In *Social behavior and organization among vertebrates* (ed. Etkin, W.). University Chicago Press.

Tinbergen, N. & Perdeck, A. C. 1951 On the stimulus situation releasing the begging response in the newly hatched Herring Gull chick (*Larus argentatus argentatus* Pont.). *Behaviour* **3**, 1-39.

Tschanz, B. 1964 Beobachtungen und Experimente zur Entstehung der 'persönlichen' Beziehung zwischen Jungvogel und Eltern bei Trottellummen. *Verh. schweiz. naturforsch. Ges.* pp. 211-216.

Weeden, J. S. & Falls, J. B. 1959 Differential responses of male Ovenbirds to recorded songs of neighbouring and more distant individuals. *Auk* **76**, 343-351.

Wenner, A. M. 1962 Sound production during the waggle dance of the Honey Bee. *Anim. Behav.* **10**, 79-95.

Wickler, W. 1959 Vergleichende Verhaltensstudien an Grundfischen. III. *Z. Tierpsychol.* **16**, 410-423.

Wickler, W. 1961 Ökologie und Stammesgesichte von Verhaltensweisen. *Fortschr. Zool.* **13**, 303-365.

Wiepkema, P. R. 1961 An ethological analysis of the reproductive behaviour of the Bitterling (*Rhodeus amarus* Bloch). *Arch. néerl. Zool.* **14**, 103-199.

Wilson, E. O. 1962 Chemical communication among workers of the Fire-ant *Solenopsis saevissima* (Fr. Smith). *Anim. Behav.* **10**, 148-158.

Zumpe, D. 1965 Laboratory observations on the aggressive behaviour of some butterfly fishes (Chaetodontidae). *Z. Tierpsychol.* **22**, 226-236.

Developments in the Study of Animal Communication

P. MARLER

It is a significant reflection, both on scientific method and on the genius of Darwin, that little real attempt was made to take up the study of animal communication where he left off. Instead, as so often happens, the subject lay fallow for half a century, until others rediscovered it. With the stimulus of new methods, the same problems were approached from a new angle, and it is in fact difficult to find any major work on animal communication which is directly and obviously inspired by *The Expression of the Emotions in Man and Animals* (London, 1872), unless it be that of J. S. Huxley. Nevertheless, perhaps von Uexküll unconsciously served as a bridge between the two generations, for several of the later workers came under his direct influence.

The change of emphasis in the new approach to animal communication has been towards the direct study of animals in natural or semi-natural environments, which we owe mainly to J. S. Huxley and K. Lorenz. With captive animals, on the other hand, H. Lissman and N. Tinbergen were pioneers in the complementary approach, exploiting the fact that some animals can be induced to respond to artificial models as they would to the social partner. By use of a wide range of models, it has often proved possible to break down apparently highly complex behaviour into surprisingly simple basic elements.

These two methods of approach have stimulated an enormous variety of work on a great many animals, the most important contributions coming from Holland, Germany and Switzerland. It is the aim of this essay to review some of these developments in order to assess how our understanding of animal communications has developed since Darwin's time, and to point out that there are still certain fields where we may look to him for further inspiration.

Perhaps Darwin's greatest limitation was his inevitably rather fragmentary knowledge of how animals actually communicate among themselves in their natural state. It is no accident that his main subjects, apart from man, were the domestic cat and dog. The need to be thoroughly intimate with the animal's life before its social communication can be really understood has since been made evident by K. Lorenz. As a result we now have a better grasp of how widespread the phenomenon of animal language is, and how complex some of the signals are which individuals exchange.

The term *communication*, which can be applied to all kinds of interaction between cells, organs and organisms, is restricted here to exchanges of information between individuals. There are various methods available to animals for signalling to each other. One of the most widespread is by chemical signals which others can either taste or smell. The substance may be carried either by diffusion or by a current to the other animal, or it may be deposited on some object where others are likely to encounter it. As we shall see, this method has many disadvantages, and more complex languages usually make use of the senses of sight and hearing. We know most about visual communication since it is the easiest for us to investigate. With the development of new techniques we are now learning more about vocal language. But the sense of smell is still rather a mystery, and the possibilities of communication by touch have scarcely been recognized, although it provides the basis for the most complex animal language so far known, discovered by K. von Frisch in the honey bee.[1]

COMMUNICATION BY TASTE AND SMELL

Because most of us neglect our chemical senses, we are apt to overlook their importance in animals. They play an important role in the life of most, with the exception of birds. A dog's life, the visual

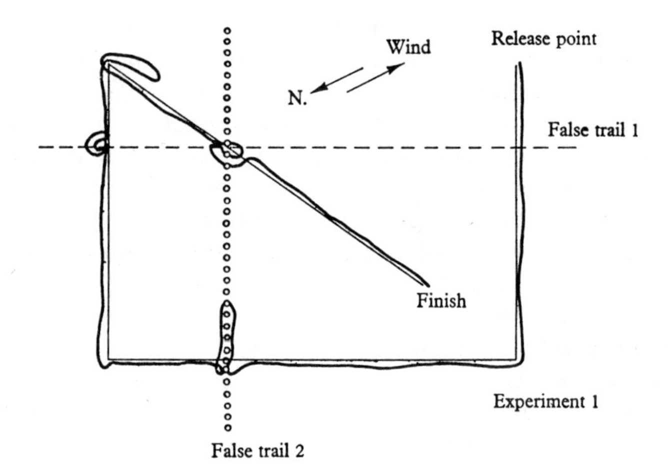

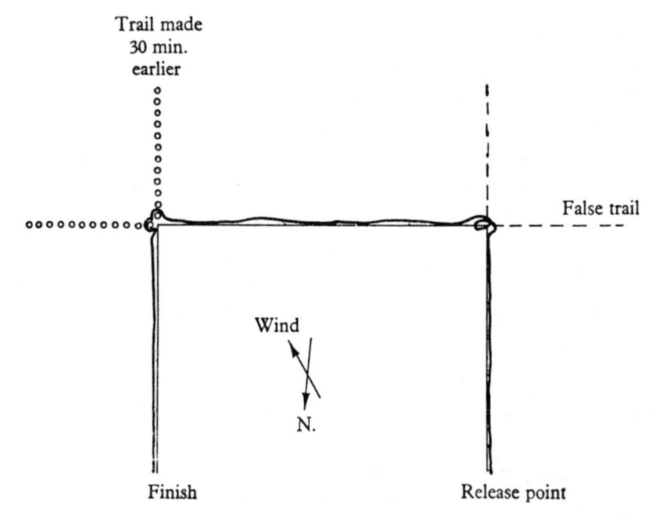

Fig. 1. Tests of the ability of a police dog to follow scent trails of other dogs. In the first experiment it successfully followed a trail without being more than momentarily confused by the false trails of two other dogs. In the second experiment it again avoided a false trail, and distinguished the fresh track from another laid by the same dog 30 minutes earlier. (After Schmid.[3])

aspect of which had such careful attention from Darwin, is probably more dominated by the sense of smell, and dogs' powers of discriminating between slightly different odours, recently confirmed in a series of experiments by Neuhaus,[2] are already familiar to anyone who has kept them. German police dogs, for example, can readily follow the fresh trail of a horse or another dog, and recognize it within a network of false tracks. They can even distinguish two tracks of the same dog, one 30 minutes older than the other[3] (fig. 1).

This ability to distinguish other individuals by smell is by no means confined to mammals. Goz[4] found that a minnow could distinguish the water passing over one member of its shoal from that passing over another. The powers of discrimination extend to other species and genera, even to other families, though they become blunted with the more distant relatives. There is one exception to this in the remarkable responses to water passing over a predatory fish, such as a pike. Exposed to this, a minnow either keeps quite still, or edges gently away, and occasionally goes into a curious trance-like state.

So fish can get a surprising amount of information about other fish by the chemical sense. In these examples it appears that the chemical signal which passes from one fish to another is an accidental by-product, probably produced more or less continuously. This is no disadvantage for communication purposes, the only requirement being that there should be little chance of two individuals producing exactly the same combination of chemicals. It probably suffices in some cases to rely on the varied diet of animals. Any two individuals are likely to eat slightly different foods, or will metabolize it in slightly different ways, so producing different excretory products.

Apparently the colony odour of bees arises in this way, where it is combined with the habit of free exchange of food between all members of the hive.[5] The repulsion of strange bees from the hive is known to be based on their different smell, as well as behaviour. Kalmus and Ribbands[6] divided a colony into three parts and periodically examined them to see if marked bees returned to the wrong part. Two groups were kept unfed and the third was given heather honey and black treacle. Within eight days, the fed group had only a small proportion of intruders, while the other two were still freely exchanging individuals. So it appears that the change in diet had already enabled the fed group to distinguish between the smells of their own comrades and those of the unfed bees. However, the actual nature of the substance secreted is still in doubt, for Renner[7] has recently shown that the bee's scent organ plays no part in the identification of the colony. Bees did not distinguish between the substances squeezed from the glands of members of different hives, so some other secretion must be involved.

Even in their simplest form, chemical signals make possible the identification of other animals down to species, colony or individual. And they can also communicate the presence of danger. Some fish will flee from a wounded companion. Von Frisch[8] and his pupil Schutz[9] demonstrated that this was a response to something released from the damaged skin. It is most common in species which form schools, though it is not confined to them, and the most effective warning signals come from the fish's own species. So this *Shreckstoff* or *fright-substance* is a quite effective method of communicating danger to other members of the species. It even helps to protect newly hatched fry from being eaten by their parents, since the adults are frightened by the substance produced if they should snap at and wound young of their own species.

Though first described in fish, the effects of these fright-substances may be much more widespread. Toad tadpoles behave in the same way[10] and there is perhaps something similar in *Paramecium, Drosophila* and mice, though this is not yet properly established.[11]

The problem of identifying a chemical signal is rather different from that of discovering the direction from which it has come. Perception of the presence of the stimulus only tells the animal that the source lies within a certain distance, depending on the concentration and characteristics of the substance, the forces carrying it from the source, and the sensitivity of the animal's receptors.

There are several methods to attract or repel animals from a particular point by chemical means. The substance can be deposited on some object, which subsequently serves as the signal source. A honey-bee leaves its odour behind when it visits a flower, which helps other bees to find it.[12] The same method can be used to establish contact between individuals if the marking animal remains near the signal points, or visits them regularly. A solitary male bumble bee marks signposts along its track of the day by biting at leaves and twigs, so depositing scent from special glands in the mouth. The track is laid in a zone which varies with the species, either in the tree canopy, in small trees or shrubs, or near the ground. He then patrols the posted area for the rest of the day. If a queen bee looking for a mate should strike this trail, she will follow the scent signals, and so eventually meet the male.[13]

Attraction to a point can also be achieved with a chemical signal from the animal's own body, as long as it keeps still for periods of time, so that the partner can track the smell down. Some of the most elementary organisms, the slime moulds, seem to form their cellular aggregations in this way; they illustrate how a complex communication system can be built up from a simple basis. Individual cells are attracted to the organizing centre by a chemical substance, acrasin, which diffuses from it. Shaffer[14] demonstrated that, although the same substance will attract the cells of more than one species, there is nevertheless a specific response. This is ensured by the secretion of a second substance which destroys acrasin. By secreting these two chemicals alternately, waves of acrasin are produced, spreading outwards from the centre with a particular interval between them. Apparently because of variations in such factors as cellular adhesiveness, each species will only aggregate in response to a particular rhythm of acrasin production, and so intraspecific communication is ensured.

For these slime moulds, simple diffusion suffices to carry the chemical, but for some purposes this is too slow, or the concentration at a distance may be very small indeed. Some improvement can be achieved if the animal creates a current over the scent gland. This may simply serve to get the scent off the gland more quickly, as in the honey-bee, or may send a concentrated signal in a particular direction. A male newt, courting his mate under water, turns to face her and curls his tail forward, so sending a current over his cloaca and towards her, apparently carrying chemical stimuli[15] (fig. 2).

A directed current will have limited value in chemical communication, unless the animal knows where to direct it. When this is not so, as in the scent signalling by which some female moths attract a mate, a natural current can be used instead, in this case air movements. Here we see some of the most remarkable achievements of this kind of communication, and also some of its inevitable limitations.

Fig. 2. A male newt directing a water current over his cloaca towards the female. (After Tinberger.[15])

In a series of carefui studies, Schwinck[16] found that the male silkworm moth can only locate the female at a distance if there is a wind blowing. He can perceive the female odour at very low concentrations, at which direct location would be inconceivable. However, he can respond to the air movement and he starts searching upwind, zig-zagging to and fro. If he loses the scent, he goes downwind and starts again. In this way he can approach close enough to change over to direct orientation, guided by the diffusion gradient around the female. The details of this second stage vary with the species.[17] One species will wheel back down-wind and return two or three times, gradually homing to the female. In another species, the male alights, and makes the last part of the search on foot. Obviously there are disadvantages in this method of communication, remarkable as its achievements are. It only works when there is a wind blowing, and the male spends a lot of time searching. Many animals have exploited visual and auditory signals which lack many of these drawbacks.

Perhaps the greatest restriction on the development of chemical language is the limited repertoire of possible signals. An animal may have several glands which produce different substances.[18] Solitary bees may have at least two distinct smells, and a tropical butterfly, *Heliconius*, probably has at least four.[19] This is a difficult subject to study and no doubt more elaborate chemical languages have still to be discovered. But no external gland is yet known to produce, as the larynx does with sound, a whole spectrum of different signals. The difficulties of rapid exchange of chemical signals between individuals are also great, though this might be partly overcome with shortlived compounds, or by destroying one substance with another,[20] as in slime moulds. Whatever further work may reveal, it seems probable that we shall always have to look elsewhere for the most elaborate forms of social communication.

VISUAL COMMUNICATION

In contrast with chemical stimuli, an animal cannot perceive a visual stimulus without also getting some idea of whence it has come. A creature with the simplest eyes may only know that the signal source is in the approximate direction in which the eye is pointing. With more elaborate eyes, each sensitive cell receives light from a particular direction, so that very accurate location of the source becomes possible. Vision is, in fact, the most efficient means many higher organisms have of locating each other. This is not even impossible for animals which are active in darkness, for some, such as many deep-sea fishes, can produce light themselves.

Fireflies, too, are well-known examples of this, making use of what must be the simplest type of visual signal, a flash of light. From this basis, they have built up a remarkably efficient system of signals for mating purposes.[21] As many as a dozen species may be active at the same time of night, each readily distinguished by its manner of flashing. Some have long flashes, others shorter ones. Some twinkle and others are steady, and some have a pattern of successive flashes like a lighthouse lamp (fig. 3). One species, *Photinus pyralis*, has been particularly carefully studied.[22] At mating time the male flies around giving a short flash at regular intervals. The female climbs a blade of grass and remains there, flashing in reply to any male who signals nearby. How she recognizes his flashes is still not known, but

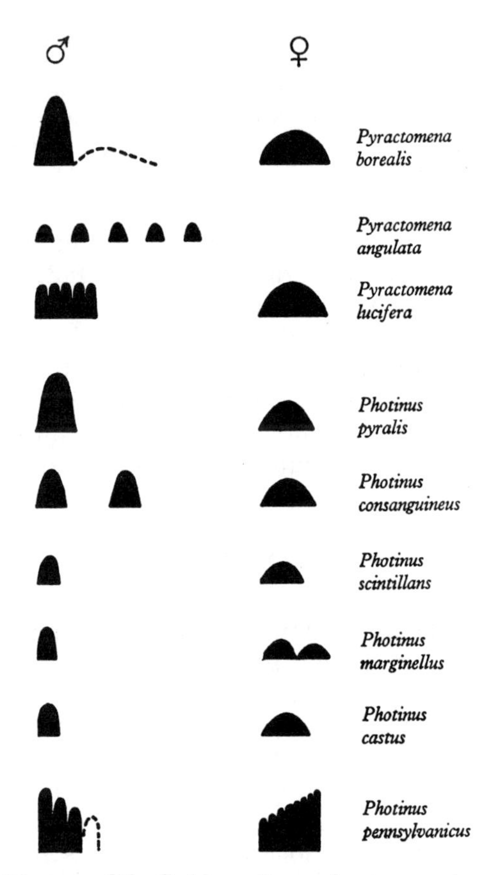

Fig. 3. Diagrams of the flashing patterns of various species of firefly. The height of each mark is roughly proportional to light intensity, the length to duration. (After McDermot.[21])

it may be because of the regular interval of about 5.8 seconds. Her response is to flash back at the male just 2 seconds afterwards, and this time interval is critical. A male has no response to other males' signals, but will approach lights of all sizes, colours and durations that flash 2 seconds after he does. These flashes are exchanged between the male and female as he approaches, until he is near enough to mate with her. In the crucial experiment, males were made to flash 2 seconds after another male by pinching them, and they were tracked down just as though they were females.

Besides being easy to locate, visual signals have many other

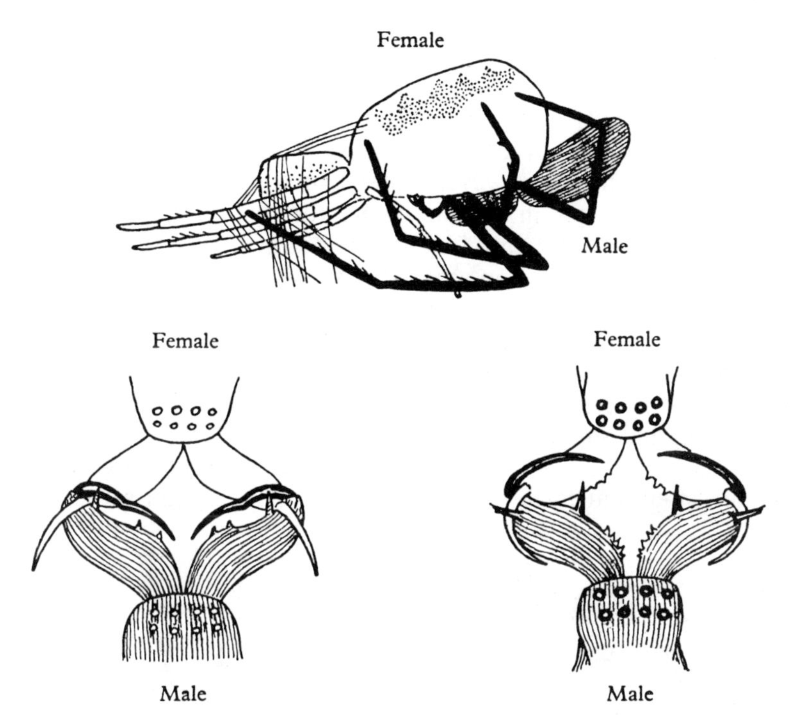

Fig. 4. The courtship of spiders. Above, the male *Xysticus lanio* copulates with his female, after fastening her down with threads. Below, the methods by which males of species of *Pathygnatha* (left) and *Tetragnatha* (right) interlock their jaws with those of the female. (After Bristowe.[24])

advantages. They are easy to produce, they can easily be turned on and off, and under the right conditions they can be received at considerable distances. However, some animals can only see detail at close range, if at all, and this has inevitable effects on their social communication.

Most spiders are short-sighted, and have to rely mainly on the senses of smell, taste and touch to identify each other. When the male approaches the female there is considerable danger that she will treat him as prey. He has to go to considerable lengths to prevent this by advancing very carefully and announcing his approach in various ways. He may jerk on her web with a particular rhythm,[23] he may stroke her, or even rush in and interlock her jaws with his own. In another species the male goes so far as to tie the female down with web, once he has subdued her (fig. 4). All of these methods of mollifying the female tend to take a long time and are not a little dangerous for the male. They seem to be made necessary by the difficulties of identification among these short-sighted spiders.

Some hunting spiders have much better vision, and their behaviour differs in many ways. Instead of waiting for their prey to enter a web, they go in search of it, running to within jumping distance and then pouncing. They can identify prey quite well by vision alone, and can be seen scanning over an object with their eyes, assessing its size. Similarly, during courtship, they have little difficulty in identifying each other at a distance, for they have evolved all kinds of elaborate movements and colours by which the males announce their species and sex (fig. 5). They avoid the risks that short-sighted spiders have to face.[24]

Again, among the insects, many have to rely on communication by smell and taste in finding mates, often because their eyes

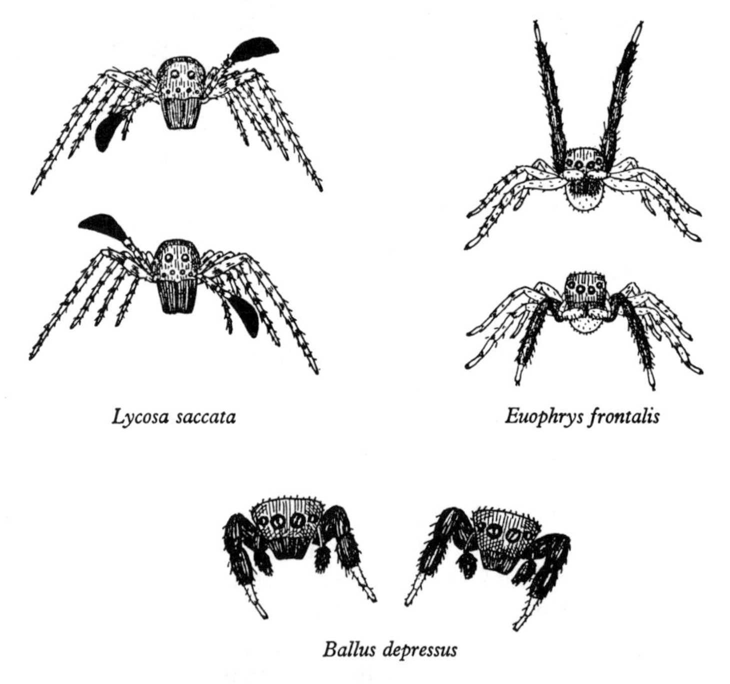

Fig. 5. The courtship of spiders with good vision. The males display in this fashion before the female by semaphore signals with the palps or forelegs, or by dancing to and fro. (After Bristowe.[24])

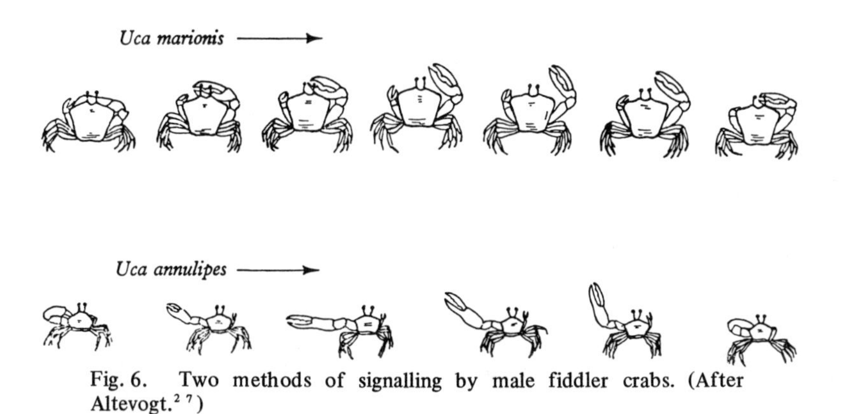

Fig. 6. Two methods of signalling by male fiddler crabs. (After Altevogt.[27])

are not very good or because they are nocturnal. Nevertheless, some day-flying insects, such as some butterflies, have an elaborate type of colour vision,[25] and quite elaborate visual signals may occur.

As in spiders, the most highly developed insect eyes occur in the more adventurous predators, such as dragonflies, and probably for this reason they rely strongly on vision in finding mates. At the other extreme we find such insects as the pond skater, *Gerris*, which uses chemical signals in finding a mate, and the Colorado beetle, *Liptinotarsa*, which seems to have no direct means of finding a mate at all, the sexes meeting fortuitously. The male even has to find which are the female's front and rear ends by trial and error.[26]

Although the eyes of many lower animals are not well-suited to form vision, they can readily detect movement. This is fully exploited in the communication of spiders, butterflies and dragonflies, and we find similar developments in some Crustacea. Best known are the little fiddler crabs which occur on the sea-shore in many parts of the world. One claw is larger than the other, and the males of each species have a characteristic way of waving it in the air which attracts females and in some cases repels males.[27] It is striking that species living together all wave in a different way, immediately revealing their identity to an experienced observer (fig. 6). Some are distinguished by the direction in which the claw is moved, some by the speed of movement and others by tilting or rocking of the body. There is also a relation between the pattern of movement and the colours of the body and claws, so that the former is made as conspicuous as possible.

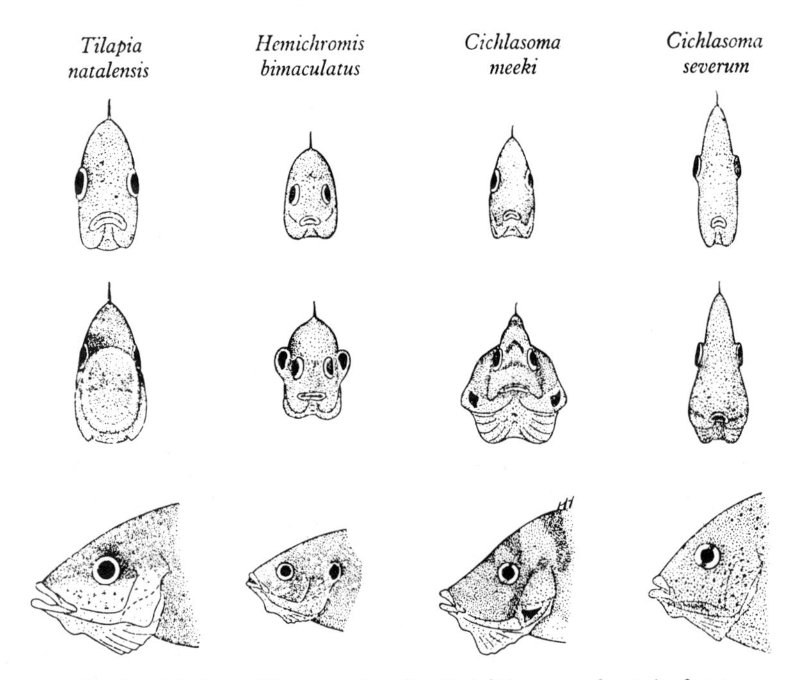

Fig. 7. Displays of four species of cichlid fishes, seen from the front and the side. Note how the visual effects are enhanced by the markings on the gill covers. (After Baerends and Baerends-van Roon.[31])

In the study of visual communication in higher animals, there are many difficulties in imitating natural forms and movements well enough to induce animals to react to models. One solution is to disguise living animals. Both methods have been tried with lizards and fish. Some lizards will respond simply to coloured Plasticene models. In species with a dull female and a blue-throated male, disguising the female with blue paint will immediately cause her mate to attack her as though she were a male.[28] Similarly among fish, the male three-spined stickleback will attack very simple models of a fish, provided that they carry the male's red underside.[29] With live jewel fish, Noble and Curtis[30] exploited the fact that the red colour of a reproductive male can be induced in a female by the injection of a drug. This red colour serves as a signal to the female; if given a choice between two males at spawning time, she selects the one with the brighter colour. Similarly, she will also respond to a red-induced female.

Sometimes the mode of behaviour of the partner is more important than colour in the visual communication of fish. Males may distinguish between the sexes solely by the way in which they respond to attack or aggressive display, other males replying with aggression, and females with a different 'inferiority' response.[31] In these exchanges between the sexes, a complete range of movements and postures is used, each playing a different role in courtship or defence of the territory (fig. 7).

Birds generally respond to models much less readily because their usually incessant movement is impossible to imitate. However, when the females of many species are ready to copulate they take up a special posture and keep quite still, while the male approaches and mounts. This is a signal we can easily represent with models, and many male birds are so completely deceived that they will mount and even deposit semen (fig. 8).

When movement is involved, we can only experiment with living animals in disguise. This method has hardly been explored yet but has great possibilities. Another pioneer, Cinat Tomson,[32] applied it to the budgerigar. The female seems to choose a mate at least partly by the spots on his collar. Given a choice between one with small spots and another with artificially large spots, applied with paint, she selects the latter. Another important signal is the cere above the bill, which is blue in males and brown in females. If a female's cere is painted blue, her mate immediately attacks her as though she were a rival male.

Fig. 8. The posture of a female chaffinch soliciting for copulation. On the right is a male, mating with a stuffed model of a female. (From photographs, after Marler.[59])

In another sexually dimorphic species, the chaffinch, the female is greenish brown, while the male has, among other things, a reddish breast. Just as in budgerigars, females disguised as males, in this case simply by staining the breast feathers with red ink, are treated as though they were males. In the winter flock, male chaffinches dominate females in the social hierarchy. Red-painted females, on the other hand, dominate other females, and may even win some fights with males.[33]

In both of these examples the colours are on display more or less permanently. The most that can be done to remove the signal is to turn in another direction, so that the colour is hidden. If the colours fall on the wings or tail or other mobile feathers, more subtle methods of concealment and display are possible. The chaffinch's wings carry two white bars, which can be concealed by the flank feathers, or exposed by raising the wing. With intermediate stages between complete exposure and concealment, a continuously varied gradation of display is possible, a development of great importance in communication (fig. 9).

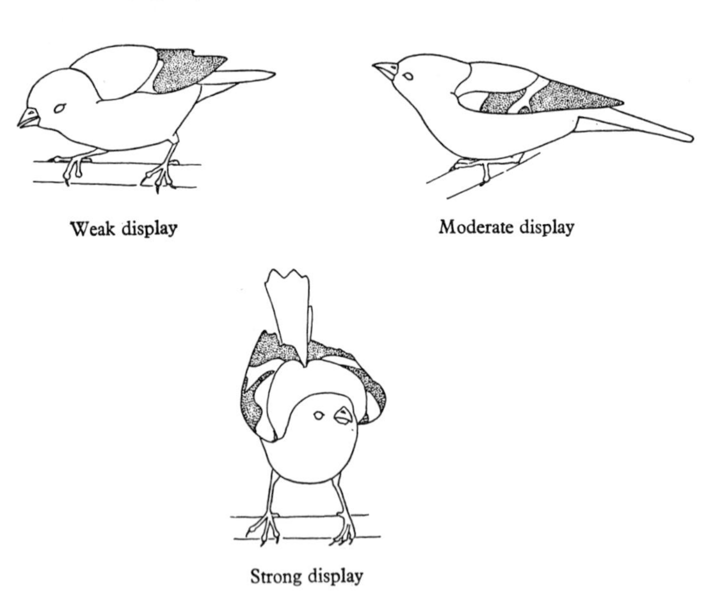

Fig. 9. Three chaffinch threat postures of increasing intensity. Note the continuous gradations of the movements of the feathers and wings. (From photographs, after Marler.[59])

Many visual signals appear in an all-or-nothing way. That is to say, each is usually true to one type and seldom grades into other signals.[34] Chaffinches have about eight special visual displays. Some of these, like the courtship displays, are either shown completely or not at all. And if we consider their communicatory function, this fits with the requirements, for a bird is either ready for courtship and mating or not.

In fighting the circumstances are different. Here each opponent is repeatedly faced with the question whether to withdraw or to press the attack. Rather than a single constant display, it is more useful to have two, grading into each other, one associated with fear, the other with aggression. In this way the slight changes in a bird's confidence as it advances and retreats are immediately manifest in its signals, and so communicated to its opponent. We can see this exchange in the close-range fighting of chaffinches in winter, and also more noticeably in the 'head-up' display with which males defend their territory. In early spring a male is commonly seen driving an opponent back with vigorous, confident display. As he advances across the boundary, elements gradually drop out of his display, to be replaced by others. When finally he gets too far into his neighbour's territory, he hesitates, his rival takes his chance and drives him back again. In this fashion the two males may spend half an hour going to and fro across the boundary.

The effectiveness with which these graded displays communicate subtle changes in mood depends on how many different changeable elements there are. The function required of the aggressive displays of chaffinches is relatively simple, and the number of transitional changes through which they pass is small. The more complex the function becomes, the more elaborate we may expect the transitions to be.

In the visual displays of the black-headed gull, Moynihan[35] discovered transitions between not just two, but several types. Here there may be several complete changes from one type to another as the relative degrees of fear and aggression change (fig. 10). As a result, slight changes of the bird's mood are registered with extraordinary accuracy. Yet even this is not the sum of the black-headed gull's visual signals. There are probably at least seven more, giving an approximate total of at least twelve, with many transitions. An equally elaborate visual language occurs in some

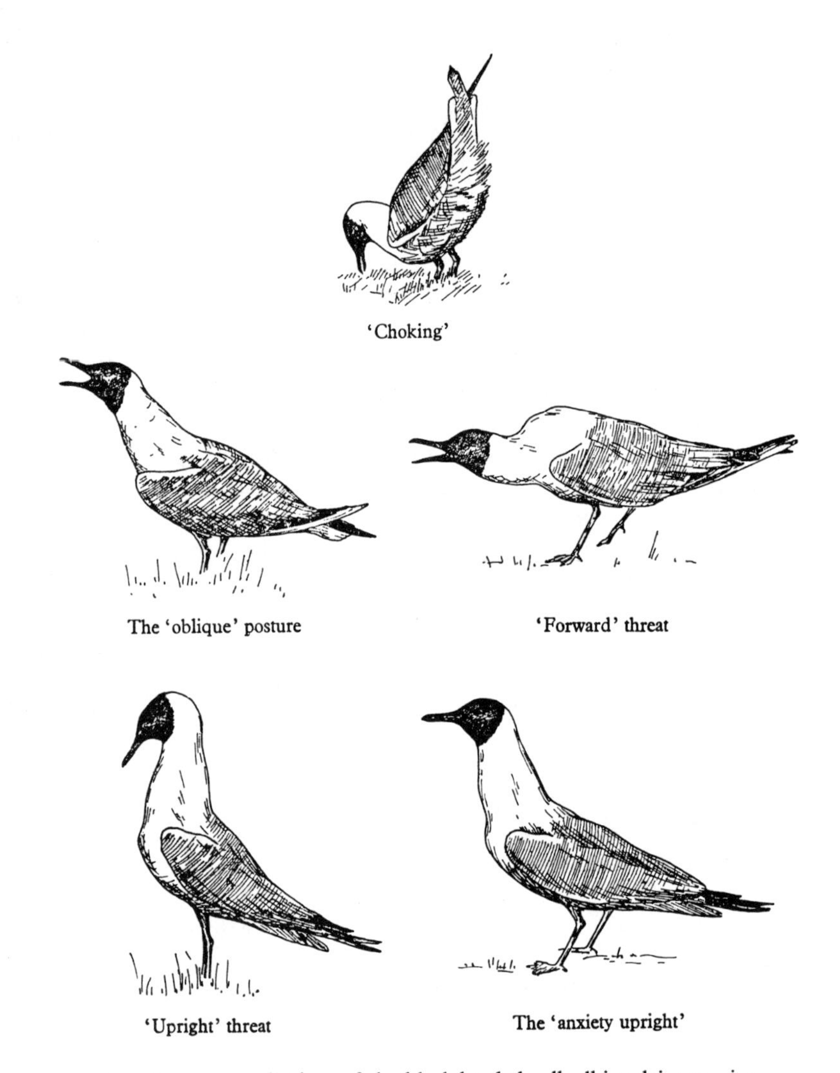

Fig. 10. Some displays of the black-headed gull, all involving varying degrees of conflict between aggressiveness and fear. Aggressiveness is relatively stronger in the postures on the left. The 'upright' and the 'anxiety upright' are associated with moderately strong aggression and fear, increasing in the 'oblique' and 'forward' postures, and reaching a maximum in 'choking'. Several of the phases grade into each other, providing continuous series of visual signals. (After Moynihan.[35])

ducks. The common mallard has at least twelve visual signals and probably more, with again many transitions which can be correlated with mood.[36]

The head and face seem to be the most important of all the parts of the body used in visual communication, perhaps partly because they can be fully exposed to the opponent while still keeping him in full view. Not only can the way in which animals look at each other be very expressive, but also the head often carries the main fighting weapons. In many species the face plays an important role in another aspect of social communication, namely individual recognition. Disguise of either a chicken or a jewel fish on the head is much more likely to prevent familiar individuals from recognizing each other than alteration of any other part of the body,[37] and Nice[38] has listed numerous other examples. This is of course especially true of ourselves.

Darwin's interest in communication largely centred on mammals, and facial expressions received much attention, especially those of dogs, cats, apes and man. The tendency to nocturnal habits in this group discourages any great development of visual communication. As Schloeth[39] has recently pointed out, the first act of many of them on meeting for the first time is to smell or lick at the nose, or the anal and genital regions (fig. 11). Nevertheless, visual signals do occur. The hamster has at least six displays,[40] and in the wolf there are many more.

The special communicatory movements of many mammals, such as ungulates, are largely confined to the ears and tail.[41] The general body posture often plays a part as well,[42] but only in animals with a more highly developed social behaviour, such as some carnivores,[43] does the face come to play a dominant role (fig. 12).

As in birds, the greatest development of communication signals occurs in mammals with a complex society. Wolves, for example, exist in highly organized groups with many communal activities. From the careful studies of Schenkel[44] we know that they use at least twenty-one communicatory signals, of which fifteen probably involve some visual elements, the others being olfactory and tactile. They take many forms, and the face is particularly expressive. Eyes, ears, mouth and the creases of the face all co-operate to give a remarkable variety of displays, aided by the

Fig. 11. Two stages in the meeting of male and female Grant zebras. First the naso-nasal contact, then the naso-genital contact. (After Schloeth.[39])

patterns of marks on the fur (fig. 13). Just as in the black-headed gull, these signals give a precise means of communicating subtle changes in mood.

When complex social habits are associated with a high intelligence, as in chimpanzees and ourselves, this trend of development may reach even further. Facial expressions become supremely important, and creases and hair tracts emphasize the disposition of the muscles. Here again expressions associated with different moods are not sharply demarcated, but grade into each other. Furthermore, in her remarkable studies on chimpanzees reared by hand, Kohts[45] has shown that there are many elements shared by several expressions (fig. 14), a conclusion also suggested by studies of human

Fig. 12. Variations in the bodily and facial expressions of cats. In each section, aggressiveness increases to the right and fear increases downward, to give a continuously graded series of signals which is ideally suited to communicate subtle changes in mood. (After Leyhausen.[43])

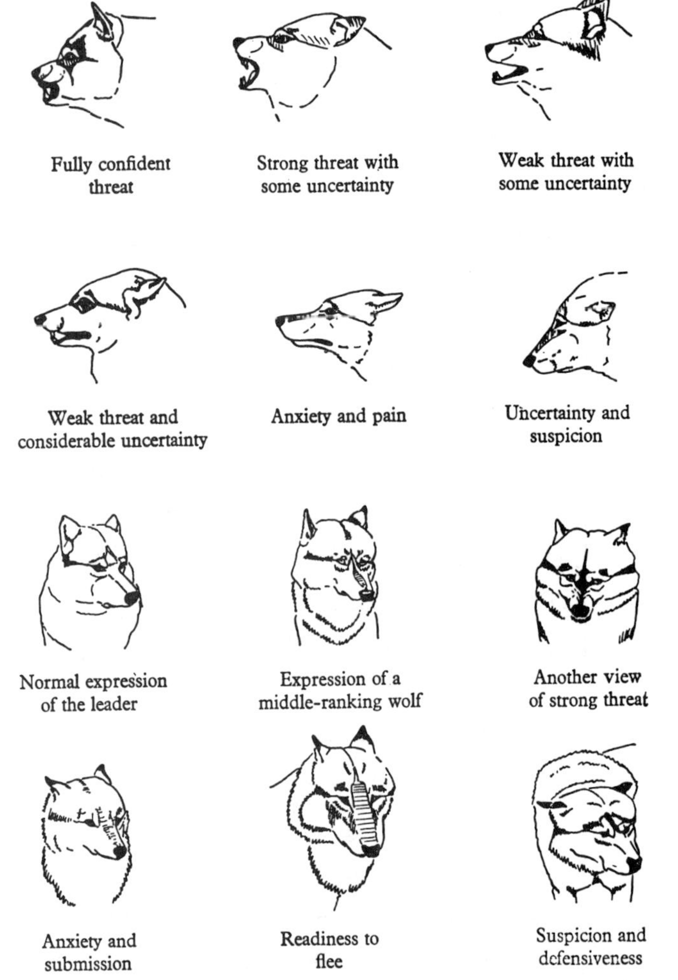

Fig. 13. Facial expressions of wolves. Slight changes in mood are accompanied by many variations, especially in the position of the ears, mouth and eyes, the changes emphasized by marks on the face. (After Schenkel.[44])

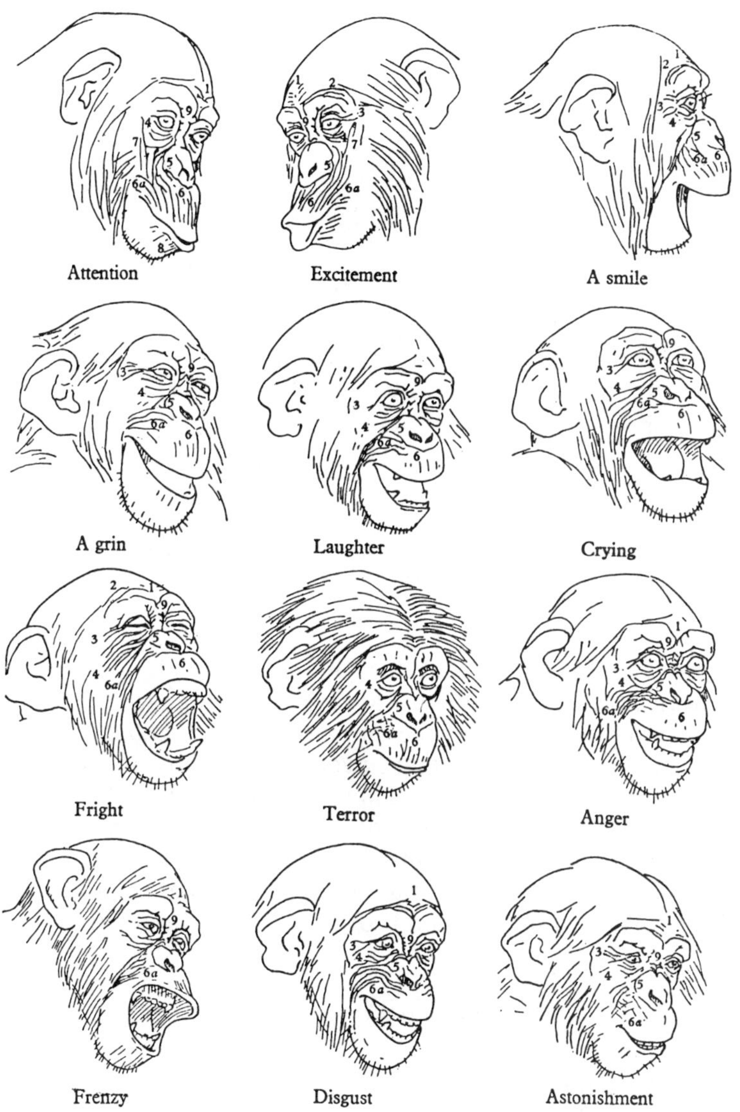

Fig. 14. Facial expressions of a young chimpanzee in various moods. Some of the creases are marked with numbers to emphasize that each is by no means confined to one expression. (After Kohts.[45])

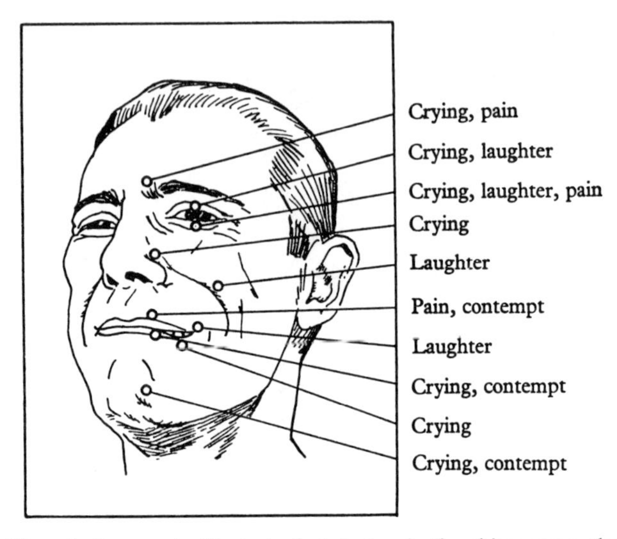

Fig. 15. A diagram to illustrate that, just as in the chimpanzee, the same fold or wrinkle in the human face may be involved in several expressions. (After Frois-Wittmann.[46])

expression (fig. 15).[46] This in turn helps to explain a point which Darwin noticed, that when people are asked to judge what emotion is portrayed in a photograph of the human face, they make a surprising number of errors. There is a great deal of ambiguity in expressions, so that some of them must be seen in their full context before they can be understood. The recognition of human expressions is thus an elaborate process, and it seems likely that visual signals are as important and as complex in man as in any animal, a fact which is sometimes forgotten in discussions of human communication.

AUDITORY COMMUNICATION

Communication by sounds presents a new set of problems, particularly with regard to production. Certain animals can make use of sounds which arise incidentally from some other function of the body. In some mosquitoes, the noise made by the female serves as a signal to the male, who hears it by means of his specially adapted antennae, which resonate to this particular note.[47] But in most species which communicate by sound, special apparatus has been developed for its production. In vertebrates this is generally associated with the respiratory apparatus, since air columns, enclosed in more or less dense tissues, form ideal resonating chambers, which can be set in vibration by a flow of air.

This method is hardly practicable for insects, though it has been suggested that the piping of a queen honey-bee may arise through vibrations induced in the air in the trachea.[48] Instead many of them have developed devices for producing sound by friction, which sets resonating surfaces in vibration.[49] There is another unique method, developed by the cicadas, which has recently been explored by Pringle.[50] A pair of drums or tymbals is set in vibration by special musculature. Under their influence the tymbals buckle and then click back at a high rate to produce a loud buzzing sound, a large tracheal air cavity beneath each acting as a resonator.

Fish have also solved the problem of sound production in a variety of ways. Some again revert to a kind of stridulation, grinding their teeth or vibrating some part of the skeleton against another.[51] The sculpin, for example, is able to produce a low-pitched hum by vibration of bones in the neck.[52] The resonating chamber is provided by the air bladder. It may be set in vibration by muscles in the wall, or by squirting air from one part of the bladder to another through a constriction. The trigger fish goes even further by beating an external membrane with the pectoral fins. As a result of these various devices, the sea is full of grunting, booming, croaking, crackling, whistling and buzzing sounds, a fact only realized since the last world war, through the investigation of marine sounds for military purposes.[53]

Our main concern is not with methods of sound production, but with the nature of the signals produced. Before we can consider this, it is necessary to review some of the fundamentals of sound and of hearing. The rate of passage of a sound wave varies with the nature of the medium; water is ideal for this purpose, transmitting sound four times more quickly than air. A given sound signal will thus also travel further in water, and it is hardly surprising that fish should have exploited the many possibilities which this situation presents.

Any sound wave has two basic properties, one the displacement of the particles or molecules of the medium, the other the change of pressure with which this is associated. While the ears of vertebrates are adapted to perceive the pressure change, those of insects register particle displacement, and this difference has far reaching effects on the ways in which sounds are heard. Consider the process involved in the most elementary function of sound signals, enabling two animals to find each other when other senses are not available as, for example, in an opaque environment. Sound location is achieved in quite different ways with the two types of ears.

Particle displacement necessarily involves direction, and this fact can be exploited in order to find the sound source. The hearing organ of a grasshopper will respond much more strongly when it is placed at right angles to the direction of a sound than when in line with it. So all that the grasshopper needs to do is to turn to and fro, listening to the sound intensity in various directions. Although it can do this with only one hearing organ, it normally uses two, and since these are directed towards the sides of the animal it only needs to steer along the line of weaker stimulation to find the source of the sound.[54] It will be obvious that, since any sound involves particle displacement, grasshoppers can locate sounds of all types equally efficiently, as long as they are within the audible range.

For vertebrates the situation is quite different. The source of a sound striking a hearing organ which responds only to pressure cannot be so easily located. An ear separated from the head would respond equally strongly however it was placed in the field of sound. The nearest approach to the method used by insects is when the head prevents the sound reaching one ear and the direction from which the sound comes is judged by the changes in intensity as the head is moved. However, this is at best an inaccurate method and normally location of sound in vertebrates relies on comparison between the stimulation of the ears on each side of the head.

A difference in the stimulation may come about in three ways. First, the head may hinder the sound from reaching one ear, resulting in a sharp difference in intensity at the two ears, from which the direction of the sound can be inferred. Secondly, if the sound comes from one side of the head, there will be a time difference between arrival at the two ears. This is very brief, but nevertheless can be perceived. Finally, there may also be a difference of phase at the two ears—that is to say the rapid changes of pressure making up the sound will occur at different moments in the two ears, and this again can give information about the direction of the sound. We can show that in contrast with insects, the detailed characteristics of a sound have a considerable effect on the efficiency of these different methods of location.[55]

Consider sound intensity at the two ears. The head acts as an obstruction in the sound field, placing the ear farthest from the source in a kind of sound shadow. However, Lord Rayleigh showed long ago that this shadowing only becomes appreciable when the obstruction is of the same order of size as the sound wavelength, or larger. In ourselves this effect only becomes appreciable with quite high-pitched notes, about an octave above the highest note of a violin. So for low-pitched sounds, this method is of little use in location.

With phase difference the reverse is true, this method being confined to low-pitched sounds. There are two reasons for this. Ambiguity arises when the wavelength is less than the distance between the ears, differences of phase becoming difficult to interpret because several oscillations may succeed before a given wave reaches the further ear. The other reason concerns the characteristics of the nerve leading from the ear, which carries only a one-to-one representation of the sound oscillations when the sound is low-pitched. After each oscillation, the nerve is unresponsive for about a thousandth of a second. So if there are more than a thousand vibrations per second in the sound, some of them are not represented by impulses in the nerve. So once again comparisons of phase will break down with sounds pitched above this critical value. In man, the limit tends to be between 1 and 2 kilocycles per second, and may be somewhat higher in birds.

The last method, relying on time difference, is unaffected by sound pitch, as long as it is within the audible range. However, it is affected by the way in which the sound starts and ends. To compare accurately the time of arrival, it is essential that there should be sharp discontinuities which can be perceived at the two ears. So a short repetitive sound will be most readily located. If we combine this with the requirements of the other two methods of location, we can derive the ideal sound needed for a vertebrate to find its source. It will include a high pitch for location by intensity difference, a low pitch for location by phase difference, and it will be sharply broken and repetitive for location by time difference.

While sounds which insects produce for locating each other need no special characteristics, in vertebrates we may expect them to find direct adaptations for this purpose. Obvious examples are the songs of birds. Many of these serve to help females locate a mate and to enable males to keep rivals from their territory.[56] In both cases, ease of localization is an advantage, and we can show that the great majority of the songs of small birds tend to conform to this ideal. The same is true of many of the calls which birds produce.

When small birds discover an owl roosting during the day, they start mobbing it conspicuously, attracting the residents from quite a wide area. It appears that the function of this behaviour is to alert others to the possibility of danger at this particular place, and once again any calls used need to be readily locateable. Many ornithologists will have noticed that these mobbing calls often have a ticking or clucking quality, involving just those characteristics which are needed for easy location. One could list many other calls with adaptations in this direction.

It is also the experience of ornithologists that some bird calls are exceedingly difficult to locate, and it was the writer's encounter with this, in the call given by a male chaffinch when a hawk flies over, which first suggested the importance of questions of sound location. If we return again to this subject for a moment, it will be evident that it is possible to design a sound which presents the maximum difficulty for localization. First, the clues for time difference can be eliminated by using a longer sound which starts and ends gradually without any sudden discontinuities or breaks. Secondly, the pitch may be narrowed down to a particular level, somewhere above the value at which location by phase difference breaks down, but below the point where intensity differences become appreciable.

It has been shown that in ourselves this intermediate zone occurs around four octaves above middle C,[57] and notes pitched in this region are quite difficult to locate. If there is a similar weakness in sound location by hawks and owls, it could be of considerable value for small birds to exploit this. There seems every reason to think that they are affected in the same way. Their heads are smaller than ours, with the ears closer together, both increasing the difficulties of sound location. Probably the refractory period of the auditory nerve prevents the one advantage they might otherwise have, of being able to use phase difference location for higher-pitched sounds. And even if they are more sensitive to intensity

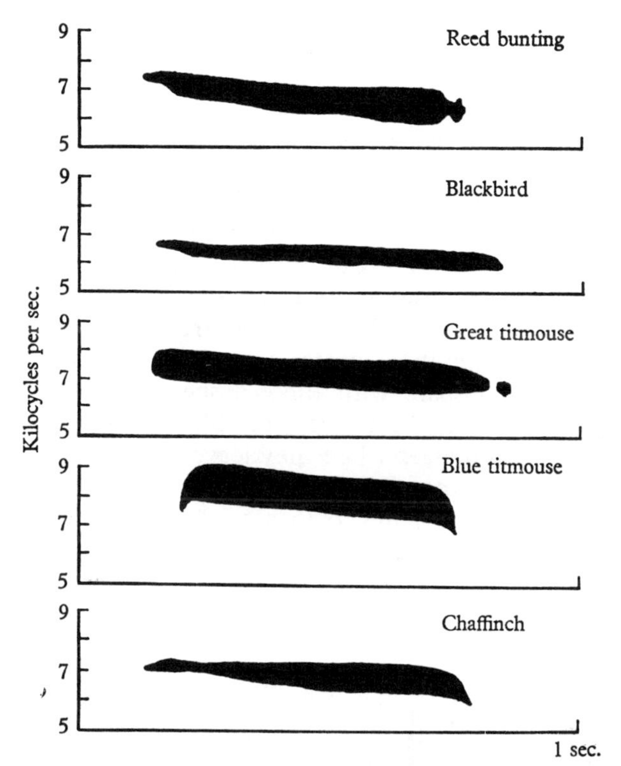

Fig. 16. The calls of five different species given when a hawk flies over. Each has a relatively narrow frequency range, somewhat overemphasized in this and all other illustrations of sonagrams, as a result of the use of wide-band pass filters. They all sound like a high, thin whistle, and are difficult to locate.

differences, which Schwartzkopff[58] has shown to be the case in song birds, there must still be a zone of minimum efficiency.

Study of calls given by various song birds, including the chaffinch, when a hawk flies over, have precisely the structure we have predicted, namely a high-pitched pure tone, beginning and ending gradually, sounding rather like the squeak of a finger on glass (fig. 16). We must conclude that these small birds have evolved a call for this particular situation that is capable of warning others of their peril while at the same time exposing themselves to a minimum of danger. Even though small birds must also have difficulty in locating this call, this is no disadvantage, for their immediate response is to fly to the nearest cover, irrespective of the direction of the call or of the hawk.[59]

We can imagine other contexts in which this type of call would be useful. Consider for example the plight of some young birds when they first leave the nest. They can hardly fly, and are extremely vulnerable to predators, yet they need a call to communicate with the parent when they are hungry. Provided that the adults can remember where the young are placed and so do not need a call to guide them, this is a circumstance in which the 'unlocateable' call can be used. The young of various species certainly have notes which we ourselves find difficult to locate—the wren for example. On the other hand, if we compare with these a species whose young can remain longer in the nest before leaving, like the hole-nesting great tit, and so are in less danger when they leave, we find that the call is easily located. It is even possible that the calls of the more vulnerable small rodents will be difficult to locate, though it is striking that shrews, somewhat protected by their repellent taste and smell, can easily be tracked down by their calls (fig. 17).

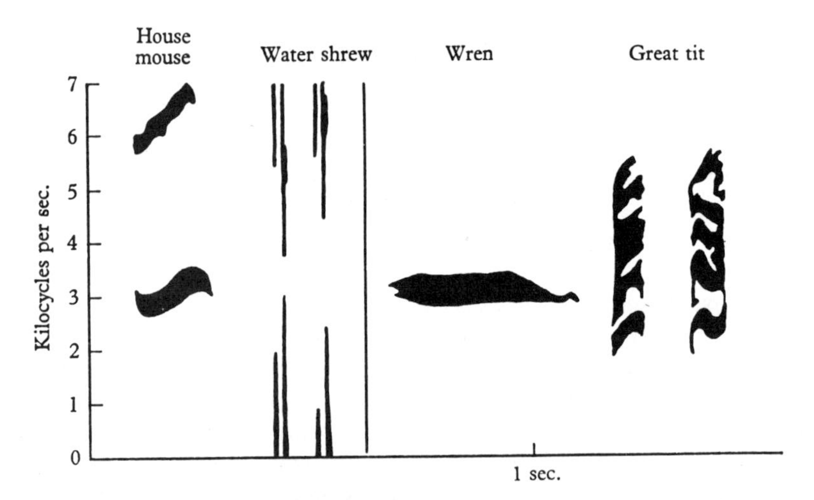

Fig. 17. A comparison of a house-mouse squeak and the chirp of a water-shrew, the first difficult to locate accurately, the second quite easy. On the right is a similar comparison of the calls of a newly fledged young wren and a great tit. Again the latter is easy to locate and the former is difficult, perhaps connected with the wren's greater vulnerability when it leaves the nest.

It is also a familiar human experience that many grasshoppers are difficult to track down by their songs. As has already been pointed out, the 'displacement' hearing organs of insects locate sound sources in a different way from vertebrate ears, and the efficiency is unaffected by the frequency of the sound, as long as it is audible. Insects therefore are freer than vertebrates in their choice of frequency. It is interesting to note that most of them, nevertheless, lie between about 6 and 14 kilocycles per second.[60] In the absence of breaks to serve as time clues, this is probably a quite difficult frequency range for those birds which prey on grasshoppers to locate. One may speculate on the possibility that some insect songs are adapted so that they are both easy for insects to track down, and difficult for vertebrates. It is noteworthy, too, that crickets, with songs which are often broken and lower-pitched, around 2 to 4 kilocycles per second and therefore easier to locate, are largely crepuscular and nocturnal. Because of this, and their cryptic and often subterranean habits, they may be less exposed to predators than some other species.

Another curious characteristic of insect hearing, discovered by Pumphrey,[61] is that, except with low-pitched notes, there is no response to the frequency of the sound. Instead they are adjusted to be sensitive to variations in the volume or amplitude. This has important implications when we consider the function of insect songs, which, like that of bird songs, is important in helping the sexes to find each other for mating. It is a prerequisite for such signals that they must differ distinctively from species to species, to avoid the possibility of confusion. Since sound frequency is not directly perceived, the specificity must lie in some other characteristic, and the pattern of amplitude variation is the obvious choice. There are two lines of evidence to suggest that this is the case. Comparative study of the songs of insects shows that there are more conspicuous differences between species' songs in the pulse pattern than in any other characteristic.[62] Haskell, for example, finds that in two very closely related bugs, *Kleidocerys resedae* and *K. ericae*, the pulse rate of one is eight per second, the other sixteen per second. The same is true of grasshopper songs[63] and also of cicada songs, as Pringle has recently demonstrated.[64] Here the various species exploit a wide range of variations, as they need to if each is to be distinguished without confusion.

Another line of evidence comes from experiments on the recognition of artificial sounds by insects. Various workers have shown that responses can be evoked by a variety of sounds produced mechanically, electrically or by mouth, often sounding to our ears quite different from the song they are supposed to imitate. In each case, it does not seem to matter which frequency is used, as long as the pattern of amplitude variation is true to type.[65]

These observations imply that there must be a strong selection pressure favouring specific distinctiveness in these communication signals concerned with reproduction. There is also good evidence for this in birds. Ornithologists are familiar with the tendency for birds living together to have distinctive songs. In at least one case this has given the first clue to taxonomic separation, for Gilbert White[66] first distinguished three species of warbler on the basis of their song.

THE EVOLUTION OF BIRD SONG

The possible effects of natural selection on bird calls would no doubt have received Darwin's attention, had he had the technical assistance which is available to us. We can still look to him for the kind of approach to adopt. In most cases our evidence can only be indirect, but we can learn a great deal from comparative study on the one hand, and from the study of variation on the other. There is obviously no direct evidence from the fossil record, but Darwin pointed out that domestication can sometimes give us information equally valuable, if we regard natural selection as represented by the animal breeder's conscious or unconscious selection of his breeding stock.

By a lucky chance we have one example of the domestication of bird song. Canaries have been bred in captivity in Germany at least from the sixteenth century. Since that time they have been transformed into a great variety of shapes and colours hardly identifiable with the greenish brown ancestor from the Canary Islands. There was also a great interest in bird song at this time, and, as an offshoot from the main stock, there arose a special breed, the roller canary, selected largely or entirely for its singing capabilities. To this day they are still matched in singing contests, championships being awarded to those which best satisfy the current fashion.

We can compare the song of the roller canary with both the wild canary and the border canary, the latter one of the breeds which has been selected for other characters. The first thing we notice is the resemblance between the wild and border canary songs. The only major difference between these two is the absence from the latter of the jumbled dissonant phrases which occur in the middle of the song of the wild bird. These are sufficiently harsh to the ear that we might expect even the fancier indifferent to song to eliminate them from his stock. Apart from this there are few consistent differences between the two, though of course both vary a great deal in detail.

Roller canary song, however, is very different from the other two. The pitch is lowered, the time pattern is transformed into long repetitive trills, the quality changed from the fluid notes of the wild and border canaries into harder sounds, sometimes with an almost metallic quality. This transformation is as great as any which Darwin describes in the form and plumage of doves or poultry, and it seems equally justifiable to conclude that bird song is also susceptible to change under the influence of selection.

The other prerequisite for evolution to occur is a certain degree of variation upon which selection can operate. With the signals of visual and chemical communication, variation is difficult to detect, since they cannot easily be described in quantitative terms. For sound signals this difficulty can be overcome with the aid of modern analytical methods. Though little has yet been done, the results are sufficiently promising to be reviewed in detail.

When we examine the repertoires of individual birds, it is remarkable how few sing exactly the same theme all the time. In Europe, perhaps the wood pigeon does, but this cannot be said of any of the song birds which the author has yet examined. The most monotonous and stereotyped singers among the warblers are perhaps the willow and wood warblers and the lesser whitethroat, but study reveals several themes for each bird. The corn bunting seemed at first to be an extreme example, but even here variations were discovered, though they could not easily be detected by ear.

In fact it almost seems to be a rule that these simple singers have several themes given in bursts, first of one theme, then of another. Typical European examples are the yellow bunting and the chaffinch, each individual having a repertoire of up to six songs. Among a total of seventy-one chaffinches, the mean number of songs per bird was 2.3. Many North American birds sing in the same way,[67] one of the best known being the song sparrow. In her intensive studies of this species, Nice[68] found from six to twenty-four songs in the repertoires of individual birds. Repertoires in the Carolina wren may be even larger; one bird is reported to have sung twenty-two different songs in twenty-four bursts of singing.[69] These are surprisingly large totals when we consider that these species give a first impression of being relatively uniform singers.

When we turn to more versatile songsters the repertoires are much larger. For example, in some preliminary studies a European robin was observed to perform a series of fifty-seven songs, every one of which was different. A mistle thrush gave twenty basic themes in forty-seven songs, but the themes could be arranged in a variety of different ways. In a series of fifty-three phrases from a song thrush, the first forty-eight included only a few repeats; then number forty-nine was a repeat of number two, number fifty was like number four, fifty-one like five, fifty-two like six and fifty-three like seven: so this bird probably had rather less than fifty themes. However, another bird gave only two repeats in eighty-five songs. And in the longest series studied so far, of 203 phrases, a song thrush gave sixty repeats; nevertheless, there were still signs that the repertoire was not exhausted, as can be seen from the distribution of the repeats:

Songs	0-50	50-100	101-150	151-200
Repeats	4	13	27	16

There was evidence of the same process which takes place in the mistle thrush, namely the recombining of old themes in new arrangements. The total of themes used at least once by this bird was 173, and allowing for up to three themes in each song there is a certain economy in building up 143 different songs in this way.

It is obvious, then, that there is ample variation of song in individuals, on which natural selection might operate. In fact the variation is sometimes unexpectedly wide. Is it simply that the limits imposed by selection are not very precise, and that some birds merely exploit all the variations between those limits because there is nothing to stop them?

Another explanation is possible. There is reason to think that birds recognize the songs of individuals they know. Male chaffinches distinguish between the songs of established rivals and newcomers, and it is possible that females recognize the song of a mate from the previous year. This could confer a definite advantage, for as well as the evidence that birds experienced in breeding produce more young,[70] considerable adjustment is needed when a pair forms for the first time. For individual recognition to occur, there must be a good chance that songs of any two birds will differ in some characteristic. The larger the repertoire, the greater will be the probability of achieving this. At least this is a plausible hypothesis, helping to explain the large number of themes which many birds sing, with perhaps some bearing on individual variation in the forms and markings of animals.[71]

For communication alone, it does not matter whether these variations are genotypic, as long as they remain stable for a reasonable period of time, so that companions can learn their characteristics. Evidence accumulating in recent years reveals wide variation in the relative contribution of learning and inheritance in the development of bird songs. Some develop quite normally when the birds are reared away from their own kind, as Sauer[72] has demonstrated in the European whitethroat and blackcap, and the same applies to the blackbird,[73] the reed bunting[74] and the corn bunting.[75] Other species will develop abnormal songs when reared in this way, as Scott[76] demonstrated in the American Baltimore oriole, and Lanyon in meadowlarks.[77] But probably the intermediate condition is most common, with the broad characteristics inherited, and the details acquired in some other way. The domestic canary, the European linnet and yellow bunting[78] have songs of this type, as well as the American song sparrow[79] and the chaffinch, the subject of careful study by Thorpe.[80] In these species the young bird learns the refinements of its song from older neighbours.

However, even in a species like the chaffinch, in which young males can be observed learning from older birds in their first spring,[81] we notice that the copies are seldom quite precise, so that each bird can generally be identified by its song in subsequent years. Either it makes a imperfect copy, or what seems more likely, there is some element of improvisation. Many species which develop normal songs in isolation also show individual characteristics. In the blackbird, Messmer[82] has shown that they arise both by learning from various neighbours, and by spontaneous recombinations of old phrases. Probably something similar occurs in the song of mistle thrushes. Even the simple and stereotyped inherited songs of the corn and reed buntings vary from bird to bird, and again an element of improvisation is probably responsible, unless, perhaps, one should regard the precise details as a matter of chance. If individual song characters are one of the ultimate objectives of this development, any of these methods will suffice.

The tendency to learn songs from neighbours results in the development of local dialects in many species,[83] including, among those mentioned above, the blackbird, yellow bunting, song sparrow and the chaffinch. Here the change from one dialect to another is most clearly marked across boundaries forming barriers to movement. In some of the isolated glens of Scotland, for example, chaffinch songs form quite distinct dialects. Reasonable stability is assured, since not only is the song learned after the male first sets up territory, but he also returns to the same place in subsequent years. Furthermore, there is a tendency to reply to rivals with a song of the same type, so that songs which are uncommon in the area may fall into disuse.

While variation in song may assist individual identification, it conflicts with the need for specific identification. Here a stereotyped song is the ideal requirement, differing as distinctively as possible from those of other birds in the area. The studies of Dilger[84] and Stein[85] have demonstrated how this specific identification is achieved in North American thrushes, both from comparative study of the songs and by observing the birds' responses to sound recordings. The most distinctive characters lie in the general timing of the song, the duration of notes, and the way in which the relative pitch changes during the song. Absolute pitch seems to be less important. The same is true of the songs of European thrushes and probably of other birds such as the chaffinch.[86] Obviously the ease with which experienced ornithologists identify birds by their song also implies fairly rigid specific characteristics, even in those species with great individual variation.

It appears that the conflict between individual and specific recognition has been resolved by relegating the variation to characteristics of the song other than those which mediate specific identification. In the thrushes, the time pattern is of specific importance, while individual characters are represented rather in the details of pitch within the general pattern. In other birds the roles might be different, and this may even be true for another member of the thrush family, the small European robin. Possibly the main specific character here is the high pitch and unusual quality of the notes, for the time pattern shows much more individual variation than in some other members of the family.

If it is correct to infer that bird songs are subject to selection pressure encouraging specific distinctness, a strong mutual influence will be exerted by species which sing together. This may explain the considerable geographical variation of song which ornithologists have described,[87] since the neighbours with which a species lives may vary in different parts of its range. Unfortunately, variations of this kind are difficult to interpret, because changes in the avifauna are so complex. However, there is a comparison which can usefully be made, namely that between the songs of a species in a dense continental avifauna and those of the same species in the sparse avifauna of a small island.

Lack and Southern[88] first drew attention to the Canary Islands as a subject for such a comparison, since the fauna consists of a sparse sample of predominantly European species or genera. They suggested that differences in bird songs between Europe and Tenerife might be explained by the reduced pressure for specific distinctness in the smaller avifauna, and visits to the Azores suggested a similar situation.[89] In 1956 the author visited Tenerife with a tape recorder, and was able to compare the bird songs with their European counterparts in detail.

The songs of some species hardly vary at all. Those of the turtle dove, great spotted woodpecker, corn bunting and blackbird do not seem to be affected significantly by island conditions. Others vary considerably, and there seem to be two main types of change, some becoming simpler and more uniform, others becoming much more variable. An example of the first group is the chaffinch, which occurs in two forms on Tenerife: the blue chaffinch, restricted to the pine forests, and the Canary Island chaffinch which occurs in the laurel woodlands. As already mentioned, the European chaffinch elaborates its song considerably by learning, and an isolated bird develops only a simple one.[90] Apparently the blue chaffinch has reverted to this simpler innate song, with a 'churr' or 'buzz' at the end, instead of the more musical flourish (fig. 18). The same has

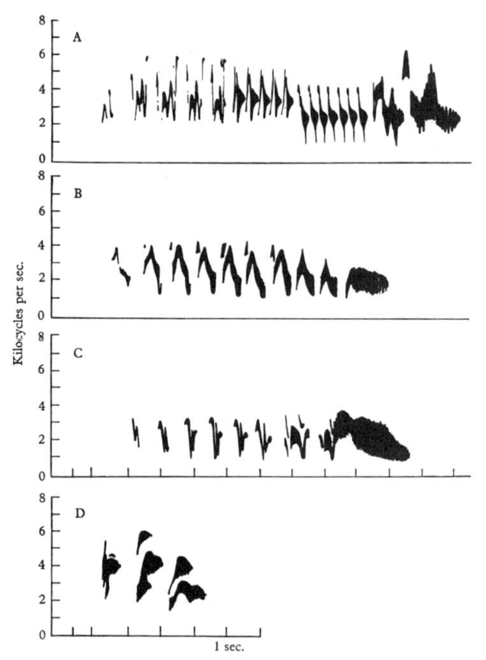

Fig. 18. Examples of chaffinch song. A is a typical song of a wild British bird. B is the song of such a bird reared out of hearing of any other chaffinch song (from experiments of W. H. Thorpe), which lacks many of the normal details. C is a song of the blue chaffinch (*Fringilla teydea*) on Tenerife. The resemblance with B is striking. D shows the 'chink' calls of a normal British chaffinch, a chaffinch reared in isolation and a Canary Island chaffinch (*Fringilla coelebs canariensis*). Again we see a resemblance between the calls of the island bird and the isolated British form.

occurred in the Canary Island chaffinch, and also in the other subspecies found in the Azores.[91] The social call of the chaffinch has met a similar fate. In Britain this call is often abnormal in isolated birds, and the Canary Island, Azores and Madeiran chaffinches all have only this innate form. It appears plausible that the smallness of the island avifauna removes the need for elaboration by learning, which takes place in Europe, and consequently the simpler and less distinctive innate forms alone occur. Yet the capacity to learn may still exist, for blue chaffinches retain slight individual characteristics in their songs.

The song of the blue titmouse shows another kind of change.

In Britain it is relatively uniform, and can easily be distinguished from the five other members of the same genus with which it lives. On Tenerife it is the only titmouse present, and has a bewildering variety of songs. Some sound more like the coal tit than any other, perhaps suggesting a closer relationship with this species than has been assumed. But the variation is very great, and the same bird may give several different songs in succession, many of them reminiscent of the songs of other species of titmouse in Britain. In the Azores, the voice of the goldcrest changes in a similar way.[91]

The chiffchaff is another case, the island bird's songs becoming more variable, sometimes sounding rather like its close relative, the willow warbler. The relationship between these two species has been of the greatest interest since Gilbert White first distinguished them by their songs. So similar are they in appearance, that the only sure way of identification apart from the song is to examine the leg colour or the wing formula. The birds themselves must rely heavily on voices for identification, which in Britain are clearly distinguishable. But where the willow warbler is absent, as on Tenerife and in southern Spain,[92] the chiffchaff's song becomes more varied, presumably because the need for a rigidly defined song pattern is reduced.

Unlike the chaffinch, the chiffchaff and the blue tit seem to be restrained from expressing their full vocal potentialities in the dense European avifauna. On Tenerife these strictures are removed, and the songs become more varied. Yet we can relate this to what happens to the chaffinch, for both types of change would involve a loss of efficiency in communication, if they took place in Europe, by hindering specific identification.

There seems to be no relationship between the tendency for song to change on islands, and the relative contributions of inheritance and learning to song development on the mainland. The corn bunting and the chiffchaff both inherit normal song in Europe, yet while the song of the former is unchanged on Tenerife, that of the latter is different. Evidently there must be plasticity in the genetic mechanism controlling chiffchaff song. While learning plays more part in the normal song of the blackbird and the blackcap than in the chiffchaff, their songs on Tenerife are not significantly changed. However, we do notice marked change in the two species in which learning plays a dominant part: the chaffinch and probably the blue tit.[93] However, our knowledge of the roles of inheritance and learning in song development is still very limited.

While discussing bird voices, it is natural that songs should receive most attention, for their function requires that they be conspicuous and distinctive. It should not be forgotten that there may be different selection pressures operating on other sound signals.[94] Consider the alarm calls of small birds discussed earlier. Here specific distinctness has been discarded altogether, and we can see that this is consistent with their function. Not only is there no advantage in having a specific call, but, if these species live together and are endangered by the same predator, there is much to be gained by having similar calls, to facilitate communication between species. This interspecific function may also affect other calls in a more subtle way. The flight calls of some finches which form mixed flocks of several species in winter are interspecific, and the same is true of the owl-mobbing calls mentioned earlier. But here the conformity is less marked (fig. 19), and this is also consistent with the fact that in other seasons and circumstances they play a part in reproduction, where some degree of specificity is an advantage.

Thus it appears that the direction in which vocal signals evolve is affected by a number of factors which can exert a selection pressure. As well as the obvious requirements of audibility, the need to avoid masking by other natural sounds, and the adaptations to facilitate or hinder localization, the relative advantages of contrast

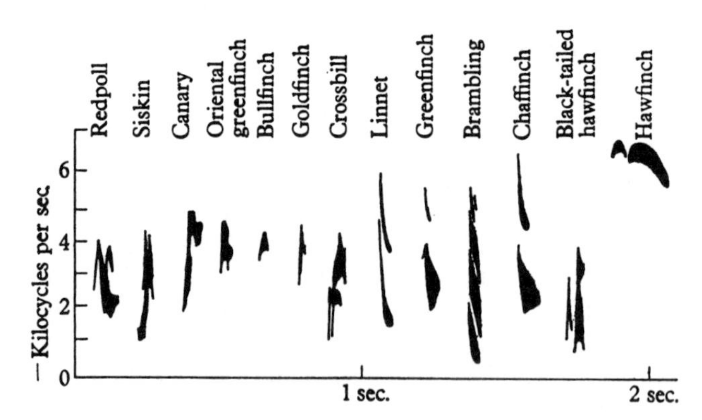

Fig. 19. The 'flight' calls of a number of finches, showing how they tend to conform to the same basic pattern, with the exception of the hawfinch.

with or resemblance to the signals of other species will vary with the function of the signal. The kind of 'sound environment' in which the signal has to operate will exert a strong influence here. The more complex this is, the more elaborate the signal has to become if it is to remain distinctive. And finally, the advantages of individual identification by voice may help to encourage the high degree of variation in some aspects, which is such a prominent characteristic of many bird songs.

There is one other method by which we can sometimes uncover clues about the evolution of sound signals, namely by study of the way in which they develop in the young bird. The chaffinch can serve as an illustration. In some respects this species is a rather divergent finch, and there has been discussion about whether it is really a close relative of the Carduelinae at all. Evidence from morphology and behaviour suggests that it is more closely related to the finches than to any other group[95] and studies of its voice support this.[96] The social and mobbing call of the chaffinch is rather unlike that of most Cardueline finches, and at first sight the gap between them is difficult to bridge (fig. 20). However, study of the development reveals a complete series of transitions, some obviously corresponding to the general finch type, from the juvenile call to that of the mature bird (fig. 21). The first call in this series, which exists only in the juvenile chaffinch, gives another clue, for it corresponds to an alarm call used in a similar form by most adult finches. The male chaffinch has instead adopted the call which is difficult to locate. Once again we can trace a developmental relationship between the original and final forms (fig. 22).

There are still other factors affecting the evolution of sound signals which have yet to be explored. The recent studies of Cullen[97] on the visual signals of the kittiwake have shown the extent to which communication methods may be modified by changes in ecology. With vocal signals, the differences between the songs of birds in open and wooded country (the former usually long and sustained, the latter short and repetitive) are so consistent that they must have significance. And it may be that body size and feeding habits affect the voice. If a bird is adjusted to a rapid metabolic turnover, and must be constantly collecting food, it cannot afford to interrupt this with long bursts of singing. Gibb[98] has pointed out that among the British titmice, the little coal tit feeds and sings at the same time, the

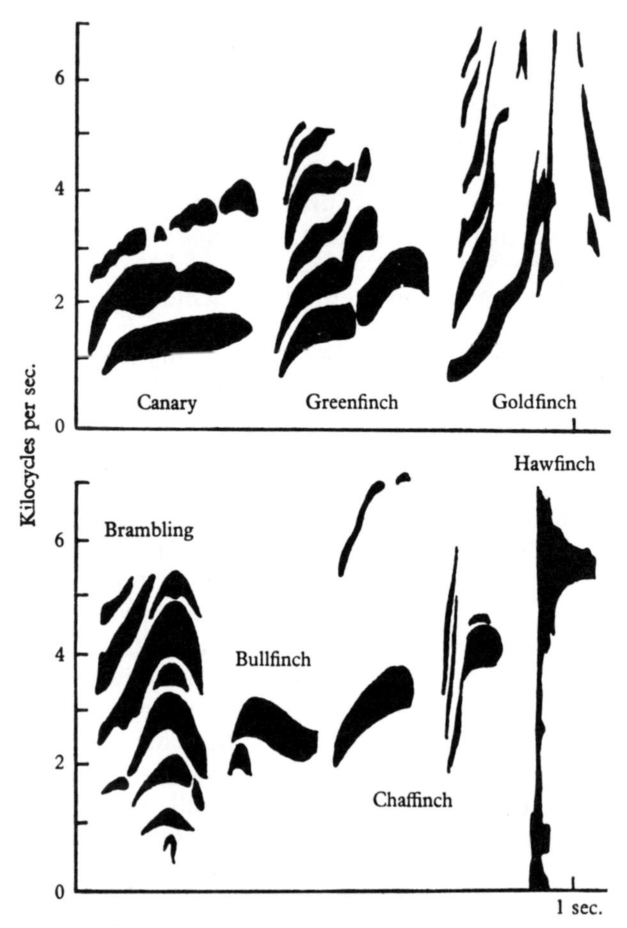

Fig. 20. The 'social' calls of various finches, all showing affinities with the same basic pattern. Those of the chaffinch and hawfinch, also used as mobbing calls, are the most divergent, but in the chaffinch at least this can be traced back to the same type (cf. fig. 21).

large blue tit sometimes stops other activities to sing, and in the still larger great tit this is the normal practice. It may be no accident that the great tit has the most elaborate vocabulary, and the coal tit perhaps the simplest. There is no doubt that many relationships will be discovered in the future between the ecology of animals and the detailed form of their communication signals.

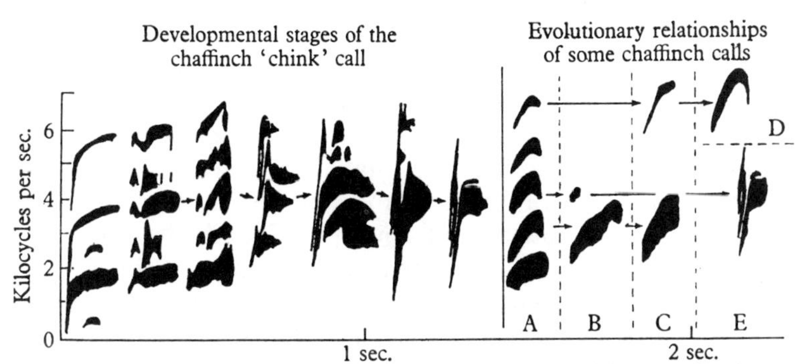

Fig. 21. On the left are shown developmental stages of the chaffinch 'chink' call, relating it to the basic finch type (fig. 30). On the right are suggested evolutionary relationships between the primitive alarm call A, used only by young chaffinches but widespread among other finches, and certain adult calls. It appears that different harmonics have been selected for the 'huit' call (C), the 'seee' hawk alarm (D; an unusual form of the call seen in fig. 17), and the 'chink' call (E). B shows an unusual form of the 'huit' call, which may correspond to an intermediate stage.

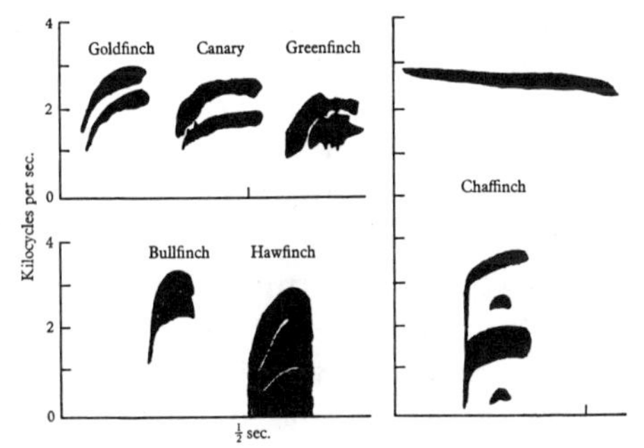

Fig. 22. Hawk alarm calls of various finches, showing the essential similarity from species to species. The chaffinch only uses this call when young (below), and in the adult male it is replaced by the type of call difficult to locate (above), which none of the other species has developed.

THE ORIGINS OF COMMUNICATION

Darwin suggested three principles governing the origin of communication signals, each of which still plays an important part in our approach to this problem to-day. The first he called the principle of associated habits. The second, the principle of antithesis, and the third, the principle of direct action, reflecting the constitution of the nervous system. Each of these coincides with ideas advanced by Lorenz,[99] Tinbergen,[100] and others, anticipating them in a remarkable way, though we can see now that Darwin was led astray in two directions. Instinctive or habitual movements, he thought, become fixed or inherited through continued practice. As he put it, 'when any sensation, desire, dislike, etc., has led during a long series of generations to some voluntary movement, then a tendency to the performance of a similar movement will almost certainly be excited whenever the same, or any analogous or associated sensation, etc., although very weak, is experienced; notwithstanding that the movement in this case may not be of the least use'. It is curious that he should have visualized a different mechanism from that proposed for the evolution of morphological characters and there is no doubt that the confusion so caused helped to dissuade subsequent workers from taking up the thread where he left off.[101]

There is also a subtle difference between the principle of antithesis and the other two which seems to have escaped his notice. It is clear that any response which has manifestations outside the animal's body is a potential communication signal, since it is capable of giving certain information to other animals. Whether natural selection encourages it in this function depends on whether the information carried has any significance for others. Thus there are two distinct problems, one concerning first origins, the other the effects of natural selection on these origins, and it is essential to keep them separate. While Darwin's first and last principles are concerned primarily with origins, the principle of antithesis, suggesting that some movements occur because they are in complete opposition or antithesis to some other attitude, is concerned with the effects of natural selection. The significance of this difference will become clearer later, when some examples have been considered.

What is known of the origins from which communication signals may have sprung? With sound signals we know very little. No doubt the stridulation of insects first arose by way of vibrating movements of the wings and other parts of the body during courtship.[102] Similarly, the sudden intake of breath of many vertebrates in alarm or pain to which Darwin drew attention may have been a precursor of some vocal signals. More is known of the origin of chemical signals, and Haldane[103] has recently drawn attention to the light this may throw on some of the mechanisms of internal communcation within the body by the endocrine system. The resemblance in chemical structure between substances used as signals and the steroid sex hormones suggests that the latter were originally concerned with communication between individuals. Furthermore, the chemical receptor in tunicates which responds to these inter-individual signals is the ciliated pit, believed to be homologous with part of the vertebrate pituitary, the centre controlling the endocrine system.

Some chemical signals have undoubtedly arisen from habits of excretion, defecation and perspiration.[104] In many mammals there are special methods of distributing urine and faeces, and it has already been suggested that excretory products can provide specific and even individual odours, as a result of variations in diet or metabolism (page 293). The scent glands which mammals carry on various parts of their body[105] may well have originated as modified sweat glands.

Most attention has been given to the origin of visual signals, both by Darwin and subsequent workers, and several recent papers have reviewed this field.[106] At least four different categories have been suggested. Most widespread are the preparatory, introductory or incomplete movements which characteristically prelude certain activities. Many elements in the visual displays of birds must have originated in this way. These are the actions now known as *intention movements*, which Darwin described as 'serviceable associated habits'.

There is a second group, explained by Darwin as results of the direct action of the excited nervous system, somewhat neglected by recent workers (though not by psychologists[107]) until Morris[108] drew attention to it once more. During emotional excitement the autonomic nervous system produces many effects which are manifest outside the body. Defecation, urination and perspiration have already been mentioned above, as well as the changes in respiration. Blushing and weeping occupy almost whole chapters in *The Expression of the Emotions*, and Darwin gives special attention to the erection of hairs and feathers, which plays an important role in many visual signals.[109]

There is another similar category of movements, perhaps not

strictly under autonomic control, which Darwin included under the same heading, and which Huxley[110] and Lack[111] refer to as 'general excited movements'. Though more difficult to identify they may play an important role in some species. Eibl-Eibesfeldt[112] has shown how the tail shivering of many excited rodents, apparently without any signal function, can come to serve in communication, as in the house-mouse.

Lastly, visual signals may originate, as described by Selous and Huxley,[113] from movements, called by Tinbergen *displacement activities,*[114] which are quite irrelevant to the situation. Good examples are the incomplete preening movements which pigeons and ducks make during courtship,[115] and there are many others.[116]

If these four categories provide the origins of visual signals, what general statements can be made about the ways in which they evolve? We may regard it as a basic function of many signals to enable others to anticipate or predict what another animal is going to do in the near future. The development of intention movements in particular can be understood in this way, as, for example, when the animal signals readiness to attack by giving movements preparatory to fighting. But movements of any origin may serve in the same way, provided that they are regular preludes of a particular activity.

Some signals, however, seem to function by making possible, not a positive prediction, but a negative one, by signifying that a response which might be expected in the circumstances will not take place in the near future. It is here that the principle of antithesis operates. Darwin pointed out that the submissive actions of dogs and cats can only be explained as being the opposite of movements during fighting. Since then, numerous other examples have been described, all in the same kind of context. During aggressive encounters between paired black-headed gulls, the 'head flagging', in which they repeatedly turn their heads away from each other, negates certain aggressive movements (fig. 23). It thus reassures the partner and acts 'as a friendly gesture, meaning something like "no offence meant".'[117] Here the movement was apparently initially an intention to escape.[118] Jackdaws and wolves have an analogous movement.[119] Another example of the principle of antithesis is the relaxed or 'fluffed' posture used by many birds to inhibit aggression (fig. 23),[120] the effects of which have been well described in Estrildine finches.[121] Most of the details of this posture can be

Fig. 23. Two examples of Darwin's principle of antithesis. Above are two black-headed gulls 'head flagging'. They turn away their faces from each other as a kind of appeasement gesture. (After Tinbergen.[29]) Below is a female chaffinch adopting the submissive posture in the face of an attack. The details of the posture are the reverse of those used in fighting and she faces away from the opponent instead of towards him. (From a photograph in Marler.[59])

regarded as the opposites of aggressive movements. It was probably originally a displacement activity[122] or even a direct result of a change of body temperature during conflict.[123] It is possible that the displacement activities of some finches (including feeding, preening and beak-wiping) may, by putting companions off their guard, have a similar social function.

There are elements in many visual signals which cannot be explained as assisting either positive or negative predictions. These are such characteristics as the colour of the skin or plumage displayed, the peculiar structures which often develop in some species, and also many of the details of the movements of hair, feathers and the limbs of the body. These are probably concerned with the effectiveness of the signal, as something to be easily perceived and recognized by others, and it is here that selection favouring specific and individual identification is likely to operate. Although these elements have received less attention than the others, they may ultimately prove of greater interest because of the more complex information they may carry. They may be imposed on any of the other categories, and once again may originate in a variety of ways.

Although the evolution in response to natural selection of any communication signal may be independent of its mode of origin, this need not necessarily be so. It is clear that many intention movements are selected because they enable others to anticipate the action which they normally prelude, as Darwin himself realized. Nevertheless, it can only hinder further progress if we are misled by this into confusing together the processes by which communication signals originate, and those by which natural selection controls their subsequent development.

ANIMAL AND HUMAN LANGUAGE

Throughout *The Expression of the Emotions*, it is assumed that the reader agrees with the original premise, namely that animals do communicate with each other by expressive sounds and movements. In *The Descent of Man* Darwin enlarges on this theme more fully, and his discussion of the relationship between animal and human language can hardly be bettered to-day. There are probably no more than two points on which we have significantly more information: the total size of the vocabulary of some animals; and the remarkable methods of social communication which von Frisch[124] has discovered in honey-bees.

Studies of visual communication have given some idea of the size of the repertoire available in certain species, but the only reliable estimates are for vocal signals, which are much easier to distinguish from the animal's general behaviour. There is a surprising consistency in the totals for the various species. Boutan,[125] in a penetrating study of the voice of gibbons, described thirteen cries, whereas howler monkeys have fifteen to twenty[126] and the black-tailed prairie-dog ten.[127] Among birds, the whitethroat has a vocabulary of twenty-eight,[128] the American song sparrow twenty-one,[129] the wren nineteen,[130] the chaffinch twenty-one,[131] and some other finches rather smaller repertoires. Although there is variation, these totals are all of the same order.

The most striking contrast between human and animal languages lies in the way in which they develop. While ours has an innate basis, the detail is very largely learned. That of animals is largely innate. Boutan[125] thought that in gibbons reared in isolation all of the calls developed normally, though his experience of the wild animals was limited. The complete vocabulary of the whitethroat is certainly innate[128] and the same probably applies to most bird calls. However, it was known to Darwin, through the work of Daines Barrington[132] that the songs of some birds are normally learned from other members of the species, as discussed earlier. And of course there are many examples of the capacity to mimic alien sounds both in birds, and to a limited extent in mammals such as the chimpanzee.[133]

Thus the difference is not that animals are incapable of learning sounds, but that this learning is restricted to certain narrow contexts. If we consider the function their language has to perform in the natural state, there is a certain consistency. The lives of most animals, and particularly birds, are generally dominated by a limited number of factors which overwhelm all others in importance. This is as true of their social life as of their interaction with the environment. For such activities as helping others to avoid danger (especially the mate and young), competing for food, keeping in contact with members of the same species and, above all, reproducing with them, it is probably most efficient to have a relatively limited vocabulary, which is instinctively used and understood the first time it is needed. Apart from certain exceptions such as bird song, where learning may have an important part to play, it appears that the more subtle advantages of elaborate communication by learned signals need a highly complex society for their value to be felt.

The dividing line between the nature of human and animal language becomes clearer when we consider the kind of information which is communicated. With animals this poses a problem, for the information can only be determined in an indirect way by observing the responses to a signal and inferring what information has been received. Consider, for example, two vocal signals of the chaffinch: the call given when a hawk flies over and the song of the male. On hearing the hawk signal, chaffinches respond just as though they had seen a hawk—by flying to a bush and hiding. We seem to be justified in inferring that the signal conveys the presence of a hawk, or at any rate of acute danger. Since the signal is difficult to locate (page 317) it does not convey information about position, and since other species use identical signals it does not convey that the signalling bird was a chaffinch. The essential simplicity of the information which we deduce to be carried by this signal becomes clear if we compare it with similar deductions about the song.

We know that the male song helps female chaffinches to find a mate in spring. Since a suitable mate needs to be both male and a chaffinch, we may infer that the song conveys both species and sex. She will ignore males not in full breeding condition, so we deduce that the song carries some information about physiological state. At times it even conveys the individual identity of the singer, as we have seen. And finally it conveys accurate information about position. It is clear that the song conveys more complex information than the hawk call, and it is significant that this difference in complexity is paralleled in the physical structure of the signals.

Of course one should not infer that chaffinches consciously communicate, or that listeners make a conscious analysis of the information which signals carry, nor that the different items are contained in different parts of the song. In fact the production and the response seem generally to be quite instinctive, except for the responses to individual characteristics. Yet the birds do respond as though they have received certain information. However, it appears that this information is available to them only from the complete set of signals. Given a limited number of signals in the vocabulary, it is most efficient to include the maximum of information in each one. Chaffinches are unable to separate the various items, and use them for new purposes.

This may be a crucial difference from our own language. Once our distant ancestors had achieved a more complex society, helping to relieve the individual of his extreme concern with personal survival in a difficult environment, a larger and more varied vocabulary would become increasingly useful. This in turn would permit separation of the complex of information in each instinctive call into a number of sounds which could then be used as separate times. Haldane[134] and Pumphrey[135] have both suggested that an increase of vocabulary, perhaps of this type, may have taken place during the technological revolution of upper Palaeolithic times, when a wide range of tools were used for the first time. Given a greatly increased number of sound signals for these objects and the way in which they are used, we might expect in time to see the first development of abstractions, grammar and so on.

However, another more subtle change from animal language is required. There are two aspects to our own language, the emotive or evocative, intimately involved with our emotional responses, and the descriptive or intelligible aspect, to which we respond rationally. It is clear that the greater part of animal communication is of the evocative type. If we visualize ourselves as chaffinches, the essential information in the hawk call is 'here is something to flee from'. It is a tremendous step for the signal to denote a hawk, as something with a particular appearance. However, we should notice that this is not essentially a change in the information carried in the signal, but rather in the way in which the information is responded to, a change in word usage rather than word structure.

There is, however, one example of the development of the descriptive aspect of language in animals. The researches of von Frisch into the social communication of the honey-bee are widely known, and have now been summarized in his two books.[136] It is for this reason that no review has been given of these studies, which are surely the most important advance in the study of animal communication since Darwin's time. During their hive dances honey-bees can transmit information to others, about the direction, distance and nature of a food source, which must be regarded as descriptive, in the same sense in which we apply this to our own language. It can be no accident that this is used by an insect with perhaps the most complex social organization of all animals.

We must conclude that there is no single characteristic which divides human language unequivocally from that of animals. Instead, as Koehler[137] has suggested, its distinctiveness results from a particular combination of attributes which, considered alone, are not unique to man. We are thus a step further towards confirming

Darwin's conclusion that the faculty of articulate speech does not offer any insuperable objection to the belief that man has developed from some lower form.

NOTES AND REFERENCES

1. Frisch, K. von (1950). *Bees, their Vision, Chemical Senses and Language.* New York.
   ——— (1954). *The Dancing Bees.* London.
2. Neuhaus, W. (1956). Die Unterscheidungsfähigkeit des Hundes für Duftgemische. *Z. vergl. Physiol.* **39**, 25-43.
3. Schmid, B. (1935). Über die Ermittelung des menschlichen und tierischen Individualgeruches durch den Hund. *Z. vergl. Physiol.* **22**, 524-38.
4. Goz, H. (1954). Über den Art- und Individualgeruch bei Fischen. *Z. vergl. Physiol.* **29**, 1-45.
5. Nixon, H. L. and Ribbands, C. R. (1952). Food transmission in the honeybee community. *Proc. Roy. Soc.* B, **140**, 43-50.
6. Kalmus, H. and Ribbands, C. R. (1952). The origin of the odours by which honey bees distinguish their companions. *Proc. Roy. Soc.* **B**, **140**, 50-9.
7. Renner, M. (1955). Neue Untersuchungen über die physiologische Wirkung des Duftorganes der Honigbiene. *Naturwissenschaften,* **21**, 589.
8. Frisch, K. von (1941). Über einen Schreckstoff der Fischhaut und seine biologische Bedeutung. *Z. verg. Physiol.* **29**, 46-145.
9. Schutz, F. (1956). Vergleichende Untersuchungen über die Schreckreaktion bei Fischen und deren Verbreitung. *Z. vergl. Physiol.* **38**, 84-135.
10. Eibl-Eibesfeldt, I. (1949). Über das Vorkommen von Schreckstoffen bei Erdkrötenquappen. *Experientia,* **5**, 236.
11. Heintz, E. (1954). Actions répulsives exercées sur divers animaux par des substances contenues dans le peau ou le corps d'animaux de même espèce. *C.R. Soc. Biol., Paris,* **148**, 585, 717.
12. Frisch, K. von (1923). Uber die 'Sprache' der Bienen. *Zool. Jb.* (Abt. 3), **40**, 1-186.
13. Haas, A. (1949). Arttypische Flugbahnen von Hummelmänchen. *Z. vergl. Physiol.* **31**, 281-307.
14. Shaffer, B. M. (1957). Aspects of cellular aggregation in cellular slime moulds. I. Orientation and chemotaxis. *Amer. Nat.* **91**, 19-35.
15. Tinbergen, N. and ter Pelkwijk, J. J. (1938). De kleine Watersalamander. *Lev. Nat.* **43**, 232-7.

16. Schwinck, I. (1954). Experimentelle Untersuchungen uber Geruchssinn und Strömungswahrnehmung in der Orientierung bei Nachtschmetterlingen. *Z. vergl. Physiol.* **37**, 19-56.
17. Kettlewell, B. D. H. (1946). Female assembling scents. *Entomologist,* **79**, 8-14.
18. Schaffer, J. (1940). *Die Hautdrüsenorgane der Säugetiere.* Berlin and Vienna.
19. Crane, J. (1955). Imaginal behaviour of a Trinidad butterfly, *Heliconius erato hydrara* Hewston, with special reference to the social use of colour. *Zoologica,* **40**, 167-95.
20. Haldane, J. B. S. (1955). Animal communication and the origin of human language. *Sci. Progr. Twent. Cent.* **43**, 385-401.
21. McDermott, F. A. (1917). Observations on the light emission of American Lampyridae. *Canad. Ent.* **49**, 53-61.
22. Buck, J. B. (1937). Studies on the firefly. II. The signal system and colour vision in *Photinus pyralis. Physiol. Zoöl.* **10**, 412-19.
23. Liesenfeld, F. J. (1956). Untersuchungen am Netz und über der Erschütterungssin von *Zygiella x-notata* (CI.) (Araneidae). *Z. vergl. Physiol.* **38**, 563-92.
24. Bristowe, W. S. (1941). *The Comity of Spiders.* II. London.
    Crane, J. (1949). Comparative biology of Salticid spiders at Rancho Grande. IV. An analysis of display. *Zoologica,* **34**, 159-214.
    Drees, O. (1952). Untersuchungen über die angeborenen Verhaltenweisen bei Springspinnen (Salticidae). *Z. Tierpsychol.* **9**, 169-207.
25. Ilse, D. (1941). The colour vision of insects. *Proc. Roy. Phil. Soc. Glasg.* **65**, 68-82.
26. Hellwig, H. and Ludwig, W. (1951). Versuche zum Frage der Arterkennung bei Insekten. *Z. Tierpsychol.* **9**, 456-62.
27. Altevogt, R. (1957). Untersuchungen zur Biologie, Ökologie und Physiologie indischer Winkerkrabben. *Z. morph. Ökol. Tiere,* **46**, 1-110.
    Crane, J. (1943). Display, breeding and relationships of Fiddler Crabs (Brachyura, genus *Uca*) in the north eastern United States. *Zoologica,* **28**, 217-23.
28. Kitzler, G. (1941). Die Paarungsbiologie einiger Eidechsen. *Z. Tierpsychol.* **4**, 353-402.
29. Tinbergen, N. (1953). *Social Behaviour in Animals.* London.
30. Noble, G. K. and Curtis, B. (1939). The social behaviour of the jewel fish, *Hemichromis bimaculatus* Gill. *Bull. Amer. Mus. Nat. Hist.* **76**, 1-46.
31. Baerends, G. P. and Baerends-van Roon, J. M. (1950). An introduction to the study of the ethology of Cichlid fishes. *Behaviour* (Suppl.), **1**.
32. Cinat Tomson, G.H. (1923). Die geschlechtliche Zuchtwahl beim Wellensittich (*Melopsittacus undulatus* Shaw). *Biol. Zbl.* **46**, 543-52.

33. Marler, P. (1955). Studies of fighting in chaffinches. (2). The effect on dominance relations of disguising females as males. *Brit. J. Anim. Behav.* **3**, 137-46.
34. Morris, D. (1957). Typical intensity and its relation to the problem of ritualisation. *Behaviour,* **11**, 1-12.
35. Moynihan, M. (1955). Some aspects of reproductive behaviour in the Black-headed Gull (*Larus r. ridibundus*) and related species. *Behaviour* (Suppl.), **4**.
36. Lorenz, K. (1941). Vergleichende Bewegungsstudien an Anatinen. *J. Ornithol.* **89**, 194-294.
    Weidmann, U. (1956). Verhaltsstudien an der Stockente *(Anas platyrhynchos* L.). I. Das Aktionssystem. *Z. Tierpsychol.* **13**, 208-71.
37. Guhl, A. M. and Ortman, M. M. (1953). Visual patterns in the recognition of individuals among chickens. *Condor,* **55**, 287-98.
    Noble, G. K. and Curtis, B. (1939). *Bull. Amer. Mus. Nat. Hist.* **76**, 1-46.
38. Nice, M. M. (1943). Studies in the life history of the Song Sparrow. II. Behaviour of the Song Sparrow and other Passerines. *Trans. Linn. Soc. N.Y.* **4**, 1-328.
39. Schloeth, R. (1956). Zur Psychologie der Begegnung zwischen Tiere. *Behaviour,* **10**, 1-79.
40. Eibl-Eibesfeldt, I. (1953). Zur Ethologie des Hamsters (*Cricetus cricetus* L.). *Z. Tierpsychol.* **10**, 204-54.
41. Schloeth, R. (1956). *Behaviour,* **10**, 1-79.
42. Eibl-Eibesfeldt, I. (1956). Einige Bemerkungen über den Ursprung von Ausdrucksbewegungen bei Säugetieren. *Z. Säugetierkunde,* **21**, 29-43.
43. Leyhausen, P. (1956). Das Verhalten der Katzen (Felidae). *Handbuch Zool.* Bd. viii, 10 (21), pp. 1-34. Berlin.
44. Schenkel, R. (1947). Ausdruckstudien an Wölfen. *Behaviour,* **1**, 81-129.
45. Kohts, N. (1935). Infant ape and human child (instincts, emotions, plays and habits) (Russian with English summary). *Sci. Mem. Mus. Darwin., Moscow,* **3**, 1-596.
46. Frois-Wittmann, J. (1930). The judgement of facial expression. *J. Exp. Psychol.* **13**, 113-51.
47. Roth, L. M. (1948). A study of mosquito behaviour. An experimental study of the sexual behaviour of *Aedes aegypti* (L). *Am. Midl. Nat.* **40**, 265-352.
48. Woods, E. F. (1956). Queen piping. *Bee World,* **37**, 185-95, 216-19.
49. Faber, A. (1953). *Leut- und Gebärdensprache bei Insekten.* Stuttgart.
    Jacobs, W. (1953). Verhaltensbiologische Studien an Feldbeuschrecken. *Tierpsychol.* (Suppl.), **1**.
    Pierce, G. (1949). *The Songs of Insects.* Cambridge, Mass.
50. Pringle, J. W. S. (1954). A physiological analysis of cicada song. *J. Exp. Biol.* **31**, 525-60.

51. Fish, M. P. (1956). Animal sounds in the sea. *Sci. Amer.* **194**, 93-102.
52. Barber, S. B. and Mowray, W. H. (1956). Mechanism of sound production in the sculpin. *Science,* **124,** 219-20.
53. Fish, M. P., Kelsey, A. S. and Mowray, W. H. (1952). Studies on the production of underwater sound by North Atlantic coastal fishes. *J. Mar. Res.* **11**, 180-93.
54. Pumphrey, R. J. (1940). Hearing in insects. *Biol. Rev.* **15**, 107-32.
55. Marler, P. (1955). Characteristics of some animal calls. *Nature, Lond.,* **176**, 6-8.
56. Howard, H. E. (1920). *Territory in Bird Life.* London.
57. Stevens, S. S. and Davis, H. (1938). *Hearing.* New York.
58. Schwartzkopff, J. (1955). On the hearing of birds. *Auk,* **72**, 340-47.
59. Marler, P. (1956). Behaviour of the chaffinch, *Fringilla coelebs. Behaviour* (Suppl.), **5**.
60. Busnel, M. C. (1953). Contribution à l'étude des émissions acoustiques des Orthoptères. *Ann. l'I.N.R.A.* **3**, 333-421.
61. Pumphrey, R. J. (1940). *Biol. Rev.* **15**, 107-32.
62. Haskell, P. T. (1957). Sound in the insect world. *New Biol.* no. 23, pp. 29-47.
63. Huber, F. (1956). Heuschrecken- und Grillenlaute und ihre Bedeutung. *Naturwissenschaften,* **14**, 317-21.
64. Pringle, J. W. S. (1954). *J. Exp. Biol.* **31**, 525-60.
65. Huber, F. (1956). *Naturwissenschaften,* **14**, 317-21.
66. White, G. (1789). *The Natural History and Antiquities of Selborne.* London.
67. Hartshorne, C. (1956). The monotony threshold in bird song. *Auk,* **73**, 176-92.
    Saunders, A. A. (1951). *A Guide to Bird Songs.* New York.
68. Nice, M. M. (1943). *Trans. Linn. Soc. N.Y.* **4**, 1-328.
69. Borror, D. J. (1956). Variation in Carolina wren songs. *Auk,* **73**, 211-29.
70. Lack, D. (1954). *The Natural Regulation of Animal Numbers*. Oxford.
71. Baerends, G. P. (1950). Specialisations in organs and movements with a releasing function. *Symp. Soc. Exp. Biol.* **4**, 337-60.
72. Sauer, F. (1955). Über Variationen der Artgesänge bei Grasmücken. *J. Ornithol.* **96**, 129-46.
73. Messmer, E. (1956). Die Entwicklung der Lautäusserungen und einiger Verhaltensweisen der Amsel (*Turdus merula merula* L.) unter natürlichen Bedingungen und nach Einzelaufsucht in schalldichten Räumen. *Z. Tierpsychol.* **13**, 341-441.
74. Poulsen, H. (1951). Inheritance and learning in the song of the chaffinch (*Fringilla coelebs* L.). *Behaviour,* **3**, 216-28.
75. Thorpe, W. H. (1956). *Learning and Instinct in Animals*. London.

76. Scott, W. E. D. (1901). Data on song in birds: observations on the song of Baltimore orioles in captivity. *Science,* **14**, 522-6.
77. Lanyon, W. E. (1957). The comparative biology of the Meadowlarks (*Sturnella*) in Wisconsin. *Publ. Nuttall Ornithol. Cl.* **1**, 1-67.
78. Poulsen, H. (1951). *Behaviour,* **3**, 216-28.
——— (1954). On the song of the Linnet (*Carduelis cannabina* (L.)). *Dansk. orn. Foren. Tidsskr.* **48**, 32-7.
79. Nice, M. M. (1943). *Trans. Linn. Soc. N.Y.* **4**, 1-328.
80. Thorpe, W. H. (1954). The process of song learning in the chaffinch, as studied by means of the sound spectrograph. *Nature, Lond.,* **173**, 465.
81. Marler, P. (1956). *Behaviour* (Suppl.), **5**.
82. Messmer, E. (1956). *Z. Tierpsychol.* **13**, 341-441.
83. Stadler, H. (1930). Vogeldialekt. *Alauda,* **2** (Suppl.), 1-66.
84. Dilger, W. C. (1956). Hostile behaviour and reproductive isolating mechanisms in the avian genera *Catharus* and *Hyocichla. Auk,* **73**, 313-53.
85. Stein, R. C. (1956). A comparative study of advertising song in the *Hyocichla* thrushes. *Auk,* **73**, 503-12.
86. Marler, P. (1952). Variation in the song of the chaffinch, *Fringilla coelebs. Ibis,* **94**, 458-72.
87. Benson, C. W. (1948). Geographical voice variation in African birds. *Ibis,* **90**, 48-71.
88. Lack, D. and Southern, H. N. (1949). Birds on Tenerife. *Ibis,* **91**, 607-26.
89. Marler, P. and Boatman, D. J. (1951). Observations on the birds of Pico, Azores. *Ibis,* **93**, 90-9.
90. Poulsen, H. (1951). *Behaviour,* **3**, 216-28.
Thorpe, W. H. (1954). The process of song learning in the chaffinch, as studied by means of the sound spectrograph. *Nature, Lond.,* **173**, 465.
91. Marler, P. and Boatman, D. J. (1951). *Ibis.* **93**, 90-9.
92. Lynes, H. (1914). Remarks on the geographical distribution of the chiffchaff and willow warbler. *Ibis,* **2**, 304-14.
93. Promptov, A. N. and Lukina, E. V. (1945). Conditioned reflectory differentiation in Passeres and its biological value. *C.R. (Dokl.) Acad. Sci. U.R.S.S.* **46**, 382-4.
94. Marler, P. (1957). Specific distinctiveness in the communication signals of birds. *Behaviour,* **11**, 13-39.
95. Mayr, E., Andrew, R. J. and Hinde, R. A. (1956). Die systematische Stellung der Gattung *Fringilla. J. Ornithol.* **97**, 258-73.
96. Marler, P. (1956). The voice of the chaffinch and its function as a language. *Ibis,* **98**, 231-61.
97. Cullen, E. (1957). Adaptations in the Kittiwake to cliff nesting. *Ibis,* **99**, 275-302.
98. Gibb, J. (1954). Feeding ecology of tits, with notes on treecreeper and goldcrest. *Ibis,* **96**, 513-43.

99. Lorenz, K. (1935). Der Kumpan in der Umwelt des Vogels. *J. Ornithol.* **79**, 67-127.
——— (1950). The comparative method in studying innate behaviour patterns. *Symp. Soc. Exp. Biol.* **4**, 221-68.
100. Tinbergen, N. (1952). Derived activities, their causation, biological significance, origin and emancipation during evolution. *Quart. Rev. Biol.* **27**, 1-32.
101. Craig, W. (1921-22). A note on Darwin's work on the expression of the emotions in man and the animals. *J. Abnorm. (Soc.) Psychol.* **16**, 356-66.
102. Kramer, S. (1957). Personal communication on insect courtship.
103. Haldane, J. B. S. (1954). La signalisation animale. *Ann. Biol.* **30**, 89-98.
——— (1956). Les aspects physico-chimiques des instincts. In *L'instinct dans le comportement des animaux et l'homme.* Paris.
104. Eibl-Eibesfeldt, I. (1956). *Z. Säugetierk.* **21**, 29-43.
105. Schaffer, J. (1940). *Die Hautdrüsenorgane der Säugetiere.*
106. Daanje, A. (1950). On the locomotory movements in birds and the intention movements derived from them. *Behaviour,* **3**, 48-98.
Eibl-Eibesfeldt, I. (1956). *Z. Säugetierk.* **21**, 29-43.
Morris, D. (1956). The feather postures of birds and the problem of the origin of social signals. *Behaviour,* **9**, 75-113.
Tinbergen, N. (1952). *Quart. Rev. Biol.* **27**, 1-32.
107. Young, P. T. (1943). *Emotion in Man and Animal.* New York.
108. Morris, D. (1956). *Behaviour,* **9**, 75-113.
109. Hingston, R. W. G. (1933). *Animal Colour and Adornment.* London.
Morris, D. (1956). *Behaviour,* **9**, 75-113.
110. Huxley, J. S. (1923). Courtship activities in the red-throated diver *Colymbus stellatus* Pontopp.); together with a discussion of the evolution of courtship in birds. *J. Linn. Soc. (Zool.)*, **35**, 253-92.
111. Lack, D. (1941). Some aspects of instinctive behaviour and display in birds. *Ibis,* **5**, 407-41.
112. Eibl-Eibesfeldt, I. (1956). *Z. Säugetierk.* **21**, 29-43.
113. Huxley, J. S. (1923). *J. Linn. Soc. (Zool.)*, **35**, 253-92.
114. Tinbergen, N. (1940). Die Übersprungbewegungen. *Z. Tierpsychol.* **4**, 1-40.
115. Lorenz, K. (1941). *J. Ornithol.* **89**, 194-294.
116. Tinbergen, N. (1940). *Z. Tierpsychol.* **4**, 1-40.
——— (1952). *Quart. Rev. Biol.* **27**, 1-32.
117. Tinbergen, N. and Moynihan, M. (1952). Head flagging in the black-headed gull. *Brit. Birds,* **45**, 19-22.
118. Moynihan, M. (1955*b*). Remarks on the original sources of displays. *Auk,* **72**, 240-6.
119. Lorenz, K. (1952). *King Solomon's Ring.* London.
120. Hinde, R. A. (1955-56). A comparative study of the courtship of certain finches (Fringillidae). *Ibis,* **97**, 706-45; *ibid.* **98**, 1-23.

121. Morris, D. (1956). *Behaviour,* **9**, 75-113.
122. Hinde, R. A. (1955-56). *Ibis,* **97**, 706-45: *ibid.* **98**, 1-23.
123. Andrew, R. J. (1956). Some remarks on behaviour in conflict situations with special reference to *Emberiza* spp. *Brit. J. Anim. Behav.* **4**, 41-4.
124. Frisch, K. von (1954). *The Dancing Bees.* London.
125. Boutan, L. (1913). Le Pseudo-langage. Observations effectuées sur un anthropoide: le Gibbon (*Hylobates leucogenys*-Ogilby). *Act. Soc. Linn. Bordeaux,* **47**, 5-81.
126. Carpenter, C. R. (1934). A field study of the behaviour and social relations of howler monkeys. *Comp. Psychol. Monogr.* **10**, 1-168.
127. King, J. A. (1955). Social behaviour, social organisation and population dynamics in a black-tailed prairie dog town in the Black Hills of South Dakota. *Contr. Lab. Vert. Zool.* **67**. Ann Arbor.
128. Sauer, F. (1954). Die Entwicklung der Lautäusserungen vom Ei ab Schallidicht gehaltener Dorngrasmucken (*Sylvia c. communis* Latham) im Vergleich mit später isolierten und mit wildlebenden Artgenossen. *Z. Tierpsychol.* **11**, 10-93.
129. Nice, M. M. (1943). *Trans. Linn Soc. N.Y.* **4**, 1-328.
130. Armstrong, E. A. (1955). *The Wren.* London.
131. Marler, P. (1956). *Ibis,* **98**, 231-61.
132. Barrington, D. (1773). Experiments and observations on the singing of birds. *Phil. Trans.* **63**, 249-91.
133. Yerkes, R. M. and Yerkes, A. W. (1929). *The Great Apes.* Yale.
134. Haldane, J. B. S. (1952). *Rationalist Ann.* pp. 37-45.
135. Pumphrey, R. J. (1951). The Origin of Language. An inaugural lecture. University of Liverpool.
136. Frisch, K. von (1950). *Bees.* New York.
——— (1954). *The Dancing Bees.* London.
137. Koehler, O. (1956). Thinking without words. *Proc. 14th Int. Congr. Zool.* p. 75. (Copenhagen, 1953.)

The Behavioral Significance of Pheromones in Vertebrates

KATHRYN K. GLEASON

JAMES H. REYNIERSE

The concept of pheromones, external chemical secretions having conspecific communication functions, is introduced and its significance for vertebrate behavior discussed. The physiological regulatory functions and communication functions of pheromones are distinguished. Physiological regulatory functions discussed are related to estrous synchrony in females and include the Lee-Boot, Whitten, and Bruce effects. Communication functions discussed include sex attractants, alarm substances, trail substances, territoriality, and individual recognition. In addition, the evolutionary significance and research implications of pheromones are noted.

Experimentation with sex attractants in insects (Kullenberg, 1956) led to the development of the concept of pheromones, a concept which is useful to entomologists and invertebrate zoologists (Karlson & Butenandt, 1959; Karlson & Lüscher, 1959) and which may have significance for the further development of behavioral research in general. Pheromones comprise a general class of chemical substances, secreted by individual organisms to the external environment, which are capable of producing specific reactions within conspecific receiving organisms. The most common instance, although not the necessary case, proposed by the originators of this concept was that wherein a chemical secreted by a single gland of one organism was perceived through the olfactory or other chemical senses of another individual.

Considering that psychologists and physiologists traditionally have devoted little time to investigations of either chemoreception or the exocrine glands, and that the commercial significance of chemoreception for applied entomology was no ordinary impetus, it is not surprising that with few notable exceptions, most of the quantitative research (Bossert & Wilson, 1963; Wilson & Bossert, 1963) as well as theoretical reviews of the pheromone concept (Butler, 1964, 1967) have been derived from studies of insect species. In much the same way, application of the pheromone concept within psychology typically has been limited to the behavior of invertebrates, especially earthworms and planaria. For example, Ressler, Cialdini, Ghoca, and Kleist (1968) identified an alarm pheromone which can account for apparent demonstrations of instrumental conditioning in annelids. Similarly, McConnell (1967) reported the facilitory effects of slime trails during planarian conditioning procedures; pheromone effects upon planarian aggregation behavior (Reynierse, 1966, 1967; Reynierse & Ellis, 1967; Reynierse, Gleason, & Ottemann, in press) agree well with these slime effects and, consistent with a pheromone interpretation, suggest the presence of a social component within the conditioning situation. But the concept is not self-limiting to these animal groups or invertebrates in general; now it may be valuable to recognize the potential significance of pheromones for vertebrate behaviors as well. The purpose of the present paper is to suggest criteria for defining the scope of the pheromone concept, to examine the evidence available for the existence of pheromones in vertebrate species, and to relate these phenomena in a significant manner to psychological research programs.

Most mammalian species, primates and seals excepted, are macrosmatic, that is, possess excellent olfactory capacities upon which they depend for detecting and recognizing faint traces of scent (Hediger, 1950). Although Wiener (1966, 1967a, 1967b) proposed that external chemical messengers influence human behavior, man is clearly not macrosmatic, and the evidence supporting pheromone influence in man is, for the present at least, tenuous. Moreover, much of the evidence Wiener presented, while perhaps indicating that man has greater olfactory sensitivity than usually supposed, still does not qualify for the more restrictive pheromone interpretation. Our discussion is limited to non-human vertebrate species.

DEFINITION OF PHEROMONES

The familiar notion of hormones as internal secretions regulating physiological processes and subsequent behaviors was the obvious analogue for Karlson's original designation of the term "pheromones," replacing earlier proposals to classify such substances as "ectohormones" (Karlson & Butenandt, 1959) or "ectocrine" (Lucas, 1947). The commonality of function shared by both groups excepted, that is, regulation of internal or external environments (Wilson, 1962), at least two defining differences distinguish pheromones from hormones: (*a*) pheromones are secreted (or excreted) to the external environment, while hormones are secreted to the internal environment; and (*b*) pheromones function as vehicles for intraspecific communication, while hormones do not conduct this additional function.

Pheromones are not just an ordinary example of olfactory sensitivity and can be differentiated from other aspects of chemoreception. Inclusion of the communicating or signaling function of pheromones necessitates that consideration of these substances be confined to substances secreted by one organism and received by another. The experimental demonstration of olfactory or other chemoreceptive acuity of species–illustrated by phenomena such as the discrimination of specific olfactory cues in steams as a basis for migration in fish (Hasler & Wisby, 1951; McBride, Fagerlund, Smith, & Tomlinson, 1964), the discrimination of individual human odors by dogs (Kalmus, 1963), the demonstration of the ability to form olfactory discriminations in toads (Martof, 1962) or rats (Valenta & Rigby, 1968), and the demonstration of the reinforcing properties of odors in rats (Long & Tapp, 1967, 1968)–implies both the capacity and probability of pheromone development to a significant degree in these species. But these reactions as presently documented do not necessarily require recourse to the pheromone concept.

Designation of pheromones as a means of intraspecific

communication further restricts use of the term. While the sensory processes involved undoubtedly are similar to those of interspecific communications such as predator-prey recognition in fish (Kleerekoper & Mogensen, 1963), the limiting of pheromones to intraspecific communication implies their potential function as species-isolating mechanisms, a distinction not necessarily implied either by the nature of the chemical compounds themselves or their secreting sources. The validity of such a distinction has been supported in part by the specific nature of the responses to sex attractants in insects (Butler, 1967; Wilson & Bossert, 1963). Wynne-Edwards (1962) indicated that all chemicals used in communication must be distinguished from poisons secreted by individual organisms. This differentiation is probably both valid and essential in considering interspecific chemical communication; restriction of pheromones to conspecific organisms precludes this additional discrimination.

It probably will be necessary in the future to distinguish pheromones from olfactory cues which function in a manner closely analogous to pheromones, but which are varied or are affected by both the quantity and combination of hormones present within the organism. Representative of the applicability of this criterion is the comparison of responses to individual sex attractants in insects, and of analogous discriminations made between estrous and nonestrous females by mammalian males. That these more general discriminations in mammals are made on the basis of pheromone functions is quite likely; but such a conclusion should not be made prima facie from the gross evidence available. The effectiveness of synthetic pheromone compounds capable of producing complete responses is the decisive criterion of pheromone function (Whitten, 1966), although, in the absence of either synthetic chemical compounds or accumulated secretions, pheromones are often inferred from less precise indices.

A final criterion which may prove useful in delineating the pheromone concept requires consideration of the secretion of a pheromone as being itself a response to some stimulus complex. What is the stimulus sufficient to produce a pheromone? The general biological principle of conservation of substances produced and excreted by the organism would seem to require that specific events would trigger the release of the pheromone. Although hardly any evidence along these lines is available, implications can be made for both the environmental stimuli which will initiate pheromone production, and for the specific central nervous system processes which precede excretion of the pheromone. Certain neurosecretory states, specific environmental stimuli, or their interactions may be the essential precursors for the production of a pheromone. An obvious analogy is that of the combination of exogenous seasonal changes and endogenous states (including hormonal changes) sufficient to produce the onset of visual courtship displays in birds (Marler & Hamilton, 1966).

Several criteria have been used in classifying pheromones. The original classification (Karlson & Butenandt, 1959) differentiated olfactorily acting and oral pheromones, thus distinguishing between the sex attractant substances and the queen or royal jelly substances of bees and termites. Butler (1964) showed the shortcoming of this dichotomy, indicating that at least part of the effect of the ingested royal jelly is olfactorily mediated.

The distinction between the primer and the releaser effects (Wilson, 1963, 1965) has been used commonly. The primer effect is said to "trigger a chain of physiological events in the recipient" while the releaser effect is a "more or less immediate and reversible change in the behavior of the recipient [Wilson, 1963, p. 100]." The releaser effects ordinarily are further differentiated by specific behavioral functions which have been associated with the pheromone (Wilson, 1965).

Wynne-Edwards (1962) proposed that not only pheromones, but all functional odors have been derived from natural selection of metabolites originally excreted for another function.

It would seem that pheromones, through evolution, have acquired two distinctly different functions, and that the most lucid classification at this state of knowledge would differentiate these functions. We shall distinguish the physiological regulatory function from the communication function.

Ultimately, the most significant identification of pheromones would be based on the individual chemical compounds, each of which, ideally, would be associated with specific physiological and communication functions. The current inability to identify and synthesize these chemicals necessitates a functional categorization of pheromones.

The specific categories discussed correspond quite closely to

Kirschenblatt's (1962) schema but without his formidable terminology. Physiological regulatory functions are limited to those effects involving stimulation and maturation or onset of reproductive processes, although Kirschenblatt proposed that such functions might also affect development of sex glands and/or modification of sex characteristics. Communication functions discussed include (*a*) sex attractants, (*b*) alarm substances, (*c*) trial substances, (*d*) territoriality, and (*e*) individual recognition.

PHYSIOLOGICAL REGULATORY FUNCTIONS

Most of the evidence for pheromones in vertebrates, meager in comparison with the literature accumulated for insect groups, is relevant for the physiological regulatory function of pheromones and, for the most part, is limited to the complex relationships between pheromones and reproductive physiology in mice and rats. Several specific effects have been documented.

Lee-Boot Effect

Induction of pseudopregnancy in the rat, resulting from stimulation of the nasal mucosa with silver nitrate (Rosen & Shelesnyak, 1937) or extirpation of the sphenopalatine ganglion (Rosen, Shelesnyak, & Zacharias, 1940), established early the relationship between olfaction and reproductive physiology. The increased incidence of spontaneous pseudopregnancy observed among grouped female mice as compared to singly housed females, now known as the Lee-Boot effect (Lee & Boot, 1955), first implicated the role of pheromones in the phenomenon. These pseudopregnancies, endocrinologically identical to those resulting from mating with sterilized males, were assumed to result from an olfactorily mediated chemical stimulus conducted through the hypothalamus to the adenohypophysis where prolactin production was affected (Lee & Boot, 1956).

In a series of experiments in which female mice were grouped, isolated, and regrouped, Dewar (1959) demonstrated that the incidence of pseudopregnancy was definitely related to the grouping variable. Failure to maintain an high rate of pseudopregnancy in isolation following grouping, and its subsequent return with regrouping, indicated the temporary nature of the effect which a pheromone interpretation would imply. Once the sufficient stimulus was no longer present, the normal cyclic activity would be expected to return. Neither the source nor the nature of such a pheromone has been identified at present.

Housing of female mice in groups of 30 produced highly significant incidences of anestrus (Whitten, 1959), contrasting with the usual Lee-Boot effect. Anestrus was both temporary and under olfactory stimulus control, probably resulting in a specific suppression of pituitary gonadotrophic secretion (Whitten, 1957). Everett (1956, 1964) concluded that both the Lee-Boot effect and the occurrence of anestrus under more highly crowded conditions resulted from secretion of varying intensities of follicle-stimulating hormone.

Whitten Effect

Early descriptions of the cyclic estrous activity in mice suggested that the introduction of males may prevent lengthening of the estrous cycle and may result in an asymmetrical distribution of impregnation throughout the cycle (Merton, 1938). Whitten's (1965a) systematic investigation of the effect indicated that either the presence of the male or his excreta produced reproductive synchrony characterized by a peak in matings on the third night after pairing. Failure to effect matings in females rendered anosmic implicated the necessity of olfaction in the effect (Whitten, 1965b). The failure to carry over the effect from cycle to cycle (Whitten, 1958) and the ability to produce synchrony of estrus in females rendered anestrous by grouping in large numbers (Whitten, 1959) give further credence to a pheromone interpretation.

Significant alterations in the pattern of estrous synchrony among grouped females exposed to the urine of males, particularly when estrous cycles are suppressed by crowding (Bronson & Marsden, 1964), indicated the source of the pheromone involved (Marsden & Bronson, 1964). Specificity of the pheromone is indicated by the significantly greater effect produced by males of the same strain as opposed to those of different strains (Marsden & Bronson, 1965). Although the active substance in the urine has not been identified, Whitten, Bronson, & Greenstein (1968) showed that the pheromone substance is volatile and probably acts through olfactory receptors.

Replication of the Whitten effect only in groups of female mice to which males were subsequently added (Lamond, 1959) indicated its function in achieving breeding synchrony. The mechanism producing this effect may be the initiation or further stimulation of follicle development (Everett, 1964; Whitten, 1958, 1966), since the presence of the male had no effect on pseudopregnancy already present, that is, pseudopregnancies were not terminated more quickly (Whitten, 1958).

Breeding synchrony for a number of other vertebrate species has been described as a function of olfactory cues, but the evidence for a specific pheromone or pheromones is entirely presumptive. In domestic sheep, the presence of the ram will stimulate ovulation in ewes not in estrus (Schinkel, 1954a), producing synchrony of estrus among ewes based on exteroceptive factors (Schinkel, 1954b). A similar phenomenon occurs in Angora goats, presumably from olfactory cues (Shelton, 1960).

Jolly (1967) reported breeding synchrony in the social lemuroids which was, at least in part, a function of olfactory cues. Here, synchrony of estrus was superimposed on the more characteristic condition among prosimians of seasonal polyestrus, perhaps indicating that the pheromone(s) involved have both a physiological as well as a communication function. Olfactory effects among prosimians constitute a special case since olfactory communication among prosimians is intermediate between that of other mammals and higher primates (Jolly, 1966; Marler, 1965). Although prosimians have several modes of scent marking, ritualized scent marking has a large visual component suggesting that communication functions are both olfactorily and visually mediated (Jolly, 1966).

The accomplishment of an event as complex as synchrony of estrus is presumed to occur as a function of two separate pheromones (Whitten, 1966). The first would act among grouped females, resulting in anestrus, and the second, from males, releasing females from such inhibition to produce cyclic activity of short duration. Marsden and Bronson (1965) demonstrated that in grouped females, the release from the grouping conditions contributed as much to the synchronization of estrus as did exposure to the urine of males.

Bruce Effect

Bruce (1960a) found that a high percentage of both pregnancies (63%) and pseudo-pregnancies (76%) failed when female mice were housed with or near strange males. It was suggested that the smell of the strange male resulted in suppression of prolactin production normally initiated by mating (Bruce & Parkes, 1960). That the pheromone was olfactory in nature was determined by finding that housing impregnated females on nesting material previously used by alien males was sufficient to produce the implantation block (Bruce, 1960b), and that recently mated females with olfactory bulb ablation did not experience the effect in the presence of strange males (Bruce & Parrott, 1960).

Origin of the pheromone was traced from products left in nesting material by males (Parkes & Bruce, 1962), implicating the urine of alien males (Dominic, 1964). The effect also occurred when sprayed or alien females were used, suggesting that the pheromone, excreted in the urine, is the product of an androgen-dependent gland (Dominic, 1965). Application, three times daily, of 0.25 cubic centimeter of fresh urine from alien males produced an effect identical with that described by Bruce (1961), distinguishing recovery from implantation block from the spontaneous return of estrus among control females (Dominic, 1966a).

The instability and volatility of the chemical factor involved (Dominic, 1964; Parkes & Bruce, 1961, 1962), the similarity in chemical composition between androgen steroids and the limits specified for pheromones (Wilson & Bossert, 1963), as well as the on-off nature of the effect (Bruce, 1963), renders a pheromone interpretation of the effect most plausible.

That the pheromone responsible for the exteroceptive block to pregnancy in mice yields reduced production of prolactin by the pituitary is a generalization implicated by several findings. Females are most sensitive to the block 48 hours after mating, that is, before implantation has occurred (Bruce, 1960b, 1961). The presence of suckling young and thus the presumably increased production of prolactin reduces the incidence of pregnancy block (Bruce & Parkes, 1961a); the administration of prolactin to females while exposed to strange males produces the same result (Bruce & Parkes, 1961b; Dominic, 1966b). Finally, the presence of ectopic pituitary grafts in females exposed to the urine of alien males results in a significantly smaller percentage of blocked pregnancies (17%) than in animals without the grafts but given the same exposure to urine of alien males (87%), indicating that the corpus luteum was being maintained by prolactin secreted by the graft in the absence of that from the organisms's own pituitary (Dominic, 1967).

Observation of an exteroceptive block to pregnancy has likewise been documented for the deer mouse, *Peromyscus maniculatus bairdii* (Eleftheriou, Bronson, & Zarrow, 1962). Although deer mice appear to be more sensitive to environmental changes in housing independent of experimental manipulation of olfactory cues, the essential time relations of the Bruce effect have been confirmed, implicating olfactory factors (Bronson & Eleftheriou, 1963). As in the laboratory mouse (Bruce, 1963), the incidence of pregnancy block in the deer mouse is independent of the number of alien males to which females are exposed (Bronson & Eleftheriou, 1963).

In lieu of behavioral quantification, speculation regarding the interrelations among the pheromones responsible for the effects reviewed produced several theories of pheromone function in mice. To account for the Bruce effect, an identifier factor was postulated in addition to the male and female pheromones postulated for synchronization of estrus to occur (Whitten, 1966). The identifying factor may be either specific or a more general signal used in individual recognition in both sexes. Either case would be compatible with the olfactory discrimination ability demonstrated for mice (Bowers & Alexander, 1967) and the potential sources of such substances available. But the general signal would seem more parsimonious since it is highly unlikely that each male would secrete a uniquely different substance. An alternative proposal is that individual discriminations basic to the Bruce effect are based on spectra of odors from individuals from the same strain (Parkes, 1960; Parkes & Bruce, 1961). This interpretation affords the combination of a general factor for the strain with individual differences sufficient to allow for discriminations based on olfactory cues.

COMMUNICATION FUNCTIONS

The evidence for pheromones as communication devices in vertebrates is considerably less well-systematized than that for physiological functions; much is only circumstantial or anecdotal at best. Yet the diversity of species involved itself suggests the occurrence of pheromone communication as a general phenomenon among vertebrates.

Sex Attractants

The function of sex attractants is implied largely from examples of sex recognition observed in several groups. While closely allied, sex attraction and sex recognition should not be assumed to be identical processes. Chemical functioning as sex attractants of necessity actively recruit approach behavior, whereas sex recognition requires only a discrimination based on olfactory or other chemical cues. The functional signifiance of sex attractants in noctuid moths, bark beetles, and other insects is quite different from that of the chemical cues used for discrimination of estrous females in mammals.

In amphibia, male newts have specialized chin glands which presumably secrete substances that attract members of the opposite sex (Young, 1950), or a male newt courting under water may send a current over his cloaca thereby sending chemical messages to his mate (Marler, 1959). The marbled salamander uses chemical secretions to attract females to the breeding ground (Noble & Bradley, 1933). Likewise, the dorsal skin gland of the kangaroo rat has a similar function in some species since its size is closely correlated with the breeding season (Quay, 1953).

Evidence for sex recognition in fish based on chemical factors dates from the early suggestions of the phenomenon in the catfish (Breder, 1935) and the blind goby (MacGinitie, 1939). Tavolga (1956) found, in another goby species, that males inititated courtship behavior when they detected ovarian fluid from the urogenital papillae of gravid females.

Discrimination between estrous and anestrous females on the basis of chemical cues is frequent in mammals and was documented for the heteromyid rodents (Eisenberg, 1963a), for marsupials (Sharman, Calaby, & Poole, 1966) where secretions of specialized apocrine glands in the pouch may initiate mating behavior (Mykytowycz & Nay, 1964), and for dogs where the urine is the source of the chemical (Beach & Gilmore, 1949).

Carr and Caul (1962) concluded that both male and females, using olfactory cues, can discriminate between sexually active and inactive animals. Sources of these cues suggested by the investigators were urine or sebaceous skin glands. These findings are substantiated further since male rats with olfactory bulb lesions are less likely to engage in mating (Heimer & Larsson, 1967). The Heimer and Larsson findings are in correspondence with earlier investigations implying that intact olfactory functioning was essential for the initiation of mating behavior in rabbits (Brooks, 1937) and horses (Hafez, Williams, & Wierzbowski, 1962), at least for inexperienced males.

Insufficient information regarding the sources, chemical composition, and mode of function for the substances implicated by these findings does not allow the definite conclusion that these substances are indeed pheromones. But the evidence is compatible with, and until otherwise indicated, most effectively handled by a pheromone interpretation.

Alarm Substances

Alarm substances ("Schreckstoff") resembling pheromones in vertebrates have been best documented for fish. Since von Frisch's (1941) initial description of the odor-dependent escape reaction ("Schreckreaktion") in minnows, similar fright reactions have been documented for many species, and have been found particularly prevalent in the *Ostariophysi* (Pfeiffer, 1962b). In all species studied, the alarm substance, although not chemically isolated, is quite likely excreted by specific club cells in the epidermis (Pfeiffer, 1962b, 1963a, 1963b); species lacking these specialized mucus-producing cells likewise lack the fright reaction, and thus, presumably, that particular alarm or fright substance released by injury to the epidermis (Pfeiffer, 1962a).

That the substance responsible for the alarm reaction is a pheromone is implicated further by two different lines of investigation bearing results corresponding closely to those of pheromone functions in insects (Butler, 1967). First, the effectiveness of the substance in high dilutions (Pfeiffer, 1962a) coincides with the more general evidence for the potency of pheromones as stimuli. Second, the correlation between the effectiveness of the substance and schooling behavior in juvenile fish corresponds to the general finding that the most extensive use of pheromones occurs in the most social of organisms (Pfeiffer, 1962b).

Investigations of a similar alarm substance and fright reaction in tadpoles of the common toad (Eibl-Eibesfeldt, 1949; Hrbacek, 1950) resulted in the preliminary conclusion that the chemical involved is probably a steroidlike substance released by injury to the epidermis. With another amphibian group, frogs, the extent of utilization of pheromones and the degree of olfactory acuity it necessitates is greater for more social species, *Bufo*, than for semisocial groups, *Rana* (Young, 1950).

Evidence of alarm substances in mammals apart from anecdotal evidence (Bourliere, 1955) is rare. Ludvigson and Sytsma (1967) propose the operation of an olfactory factor in white rats which interferes with straight alley running performance in a manner analogous to an alarm pheromone. From a methodological point of view, this is particularly significant for reward-shift (Crespi-type experiments) and extinction conditions. Indeed, as Ludvigson and Sytsma (1967) correctly concluded, "there have probably been very few extinction studies ever conducted on runway behavior of rats in which, in addition to the removal of reward, there was not also a strong accumulation of an external stimulus–odor associated with nonreward." Additional evidence supporting the role of these olfactory cues has been obtained for differential conditioning (McHose & Ludvigson, 1966), patterned running under patterned schedules of reward and nonreward (McHose, 1967), resistance to extinction (McHose, Jacoby & Meyer, 1967), and spontaneous alternation in the T maze (Douglas, 1966).

Trail Substances

Trail marking has been frequently described in vertebrates (Bourliere, 1955; Hediger, 1950, 1955; Wynne-Edwards, 1962; Young, 1950), but little quantitative research has been completed. The trail substances likely serve several behavioral functions including alarm, sex identification, regulation of population density, and foraging purposes; as yet, these have not been isolated from the more general process of trail marking. During the period of sexual receptivity, female dogs urinate in several places, advertising both their location and receptive state; when males visit these urine trails, they become highly excited and pursue the female (Scott & Fuller, 1965). Rats, too, leave odor trails that are followed by other rats (Barnett, 1963).

Several factors favor a pheromone interpretation of the trail substances despite the paucity of experimental evidence accumulated. The specific information carried by the trails, the on-off nature of the signal, and the relative permanence of the chemicals responsible for trail marking in vertebrates coincide with the evidence relevant for insect trails (Wilson & Bossert, 1963). Still, vertebrate and insect trail marking are almost certainly mediated by different mechanisms, and the behavior of vertebrates following trails is probably more variable than that shown in response to insect trails.

Territoriality

Simple definitions of territoriality emphasize any area that is defended (Burt, 1943; Noble, 1939). Hediger (1950), however, emphasized that the concept of territory includes marking as well as defense. While territorial demarcation may depend upon auditory signals (e.g., birdsong), or visual signals (e.g., displays), territorial defense requires the presence of the resident if these signals are exclusively relied upon. On the other hand, marking territories with scents has the advantage of advertising ownership even when the resident is absent (Hediger, 1955). Frequently a territory is marked by several means, for example, auditory and olfactory in alligators and visual and olfactory in bears (Hediger, 1950).

Territorial demarcation with scents, dung, urine, or other glandular secretions usually are placed on prominent and salient features of the environment, for example, prominent twigs, branches, tree stumps and stones. Deer and antelope have a gland above the eye, the antorbital gland, which produces an oily, strong-smelling substance and which wards off conspecific intruders when they enter the occupied territory (Hediger, 1955). East African mongooses use anal glands (Hediger, 1955), titi monkeys use chest glands (Moynihan, 1966), rabbits use chin glands (Mykytowycz, 1962, 1965), Mongolian gerbils a midventral sebaceous gland (Thiessen, Friend, & Lindzey, 1968) in territorial marking. Heteromyid rodents depress their anal-genital area against the substrate, and this marking behavior is one component of the integrated sandbathing movements (Eisenberg, 1963b).

Scent marking by chinning is present in social rabbits but absent in solitary rabbits and hares (Marsden & Holler, 1964;

Mykytowycz, 1965), corresponding to the smaller chin glands in solitary species and to increases in gland size during the breeding season when territoriality is strong (Mykytowycz, 1965). Likewise, the scent glands of shrews are believed to have a territorial function, although undoubtedly they also function for sex identification (Pearson, 1946), while the scent glands in lemurs (Jolly, 1966) and prairie dogs (King, 1955) may have an agonistic social function during territorial defense. Epple & Lorenz (1967) examined the sternal gland in most *Platyrrhini* (New World primates) genera and found that marking is maximum in dominant males, and gland size is directly related to the dominance hierarchy. Although marking is related to sexual and aggressive behaviors, whether or not it has a territorial function is not clear. Thus, Mason (1966) reported sternal gland marking in *Callicbeus.* Although this New World monkey occurs in small family units having territories, and marking occurs most frequently after an encounter between two groups, marking does not always occur on territorial boundaries; Mason never observed animals reacting to the marks of another. A whole family of mammals, the *Mustelidae*, leave musk deposits, an oily, strongly odoriferous substance. Mink (Svihla, 1931), weasels, and otters (Wynne-Edwards, 1962) probably leave musk deposits for territorial demarcation as well as for individual recognition. The North American muskrat (Wynne-Edwards, 1962) deposits both dung and musk for these purposes. Lederer (1950) provided a more detailed survey of the communication functions of musk.

Urination and defecation are frequently used for territorial demarcation in which both anatomical characteristics and physiological requirements of elimination ensure that the territory is regularly impregnated with the scent (Hediger, 1950). The dwarf hippopotamus (Hediger, 1950) marks its territory with urine and dung, the Indian rhinoceros (Wynne-Edwards, 1962) uses dung markings at least partially for territorial defense, and male lemurs (Ilse, 1955) and the big cats (Hediger, 1950) mark their territories with urine. Large predatory and free-roaming species often share a large moving territory with temporal rather than spatial boundaries (Eaton, 1968; Lehausen & Wolff, 1959). Cheetah (Eaton, 1968) and housecats (Lehausen & Wolff, 1959) have these time-plan territories which are marked with urine. Fresh markings provide temporary boundaries which deter intruding conspecifics; older signals, while noticed, are not respected. Contrary to frequent belief, urination does not seem to have territorial significance in domestic dogs or wolves, since strange dogs will enter and mark an inhabited area when the resident dog is away, while wolves only defend the area close to their den (Scott & Fuller, 1965).

A large body of evidence indicates that territorial marking is under androgen control. In both gerbils (Thiessen et al., 1968) and rabbits (Mykytowycz, 1965), males mark more often than females, marking is reduced in castrated males, and in the gerbil, testosterone replacement therapy returns marking incidence to original levels. Territorial marking and reproductive behavior in males are both androgen mediated. Its biological significance, however, does not only derive from the increased aggressiveness during the breeding season, which territorial defense directed toward intruding conspecific males implies. Establishing and defending a territory only increases the probability that reproductive behavior will take place; marking a territory has a physiological regulating function controlling female estrous cycle and increases the probability that fertile mating will take place. One hormone, androgen, directly controls the reproductive competence of males and, indirectly, through territorial markings, the reproductive competence of females.

Individual Recognition

Individual recognition on the basis of pheromones is a more general phenomenon than the sex recognition discussed earlier. It is best documented by evidence of mother-young recognition dependent on olfactory or chemical cues in Alaskan fur seals (Bartholomew, 1959), goats (Blauvelt, 1954; Klopfer, Adams, & Klopfer, 1964), dogs, (Menzel & Menzel, 1953, cited by Johnson, Goy, & Michels, 1962), and in the jewel fish (Kühme, 1964, cited by Marler & Hamilton, 1966). Chemical cues also have been implicated in the retrieval behavior of female rats (Beach & Jaynes, 1956).

Other examples of individual recognition dependent upon chemical cues include identification of prairie dogs through the "kiss" which has an olfactory component (King, 1955), individual discrimination in minnows (Göz, 1954, cited by Marler, 1959), discrimination in bullheads where individual recognition is related to dominance (Todd, Atema, & Bardach, 1967), mice which can discriminate between two males of a single inbred strain (Bowers & Alexander, 1967), and dogs following an individual trail consisting of specific body odors (Le Magnen, 1963).

Due to the general nature of the cues implicated, this body of information cannot be construed as commanding evidence for the functioning of specific pheromones in either maternal-young relations or individual recognition. It does, however, indicate the presence of the olfactory acuity required for the operation of pheromones.

EVOLUTIONARY SIGNIFICANCE

Wynne-Edwards (1962) suggested that the origin of all functional odors, regardless of type, was derived by natural selection from metabolites produced for some other function. Certainly this general viewpoint can be ascribed to the development of chemical communication through pheromones. The close similarity both in chemical composition (Whitten, 1966) and function, between pheromones and hormones, would indicate that it is feasible to consider the physiological regulatory function of pheromones as the precursory function of these substances from an evolutionary point of view. Similarly, as Lenhoff (1968) suggested, chemical receptors in lower forms, for example, the receptor sites for glutathione in hydra, may have given rise to the olfactory, hormonal, and pheromonal chemical receptors of higher vertebrates.

The lack of comparative studies, fossil records, or even a technology sufficiently refined to differentiate among the quantifiable aspects of compounds functioning as pheromones renders the problem of the evolutionary course of pheromone development little more than a considered guess. Several suggestions appear feasible and interesting to incorporate into a research program. Klopfer (1962), in discussing the development of mimicry among birds, suggested that one organism upon contact with a specific stimulus may emit a signal which then serves as an unconditioned stimulus for a non-participating observer. In fish, the chemically based fright reaction may be communicated visually to other individuals not exposed to the alarm substance (Pfeiffer, 1962b).

While the process hypothesized is most amenable to the

incorporation of visual behavior patterns into communication systems, particularly the specific instance of mimicry, the modification of rat behavior after olfactory cues were produced by other rats in learning tasks comparable to alarming situations has been suggested (Ludvigson & Sytsma, 1967). Clearly, this process could account for maintenance of the communication system by chemical cues, although the initial operation of the system is more likely to have been a function of the stimulus contrasts provided by the pheromone secretion and the resultant attention given it.

Andrew (1964) proposed an alternative to Morris' (1956) hypothesis of the incorporation of secretions into visual displays by means of autonomic activity, and favored a stimulus contrast interpretation. Initial marking of novel stimuli by lemurs and galagoes could be accounted for by stimulus contrast, whereas a simple autonomic hypothesis could not predict such discriminative marking necessary for the eventual incorporation of olfactory signals into specific displays or patterns.

Further indirect evidence favoring such development of pheromone communication is the apparent correlation between degree of sociality of a species and the extent to which pheromones are known to function. In frogs, the more social species (*Bufo*) appear to use pheromones for communication more than less social (*Rana*) (Young, 1950), concurring with Karlson's original tenet that pheromones as chemical communication presuppose social behavior.

If the ritualization and evolution of visual displays as signaling devices is but a particular example of the more general case of change in function as a result of evolution (Tinbergen, 1964), the analysis of the development of visual displays in birds (Etkin, 1964) provides a useful analogy for the possible evolution of communication by pheromones. Ritualization of visual patterns into functional displays ensued from the gradual development of distinctiveness and conspicuousness of certain groups of feathers, sequences of motor movements, or a combination of both. The conclusion that pheromones have indeed developed both the distinctiveness and conspicuousness necessary for signaling function is best documented in insects, where species-specificity obtains for many sex attractants (Butler, 1967), and where the smallest effective amounts of pheromone excreted may approximate only a few molecules each time (Wilson & Bossert, 1963). The extent to which the communication function attributable to pheromones is a function of the chemical structure per se or of the combination with other attendant odors or secretions requires a behavioral assay of the synthesized compound, as yet noticeably absent from the pheromone literature of vertebrates.

Target examples appropriate for the comparative investigation of evolutionary hypotheses include instances such as the kangaroo rat in which secretion from the dorsal skin gland is correlated with the breeding season, functioning specifically for sex recognition in some species, and is used throughout the year for general recognition in other species (Quay, 1953).

RESEARCH IMPLICATIONS

Several factors contribute to the import of pheromones for behavioral research in general: (*a*) Pheromones are not phenomena limited to invertebrate groups, but appear to be characteristic of many vertebrates as well; (*b*) in addition to a physiological function, pheromones serve also as communication media; and (*c*) when quantified by chemical analysis and behavioral assay, pheromones are appropriate units for the quantification of other associated behaviors.

The consideration of pheromones is particularly germane to investigations of sensory processes. Aside from the usual pertinent questions related to sensory physiology (e.g., the nature of the sufficient stimulus, the range of effectiveness of the sufficient stimulus, the function and sensitivity of the receptor organ[s], etc.), research regarding the sensory basis of pheromones would also include whether or not the receptor organs and nervous physiology involved are the same for both the physiological and communication functions of pheromones. Furthermore, the ecology of a species may prohibit reliance upon vision or audition while simultaneously providing ideal conditions for chemoreception and chemical communication (Marler, 1967).

Or, from an ontogenetic viewpoint, the question may be asked, which response is the organism first able to make—that of secreting the pheromone in the appropriate environmental setting, or that of responding appropriately to the pheromone excretion of another organism? Because chemical signals are usually available as an information source to the sender as well as to the recipient, the empirical question is whether or not experience in secreting a chemical stimulus is necessary for the development of the chemoreceptive acuity enabling an organism to perceive that stimulus as well as to behave in a socially appropriate manner upon being stimulated by it.

Review of the literature of vertebrate reproductive physiology clearly indicates the necessity of considering the role of pheromones, or at least, more general olfactory cues. There are obvious implications for laboratory procedures relevant for housing of males and females, the effectiveness of induced pair-formations, and the precision of base-line data regarding estrous cycles, incidence of mating, and occurrence of either pseudopregnancies or blocked pregnancies. Pheromones may represent factors to be controlled as extraneous to the process of interest, or as an integral factor in normal reproductive physiology. Little, if any, information is available for vertebrates regarding possible effects of pheromones on the development and maturation of reproductive processes. It is unlikely that an effect as compelling as that of the queen-substance in honeybees (Butler, 1967) or the accelerating pheromones of desert locusts (Loher, 1961) and crickets (McFarlane, 1966) is operative in vertebrates. But, the effects of pheromones have not been systematically eliminated in research on the effects of mother-young relationships on adult social-sexual behaviors.

As communication media, pheromones afford an interesting opportunity to investigate the development of a communication system based on a unit, the pheromone, permitting precise quantification and identification. The information transmitted by the components of a visual signal can never be quantified in the same manner as a specific dilution of a chemical distributed over a given area, even though the duration of the effect of that chemical cannot always be regulated. Within a species, interesting questions can be raised regarding the amount and type of information transmitted by a given pheromone in different dilutions or in combinations with different, more general olfactory cues and/or visual or auditory signals. Between species or groups, questions may be asked concerning the extent to which the same chemical in a given dilution and setting carries the same information in one group as it does in another group; or, conversely, the question may be phrased as to the means and setting for the transmission of the same bit of information for two different groups. In either case, an index of the process of development and maintenance of a communication system which can be precisely quantified would add to the total literature of behaviors associated with communication and language. Marler (1959) pointed out the restrictive nature of chemical language, that is, glands do not produce a whole spectrum of different chemical signals. But this limitation should not restrict the comparative research proposed. While this characteristic may limit the richness of the language, it is also ideally suited as a species-isolating mechanism in which only intraspecific communication is possible.

But the overwhelming significance of pheromones for the conduct of behavioral research derives from the recognition that olfactory cues in general comprise an important class of variables requiring control in laboratory experiments. Systematic elimination of olfactory cues either within or between groups of subjects, for example, has not been a general operative procedure in most learning experiments. Consequently, confusing or conflicting empirical results may be resolved when appropriate control of the discriminative olfactory cues produced by the subjects themselves in response to a changing environmental situation is obtained (Ludvigson & Sytsma, 1967).

Behavioral (Bowers & Alexander, 1967) and physiological (Ottoson & Shepherd, 1967) evidence has indicated a degree of olfactory acuity in rodents requiring stringent olfactory control in experimental investigations with these animals, whether the salient cues originate from pheromones or not. Pheromones represent only a specific instance of the general manner in which animals may alter the experimental environment subsequent to a treatment procedure, resulting in unconditioned responses to these new cues by other animals, but which may appear to the experimenter as conditioned responses to an experimental treatment.

Neither can species traditionally considered micronosmic be excluded a priori from the rigorous controls required for olfactory cues. Birds, for example, have been shown to have the capacity for olfactory acuity which far supersedes traditional estimations, and in some nocturnal bird species, the operation of pheromones has been specifically implied (Bang, 1960).

Finally, it would seem appropriate, in the light of evidence which implicates the compelling effects of hitherto unnoticed cues produced by pheromones and related compounds, to begin to control systematically all aspects of the environmental situation in which experimental subjects are placed.

REFERENCES

Andrew, R. J. The displays of the primates. In J. Buettner-Janusch (Ed.), *Evolutionary and genetic biology of primates.* Vol. 2. New York: Academic Press, 1964.

Bang, B. G. Anatomical evidence for olfactory function in some species of birds. *Nature*, 1960, **188**, 547-548.

Barnett, S. A. *The rat: A study in behaviour.* Chicago: Aldine, 1963.

Bartholomew, G. A. Mother-young relations and the maturation of pup behavior in the Alaskan fur seal. *Animal Behaviour,* 1959, **7**, 163-171.

Beach, F. A., & Gilmore, R. W. Response of male dogs to urine from females in heat. *Journal of Mammalogy*, 1949, **30**, 391-392.

Beach, F. A., & Jaynes, J. Studies of maternal retrieving in rats. III. Sensory cues involved in the lactating female's response to her young. *Behaviour,* 1956, **10**, 104-125.

Blauvelt, H. Dynamics of the mother-newborn relationship in goats. In B. Schaffner (Ed.), *Group processes.* New York: Josiah Macy, Jr., Foundation, 1954.

Bossert, W. H., & Wilson, E. O. The analysis of olfactory communication among animals. *Journal of Theoretical Biology*, 1963, **5**, 443-469.

Bourliere, F. *The natural history of mammals.* New York: A. A. Knopf, 1955.

Bowers, J. M., & Alexander, B. K. Mice: Individual recognition by olfactory cues. *Science*, 1967, **158**, 1208-1210.

Breder, C. M., Jr. The reproductive habits of the common catfish, *Ameiurus nebulosus*, with a discussion of their significance in ontogeny and phylogeny. *Zoologica*, 1935, **19**, 143-185.

Bronson, F. H., & Eleftheriou, B. E. Influence of strange males on implantation in the deermouse. *General and Comparative Endocrinology*, 1963, **3**, 515-518.

Bronson, F. H., & Marsden, H. M. Male-induced synchrony of estrus in deermice. *General and Comparative Endocrinology*, 1964, **4**, 634-637.

Brooks, C. McC. The role of the cerebral cortex and of various sense organs in the excitation and execution of mating activity in the rabbit. *American Journal of Physiology*, 1937, **120**, 544-553.

Bruce, H. M. A block to pregnancy in the mouse caused by proximity of strange males. *Journal of Reproduction and Fertility*, 1960, **1**, 96-103. (a)

Bruce, H. M. Further observations on pregnancy block in mice caused by proximity of strange males. *Journal of Reproduction and Fertility*, 1960, **1**, 311-312. (b)

Bruce, H. M. Time relations in the pregnancy block induced in mice by strange males. *Journal of Reproduction and Fertility*, 1961, **2**, 138-142.

Bruce, H. M. Olfactory block to pregnancy among grouped mice. *Journal of Reproduction and Fertility*, 1963, **6**, 451-460.

Bruce, H. M., & Parkes, A. S. Hormonal factors in exteroceptive block to pregnancy in mice. *Journal of Endocrinology*, 1960, **20**, XXIX.

Bruce, H. M., & Parkes, A. S. The effect of concurrent lactation on the olfactory block to pregnancy in the mouse. *Journal of Endocrinology*, 1961, **22**, VI-VII. (a)

Bruce, H. M., & Parkes, A. S. An olfactory block to implantation in mice. *Journal of Reproduction and Fertility*, 1961, **2**, 195-196. (b)

Bruce, H. M., & Parrott, D. V. M. Role of olfactory sense in pregnancy block by strange males. *Science*, 1960, **131**, 1526.

Burt, W. H. Territoriality and home range concepts as applied to mammals. *Journal of Mammalogy*, 1943, **24**, 346-352.

Butler, C. G. Pheromones in sexual processes in insects. In K. C. Highman (Ed.), *Insect reproduction.* Symposium No. 2. London: Royal Entomological Society, 1964.

Butler, C. G. Insect pheromones. *Biological Review*, 1967, **42**, 42-87.

Carr, W. J., & Caul, W. F. The effect of castration in rat upon the discrimination of sex odours. *Animal Behaviour*, 1962, **10**, 20-27.

Dewar, A. D. Observations on pseudopregnancy in the mouse. *Journal of Endocrinology*, 1959, **18**, 186-190.

Dominic, C. J. Source of the male odour causing pregnancy block in mice. *Journal of Reproduction and Fertility*, 1964, **8**, 266-267.

Dominic, C. J. The origin of the pheromones causing pregnancy block in mice. *Journal of Reproduction and Fertility*, 1965, **10**, 469-472.

Dominic, C. J. Observations on the reproductive pheromones of mice. I. Source. *Journal of Reproduction and Fertility*, 1966, **11**, 407-414. (a)

Dominic, C. J. Observations on the reproductive pheromones of mice. II. Neuroendocrine mechanisms involved in the olfactory block to pregnancy. *Journal of Reproduction and Fertility*, 1966, **11**, 415-421. (b)

Dominic, C. J. Effect of ectopic pituitary grafts on the olfactory block to pregnancy in mice. *Nature*, 1967, **213**, 1242.

Douglas, R. J. Cues for spontaneous alternation. *Journal of Comparative and Physiological Psychology*, 1966, **62**, 171-183.

Eaton, R. L. Group interactions, spacing, and territoriality in cheetah. Paper presented at the meeting of the Midwestern Psychological Association, Chicago, May 1968.

Eibl-Eibesfeldt, I. Über das Vorkommen von Schreckstoffen bei Erdkrotenquappen. *Experentia*, 1949, **5**, 236. (English summary)

Eisenberg, J. F. The behavior of heteromyid rodents. *University of California Publication in Zoology*, 1963, **69** 1-114. (a)

Eisenberg, J. F. A comparative study of sandbathing behavior in heteromyid rodents. *Behaviour*, 1963, **22**, 16-23. (b)

Eleftheriou, B. C., Bronson, F. H., & Zarrow, M. X. Interaction of olfactory and other environmental stimuli on implantation in the deermouse. *Science*, 1962, **137**, 764.

Epple, G., & Lorenz, R. Vorkommen, morphologie und funktion der oternal-drüse bei den platyrrhini. *Folio prumatologica*, 1967, **7**, 98-126.

Etkin, W. (Ed.) Theories of animal socialization and communication. *Social behavior and organization among vertebrates*. Chicago: University of Chicago Press, 1964.

Everett, J. W. Functional corpora lutea maintained for months by autografts of rat hypophysis. *Endocrinology*, 1956, **58**, 786-796.

Everett, J. W. Neural control of reproductive function of the adenohypophysis. *Physiological Review*, 1964, **44**, 373-431.

Frisch, K. von. Über einen Schreckstoff der Fischhaut umd seine biologische Bedeutung. *Zeitschrift füer Vergleichende Physiologie*, 1941, **29**, 46-145.

Goz, H. Über den Art- und Individualgeruch bei Fischen. *Zeitschrift füer Vergleichende Physiologie*, 1954, **29**, 1-45. Cited by P. R. Marler, *Developments in the study of animal communication.* In P. R. Bell (Ed.), *Darwin's Biological Work.* Cambridge: Cambridge University Press, 1959. P. 153.

Hafez, E. S. E., Williams, N., & Wierzbowski, S. The behavior of horses. In E. S. E. Hafez (Ed.), *The behaviour of domestic animals.* Baltimore: Williams & Wilkins, 1962.

Hasler, A. D., & Wisby, W. J. Discrimination of stream odors by fishes and its relation to parent stream behavior. *American Naturalist*, 1951, **85**, 223-238.

Hediger, H. *Wild animals in captivity*. London: Butterworth & Co. 1950.

Hediger, H. *Studies of the psychology and behaviour of captive animals in zoos and circuses.* New York: Criterion Books, 1955.

Heimer, L., & Larsson, K. Mating behavior of male rats after olfactory bulb lesion. *Physiology and Behavior*, 1967, **2**, 207-209.

Hrbacek, I. On the flight reaction of tadpoles of the common toad caused by chemical substances. *Experentia*, 1950, **6** 100-101.

Ilse, D. R. Olfactory marking of territory in two young male loris, *Loris tardigradus lydekkerianus*, kept in captivity in Poona. *British Journal of Animal Behaviour,* 1955, **3**, 118-120.

Jolly, A. *Lemur behavior.* Chicago: University of Chicago Press, 1966.

Jolly, A. Breeding synchrony in wild *Lemur catta*. In S. A. Altmann (Ed.), *Social communication among primates*. Chicago: University of Chicago Press, 1967.

Kalmus, H. The discrimination by the nose of the dog of individual human odours and in particular of the odours of twins. *British Journal of Animal Behaviour*, 1963, **3**, 25-31.

Karlson, P., & Butenandt, A. Pheromones (ectohormones) in insects. *Annual Review of Entomology*, 1959, **4**, 39-58.
Karlson, P., & Lüscher, M. 'Pheromones': A new term for a class of biologically active substances. *Nature*, 1959, **183**, 55-56.
King, J. A. Social behavior, social organization, and population dynamics in a black-tailed prairie dog town in the Black Hills of South Dakota. *Contributions of the Laboratory of Vertebrate Biology*, No. 67, Ann Arbor: University of Michigan Press, 1955.
Kirschenblatt, J. Terminology of some biologically active substances and validity of the term "pheromones." *Nature*, 1962, **195**, 916-917.
Kleerekoper, H., & Mogensen, J. Role of olfaction in the orientation of *Petromyzon marinus.* I. Response to a single amine in prey's body odor. *Physiological Zoology*, 1963, **36**, 347-360.
Klopfer, P., Adams, D. K., & Klopfer, M. S. Maternal "imprinting" in goats. *Proceedings of the National Academy of Science*, 1964, **52**, 911-914.
Kühme, W. Eine chemisch ausgelöste Schwarmreaktion bei jungen Cichliden (Pisces). *Naturwissenschaften*, 1964, **51**, 120-121. Cited by P. R. Marler & W. J. Hamilton, III, *Mechanisms of animal behavior.* New York: Wiley, 1966. P. 305.
Kullenberg, B. Field experiments with chemical sexual attractants on *Aculeate hymenoptera* males. *Zoologiska Bidrag Uppsala*, 1956, **31**, 253-354.
Lamond, D. R. Effect of stimulation derived from other animals of the same species on estrous cycles in mice. *Journal of Endocrinology*, 1959, **18**, 343-349.
Lederer, E. Odeurs et parfums des animaux. *Fortschritte der chemie organischer naturstoffe*, 1950, **6**, 87-153.
Lee, S. van der., & Boot, L. M. Spontaneous pseudopregnancy in mice. *Acta Physiologica et Pharmacologica Neerlandica*, 1955, **4**, 442-444.
Lee, S. van der., & Boot, L. M. Spontaneous pseudopregnancy in mice. II. *Acta Physiologica et Pharmacologica Neerlandica*, 1956, **5**, 213-215.
Lehausen, P., & Wolff, R. Das revier einer haskatze. *Zeitschrift für Tierpsychologie*, 1959, **16**, 666-670.
LeMagnen, J. Olfactory identification of chemical units and mixtures and its role in behavior. In Y. Zotterman (Ed.), *Olfaction and taste.* New York: Macmillan, 1963.
Lenhoff, H. M. Behavior, hormones, and hydra. *Science*, 1968, **161**, 434-442.
Loher, W. The chemical acceleration of the maturation process and its hormonal control in the male of the desert locust. *Proceedings of the Royal Society, Series B*, 1961, **153**, 380-397.
Long, C. J., & Tapp, J. T. Reinforcing properties of odors for the albino rat. *Psychonomic Science*, 1967, **7**, 17-18.
Long, C. J., & Tapp, J. T. An apparatus for the assessment of the reinforcing properties of odors in small animals. *Journal of the Experimental Analysis of Behavior*, 1968, **11**, 49-51.

Lucas, C. E. Ecological effects of external metabolites. *Biological Review*, 1947, **22**, 270-295.

Ludvigson, H. W., & Sytsma, D. The sweet smell of success: Apparent double alternation in the rat. *Psychonomic Science*, 1967, **9**(5), 283-284.

MacGinitie, G. E. The natural history of the blind goby, *Typhlogobius californiensis steindachner. American Midland Naturalist*, 1939, **21**, 489-505.

Marler, P. Developments in the study of animal communication. In P. R. Bell (Ed.), *Darwin's Biological Work*. Cambridge: Cambridge University Press, 1959.

Marler, P. Communication in monkeys and apes. In I. DeVore (Ed.), *Primate Behavior*. New York: Holt, Rinehart & Winston, 1965.

Marler, P. Animal communication signals. *Science*, 1967, **157**, 769-774.

Marler, P. R., & Hamilton, W. J., III. *Mechanisms of animal behavior*. New York: Wiley, 1966.

Marsden, H. M., & Bronson, F. H. Estrous synchrony in mice: Alteration by exposure to male urine. *Science*, 1964, **144**, 1469.

Marsden, H. M., & Bronson, F. H. The synchrony of estrus in mice: Relative roles of the male and female environments. *Journal of Endocrinology*, 1965, **32**, 313-319.

Marsden, H. M., & Holler, N. R. Social behaviour in confined populations of the cottontail and the swamp rabbit. *Wildlife Monographs*, 1964, No. 13. Washington, D. C.: Wildlife Society.

Martof, B. S. Some observations on the role of olfaction among salientian amphibia. *Physiological Zoology*, 1962, **35**, 270-272.

Mason, W. A. Social organization of the South American monkey *Callicebus moloch:* A preliminary report. *Tulane Studies in Zoology*, 1966, **13**, 23-28.

McBride, J. R., Fagerlund, U. H. M., Smith, M., & Tomlinson, N. Olfactory perception in juvenile salmon. II. Conditioned response of juvenile sockeye salmon to lake waters. *Canadian Journal of Zoology*, 1964, **42**, 245-248.

McConnell, J. V. Specific factors influencing planarian behavior. In W. C. Corning & S. C. Ratner (Eds.), *Chemistry of learning*. New York: Plenum Press, 1967.

McFarlane, J. E. Studies on group effects on crickets. I. Effect of methyl linolenate, methyl linoleate and vitamin E. *Journal of Insect Physiology*, 1966, **12**, 179-188.

McHose, J. H. Patterned running as a function of the sequence of trial administration. *Psychonomic Science*, 1967, **9**, 281-282.

McHose, J. H., Jacoby, L. L., & Meyer, P. A. Extinction as a function of number of reinforced trials and squad composition. *Psychonomic Science*, 1967, **9**, 401-402.

McHose, J. H., & Ludvigson, H. W. Differential conditioning with nondifferential reinforcement. *Psychonomic Science*, 1966, **6**, 485-486.

Menzel, R., & Menzel, R. Einiges aus der Pflegewelt der mutterhündin. *Behaviour*, 1953, **5**, 289-304. Cited by J. I. Johnson, R. W. Goy, & K. M. Michels, *Physiological mechanisms and behaviour patterns.* In E. S. E. Hafez (Ed.), *The behaviour of domestic animals.* Baltimore: Williams & Wilkins, 1962. P. 161.

Merton, H. Vii. Studies on reproduction in the albino mouse. *Proceedings of the Royal Society of Edinburgh*, 1938, **58**, 80-96.

Morris, D. The feather postures of birds and the problem of the origin of social signals. *Behaviour*, 1956, **9**, 75-113.

Moynihan, M. Communication in the titi monkey, *Callicebus. Journal of Zoology*, 1966, **150**, 77-127.

Mykytowycz, R. Territorial function of chin gland secretion in the rabbit, *Oryctolagus cuniculus (L). Nature*, 1962, **193**, 799.

Mykytowycz, R. Further observations on the territorial function and history of the submandibular cutaneous (chin) glands in the rabbit. *Oryctolagus cuniculus. Animal Behaviour*, 1965, **13**, 400-412.

Mykytowycz, R., & Nay, T. Studies on the cutaneous glands and hair follicles of some species of *Macropodidae. Commonwealth Scientific and Industrial Research Organization Wildlife Research*, 1964, **9**, 200.

Noble, G. K. The role of dominance in the life of birds. *Auk*, 1939, **56**, 263-273.

Noble, G. K., & Bradley, H. T. The relation of the thyroid and the hypophysis to the moulting process in the lizard, *Hemidactylus helleri. Biological Bulletin*, 1933, **64**, 289-298.

Ottoson, D., & Shepherd, G. M. Experiments and concepts in olfactory physiology. In Y. Zotterman (Ed.), *Progress in brain research*. Vol. 23. New York: Elsevier, 1967.

Parkes, A. S. The role of odorous substances in mammalian reproduction. *Journal of Reproduction and Fertility*, 1960, **1**, 312-314.

Parkes, A. S., & Bruce, H. M. Olfactory stimuli in mammalian reproduction. *Science*, 1961, **134**, 1049-1054.

Parkes, A. S., & Bruce, H. M. Pregnancy-block in female mice placed in boxes soiled by males. *Journal of Reproduction and Fertility*, 1962, **4**, 303-308.

Pearson, O. P. Scent glands of the short-tailed shrew. *Anatomical Record*, 1946, **94**, 615-629.

Pfeiffer, W. The fright reaction in American fish. *American Zoologist*, 1962, **2**, 436. (Abstract) (a)

Pfeiffer, W. The fright reaction of fish. *Biological Reviews*, 1962, **37**, 495-511. (b)

Pfeiffer, W. The fright reaction in North American fish. *Canadian Journal of Zoology*, 1963, **41**, 69-77. (a)

Pfeiffer, W. Alarm substances. *Experentia*, 1963; **19**, 113-123. (b)

Quay, W. B. Seasonal and sexual differences in the dorsal skin gland of the kangaroo rat, *Dipodomys. Journal of Mammalogy*, 1953, **34**, 1-14.

Ressler, R. H., Cialdini, R. B., Ghoca, M. L., & Kleist, S. M. Alarm pheromone in the earthworm, *Lumbricus terrestris:* An alternative to learning. *Science*, 1968, **161**, 597-599.

Reynierse, J. H. Some effects of light on the formation of aggregations in planaria, *Phagocata gracilis. Animal Behaviour*, 1966, **14**, 246-250.

Reynierse, J. H. Aggregation formation in planaria, *Phagocata gracilis* and *Cura foremani:* Species differentiation. *Animal Behaviour*, 1967, **15**, 270-272.

Reynierse, J. H., & Ellis, R. R. Aggregation formation in three species of planaria: Distance to nearest neighbour. *Nature*, 1967, **214**, 895-896.

Reynierse, J. H., Gleason, K. K., & Ottemann, R. Mechanisms producing aggregations in planaria. *Animal Behaviour*, in press.

Rosen, R., & Shelesnyak, M. C. Introduction of pseudopregnancy in rat by silver nitrate on nasal mucosa. *Proceedings of the Society for Experimental Biology and Medicine*, 1937, **36**, 832-834.

Rosen, S., Shelesnyak, M. C., & Zacharias, L. R. Naso-genital relationship. II. Pseudopregnancy following extirpation of the sphenopalatine ganglion in the rat. *Endocrinology*, 1940, **27**, 463-468.

Schinkel, P. G. Effect of presence of ram on ovarian activity of the ewe. *Australian Journal of Agricultural Research*, 1954, **5**, 465-469. (a)

Schinkel, P. G. The effect of the ram on the incidence and occurrence of oestrus in ewes. *Australian Veterinary Journal*, 1954, **30**, 189-195. (b)

Scott, J. P., & Fuller, J. L. *Genetics and the social behavior of the dog.* Chicago: University of Chicago Press, 1965.

Sharman, G. B., Calaby, J. H., & Poole, W. E. Patterns of reproduction in female diprotodont marsupials. In I. W. Rowlands (Ed.), *Symposia of the Zoological Society of London*, 1966, **15**, 205-232.

Shelton, M. Influence of the presence of a male goat on the initiation of estrous cycling and ovulation in Angora does. *Journal of Animal Science*, 1960, **19**, 368-375.

Svihla, A. Habits of the Louisiana mink. *Journal of Mammalogy*, 1931, **13**, 366-368.

Tavolga, W. N. Visual, chemical and sound stimuli as cues in the sex discriminatory behavior of the *Gobiid* fish *Bathygobius soporator. Zoologica,* 1956, **41**, 49-64.

Thiessen, D. D., Friend, H. C., & Lindzey, G. Androgen control of territorial marking in the Mongolian gerbil. *Science*, 1968, **160**, 432-433.

Tinbergen, N. The evaluation of signaling devices. In W. Etkin (Ed.), *Social behavior and organization in vertebrates.* Chicago: University of Chicago Press, 1964.

Todd, J. H., Atema, J., & Bardach, J. E. Chemical communication in social behavior of a fish, the yellow bullhead (*Ictolurus natolis*). *Science*, 1967, **158**, 672-673.

Valenta, J. G., & Rigby, M. K. Discrimination of the odor of stressed rats. *Science*, 1968, **161**, 599-601.

Whitten, W. K. Modification of the estrous cycle of the mouse by external stimuli associated with the male. *Journal of Endocrinology*, 1956, **13**, 399-404. (a)

Whitten, W. K. The effect of the removal of the olfactory bulbs on the gonads of mice. *Journal of Endocrinology*, 1956, **14**, 160-163. (b)

Whitten, W. K. Effect of exteroceptive factors on the estrous cycle of mice. *Nature*, 1957, **180**, 1436.

Whitten, W. K. Modification of the estrous cycle of the mouse by external stimuli associated with the male. Changes in the estrous cycle determined by vaginal smears. *Journal of Endocrinology*, 1958, **17**, 307-313.

Whitten, W. K. Occurrence of anestrous in mice caged in groups. *Journal of Endocrinology*, 1959, **18**, 102-107.

Whitten, W. K. Pheromones and mammalian reproduction. In A. McLaren (Ed.), *Advances in reproductive physiology*. New York: Academic Press, 1966.

Whitten, W. K., Bronson, F. H., and Greenstein, J. A. Estrus-inducing pheromone of male mice: Transport by movement of air. *Science*, 1968, **161**, 584-585.

Wiener, H. External chemical messengers. I. Emission and reception in man. *New York State Journal of Medicine*, 1966, **66**, 3153-3170.

Wiener, H. External chemical messengers. II. Natural history of schizophrenia. *New York State Journal of Medicine*, 1967, **67**, 1144-1165. (a)

Wiener, H. External chemical messengers. III. Mind and body in schizophrenia. *New York State Journal of Medicine*, 1967, **67**, 1287-1310. (b)

Wilson, E. O. Chemical communication among workers of the fire ant *Solenopsis sacuissima*. I. The organization of mass-foraging. *Animal Behaviour*, 1962, **10**, 134-164.

Wilson, E. O. Pheromones. *Scientific American*, 1963, **208**, 100-114.

Wilson, E. O. Chemical communication (pheromone) function in the social insects. *Science*, 1965, **149**, 1064-1071.

Wilson, E. O., & Bossert, W. H. Chemical communication among animals. In G. Pincus (Ed.), *Recent progress in hormone research*. Vol. 19. New York: Academic Press, 1963.

Wynne-Edwards, V. C. *Animal dispersion in relation to social behaviour*. Edinburgh: Oliver & Boyd, 1962.

Young, J. Z. *The life of vertebrates*. Oxford: Clarendon Press, 1950.

SUGGESTIONS FOR FURTHER READING

Archer, J. Effects of population density on behavior in rodents. In J. H. Crook (Ed.), *Social behavior in birds and mammals.* New York: Academic Press, 1970. Pp. 169-210.

Bastock, M. *Courtship: A zoological study*. London: Heinemann, 1967.

Crook, J. H. (Ed.) *Social behavior in birds and mammals.* New York: Academic Press, 1970.

Crook, J. H. The socio-ecology of primates. In *Social behavior in birds and mammals.* New York: Academic Press, 1970. Pp. 103-166.

*Dimond, S. J. *Social behavior of animals.* New York: Harper & Row, 1970.

Etkin, W. (Ed.) *Social behavior of organization among vertebrates.* Chicago: University of Chicago Press, 1964.

*Etkin, W. (Ed.) *Social behavior from fish to man.* Chicago: University of Chicago Press, 1967.

*Frings, H., & Frings, M. *Animal communication*. New York: Blaisdell, 1964.

Sebeok, T. A. (Ed.) *Animal communication*. Bloomington: Indiana University Press, 1968.

*Tinbergen, N. *Social behaviour in animals*. Science Paperbacks. London: Methuen, 1966.

Vine, I. Communication by facial-visual signals. In J. H. Crook (Ed.), *Social behavior in birds and mammals.* New York: Academic Press, 1970. Pp. 279-345.

*Introductory reviews.

IV BEHAVIOR GENETICS

The behavior observed in any organism would not be there if the organism did not have the receptors and effectors to perceive and respond to stimulation. Perception and responsiveness may change as a consequence of *maturation* of receptors and effectors and as a consequence of *experience* or learning; but the underlying mechanisms are innate, or genetically determined. How (and to what) the animal responds and perceives is therefore a consequence of inheritance and experience. (The relationships between the contributions of genetic and experiential factors to the development and actuation of behavior are summarized in the reading by Fox in Chapter V.) Through reciprocal interaction, genetic and environmental factors can influence ontogeny or development and subsequent expression of behavior—the behavioral phenotype.

It is logical to propose that if all environmental factors are kept at a constant and individuals behave differently, these individual differences point to some underlying genetic variable. After appropriate behavioral tests of several individuals (i.e., a random heterogenous population) and an analysis of individual differences, subjects that had high scores and others with low scores on the behavior being studied (e.g., maze-running or mating speed) may be selectively bred. In this way, two strains or lines can be developed (e.g., slow and fast maze-runners). We may then determine the heritability of such traits and develop strains or lines of selectively bred subjects possessing these traits. Differences in behavior may be found in the frequency, amplitude, and duration of a particular action in different strains or hybrids. A good example is the prey-catching fore-limb stab in coyotes. In coyote x dog hybrids it is seen at a lower frequency and amplitude than in coyotes, while it is rarely seen in domesticated dogs. The sequence position of an action in relation to other actions in a temporal sequence and its ease of elicitation (or threshold) may also be modified. Thus the pattern of carrying nest materials tucked in the wing feathers (a characteristic of one species of love bird) may occur out of sequence and be disrupted by a strong tendency to carry the material in the bill in hybrids (a characteristic of another species). Combined actions from two species in their hybrids can thus cause marked changes in behavior sequences. Threshold may also be changed, as exemplified by a partially inhibited prey-killing bite in several F_2 coyote x beagles: coyotes of the same age show no bite inhibition, whereas beagles have "soft mouths" and do not kill the prey. Physiological and emotional-reactivity differences may also be identified (e.g., in locomotor activity and in defecation rates in a strange "open-field" situation). The "open-field" test simply consists of placing the subject in a brightly lighted enclosure, the floor of which is marked off in squares so that the number of squares crossed in a given time can be counted. A fearful rat usually freezes and defecates a good deal. Biochemical differences in brain serotonin levels, of thyroid metabolism, or of blood corticosteroid levels may also be identified.

Another method employed by behavior geneticists is to compare different inbred strains or species and subspecies (usually of fruit flies and mice, because they provide the greatest variety of strains). In all such studies the strains must be raised under similar environmental conditions, because the environment may alter the behavioral phenotype (such as the emotionality or sociability of the animal) and consequently introduce an uncontrolled nongenetic variable into the experiment. Once the behavioral profiles of the strains chosen for study have been determined, the effects of environmental influences upon different genotypes may be advantageously studied. For example, the sensitive period for handling (see Ch. V) and the effects of handling may vary from one strain of mice to the next. Cross-breeding experiments may also be conducted to elucidate the mode of inheritance of certain traits (e.g., whether dominant, recessive, or sex-linked). Following the earlier species-comparison studies of earlier ethologists, exemplified by Lorenz's studies of ducks and geese and their hybrids, the behavior geneticist may focus upon species-isolating mechanisms (e.g., ethological barriers), which in nature prevent hybridization between sympatric species; or he may study the behavior genetics of closely related species or subspecies that have evolved and adapted to different ecological niches. Behavior genetics opens up the door to other problems—for instance, the biochemical bases for differences in behavior and neural and hormonal differences.

The readings in this chapter give a representative picture of this relatively new field of research. The influence of genes on the evolution of behavior is reviewed by Manning, who has spent several years studying the behavior genetics of fruit flies. Of other species, perhaps the most work done on mammals has been on various strains of mice. The readings of van Abeelen and Bruell give an excellent overview of the measures that can be used to determine behavior differences attributable to genetic influences. The paper by Quadagno and Banks focuses on the complex issue of the effects of early environmental influences (e.g., behavior of the mother) on offspring of different genotypes, these authors employing the method of cross fostering as part of their experimental design. For more detailed reports on the behavior genetics in birds, canids, and other species, the reader is urged to consult the list of suggested further readings.

Genes and the Evolution of Insect Behavior

AUBREY MANNING

AN INTRODUCTION TO THE PROBLEM

This chapter will draw together what is known about the effects of genes upon insect behavior and will examine how far this knowledge helps in understanding its evolution. There is no attempt to provide a complete review of the literature, and much that is relevant has been omitted.

At the outset it is necessary to consider what we mean by saying that behavior is inherited. The phrase can imply only that a potentiality is transmitted. An animal possesses the potentiality to perform such and such behavior, given a particular stimulus situation and having been exposed to a particular range of environments in the period prior to testing.

For some types of behavior this environmental range may be quite broad. It matters rather little what the animal's previous experience has been; the same behavior appears at the same sort of stimulus and looks much the same when performed. Such behavior is characterized by rigid patterns of movement or posture and is often evoked by special key stimuli in the environment. It has often been called "instinctive" (e.g., Tinbergen, 1951). In spite of the numerous objections leveled at this term because of past misuse, it has no adequate substitute and is still useful, especially in behavior genetics. Instinctive behavior must be a property of the inherited structure of the nervous system, hormones, etc. This is not to imply that it is not capable of modification, but the basic properties of the sensorimotor patterns and often the responsiveness to particular stimuli are laid down with the developing nervous system. They must depend in some fashion on the physical and functional connectivity of neurons.

At the other end of the scale, behavior may be almost completely dependent in its form and elicitability upon the animal's individual history and exhibit all those characteristics we may subsume under the term "learning." This too must be related to the inherited structure of the nervous system, but in a less direct manner than instinctive behavior. We know that, just as a phylogenetic series can be traced through the vertebrates, showing increasing size and complexity of brain structure, so there is a corresponding increase in the ability for complex learning. All that can be stated is in terms of potentialities. Neither rats nor monkeys normally manifest the behavior associated with the solution of triple ambiguity problems, but the nervous system of the monkey possesses the inherited ability to organize such behavior; that of the rat does not (Harlow, 1958).

Between these two extremes of purely instinctive and purely learned behavior there are all possible intermediates. Most overt behavior depends on elements of both. The interactions between the two are sometimes complex for, as Hinde and Tinbergen (1958) point out, it may be a predisposition to learn particular things that is inherited. Various workers, e.g., Hebb (1953), Lehrman (1953) and Verplanck (1955), have suggested that the instinct-learning dichotomy is no longer a useful one for the study of the development and organization of behavior. For instance, Lehrman has shown that the knowledge that a piece of behavior is inherited does not enable one to predict the nature of its ontogeny or to separate it rigidly from acquired behavior. Nevertheless, the identification of instinctive behavior is still useful for genetic analysis, because it is so much simpler to study the inheritance of those patterns that are well buffered against environmental fluctuations during development and in adult life.

The insects are a particularly appropriate group for this kind of work. Their short life-span with attendant lack of parental care and their compact nervous system have favored the evolution of rigid patterns that require no learning. Insects can learn, but usually such learning serves only to modify the orientation of instinctive responses which are themselves unchanged. The Hymenoptera (ants, bees, and wasps) show extraordinary facility for this type of learning, and it plays an important part in their normal life. By contrast, the Diptera (two-winged flies) exhibit little trace of learning under natural conditions. Indeed, it is extremely difficult to demonstrate experimentally even simple conditioning of a fly; Frings (1941) might be the only worker to report success. The life of Diptera is tied, completely successfully, to a series of rigid, inherited responses to food, mate, and shelter. The ability to modify these responses rapidly apparently confers no noticeable selective advantage.

In general, then, the insect-behavior geneticist is able to study the effects of selection or gene substitution against a clear background of inherited behavior, with the experience of individual insects playing a relatively minor role. He has to choose "units" of behavior for genetic analysis, and behavior is often so complex and diffuse that this is likely to be a difficult task. With much of insect behavior one has a natural grouping into units—the "fixed action patterns" of ethologists—which are distinct and relatively invariable in form (see Hess, 1962). Each of these often consists of a series of muscle contractions which it may be possible to break down further into units. The work of Rothenbuhler (1958) shows that interesting and meaningful results can be achieved by selecting fixed action patterns which are functionally distinct and which turn out to be genetically distinct also. Certainly the empirical approach has much to commend it. At a certain stage in the history of systematics Darwin's definition of a species as "what any competent taxonomist chooses to call one" served its purpose. At this stage in behavior genetics we might well use a comparable definition of a behavior unit.

THE EFFECTS OF GENES ON NERVOUS STRUCTURE

Sperry (1958) has suggested that inherited changes in the nervous system may be due to changes in (1) size, (2) number, (3) connectivity, and (4) excitatory properties of nerve cells. It can be argued, justifiably, that this is but one way of considering genetic effects on the nervous system and that it may be more realistic to choose a completely different system. Nevertheless, Sperry's categories serve to emphasize types of genetic effect whose behavioral results must be profound but which are often overlooked. Although it is a problem of the greatest importance for behavioral evolution, we have little knowledge of how genes operate to affect behavior via the first three categories. These are effects on nervous structure, and we know very little of how far the nervous system shows the structural variability characteristic of all morphological features.

We are unlikely to be able to identify and relate altered structure to altered behavior except in extreme cases. No one is surprised that congenital microcephalics have altered behavior or that the various "waltzer"-type genes of the mouse (Grüneberg, 1952) have postural and locomotor effects commensurate with the middle-ear abnormalities they produce.

An equally profound behavioral result may be expected when the number of chromosome sets is altered. Tetraploid animals, which have twice the normal number, are usually much the same size as normals, but their cells are approximately twice normal size (Fankhauser, 1945, 1955). This means the animals have only one-half the normal number of cells, brain cells included. It is fairly easy to obtain salamanders with three, four, five, or even eight sets of chromosomes and, although they are often rather sickly animals, they are potentially of great interest for behavior studies. Fankhauser et al. (1955) and Vernon and Butsch (1957) have shown that triploid and tetraploid salamanders with 33⅓ and 50 percent reduction in cell number, respectively, have markedly impaired learning ability. It would be interesting to know what happens to their instinctive behavior.

Haploid animals, with only a single chromosome set, have a doubled cell number. Among vertebrates they show very reduced viability, perhaps because of the total unmasking of deleterious recessive genes. This makes the Hymenoptera of particular interest because, with their method of sex determination, males normally develop from unfertilized eggs and are haploid in origin. Presumably the ancestral Hymenoptera had males with doubled cell number, but selection has favored genes that increase cell size and reduce cell number to normal. Haploid-male cells are about the same size as those of diploid females among *Habrobracon* (Speicher, 1935) and the honeybee (Oehninger, 1913). The situation among honeybees is complicated by the normal occurrence of endopolyploidy, where the chromosome number of various tissues or organs is multiplied (Merriam and Ris, 1954).

As far as the genetic effects on the structure of the insect nervous system are concerned, there is only the work of Power (1943). He showed that the gene *bar* which reduces the number of ommatidia in Drosophila also affects the structure of the brain. Fibers develop centripetally from the retinal cells, and there are consequently many fewer in bar-eyed flies. This reduction extends beyond the first synapses in the visual system into the internal glomerulus and even beyond, though with diminishing effect. Thus, bar-eyed flies are deprived not only of receptors but also of the corresponding parts of the visual nervous system. Many genes which affect sense organs must have similar repercussions on the nervous system. The bristle genes of Drosophila, which affect tactile receptors primarily, spring to mind, and also the gene *antennaless*. The behavioral effects of this gene (Begg and Packman, 1951) go far beyond those produced by amputating the antennae of normal flies (Manning, 1959a). Part of this difference may be due to effects on the antennal nerves and sensory centers as well as general debilitation.

THE EFFECTS OF GENES ON BEHAVIOR

Because there is so little information on the structural effects of genes, we must rely mostly on behavioral descriptions of gene action. The examples in insects differ widely in the degree to which they have been analyzed, but they point toward one obvious conclusion. The commonest effect that mutations have upon behavior is to alter, not the nature of the patterns involved, but their threshold and the frequency with which they are performed.

In Drosophila, for example, no gene has been described which affects the qualitative form of a behavior pattern. There is no behavioral equivalent of a morphological mutant like *aristapedia* where an antenna is replaced by an abortive leg [at least, if we except the anomalous *transformer* gene which changes a genotypic female into a male with male behavior (Sturtevant, 1945)]. Rather, there is the equivalent of many bristle genes that alter the length and number of bristles but retain their basic form.

Various genes of *Drosophila melanogaster* have been shown to have a deleterious effect on the mating success of male flies which carry them, e.g., *ebony* and *vestigial* (Rendel, 1951); *white* (Reed and Reed, 1950; Petit, 1958); *yellow* (Bastock, 1956). It is worth examining one of the best-analyzed examples in more detail. Bastock (1956) has shown that the reduced success of *yellow* males is due to the poorer stimulating effect of their courtship behavior. *Melanogaster's* courtship can be divided into four basic behavior patterns: (1) "orientation," in which the male stands close to or follows the female, (2) "vibration," in which he rapidly vibrates that wing closest to the female's head, (3) "licking," in which he extends his proboscis and licks the female's ovipositor, and (4) "attempted copulation," in which he tries to mount her (Bastock and Manning, 1955). Vibration and licking are certainly the most important elements in stimulating the female and causing her to become receptive. *Yellow* males perform these and other elements in a precisely normal fashion. They also court as persistently as normal males, but their courtship has a smaller proportion of vibration and licking and is therefore less stimulating.

The *yellow* gene's effect is thus a subtle one, and we have no idea where the gene operates in the chain between the male's perceiving the female and performing various sequences of muscle contractions. Similarly, Williams and Reed (1944) have shown that various genes produce small, but significant, changes in the normal wing-beat frequency of Drosophila. The stimulus-response chain is simpler than in the case of courtship, but the genes could still operate via any of a large number of combinations of sense organs, nerves, or muscles.

Apart from single-gene effects, changes in the genotype as a result of selection or domestication also have behavioral repercussions. For example, Bösiger (1960) finds that the reduced mating success of various mutant stocks of *D. melanogaster* is not due to the marker genes but results from the accumulation of a large number of genes during many generations of domestication. Ewing (1961) shows that the genotypic changes produced by selection for large and small body size, again in *D. melanogaster*, also affect the courtship behavior of males. Small flies have a higher proportion of vibration and licking in their display than large or control flies. Ewing demonstrates convincingly that this is not a direct result of the genetic changes that have altered size. It is produced by secondary selection within the culture bottles of small flies which "compensates" for their reduced wing area and the reduced stimulating ability that follows.

Clearly, some very rapid evolution can take place in a Drosophila bottle. Various artificial-selection experiments show how much variability for genes that affect behavior is present in ordinary populations.

Hirsch and his coworkers (see Hirsch, 1962) have shown how readily accessible to selection are the numerous genes which affect the levels of simple photo- and geotactic responses. Their experiments are described in more detail elsewhere in this volume. A similarly marked response to selection was found by Manning (1961), using the mating speed of Drosophila. Fifty pairs of virgin flies were introduced into a bottle and pairs removed as they began to copulate, the fastest and slowest being used for breeding. With unselected control flies, 25 pairs had mated in the bottle after about 6 minutes. After seven generations of selection, this was reduced to some 3 minutes by the fast-mating lines, while the slow-mating lines took 30 minutes or more. Natural selection clearly keeps mating speed in normal populations quite close to the maximum.

In this case, selection changed the behavior of both sexes, but primarily the males. They showed a changed pattern of courtship comparable to that produced by the *yellow* gene described above. The genes which had accumulated in the fast-mating lines increased the frequency with which the vibration and licking elements were performed. In the slow lines these elements occurred less frequently than normal. Mating speed is a complex and somewhat arbitrary character, and it was only to be expected that sexual behavior was not the only thing affected by selection. Changes in the general locomotor activity of the flies had just as great an effect upon mating speed. These changes were not in the same direction as those in sexual behavior. The slow-mating lines were slow partly because they were so intensely active when put into the mating bottle that it was many minutes before any began courting. Conversely, the fast-mating flies were very sluggish in all but sexual responses. Unselected controls were intermediate in both respects and probably had an optimum "balance" between sexual and general activity. The genetic basis of these two aspects of behavior is certainly fairly distinct, and they can be changed independently as a result of strong selection. Their essential independence is further demonstrated by the fact that, with a different selection technique, slow-mating lines of flies were produced which also showed lowered general activity (Manning, 1963).

This short account of gene effects on Drosophila behavior serves to emphasize the lability of behavioral thresholds. It is tempting to speculate that genes may operate directly on the nervous system in a manner related to Sperry's fourth category listed above, that of the excitatory properties of neurons. This might involve changes in membrane permeability, enzyme secretion, or anything that can affect a neuron's threshold. In no case do we have any of the relevant details of gene action so that little is gained by attempting to be more precise.

The evidence that genes can affect neural thresholds directly is purely circumstantial, but the slow-mating flies of Manning (1961) might be considered as an example. Their poor mating performance does not appear to be the result of gene action on the flies' general metabolism or muscular efficiency. The same muscles that work at low intensity in a sexual situation are involved in high-intensity activity in other situations. Again, their sense organs may be impaired, but none operate exclusively in a sexual context and there is no other sign of impairment. In many respects the nervous system itself is the most plausible site for gene action.

It is not surprising that this should be so. The nervous system is in constant activity; the second-to-second changes in behavior are not produced by the initiation and termination of impulse trains in particular tracts. Rather, as a response to changing sensory inflow, there are changes in the frequencies of both excitatory and inhibitory impulses in tracts that are continuously active at some level. The infinite subtlety of threshold changes in such a system provides plenty of scope for gene action. In addition, there are important parts of the nervous system whose main function seems to be modifying the level of discharge in others. The supra- and subesophageal ganglia of insects appear to exercise this kind of control over the lower segmental centers of the thorax and abdomen. It is in the latter that the motor coordination of discrete behavior patterns is organized, but their discharge is dependent on the interplay of descending facilitatory and inhibitory impulses from the brain (see Vowles, 1961a, 1961b). For example, if the head of a male praying mantis is removed, it begins incessant walking movements. If it encounters a female, incessant copulatory movements begin, which may end with normal and successful copulation (Roeder, 1935). Roeder et al. (1960) have shown that this behavior is the result of greatly increased spontaneous activity in the thoracic and abdominal ganglia of the mantis following the severance of connections with the brain.

THE BEHAVIOR OF GYNANDROMORPHS

At this point, when considering the neurological basis of insect behavior, it is relevant to consider briefly one special type of genetic aberration which yields some interesting behavioral information. Gynandromorphs are mosaic individuals, some of whose cells are genetically male and others female. Unlike vertebrates, in insects the gonads do not produce a hormone that coordinates the development of secondary sexual characters. Thus transplanting ovaries into a castrated-male-insect larva does not affect the development of normal male characters and behavior. Sex is determined entirely by the chromosomes, and it is perfectly possible to have a male head and thorax joined to a female abdomen containing fertile ovaries. The various genetic situations that give rise to gynandromorphs are described by Sinnott et al. (1958).

The behavior of gynandromorphs has been described only in two types of Diptera, *Drosophila* (Morgan and Bridges, 1919; Hollingsworth, 1955) and the housefly, *Musca domestica* (Milani and Rivosecchi, 1954), and in two types of Hymenoptera, the parasitic wasp, *Habrobracon juglandis* (Whiting, 1932), and the honeybee, *Apis mellifera* (Sakagami and Takahashi, 1956). In addition, the behavior of "intersex" Drosophila (which show a varying mixture of male and female characters but are not true gynandromorphs) has been described by Sturtevant (1920) and Hollingsworth (1959).

Gynandromorphs are interesting because they provide a unique means of assessing the relative roles of the brain and the more peripheral centers. How does an insect behave, say, when its brain is male, but its thoracic and abdominal ganglia are female?

It is impossible as yet to give a clear-cut answer to this question, for the evidence is incomplete and conflicting. The evidence from *Drosophila* and *Habrobracon* agrees in finding that the sex of the brain determines behavior. Whiting's (1932) evidence is particularly interesting. In *Habrobracon* both sexes have distinctive behavior and, in particular, female behavior is not revealed merely by an absence of male patterns, which is often all that can be observed in *Drosophila.* Only female *Habrobracon* mount, palpate, and sting caterpillars which are their normal hosts; males ignore them. Whiting observed 62 gynandromorphs and, in those which had a head of one sex and abdomen of the other, found a clear dependence on the head. Thus wasps with female heads and male abdomens would mount and palpate caterpillars, try to sting them, and even make egg-laying movements with their completely male abdomens.

Whiting had some wasps which were male on one side and female on the other; their brains thus contained both types of cell. Such wasps showed signs of both male *and* female behavior, though rarely in a complete fashion. Left/right gynandromorphs also had a tendency to show inappropriate responses to external stimuli. Presented with a caterpillar they sometimes made male courtship movements or would try to sting a female wasp instead of courting her.

Such a full correspondence between the sex of the brain and behavior might not be expected, in view of the neurophysiological evidence given above. The insect brain operates primarily as a general modifier on behavior patterns which are themselves organized in the thoracic and abdominal centers. We might predict that these lower centers would sometimes "break through" in a gynandromorph to reveal their own potentialities.

Something approaching this has been found in gynandromorph houseflies and honeybees. Milani and Rivosecchi (1954) have a few observations on *Musca* and report that sex behavior follows the sex of the abdomen. Flies with female heads on male bodies successfully attempted copulation with normal females. Sakagami and Takahashi (1956) have records of the behavior of some 40 gynandromorph honeybees with a varying mixture of male and female parts. They could not observe specifically sexual behavior because the female workers are sterile and there is very little characteristic drone behavior. However, drones normally move about the hive in a more sluggish manner than workers. On the whole they found that this character in gynandromorphs agreed with the degree of "maleness" of the head. This was not true of the complex series of social patterns such as cell cleaning, mutual feeding, and hive ventilation, which are normally performed only by workers. Sakagami and Takahashi found that even gynandromorphs with completely male head and female body showed many of these patterns in completely normal form. This is the more striking in that the structure of the brain is very different in the two sexes. Drones have enormous eyes and correspondingly enlarged visual centers, and their corpora pedunculata or mushroom bodies are much reduced compared with those of a worker's brain.

Sakagami and Takahashi suggest several possible explanations for their results. Considering them alongside the other gynandromorph evidence, it seems certain that both male and female insects inherit a nervous system capable of all the behavior shown by the species. This is also the case among vertebrates where the hormonal balance determines which type of behavior is evoked. Some other kind of switch mechanism must operate in insects. In *Drosophila* and *Habrobracon* the switch appears to operate primarily upon the brain which in turn evokes behavior of the corresponding sex from the lower centers. However, in *Musca*, a relative of *Drosophila*, and the honeybee, a relative of *Habrobracon*, the sex of the brain has apparently less influence. These inconsistencies between relatives are unexpected and we must simply wait for more detailed information.

HOW ARE GENE-CONTROLLED CHANGES RELATED TO THE EVOLUTION OF INSECT BEHAVIOR?

We have seen that the usual effect of genes is to alter behavior in a quantitative, rather than qualitative, fashion. This dichotomy is not absolute. If, during evolution, a series of quantitative changes gradually reduces the performance frequency of a behavior pattern to zero, a qualitative change in the animal's behavior repertoire has resulted. Further, it can be argued that, if the units chosen for analysis are small enough, any change is a quantitative one. Nevertheless, the dichotomy is useful when considering the manner in which behavior evolves.

We must now examine how the divergence of behavior between species and races may be related to gene action. Can we understand behavioral evolution in terms of natural selection operating over a long period on small inherited changes?

We need data from a range of closely related species, and fortunately there have recently been a number of excellent comparative studies of various insect groups. Among the investigators, we may list Spieth (1952) who contributed a study of the courtship displays of some 100 species of Drosophila, Blest (1957) who analyzed the defensive displays of a number of Saturniid and Sphingid moths, and Crane who studied the analogous displays of some Mantids (1952) and the courtship of Heliconiid butterflies (1957a). Still within the bounds of the Arthropods, Crane also made comparative studies of courtship by Salticid spiders (1949) and fiddler crabs (1957b). All these workers have studied a range of related species, and all have been particularly interested in the evolution of the behavior they describe.

In all these groups it is found, not unexpectedly, that the instinctive-behavior repertoire is quite conservative. There is a limited set of behavior units, just as morphological features are also limited. It is clear that, while distant relatives may show behavior differences which appear to be "qualitative," closer relatives differ in a more simple "quantitative" way. This point has already been stressed by Tinbergen (1959a) and relates very well to what is known of gene action.

We can examine the nature of the behavior changes within a group in more detail. Nearly all the behavior under consideration has the function of communicating something to conspecifics or to potential predators. Historically, responses that serve such a function have been derived from various sources in the insects' repertoire. And they have been modified to make them distinctive and conspicuous. This type of evolutionary change has been called "ritualization" (Tinbergen, 1952). Blest (1961) provides a full discussion of the ritualization concept and, following him, the basic features of the process may be considered under two headings.

Changes in the Releasing Mechanism

In many cases we find that related species have different thresholds for the production of homologous responses to the same stimulus. Some moths of the genus *Automeris* perform a defense display in response to tactile stimulation, but their thresholds vary. Different parts of the display vary in their thresholds independently of each other (Blest, 1957). Crane (1952) describes similar threshold differences for the defensive displays of Mantids. Again, *Drosophila* species appear to differ in their sexual-behavior thresholds as measured by the latency from the introduction of the sexes to the beginning of courtship (Spieth, 1952; Manning, 1959b). Differences of this type are very easily related to genetic changes. They exactly resemble the changes produced in *Drosophila* by artificial selection (Manning, 1961).

Often relatives differ in the dominant sensory modality concerned in evoking homologous responses. *Drosophila* species vary greatly in their dependence on visual stimulation during courtship. *D. subobscura* never mates in the absence of light, but its close relatives *pseudoobscura* and *persimilis* are little affected by darkness (Wallace and Dobzhansky, 1946). Spieth and Hsu (1950) describe a parallel case in the *melanogaster*-species group. At one end of the scale is *auraria*, like *subobscura* quite inactive sexually if kept in the dark. At the other end is *melanogaster* itself, which is scarcely affected. *Melanogaster's* closest relative, *simulans*, is strongly affected by the absence of light. These two species form a sibling pair which must have diverged very recently, yet already they show considerable differences in behavior. The courtship of both types of male is quite similar, but while *melanogaster* females are most responsive to the chemical and tactile stimuli the male provides, *simulans* responds mainly to the visual stimuli. *Simulans* females probably have lowered thresholds somewhere in the visual system, and they also have more visual receptors. Their eyes have more ommatidia than those of *melanogaster*, and this means more neurons in the visual nervous system (Manning, 1959b).

Crane (1949) has found a comparable situation among Salticid spiders, where a series based upon increasing light dependence can be traced. Here, however, the dependence on vision is not restricted to the sexual situation (we do not know that it is in *D. simulans*) but extends through all the spiders' behavior.

Changes in Coordination

This is essentially a blanket category. We have too little knowledge of the mechanisms underlying the performance of an instinctive-behavior pattern to be able to classify coordination changes meaningfully. Morris (1957) and Blest (1961) consider more fully a number of changes which might come under this heading. The "aim" of ritualization has been to produce a distinctive, unambiguous signal. One conspicuous way in which homologous patterns differ between relatives is in the degree to which various elements of the pattern are emphasized.

Male fiddler crabs of the genus *Uca* all show a rhythmic claw waving in their courtship display. The genus falls into two groups behaviorally. One accentuates the lateral movement of the claw during the wave; the other accentuates the vertical component. Species also differ in the degree to which the body is raised on the ambulatory legs during the wave (Crane, 1957b). Brown (1965) describes how the courtship wing vibration of various members of the *Drosophila obscura* species group differs in the degree to which the trailing edge of the wing is lowered. Female Heliconiid butterflies show similar variations in their wing movements during courtship (Crane, 1957a). These are Arthropod examples, but numerous cases of this type are described for birds, where some displays are very fully analyzed (e.g., Tinbergen, 1959b).

A second type of coordination change which may accompany ritualization is an increase or decrease in the speed of a movement. Blest (1957) describes variation in display speed among moths. Lindauer (1957) compares the speed and rhythm of the waggle dance by the four species of *Apis* (honeybees). To indicate a distance of 100 meters to the food source, the domestic honeybee, *A. mellifera*, shows 10 runs per 15 seconds. *A. dorsata* shows 9 runs to indicate the same distance, *A. indica* shows 7.5, and *A. florea* only 6. The same kinds of variations are found between different strains of the domestic honeybee (Boch, 1957).

These are but a few examples of some of the more important changes which have occurred repeatedly during the microevolution of behavior; a more complete review is provided by Manning (1965). It is perfectly reasonable to consider them as a result of the accumulation of small quantitative effects produced by gene mutation. Changes in the threshold of responses are, as we have seen, typical results of mutation. The exaggerations of particular parts of a movement or changes in its speed may well result from threshold changes also. A group of muscles is active earlier or later in a sequence and maintains its activity for a longer or shorter time. The time occupied by sequences may be varied and so on. If correct, these interpretations require that genes are able to exert their effects at particular sites in the nervous system or upon particular sense organs or muscles. This speculation can be checked with suitable material, and there is some circumstantial evidence in favor of it; e.g., Rothenbuhler (1958) has found that different parts of a behavior sequence are affected individually by different genes. Certainly the nervous system is diverse enough in histology and biochemistry to make limited gene action quite feasible.

THE INHERITANCE OF BEHAVIOR PATTERNS THEMSELVES

So far we have considered only how existing behavior patterns are modified by genes. We must now consider the inheritance of "whole" units of behavior. Instinctive behavior is usually efficiently adapted to an animal's normal environment. It is probable that some of its adaptiveness has been attained by means of "genetic assimilation" (Waddington, 1961). This is the process of accumulating genes that enable the organism to make an adaptive response to an environmental stimulus. The threshold for this response becomes lowered over successive generations, provided the environmental stimulus is consistently present. Eventually individuals are produced which develop the response even in the absence of the original stimulus.

Waddington has demonstrated genetic assimilation experimentally for some morphological and physiological responses to external stimuli by *Drosophila*. In behavioral terms it could lead to acquired behavior patterns becoming inherited ones. For example, Thorpe and others have studied a form of "larval conditioning" to host caterpillars in the parasitic Ichneumonoid, *Nemeritis* (Thorpe and Jones, 1937; Thorpe, 1938), and also the conditioning of *Drosophila* to contaminants in food (Thorpe, 1939). Here the insects have an inherited preference for the normal situation, but their aversion to abnormal stimuli can be significantly reduced by exposure to them during the larval period. Consistent selection for the insects that responded best might well lead to the development of strains that showed inherited preferences for the new situation. A start has been made on experiments of this type, using Drosophila and peppermint oil as a contaminant in their food (Moray and Connolly, 1963; Moray and Arnold, 1964). Although there are some signs of assimilation, the situation is complicated by the relative toxicity of peppermint oil.

Whether or not it arose in this way, the inheritance of any behavior unit is likely to be controlled by many genes. Caspari (1958, 1963) and others have suggested this previously, and all the argument of the preceding sections supports this view. We can only envisage the construction of the necessary neural mechanism by many small steps. Large, sudden changes are almost certain to be disadvantageous both for their physiological effects and because they are likely to be maladaptive behaviorally.

Unfortunately, it is very difficult to obtain direct evidence of the inheritance of behavior patterns. In hybrids the behavior patterns rarely show any sign of breaking up into smaller units, although these might be impossible to recognize anyway. As Caspari (1963) points out, F_2 hybrids and backcrosses are needed if units of behavior that correspond to genetic units are to be isolated. Only rarely can these be obtained, save from species which are so closely related that their behavioral repertoires are very similar. Such species usually differ by genes that affect only the frequency of performance of patterns common to both. Even if a pattern is apparently absent in one parent species, the necessary neural mechanism may be present, though with a very high threshold. "Scissoring," a courtship movement typical of *Drosophila simulans* males, is not normally seen in *D. melanogaster.* Nevertheless, it can be evoked under abnormal conditions (Manning, 1959b). Sometimes a behavior pattern present in both parent species is absent in the hybrid. Ehrman (1960) describes how the female hybrids between two subspecies of *D. paulistorum* are completely unreceptive to the courtship of males and never mate. This too may be a result of a greatly elevated threshold.

If the performance frequency of a behavior pattern in the hybrids is intermediate between those of the parent species, and if the F_2 generation shows a full range of frequencies, we can argue little about the pattern's actual inheritance. We know only that multiple loci affect its performance threshold. Sometimes a single locus seems to determine whether or not a pattern occurs. For example, Hörmann-Heck (1957) studied the inheritance of a number of the courtship patterns in two crickets, *Gryllus campestris* and *G.*

maculatus. Some of them appeared to be controlled by a single locus, but this is only a shorthand way of saying that this locus controlled the performance threshold of the pattern in a rather switchlike manner. The underlying mechanisms must depend on numerous loci for their development, although selection may have caused these loci to become linked, perhaps within an inversion, so that they are inherited as a block. Systems of this type have been shown to control the inheritance of color and mimicry patterns of Lepidoptera (Sheppard, 1961).

An important advance in the study of behavioral inheritance may come from the analysis of animal sounds. The sound spectograph enables an exact record to be made of a most complex, ritualized series of muscular movements. The breakdown of parental patterns in hybrids may be detected with far more certainty than is normally possible. There is already some work with hybrids among grasshoppers (Perdeck, 1958) and doves (Lade and Thorpe, 1964), although F_2 hybrids and backcrosses are difficult to obtain because of the near sterility of the F_1 hybrids.

GENES AND SEXUAL ISOLATION

Hitherto we have considered how insect behavior has been changed by evolution. However, the influence is not in a single direction. In conclusion, we must give some account of how behavior influences the course that evolution takes, and the study of sexual isolation has been foremost in this connection. Sexual isolation may be defined as the reduction of hybridization by behavioral barriers to mating between species or strains.

Sexual-isolation studies gained great impetus from the publication of two books, Dobzhansky's *Genetics and the Origin of Species* (1937) and Mayr's *Systematics and the Origin of Species* (1942). One central problem was how divergent species emerge from a common ancestral population. Must populations be geographically isolated before divergence can occur? How stable are the genetic differences which have arisen between populations in isolation if they subsequently meet?

Some barrier to prevent hybridization must be present if previously isolated populations are not to mingle once more. Müller

(1942) suggested that sexual isolation could arise as one consequence of genetic divergence while two populations are still separated. When they meet again a barrier already exists and they do not interbreed. Dobzhansky considered this unlikely but envisaged sexual isolation arising rather quickly after the populations meet. If divergence has proceeded far enough to render the hybrids at a disadvantage, selection will favor the rapid evolution of a sexual-isolation mechanism.

Evidence favoring each point of view has been put forward, but nearly everybody now agrees that they are not mutually exclusive and must reinforce one another in many cases. It was important to discover how small a genetic divergence could produce sexual isolation. Many people have looked for isolation between different strains of the same species, different inbred lines, and between stocks differing by only a single gene. Nearly all the work is on Drosophila, and Patterson and Stone (1952) give a very full account of the literature to that date. Much of it suffers from a total disinterest in behavior as such. Often isolation has been detected simply by scoring the genotype of the progeny, with no direct observation. In some cases where the insects have been watched, the courtship of a male Drosophila has been considered simply as a vehicle by which he expresses the degree of his sexual isolation from the female he is courting. Thus males that copulate at random with females of their own and a foreign strain have nevertheless been described as showing "courtship discrimination" between them.

Sexual isolation among insects is based on a variety of sensory discriminations. In many *Drosophila* species it is primarily chemical, either from contact chemoreceptors on the tarsi or via the antennae (Miller, 1950; Spieth, 1952; Manning, 1959a). Females usually discriminate more strongly than males. It is not disadvantageous for males to be aroused by a wide range of stimuli for they can mate many times, but females mate less often (sometimes only once), and their choice of male is critical.

Chemical differences between populations are almost certain to arise at a very early stage in divergence and thus are well adapted to form the basis for isolation. Kessler (1962) shows that isolation based upon contact-chemical differences has already developed between geographical races of *D. paulistorum*, which must be of very recent origin.

Visual discrimination against foreign mates is probably rare in insects; they do not possess fine enough form vision. Among the insects that use visual stimuli in courtship, such as butterflies, the males approach female models of almost any color (Tinbergen et al., 1942; Stride, 1957; Magnus, 1958). But when they come closer, they usually court only those models of roughly the correct color. Chemical stimuli are concerned in the final stages of butterfly courtship, and these are presumably more critical.

Perdeck (1958) describes a remarkable example of sexual isolation between two sibling grasshopper species (*Chorthippus brunneus* and *C. biguttulus*), which is based entirely on sound stimuli. The females are attracted to their males by their distinctive songs. If they are artificially lured into the vicinity of foreign males they show no subsequent discrimination at all.

Genes appear to affect sexual isolation in a typically quantitative fashion. Laboratory stocks of *Drosophila melanogaster* and *D. simulans* vary in the degree of isolation between the species (Barker, 1962). Koopman (1950) showed by artificial selection that *D. pseudoobscura* and *D. persimilis* normally show considerable variability for genes affecting the sexual isolation between them. By eliminating hybrids from mixed populations, he was able to increase isolation markedly within a few generations, mostly by increasing the discrimination of *persimilis* males.

We have seen that single-gene mutations often reduce the mating success of males that carry them. However, it is less common for them to affect the receptivity of females; thus mutant males may be at a disadvantage both with mutant and normal females. This "one-sided mating preference" in *D. melanogaster* has been described for the mutants *yellow* (Merrell, 1949; Bastock, 1956), *raspberry* (Merrell, 1949), and *white* (Reed and Reed, 1950). The extent to which this situation could represent an initial stage in the evolution of true sexual isolation has been disputed. Merrell (1953), for example, argues that it has little relevance because the mutant males are always at a disadvantage in mixed populations. He has indeed shown that various genes are eliminated at the rate predicted from the mating deficiency of the carrier males.

In an isolated population, however, a change in the courtship behavior of one sex immediately imposes a new selection pressure on the other. Bastock (1956) finds that *yellow* females taken from stocks that have carried the gene for many generations are more receptive than normal females. This difference helps to "compensate" for the courtship deficiency of *yellow* males, which now inseminate *yellow* females at nearly the same rate as normal males. This increased receptivity is not an effect of the *yellow* gene itself. It has been produced by selection in *yellow* stocks where the courtship of males is poor, but the usual selection pressure to mate and lay eggs quickly remains.

If in an isolated population there appears a gene that is generally advantageous but has an effect comparable to *yellow* on the courtship of males, selection will not favor an increase of female receptivity beyond a certain point. The reasons for this appear to be twofold in *Drosophila*. Firstly, a degree of unwillingness enables females to "sample" the courtship of males and to discriminate against those which are deficient. Smith (1958) has discussed this type of sexual selection and shows how it enables *D. subobscura* females to avoid mating with inbred males of low fertility. Bösiger (1960) puts forward similar ideas. Secondly, if female receptivity increases too far, they may accept foreign males and be rendered effectively sterile since they mate only once.

Would, then, a gene such as *yellow*, if it confers other advantages, spread only rather slowly through a population, having to overcome its behavioral disadvantage? Bastock argues that selection favors females that respond preferentially to some aspect of their males' courtship which is less affected by the gene. If vibration and licking are reduced, as by *yellow*, the females might respond more to visual aspects of the orientation part of the display. This, in turn, will result in selection for males which accentuate this part of courtship. Eventually this mutual selection process will lead to sexual isolation from other populations which still rely most on vibration and licking. The divergence of *D. melanogaster* and *D. simulans* from a common ancestor is most reasonably explained in this way. *Simulans* males are more sluggish and court less actively than *melanogaster*, but their females respond to visual aspects of the display and, if anything, accept them more easily than *melanogaster* females accept their males (Manning, 1959b). Such a system agrees well with what is known of the behavior differences between other closely related *Drosophila* species. It means that quite small genetic changes might lay the foundations for sexual isolation in geographically isolated populations. These will be quickly strengthened by selection if they subsequently meet and have disadvantageous hybrids.

The effects which genes have on habitat selection also have repercussions on sexual isolation. Quite often the isolation found between species in the laboratory seems insufficient to account for the rarity of naturally occurring hybrids. *D. pseudoobscura* and *D. persimilis* are a case in point. Clearly their sexual isolation is reinforced by the fact that where they are sympatric they choose different microhabitats within an area (Pittendrigh, 1958). Waddington et al. (1954) have demonstrated that genetic divergence such as occurs in domestic Drosophila stocks has a direct effect on habitat selection and presumably Drosophila choose those environments where they survive best. Kalmus (1941) shows that, under particular circumstances, genes that are normally disadvantageous may show improved survival. *Yellow*, for example, survives starvation in a moist atmosphere better than wild types.

Differences in habitat selection and survival ability are of greatest importance in those areas where two closely related species overlap. In the absence of competition they may have a wide range of microhabitats but, when they compete, each species is forced to occupy only those where it can survive better than its relative. Among birds there are good examples of habitat selection expanding and contracting according to competition. The willow warbler (*Phylloscopus trochilus*) and its close relative the chiffchaff (*P. collybita*) both breed over a wide area of Europe. The willow warbler normally lives in low bushes and scrub whereas the chiffchaff occupies trees and tall bushes. In the Canary Islands, the willow warbler is absent; there the chiffchaff frequents both types of habitat (Lack and Southern, 1949). Similarly, in the Sierra Nevada of California, *Drosophila pseudoobscura* is forced, by competition with *D. persimilis*, into woodlands that are drier than those it prefers in the more eastern and southern portions of its range where the latter species is absent (Pittendrigh, 1958).

Even within a Drosophila population cage in the laboratory there may be a sufficient range of habitats for microgeographical isolation to exist between strains. Knight et al. (1956) and Crossley (1963) have attempted to select for sexual isolation between different mutants of *D. melanogaster*. They mixed stocks which were genotypically similar, except that one was homozygous for the gene *vestigial*, which greatly reduces wing development, and the other for *ebony*, which affects body color and also impairs vision. They imposed selection for isolation by removing the hybrids, which are phenotypically wild, each generation. Both found that the stocks did not always mix and mate at random in population cages and jars. One result of the presence of the *ebony* and *vestigial* genes was to cause the two stocks to react differently to light and other features of the containers when they were first introduced as virgins. This microhabitat selection was certainly increased by their selection and reinforced any true sexual isolation.

Another example is that given by Hovanitz (1953) who describes how a gene affecting wing color in the butterfly *Colias eurythme* also changes its optimum temperature and light intensity for flight. White females are most active in the early morning and just before sunset, when temperature and light are low. Yellow and orange females show a peak of activity at noon. The white gene does not affect the color of males, but if it affects their activity in a similar way to that of females, it may well influence the frequency of mating between the different genotypes. Genes that affect habitat selection in this way are to some extent "autoisolating," and this is bound to influence, and perhaps accelerate, the evolution of sexual isolation.

CONCLUSION

The speculation-to-fact ratio in this discussion has inevitably been rather high. Yet we can understand in principle if not in detail how insect behavior has evolved by the accumulation of small inherited changes. One urgent need is for more physiological data on how genes affect the nervous system and its operation. Behavior genetics is a rapidly expanding field, and it is certain that insects will prove as valuable here as they have in other branches of biology in elucidating mechanisms that are of universal importance.

REFERENCES

Barker, J. S. F. Sexual isolation between *Drosophila melanogaster* and *Drosophila simulans. Amer. Nat.*, 96: 105-115, 1962.

Bastock, M. A gene mutation which changes a behavior pattern. *Evolution,* 10: 421-439, 1956.

Bastock, M., & Manning, A. The courtship of *Drosophila melanogaster. Behavior,* 8: 85-111, 1955.

Begg, M., & Packman, E. Antennae and mating behavior in *Drosophila melanogaster. Nature,* 168: 953, 1951.

Blest, A. D. The evolution of protective displays in the Saturnoidea and Sphingidae (Lepidoptera). *Behaviour,* 11: 247-309, 1957.

Blest, A. D. The concept of ritualization. In W. H. Thorpe & O. L. Zangwill (Eds.), *Current Problems in Animal Behaviour*, pp. 102-124. London: Cambridge University Press, 1961.

Boch, R. Rassenmässige Unterschiede bei den Tänzen der Honigbeine (*Apis mellifica* L.) *Z. Vergl. Physiol.*, 40: 289-320, 1957.

Bösiger, E. Sur la role de la selection sexuelle dans l'evolution. *Experientia,* 16: 270-273, 1960.

Brown, R. G. B. Courtship behaviour in the *Drosophila obscura* group. Part II. Comparative studies. *Behaviour,* 25: 281-323, 1965.

Caspari, E. Genetic basis of behavior. In A. Rose & G. G. Simpson (Eds.), *Behavior and Evolution,* pp. 103-127. New Haven, Conn.: Yale University Press, 1958.

Caspari, E. Genes and the study of behavior. *Amer. Zool.,* 3:97-100, 1963.

Crane, J. The comparative biology of Salticid spiders at Rancho Grande, Venezuela. IV. An analysis of display. *Zoologica,* 34: 159-214, 1949.

Crane, J. A comparative study of innate defensive behavior in Trinidad Mantids (Orthoptera, Mantoidea). *Zoologica,* 37: 259-293, 1952.

Crane, J. Imaginal behavior in butterflies of the family Heliconiidae: changing social patterns and irrelevant actions. *Zoologica,* 42: 135-145, 1957a.

Crane, J. Basic patterns of display in fiddler crabs (Ocypodidae, genus *Uca*). *Zoologica*, 42: 69-82, 1957b.

Crossley, S. An experimental study of sexual isolation within a species of Drosophila. Ph.D thesis. Oxford University, 1963.

Dobzhansky, T. *Genetics and the Origin of Species.* New York: Columbia Univerisity Press, 1937.

Ehrman, L. A genetic constitution frustrating the sexual drive of *Drosophila paulistorum. Science*, 131: 1381-1382, 1960.

Ewing, A. W. Body size and courtship behaviour in *Drosophila melanogaster. Anim. Behav.*, 9: 93-99, 1961.

Fankhauser, G. The effects of changes in chromosome number on amphibian development. *Quart. Rev. Biol.,* 20: 20-78, 1945.

Fankhauser, G. The role of nucleus and cytoplasm. In B. H. Willier, P. A. Weiss, & V. Hamburger (Eds.), *Analysis of Development*, pp. 126-150. Philadelphia: W. B. Saunders Company, 1955.

Fankhauser, G., Vernon, J. A., Frank, W. H., & Slack, W. V. Effect of size and number of brain cells on learning in larvae of the salamander, *Triturus viridescens. Science,* 122: 602-693, 1955.

Frings, H. The loci of olfactory end-organs in the blowfly, *Cynomyia cadaverina* Desvoidy. *J. Exp. Zool.,* 88: 65-93, 1941.

Grüneberg, H. *The Genetics of the Mouse*, 2nd ed. The Hague: Martinus Nijhoff, 1952.

Harlow, H. F. The evolution of learning. In A. Roe & G. G. Simpson, (Eds.), *Behavior and Evolution*, pp. 269-290. New Haven, Conn.: Yale University Press, 1958.

Hebb, D. O. Heredity and environment. *Brit. J. Anim. Behav.,* 1: 43-47, 1953.

Hess, E. H. Ethology, an approach towards the complete analysis of behavior. In R. Brown, E. Galanter, E. H. Hess, & G. Mandler, *New Directions in Psychology*, pp. 159-266. New York: Holt, Rinehart and Winston, Inc., 1962.

Hinde, R. A., & Tinbergen, N. The comparative study of species-specific behavior. In A. Roe & G. G. Simpson (Eds.), *Behavior and Evolution*, pp. 251-268. New Haven, Conn.: Yale University Press, 1958.

Hirsch, J. Individual differences in behavior and their genetic basis. In E. L. Bliss (Ed.), *Roots of Behavior: Genetics, Instinct, and Socialization in Animal Behavior*, pp. 3-23. New York: Paul B. Hoeber, Inc., medical book department of Harper & Row, Publishers, Incorporated, 1962.

Hollingsworth, M. J. A gynandromorph segregating for autosomal mutants in *Drosophila subobscura. J. Genet.,* 53: 131-135, 1955.

Hollingsworth, M. J. Observations on the sexual behaviour of intersexes in *Drosophila subobscura. Anim. Behav.,* 7: 57-59, 1959.

Hörmann-Heck, S. von. Untersuchengen über den Erbgang einiger Verhaltensweisen bei Grillenbastarden (*Gryllus campestris* L. x *Gryllus bimaculatus* De Geer). *Z. Tierpsychol.,* 14: 137-183, 1957.

Hovanitz, W. Polymorphism and evolution. *Sympos. Soc. Exp. Biol.,* 7: 238-253, 1953.

Kalmus, H. The resistance to desiccation of Drosophila mutants affecting body colour. *Proc. Roy. Soc.* (London), (B) 130: 185-201, 1941.

Kessler, S. Courtship rituals and reproductive isolation between the races or incipient species of *Drosophila paulistorum. Amer. Nat.,* 96: 117-121, 1962.

Knight, G. R., Robertson, A., & Waddington, C. H. Selection for sexual isolation within a species. *Evolution,* 10: 14-22, 1956.

Koopman, K. F. Natural selection for reproductive isolation between *Drosophila pseudoobscura* and *Drosophila persimilis*. *Evolution*, 4: 135-148, 1950.
Lack, D., & Southern, H. N. Birds on Tenerife. *Ibis*, 91: 607-626, 1949.
Lade, B. I., & Thorpe, W. H. Dove songs as innately coded patterns of specific behaviour. *Nature*, 202: 366-368, 1964.
Lehrman, D. S. A critique of Konrad Lorenz's theory of instinctive behavior. *Quart. Rev. Biol.*, 28: 337-363, 1953.
Lindauer, M. Communication among the honeybees and stingless bees of India. *Bee World*, 38: 3-13, 34-39, 1957.
Magnus, D. B. E. Experimentelle Untersuchungen zur Bionomie und Ethologie des Kaisermantels *Argynis paphia* L. (Lep. Nymph.). I. Über optische Auslöser von Anfleigereaktion und ihre Bedeutung für das Sichfinden der Geschlechter. *Z. Tierpsychol.*, 15: 397-426, 1958.
Manning, A. The sexual isolation between *Drosophila melanogaster* and *Drosophila simulans*. *Anim. Behav.*, 7: 60-65, 1959a.
Manning, A. The sexual behaviour of two sibling *Drosophila* species. *Behaviour*, 15: 123-145, 1959b.
Manning, A. The effects of artificial selection for mating speed in *Drosophila melanogaster*. *Anim. Behav.*, 9: 82-92, 1961.
Manning, A. Selection for mating speed in *Drosophila melanogaster* based on the behaviour of one sex. *Anim. Behav.*, 11: 116-120, 1963.
Manning, A. Drosophila, and the evolution of behaviour. *Viewpoints in Biol.*, 4: 123-167, 1965.
Mayr, E. *Systematics and the Origin of Species*. New York: Columbia University Press, 1942.
Merrell, D. J. Selective mating in *D. melanogaster*. *Genetics*, 34: 370-389, 1949.
Merrell, D. J. Selective mating as a cause of gene frequency changes in laboratory populations of *Drosophila melanogaster*. *Evolution*, 7: 287-296, 1953.
Merriam, R. W., & Ris, H. Size and DNA content of nuclei in various tissues of male, female and worker honeybees. *Chromosoma*, 6: 522-538, 1954.
Milani, R., & Rivosecchi, L. Gynandromorphism and intersexuality in *M. domestica*. *Drosophila Information Service*, 28: 135-136, 1954.
Miller, D. D. Mating behavior in *Drosophila affins* and *Drosophila algonguin*. *Evolution*, 4: 123-134, 1950.
Morgan, T. H., & Bridges, C. B. The origin of gynandromorphs. *Carnegie Inst. Wash. Publ.*, no. 287, pp. 22-23, 1919.
Moray, N., & Arnold, P. Confirmation of apparent genetical assimilation of behaviour in *Drosophila melanogaster*. *Nature*, 204: 504, 1964.
Moray, N. & Connolly, K. A possible case of genetic assimilation of behaviour. *Nature*, 199: 358-360, 1963.
Morris, D. "Typical intensity" and its relationship to the problem of ritualization. *Behaviour*, 11: 1-13, 1957.

Müller, H. J. Isolating mechanisms, evolution and temperature. *Biol. Sympos.,* 6: 71-122, 1942.

Oehninger, M. Ueber Kerngrössen bei Bienen. *Verh. Phys.-Med. Ges. Wurzburg,* 42: 135-149, 1913.

Patterson, J. T., & Stone, W. S. *Evolution in the Genus Drosophila.* New York: The Macmillan Company, 1952.

Perdeck, A. C. The isolating value of specific song patterns in two sibling species of grasshoppers (*Chorthippus brunneus* Thunb. and *C. biguttulus* L.). *Behaviour,* 12: 1-75, 1958.

Petit, C. La determinisme genetique et psychophysiologique de la competition sexuelle chez *Drosophila melanogaster. Bull. Biol.,* 92: 248-329, 1958.

Pittendrigh, C. S. Adaptation, natural selection and behavior. In A. Roe & G. G. Simpson (Eds.), *Behavior and Evolution,* pp. 390-416. New Haven, Conn.: Yale University Press, 1958.

Power, M. E. The effect of reduction in numbers of ommatidia upon the brain of *Drosophila melanogaster. J. Exp. Zool.,* 94: 33-71, 1943.

Reed, S. C., & Reed, E. W. Natural selection in laboratory populations of *Drosophila.* II. Competition between white-eye gene and its wild type allele. *Evolution,* 4: 34-42, 1950.

Rendel, J. M. Mating of ebony, vestigial and wild type *Drosophila melanogaster* in light and dark. *Evolution,* **5**: 226-230, 1951.

Roeder, K. D. An experimental analysis of the sexual behaviour of the praying mantis. *Biol. Bull.,* 69: 203-220, 1935.

Roeder, K. D., Tozian, L., & Weiant, E. A. Endogenous nerve activity and behavior in the mantis and cockroach. *J. Insect Physiol.,* 4: 35-62, 1960.

Rothenbuhler, W. C. Genetics of a behavior difference in honeybees. *Proc. 10th Int. Congr. Genet.,* 2: 252, 1958.

Sakagami, S. F., & Takahashi, H. Beobachtungen über die gynandromorphen Honigbienen, mit besonderer Berücksichtingung ihrer Handlungen innerhalb des Volkes. *Ins. Soc.,* 3: 513-529, 1956.

Sheppard, P. M. Some contributions to population genetics resulting from the study of the hepidoptera. *Adv. Genet.,* 10: 165-216, 1961.

Smith, J. M. Sexual selection. In S. A. Barnett (Ed.), *A Century of Darwin,* pp. 231-244. London: William Heinemann, Ltd., 1958.

Speicher, B. R. Cell size and chromosomal types in *Habrobracon. Amer. Nat.,* 69: 79-80, 1935.

Sperry, R. W. Development basis of behavior. In A. Roe & G. G. Simpson (Eds.), *Behavior and Evolution,* pp. 128-139. New Haven, Conn.: Yale University Press, 1958.

Spieth, H. T. Mating behavior within the genus *Drosophila* (Diptera). *Bull. Amer. Mus. Nat. Hist.,* 99: 394-474, 1952.

Spieth, H. T., & Hsu, T. C. The influence of light on seven species of the *Drosophila melanogaster* group. *Evolution,* 4: 316-325, 1950.

Stride, G. O. Investigations into the courtship behaviour of the male of *Hypolimnas misippus* (Lepidoptera, Nymphalidae) with special reference to the role of visual stimuli. *Brit. J. Anim. Behav.*, 5: 153-167, 1957.

Sturtevant, A. H. Intersexes in *Drosophila simulans. Science,* 51: 352-353, 1920.

Sturtevant, A. H. A gene in *Drosophila melanogaster* that transforms females into males. *Genetics,* 30: 297-299, 1945.

Thorpe, W. H. Further experiments on olfactory conditioning in a parasitic insect. The nature of the conditioning process. *Proc. Roy. Soc.* (*London*), (*B*) 126: 370-397, 1938.

Thorpe, W. H. Further experiments on pre-imaginal conditioning in insects. *Proc. Roy. Soc.* (*London*), (*B*) 127: 424-433, 1939.

Thorpe, W. H., & Jones, F. G. W. Olfactory conditioning and its relation to the problem of host selection. *Proc. Roy. Soc. (London), (B)* 124: 56-81, 1937.

Tinbergen, N. *The Study of Instinct.* London: Oxford University Press, 1951.

Tinbergen, N. "Derived" activities; their causation, biological significance, origin and emancipation during evolution. *Quart. Rev. Biol.*, 27: 1-32, 1952.

Tinbergen, N. Behaviour, systematics and natural selection. *Ibis,* 101: 318-330, 1959a.

Tinbergen, N. Comparative studies of the behaviour of gulls (Laridae): a progress report. *Behaviour,* 15: 1-70, 1959b.

Tinbergen, N., Meeuse, B. J. D., Boerema, L. K., & Varossieau, W. W. Die Galz des Samtfalters, *Eumenis* (=*Satyrus*) *semele* (L.). *Z. Tierpsychol.*, 5:182-226, 1942.

Vernon, J. A., & Butsch, J. Effect of tetrapolidy on learning and retention in the salamander. *Science*, 125: 1033-1034, 1957.

Verplanck, W. S. Since learned behaviour is innate, and vice versa, what now? *Psychol. Rev.*, 62: 139-144, 1955.

Vowles, D. M. Neural mechanisms in insect behaviour. In W. H. Thorpe & O. L. Zangwill (Eds.), *Current Problems in Animal Behaviour,* pp. 5-29. London: Cambridge University Press, 1961a.

Vowles, D. M. The physiology of the insect nervous system. *Int. Rev. Neurobiol.*, 3: 349-373, 1961b.

Waddington, C. H. Genetic assimilation. *Adv. Genet.*, 10: 257-293, 1961.

Waddington, C. H., Woolf, B., & Perry, M. Environment selection by *Drosophila* mutants. *Evolution,* 8: 89-96, 1954.

Wallace, B., & Dobzhansky, T. Experiments on sexual isolation in *Drosophila.* VIII. Influence of light on the mating behavior of *Drosophila subobscura, Drosophila persimilis* and *Drosophila pseudoobscura. Proc. Natl. Acad. Sci.*, 32: 226-234, 1946.

Whiting, P. W. Reproductive reactions of sex mosaics of a parasitic wasp, *Habrobracon juglandis. J. Comp. Psychol.*, 14: 345-363, 1932.

Williams, C. M., & Reed, S. C. Physiological effects of genes: The flight of *Drosophila* considered in relation to gene mutations. *Amer. Nat.*, 78: 214-223, 1944.

Effects of Genotype on Mouse Behaviour

J. H. F. VAN ABEELEN

The purpose of this investigation is to measure variations in the behaviour of house mice, and to examine their relation to polygenic differences and to a monogenic difference.

Behavioural differences between strains have been firmly established (see McClearn, 1965). A survey of the literature on strains DBA/2, C57BL/6, and their F_1-hybrid (Table I) shows that the parental strains are quite distinct in many respects. In order to study more closely their characteristics, and to look for heterosis in the hybrid strain (see Bruell, 1964, for discussion), I observed stereotyped behaviour patterns, general activity, and a simple learning response displayed by them.

Behavioural differences between mutants and non-mutants, on the other hand, have been detected by means of gene substitutions (see, for instance, van Abeelen, 1963a, b, c, 1965). In view of the skeletal, vascular, and renal anomalies associated with the short-ear (*se*) locus in mice (see for review: Grüneberg, 1963, p. 32-36), and its effect on body size (McNutt, 1958), one would expect pleiotropic effects upon behaviour as well. Thus, although previous work with *se* has yielded virtually negative results in a variety of behavioural tests (Bundy, 1950; Ashman, 1957; Les, 1958; Denenberg, Ross & Blumenfield, 1963), research on this allele is continued here, using the same categories of behaviour as mentioned in the preceding paragraph.

Table I. Some behavioural characteristics of strains DBA/2, C57BL/6, and their F_1 as reported in the literature.

Variable	*DBA/2*	*C57BL/6*	F_1	*Authors*
Locomotor activity	Low	High	–	Thompson (1953)
	Low	High	Rather low	Mordkoff *et al.* (1959)
	Low	High	Intermediate	Schlesinger *et al.* (1963)
	High	Low	–	Foshee *et al.* (1965)
Exploratory sniffing rate	Low	High	–	Vanderpool *et al.* (1962)
	Low	High	–	Foshee *et al.* (1965)
Defecation rate	High	Low	–	Thompson (1953)
Grooming rate	High	Low	–	Vanderpool *et al.* (1962)
Grooming duration (moderate temp.)	Long	Short	Long	Mordkoff *et al.* (1964)
Mounting latency	High	Low	Low	McGill *et al.* (1963b)
Intromission latency	High	Rather low	Low	McGill *et al.* (1963b)
Recovery of sex drive	Quick	Slow	Quick	McGill *et al.* (1963a)
Sex drive	Strong	Weak	Strong	McGill *et al.* (1964)
Avoidance conditioning	Good*	Poor	–	Royce *et al.* (1960)
Audiogenic seizure susceptibility	High	Low	Intermediate	Fuller *et al.* (1950)
	High	Low	–	Ginsburg (1954)
Alcohol preference	Low	High	Rather high	Fuller (1964)

*Sub-strain of DBA not specified.

EXPERIMENT I

The ethological method of constructing inventories of basic behavioural elements was applied in this series of direct observations. The mice were placed singly or in pairs into a large observation cage, thus enabling me to make frequency counts of the acts performed and the postures assumed in both an exploratory and an agonistic situation.

Method

SUBJECTS. DBA/2J, C57BL/6J, and B6D2F_1 mice (Staats, 1964) were used for studying strain effects. The left ear was coloured with a fuchsin dye in half of them for identification in the paired situation. In the comparison of mutants (*se/se*) with nonmutants (*se*/+), mice of the co-isogenic stock SEC/1Gn (Staats, 1964) were subjects (F_{72}-F_{75}; homozygous and heterozygous litter-mates). In addition to punching, their ears were dyed in the same way.

Each group[1] included twenty males about 2½ months of age that had been isolated for 1 month before testing. The mice were subjected to as similar environments as possible. They were born and raised in double compartment, metal cages with wood shaving bedding. Food pellets and water were supplied *ad libitum*. In the air-conditioned mouse room the natural day-night periodicity prevailed. Weaning took place at the age of 1 month. Prior to observation, the animals were transferred, while staying in their home cages, to another mouse room. From there they were taken to the observation cage by means of a cardboard box, without touching them by hand. After testing, they were again isolated.

APPARATUS. The observation cage measured 35 x 15 x 18 in. Except for the Plexiglas front pane through which the animals could be viewed at eye level, it was constructed of hardboard painted in dark green. A sliding partition could be used to divide the terrarium in equal halves. A mineral bedding covered the floor, with some food pellets scattered randomly over it, permitting the mice to display digging, pushing, eating, etc. Because the cage was not cleaned until all experiments were completed, the scent tracks left by the animals were probably all over its interior. Against the back wall stood a small wire mesh cube, providing the mice with an opportunity for sniffing and climbing. A small wooden cube that could be lowered quietly by means of a pulley during the tests (the novel object in the solitary situation) offered an extra stimulus for investigative behaviour. Three light beams, directed upon three photoelectric cells, divided the floor into four equal areas. Interruption of any beam actuated a counter so that measures of general activity could be included. The apparatus was lit from above by eight 40 W fluorescent tubes shielded with plastic covers.

PROCEDURE. Each animal was observed twice: 20 min in the solitary situation, during which the novel object was introduced

[1] In each group one half of the animals received a moderate dose of chlorpromazine in isotonic saline injected intraperitoneally 1 hr before testing, the other half received saline only. Statistical analysis did not reveal significant drug effects for a large majority of the behavioural components; consequently, in these cases the scores for the sub-groups have been pooled. Furthermore, I failed to discover any influence of saline injection or puncture upon ambulatory and agonistic behaviour of C57BL/6J mice (van Abeelen, 1965, unpublished results).

15 min after the beginning, and 15 min in the paired situation, in that order and on different afternoons. The frequencies of twenty-two behavioural components carried out by solitary males and twelve components carried out by pairs of males were recorded in a standard fashion on checklists. Descriptions, together with some figures, of these thirty-four postures and acts (except pushing) have been published previously (van Abeelen, 1963a, 1965); their names can be found in Tables II and III of the present paper. By pushing was meant: the mouse made very rapid alternating movements with the forepaws, displacing the bedding material in a forward direction.

In the solitary situation, 'freezing' of the mouse is fairly common. Because it is sometimes time-consuming, I prolonged a session with n min in case the mouse froze for a total duration of n min in that session.

In the paired situation the behaviour of both males was registered simultaneously. At that time, the pairs were already familiar with the terrarium, having explored it before. Moreover, in the morning before the paired test they were put for an additional 15 min into one compartment of the cage.

The following nonparametric statistical tests were applied for evaluation of the results (Siegel, 1956, pp. 116 and 96): first, the two-tailed Mann-Whitney U test for comparisons with regard to components of which the total frequency in each group was higher than half the total number of animals in such group (probabilities are indicated in the tables by symbol u), and secondly, Fisher's two-tailed exact test for 2 x 2 contingency tables, for components with lower frequencies (probabilities are indicated in the tables by symbol e).

Results

STRAINS. Table II shows that strain DBA/2 is characterized by its low locomotor activity, its low scores for exploratory sniffing (wire cube, novel object, food), reconnoitering, climbing (wire cube, novel object), and shaking the fur, and its higher frequencies of hair fluffing and gnawing at the wall. Qualitatively, these mice differ from the other strains by their tendency to keep the abdomen close to the floor when walking. No spontaneous seizures occurred during the observations. Strain C57BL/6, on the other hand, is conspicuous by demonstrating carrying food, eating, defecating, vibrating with the

Table II. Mean frequencies of behavioural components performed by solitary males of the two parental strains and the F_1 and the results of the statistical tests.

Components	*Mean frequencies*			*Differences between strains: results of tests*		
	DBA/2J	*C57BL/6J*	*B6D2F₁*	*DBA/2J v. C57BL/6J*	*DBA/2J v. B6D2F₁*	*C57BL/6J v. B6D2F₁*
Staring at observer	1.0	0.4	0.8	–	–	–
Hair fluffing	0.5	0.1	0.3	e	–	–
Tail rattling	0.0	0.5	0.1	ee	–	e
Sniffing at wire cube	13.9	25.6	26.6*	uu	uu	–
Reconnoitering	7.8	27.6	32.0	uu	uu	–
Lifting forepaw	3.0	5.6	3.8	u	–	–
Leaning against wall	26.1	27.4	46.5	–	uu	uu
Gnawing at wall	1.3	0.2	0.5	ee	u	–
Climbing wire cube	2.7	8.7	13.0	uu	uu	–
Jumping	0.0	0.0	0.0	–	–	–
Sniffing at food	1.6	3.9	2.8	uu	u	–
Carrying food	0.6	0.0	0.6	ee	–	ee
Eating	7.9	3.1	8.0	uu	–	uu
Defecating	0.8	0.1	0.7	e	–	ee
Shaking the fur	1.3	7.5*	3.6	uu	uu	u
Vibrating paws	0.9*	0.2	1.0	e	–	ee
Grooming	4.0	2.1	5.0	uu	–	uu
Digging	9.9	15.5	23.6*	–	u	u
Pushing	2.9	2.6	5.5	uu	–	u
Sniffing novel object	2.6	7.2	7.8*	uu	uu	–
Leaning novel object	2.2	3.3	4.8	–	uu	–
Climbing novel object	0.3	2.2	4.1	e	uu	u
Freezing duration (sec)	7.4	10.1	18.9	–	–	–
Activity count	43.7	142.4	135.1	uu	uu	–

The number of animals in each group is twenty, except for cases marked by * (n = 10; see footnote 1). For the activity count n = 12. Duration of observation: 20 min per animal, except for components directed towards the novel object (5 min). Differences are indicated by uu or ee ($P<0.01$) and by u or e ($P<0.05$).

forepaws, grooming, and pushing less often; and tail rattling, lifting one forepaw, and shaking the fur more often. In the F_1 the frequencies of leaning (wall, novel object), climbing (novel object, wire cube), digging, and pushing exceeded those of the parental strains (in three instances not significantly).

Table III. Mean frequencies of behavioural components performed by pairs of males of the two parental strains and the F_1, and the results of the statistical tests.

Components	*Mean frequencies*			*Differences between strains: results of tests*		
	DBA/2J	*C57BL/6J*	*B6D2F$_1$*	*DBA/2J v. C57BL/6J*	*DBA/2J v. B6D2F$_1$*	*C57BL/6J v. B6D2F$_1$*
Fixing	2.7	3.2	7.6	–	u	u
Hair fluffing	1.3	1.5	1.1	–	–	–
Tail rattling	5.1	0.2	6.8	–	–	e
Wrestling	3.4	0.0	0.8	e	–	–
Chasing	1.3	0.0	5.3	e	–	ee
Fleeing	2.0	0.0	10.8*	e	u	ee
Subm. posture	1.0	0.0	2.8	e	–	e
Nosing	17.6	18.6	14.0	–	–	–
Touching	0.5	1.0	0.4	–	–	–
Mounting	0.0	0.6	0.0	–	–	–
Grooming	7.6	6.8*	9.6	–	–	–
Digging	3.2	14.3	11.8	u	u	–
No. of fights	0.7	0.0	0.8	ee	–	ee

The number of pairs in each group is ten, except for cases marked by * (five pairs; see footnote 1). The values for the members of a pair are added. Duration of observation: 15 min per pair. Differences are indicated by ee ($P<0.01$) and by u or e ($P<0.05$).

The data pertaining to the agonistic situation are arranged in Table III. Except for fixing and digging, the behaviour of DBA/2 resembled that of the F_1, although the latter gave the impression of being more aggressive. In C57BL/6 mice, in spite of their having frequent bodily contacts (e.g. nosing), aggressiveness was almost completely absent, there was only some tail rattling, but no wrestling, chasing, fleeing or submissive posture took place.

MUTANTS. The results with strain SEC/1Gn can be dealt with briefly. The tables compiled are omitted here, because neither in the exploratory situation, nor in the agonistic situation, the comparison of mutants and non-mutants produced a single difference in respect of the more than thirty items of the ethogram.

Discussion

First of all, it should be kept in mind, that in a long list of behaviours as examined here one is apt to find a few significant differences that are exclusively due to chance.

The results obtained for locomotor activity, exploratory sniffing, defecation, and grooming in DBA/2 and C57BL/6 confirm the data surveyed in Table I, if we exclude the results of Foshee and collaborators for locomotor activity. In addition, many other strain differences were demonstrated to exist. The screening techniques applied here prove to be well-suited for the rapid detection of such differences. The F_1 seems to show dominance for some components and intermediacy for others. In some respects (leaning against wall, digging, climbing novel object, fleeing) these mice turned out to be very mobile animals, indicating the effect of heterosis. As yet no exact identification of responsible genes is possible.

The absence of any behavioural effect of the *se* allele in experiment I is in keeping with previous work already referred to. The locus does affect conditioning, as we shall see below.

EXPERIMENT II

These tests were intended to investigate active avoidance conditioning in mice of different genotypes, using an electric shock escape device. Originally, this 'jumping box' had been devised by Dr. R. E. Wimer, Bar Harbor, Maine; I modified it somewhat for the purpose of the present study. The measures taken per trial were the number of shock series (one or zero) and the escape latencies (in sec).

Method

SUBJECTS.[2] The same individuals used in experiment I were examined, but this time the strains DBA/2J, C57BL/6J, and B6D2F_1 each comprised eighteen animals of 3 months; the age of the twenty *se/se* mice and twenty *se*/+ mice varied between 3 and 4½ months. They were transferred to the shock escape device again by means of a cardboard box.

APPARATUS. The jumping box measured 6.25 x 6.25 x 6 in. and consisted of opaque Plexiglas walls, a metal grid for floor, and a

[2] Since the subjects had already been used in an experiment involving chlorpromazine (see footnote 1), there might have been after-effects of treatment upon performance in the avoidance tests. This turned out to be not the case for either genotype.

transparent Plexiglas lid. Inside was a rotatable platform, 2.5 in. above the grid and protruding 2.75 in. from the wall. The grid could be electrified by operating a switch connected to a Grason-Stadler shock generator (E 1064 GS).

PROCEDURE. Trials were given in massed practice. Before the first trial, the mouse was allowed to explore the platform for 30 sec, then, by rotating the shelf, he was forced on the grid and given 30 sec exploration time more. Next, shocks of 340 V d.c. were administered until he jumped or scrambled onto the shelf, after which he was left alone for 30 sec. First trials started with shocks of 0.13 mA. A few mice turned out to be relatively insensitive to this amperage which, in that case, was stepped up to 0.16 or 0.20 mA and maintained at that level in that trial. If a mouse showed freezing, the strength was increased tenfold for a split second.

In the second trial the mouse was forced on the grid again, but shocking was delayed 15 sec, in order to give him an opportunity to escape without being shocked (if he did so, latency equalled zero). The whole procedure was then repeated. The criterion for the end of the series of trials was three consecutive periods in which the mouse jumped onto the platform within 15 sec without being shocked, and stayed there for at least 5 sec. In a few instances, observation was discontinued after forty trials if a particular animal had not accomplished the learning task by then. The data were evaluated by applying the two-tailed Mann-Whitney U test.

Results

STRAINS. As Table IV shows, the parental strains did not differ significantly from each other, but each of them was highly different from the F_1, which performed better in both measures. Half of the F_1 mice reached the criterion at trial 9, half of the C57BL/6 animals at trial 14, and for DBA/2 animals the median was trial 16. One mouse of strain C57BL/6 and two mice of strain DBA/2 did not accomplish the task at all. Thus, the F_1 was definitely superior; there were only some slight indications that DBA/2 mice tend to perform more poorly than C57BL/6 mice.

MUTANTS. It appears that the mice heterozygous for short-ear performed better in the learning task than the homozygous animals;

Table IV. Mean escape latencies and mean number of shocks required to meet criterion, and the results of the statistical tests for males of the two parental strains and the F_1.

	Means			*Results of tests*		
	DBA/2J	*C57BL/6J*	*B6D2F₁*	*DBA/2J v. C57BL/6J*	*DBA/2J v. B6D2F₁*	*C57BL/6J v. B6D2F₁*
Escape latency	129.72	100.28	39.28	–	uu	uu
No. of shocks	12.17	11.44	5.83	–	u	u

The number of animals in each group is eighteen. Differences are indicated by uu ($P < 0.01$) and by u ($P < 0.05$).

Table V. Mean escape latencies and mean number of shocks required to meet criterion for males of strain SEC/1Gn.

	Means		
	se/se	*se/+*	*Results of tests*
Escape latency	80.30	51.65	u
No. of shocks	6.40	4.60	–

The number of animals in each group is twenty. A difference is indicated by u ($P < 0.05$).

the difference for latency is significant (see Table V). Two types of learning curves are presented. The one in Fig. 1 is based on the total escape latencies per trial, the one in Fig. 2 is made according to the total number of shock series per trial. The more relevant parts of the curves lie approximately between trial 3 and trial 16. Due to large individual variations, the curves in Fig. 1 fluctuate a good deal; in Fig. 2, however, they are smoother and well apart. Half of the *se/+* group reached the criterion at trial 6, this was for the *se/se* mice trial 9. All individuals achieved the goal within twenty-seven trials.

Discussion

Royce & Covington (1960) state that C57BL/6J mice condition very poorly, and DBA/J mice (not further specified) condition well in an electric shock avoidance experiment, using a buzzer for stimulus. This learning inferiority of C57BL/6 did not materialize in the present study, which was designed somewhat differently, though.

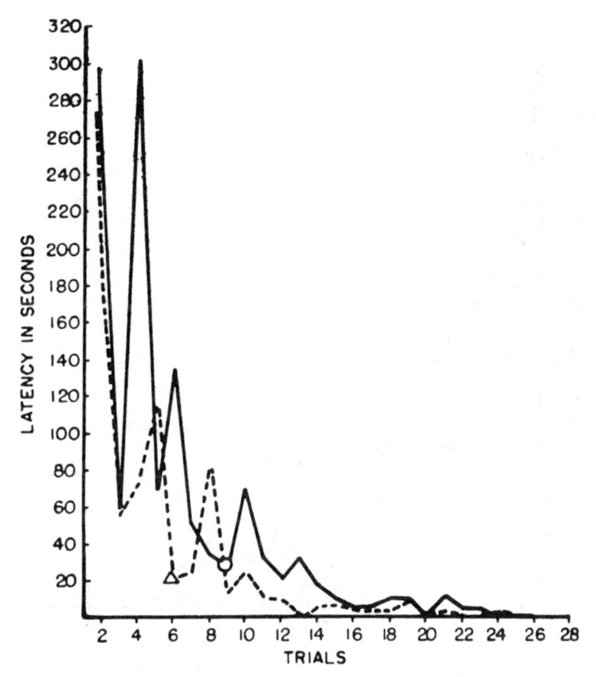

Fig. 1. Learning curves of *se/se* (———) and *se*/+ (– – –) mice, based on escape latencies.

The behaviour of the F_1 was clearly heterotic, which might be indicative of a selective advantage of avoidance learning (see Bruell, 1964).

Bundy (1950), Ashman (1957), and Denenberg *et al.* (1963), using fewer subjects, have obtained negative results for the *se* locus in shock escape tests. However, now there seems indeed to be an association between this locus and avoidance behaviour, as this experiment, using twenty pairs, suggests. Because of the high degree of inbreeding of this strain, it is very unlikely that closely linked genes are responsible for it. Thus, at least part of the relevant genetical material is known; however, its behavioural effect need not be the outcome of a primary gene action.

The finding that differences between strains emerged mainly in experiment I, whereas a difference between mutants and non-mutants appeared in experiment II only, stresses the importance of

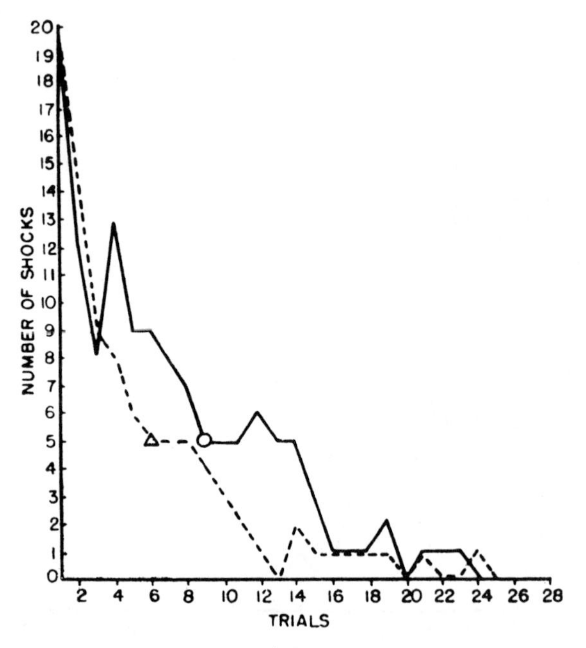

Fig. 2. Learning curves of *se/se* (———) and *se*/+ (– – –) mice, based on number of shocks.

measuring many aspects of the behavioural phenotype when studying genetically different groups.

Finally, it is profitable to employ the jumping box in such a way that even the slowest subject has in each trial ample opportunity to escape without being shocked. Then, learning performance is not so easily confounded with locomotory and climbing abilities.

SUMMARY

1. Behavioural differences between (i) the strains DBA/2J, C57BL/6J, and their F_1 hybrids, and (ii) homozygous and heterozygous short-ear (*se*,) animals, were examined. For this purpose more than thirty stereotyped behavioural components performed by single male house mice and by pairs of males when placed into an observation cage, and avoidance behaviour in a shock escape box were taken into consideration.

2. Many strain differences not described previously were established; others generally confirmed earlier findings. Strain DBA/2J is mainly characterized by low scores for various locomotory and exploratory activities, and strain C57BL/6J by low values for feeding behaviour, defecation, grooming, and aggressiveness. There was no clear-cut difference in active avoidance learning between these strains. The B6D2F_1 hybrid showed evidence of hybrid vigour, they rated high particularly with regard to leaning postures, climbing, manipulation of bedding material, and learning performance.

3. The *se* locus was found to influence avoidance behaviour; mutants did less well than non-mutants. No effect upon the frequencies of fixed action patterns or upon general activity was observed.

REFERENCES

Abeelen, J. H. F. van (1963a). Mouse mutants studied by means of ethological methods. I. Ethogram. *Genetica*, **34**, 79-94.

Abeelen, J. H. F. van (1963b). II. Mutants and methods. *Genetica*, **34**, 95-101.

Abeelen, J. H. F. van (1963c). III. Results with *yellow, pink-eyed dilution, brown* and *jerker. Genetica*, **34**, 270-286.

Abeelen, J. H. F. van (1965). An ethologcigal investigation of single-gene differences in mice. Doctoral dissertation, University of Nijmegen, Netherlands.

Ashman, R. F. (1957). An attempt to discover behavioral effects of single-gene differences in mice. Student report, The Jackson Laboratory, Bar Harbor, Maine.

Bruell, J. H. (1964). Inheritance of behavioral and physiological characters of mice and the problem of heterosis. *Am. Zool.*, **4**, 125-138.

Bundy, R. E. (1950). A search for some effects of the "*short-ear*" gene on behavior in mice. *Am. Nat.*, **84**, 393-399.

Denenberg, V. H., Ross, S. & Blumenfield, M. (1963). Behavioral differences between mutant and non-mutant mice. *J. comp. physiol. Psychol.*, **56**, 290-293.

Foshee, D. P., Vierck, Jr, C. J., Meier, G. W. & Federspiel, C. (1965). Simultaneous measure of general activity and exploratory behavior. *Percept. Mot. Skills*, **20**, 445-451.

Fuller, J. L. (1964). Measurement of alcohol preference in genetic experiments. *J. comp. physiol. Psychol.*, **57**, 85-88.

Fuller, J. L., Easler, C. & Smith, M. E. (1950). Inheritance of audiogenic seizure susceptibility in the mouse. *Genetics, Princeton*, **35**, 622-632.

Ginsburg, B. E. (1954). Genetics and the physiology of the nervous system. *Res. Publs. Ass. Res. nerv. ment. Dis.*, **33**, 39-56.

Grüneberg, H. (1963). *The Pathology of Development. A study of inherited skeletal disorders in animals.* Oxford: Blackwell Scientific Publications.

Les, E. P. (1958). A study of the effects of single locus heterozygosity on traits which may have survival value in eight stocks of laboratory mice. Ph.D. dissertation, Ohio State University.

McClearn, G. E. (1965). Genotype and mouse behaviour. *Genetics Today* (Ed. by S. J. Geerts). *Proc. XI Int. Congr. Genet.*, Vol. 3, pp. 795-805. Oxford: Pergamon Press.

McGill, T. E. & Blight, W. C. (1963a). Effects of genotype on the recovery of sex drive in the male mouse. *J. comp. physiol. Psychol.*, **56**, 887-888.

McGill, T. E. & Blight, W. C. (1963b). The sexual behaviour of hybrid male mice compared with the sexual behaviour of the inbred parent strains. *Anim. Behav.*, **11**, 480-483.

McGill, T. E. & Tucker, G. R. (1964). Genotype and sex drive in intact and in castrate male mice. *Science, N.Y.*, **145**, 514-515.

McNutt, W. (1958). The effect of the *short-ear* gene on body size in the mouse. *Anat. Rec.*, **130**, 337 (abstract).

Mordkoff, A. M. & Fuller, J. L. (1939). Variability in activity within inbred and crossbred mice: A study in behavior genetics. *J. Hered.*, **50**, 6-8.

Mordkoff, A. M., Schlesinger, K. & Lavine, R. A. (1964). Developmental homeostasis in behavior of mice: Locomotor activity and grooming. *J. Hered.*, **55**, 84-88.

Royce, J. R. & Covington, M. (1960). Genetic differences in the avoidance conditioning of mice. *J. comp. physiol. Psychol.*, **53**, 197-200.

Schlesinger, K. & Mordkoff, A. M. (1963). Locomotor activity and oxygen consumption. Variability in two inbred strains of mice and their F_1 hybrids. *J. Hered.*, **54**, 177-182.

Siegel, S. (1956). *Nonparametric Statistics for the Behavioral Sciences*. New York: McGraw-Hill.

Staats, J. (1964). Standardized nomenclature for inbred strains of mice. Third listing. *Cancer Res.*, **24**, 147-168.

Thompson, W. R. (1953). The inheritance of behaviour: behavioural differences in fifteen mouse strains. *Can. J. Psychol.*, **7**, 145-155.

Vanderpool, D. L. & Davis, R. T. (1962). Differences in spontaneous behavior among inbred strains of mice. *Psychol. Rep.*, **10**, 123-130.

Inheritance of Behavioral and Physiological Characters of Mice and the Problem of Heterosis

JAN H. BRUELL

Heterosis has been studied extensively in plants and animals (Gowen, 1952; Cold Spring Harbor, 1955) but there exist few behavior genetic studies of it (Fuller and Thompson, 1960). I will present results of several behavior genetic studies demonstrating heterotic inheritance of some forms of mouse behavior. Two examples of intermediate nonheterotic inheritance of physiological characters of mice will also be given. The empirical part of the paper will be followed by a discussion of some current views regarding the genetics and evolution of heterosis. My aim will be to show that it is possible to study the mode of inheritance of behavioral traits, and that the study of behavioral heterosis and behavioral inbreeding depression may contribute to the study of evolution.

Heterosis is a descriptive term used to designate the relative positions on a measuring scale occupied by an F_1 hybrid and its inbred parents. Figure 1 shows a measuring scale, and two points on it occupied by inbred parent strains P_1 and P_2. The position midway between the parents is called midparent, MP. The F_1 hybrids resulting from cross $P_1 \times P_2$ can occupy any position on the measuring scale. If the F_1 mean coincides with the midparent, one speaks of intermediate inheritance: if it occupies any other position on the scale, inheritance is called heterotic.

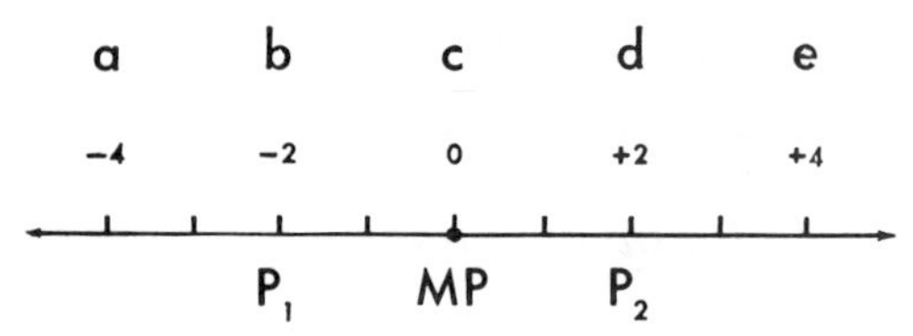

Fig. 1. Represented is a measuring scale and positions on this scale occupied by two inbred strains, P_1 and P_2. The point midway between the parents, the so-called midparent (MP), is also shown. Marked by letters above the scale are positions which may be occupied by F_1 hybrid offspring of the parent strains. Inheritance is called intermediate if the F_1 hybrid scores in position (c), heterotic when the F_1 mean falls into any other place. It is customary to speak of hybrid vigor when the hybrid scores outside the range bracketed in by the parents, e.g., in position (a) or (e). The letters correspond to those given in Table 4 and the text.

METHOD

Subjects

More than 4,000 mice belonging to 13 inbred strains, and 31 populations of F_1 hybrids were tested. These strains and strain crosses are listed in Tables 1 and 2. Each inbred strain is listed by its standard name (Committee, 1960) and a two digit code number. F_1 hybrids are indicated by combinations of these code numbers, *e.g.*, an F_1 hybrid derived from the mating of an A/J ♀ (01) to a C57B1/10 (05) ♂, is named 0105. The reciprocal hybrid derived from the mating of an 05♀ to an 01♂ is called 0501.

Our colony of inbred strains was set up in 1958. At that time the Jackson Laboratories, Bar Harbor, Maine, supplied us with pedigreed breeder pairs belonging to strains 01 to 05, and 07 to 09. Breeder pairs of strains 06, and 10 to 13 were kindly supplied to us by Dr. Edwin P. Les, of the Jackson Laboratories. All strains except 06, 11, and 12, were highly inbred. For purposes of this study it is important to note certain blood ties existing among the inbred strains we used. All 13 strains can be traced back to a few, presumably unrelated, ancestral groups, namely, H. J. Bagg's albinos, C. C. Little's albinos, DBA, and C57, and J. Furth's AKR and RFM (Committee, 1960; Russel and Gerald, 1958).

DESCENDANTS OF BAGG'S ALBINOS. In 1913 H. J. Bagg obtained albino mice from a dealer in Ohio. These are among the ancestors of strain 01-A/J, 03-Balb/c, 04-C3H, 10-SEC/1, 12-HRS, and 13-SEC/2. A/J mice stem from a mating of an albino from Bagg's colony to an albino of Little. C3H mice are derived from a cross between a Bagg albino and a DBA of Little. Finally, Balb/c mice are descendants of Bagg's albinos. After Balb/c had reached a high degree of inbreeding, E. Green crossed a Balb/c to an NB mouse from his colony and obtained SEC mice which gave rise to two sublines, SEC/1 and SEC/2. Green also mated a Balb/c to a hairless mouse which he had obtained from H. R. Chase and thus started the HRS strain.

DESCENDANTS OF LITTLE'S DBA. These mice had been bred by Little since 1909 and used in coat color experiments. The 08-DBA/1 mice used in this study are descendants of these mice. A cross between a DBA mouse and a Bagg albino started the 04-C3H strain.

DESCENDANTS OF LITTLE'S C57. All C57 mice are descendants of one pair of mice which Little obtained from A. E. C. Lathrop in 1921. The 05-C57B1/10 and 07-C57L mice are bred by the Jackson Memorial Laboratory. The 06-C57B1/6 were produced by E. Russel by placing the a^t gene from a mouse of H. R. Chase on a C57B1/6 background by seven generations of backcrossing. The line was then continued by E. Les by forced heterozygosis in brother x sister matings of type $a^t a \times aa$ for another seven generations before we received a breeder pair from Les. Our data are based on scores of both C57B1/6 $a^t a$ and aa mice.

The 11-C57B1/6 $A^y a$ strain was also developed by E. Russel. In this case she placed the A^y gene of a mouse from H. B. Chase's colony on a C57B1/6 background by 12 generations of backcrossing. The line was then continued by E. Les by forced heterozygosis in brother x sister matings of type $A^y a \times aa$ for four generations before we received a breeder pair from Les. Our data are based on scores of 11-C57B1/6 aa animals only. No yellow animals were included.

FURTH'S AKR AND RFM. The 02-AKR and the 09-RFM strains were developed by J. Furth for leukemia research prior to 1930.

AKR are high leukemia mice while RFM are a low leukemia strain. These mice presumably are not related to each other or any of the other strains used in this study.

In our laboratory, matings were between siblings only, and exact records of matings and births of litters were kept. The choice of the inbred strains used in this study was not guided by specific knowledge of their behavior. The F_1 crosses between the inbreds were also made without special consideration of the behavioral performance of the parent strains.

The animals were housed on cedar shavings in aluminum baking pans covered with wire mesh. The size of these cages was $9\frac{5}{8}'' \times 5\frac{1}{2}'' \times 2\frac{3}{4}''$. Except during testing, all animals had free access to Purina Mouse Breeder Chow and water. The temperature in animal quarters and testing rooms was kept at $73°F \pm 3°$. Rooms were ventilated, but humidity was not controlled. The lights remained on 12 hours per day. All animals were handled at regular intervals, about every seven to twelve days when they were transferred to a clean cage. Young were weaned when one month old and litter mates of the same sex were kept in the same cage until they reached the testing age of 80 to 100 days. The plan was to test all animals during their fourth month of life. However, when many animals reached testing age simultaneously, testing of some of them had to be postponed; others again, had to be tested before they were 90 days old.

Tests continued throughout 1960 and 1961. The testing of the various strains and crosses did not follow any predetermined pattern. Animals were tested as they reached testing age: this could occur during any season or month of the two year testing program. All animals that became available during these two years were tested and are included in this report.

Apparatus and Procedure

EXPLORATORY BEHAVIOR. Mice placed in a strange environment behave as if exploring it. To obtain a measure of such activity we placed mice individually in a four compartment maze. As the mouse moved from one compartment of the maze to another, it interrupted a light beam and activated a photorelay and counter. The exploration score for an animal consisted of the total count registered in ten minutes of testing. A photograph of the apparatus has been published (Bruell, 1961).

OTHER TESTS. Results of other behavioral and physiological tests will be presented in the next section, and necessary details regarding subjects and procedure will be given there.

RESULTS

Exploratory Behavior

Means and standard deviations for females and males of the 44 genotypes tested are given in Tables 1 and 2. These data will permit the reader, depending on his special interests, to carry out various correlations and tests of significance. For purposes of this presentation, however, only the means given in the two tables will be used. They will be treated as if they were scores for individual mice, albeit scores based on N repeated measurements. Thus the data are comparable to a set of scores obtained by measuring exploratory behavior of 44 sibling pairs. Thirteen of those pairs were inbred (Table 1) and 21 were hybrid organisms (Table 2). Some of the inbred animals were the mothers or sires of the hybrids. Some of the

Table 1. Exploratory behavior in 13 inbred strains of mice.

Code number and name of strain	*N*		*Females*		*Males*	
	♀	♂	*Mean*	*S.D.*	*Mean*	*S.D.*
01 A/J	70	65	132	27.68	125	26.74
02 AKR	47	60	178	48.01	176	66.05
03 Balb/c	54	47	168	30.90	152	36.24
04 C3H	69	80	109	36.63	118	41.24
05 C57BL/10	60	52	155	30.23	146	31.26
06 C57BL/6a^ta	80	81	161	39.59	165	43.51
07 C57L	27	33	181	42.17	171	35.99
08 DBA/1	92	96	144	39.06	156	44.56
09 RFM	52	47	195	57.46	182	39.80
10 SEC/1	117	129	167	38.57	172	40.96
11 C57BL/6 *aa*	68	74	162	46.89	148	45.02
12 HRS Hr hr	36	27	173	47.65	175	37.75
13 SEC/2	84	69	168	42.10	169	44.42

Table 2. Exploratory behavior in 31 F_1 hybrid groups of mice.

	N		*Females*		*Males*	
*Genotype**	♀	♂	*Mean*	*S.D.*	*Mean*	*S.D.*
0103	12	19	143	20.49	132	21.12
0104	19	31	144	38.13	155	38.52
0105	28	27	139	33.63	138	19.10
0106	48	63	159	30.68	148	37.30
0110	38	49	153	40.80	153	38.94
0301	38	42	140	24.60	147	30.38
0304	26	26	175	44.06	167	32.17
0306	34	27	203	34.71	185	45.45
0308	10	12	190	20.95	221	15.91
0310	26	23	180	54.72	171	35.57
0401	25	37	152	38.25	159	43.61
0405	42	57	171	38.43	179	31.24
0501	32	27	145	24.12	134	21.82
0502	62	53	192	42.40	186	36.77
0504	35	40	144	26.46	160	42.01
0506	42	43	191	51.08	163	43.07
0508	54	47	179	39.20	206	28.53
0509	49	42	195	56.49	189	41.15
0510	62	41	195	55.50	190	51.72
0511	12	15	147	28.93	142	33.45
0601	71	109	150	37.11	156	36.17
0603	83	65	182	45.48	185	50.00
0604	16	21	174	41.39	200	33.79
0605	73	71	178	52.51	173	37.20
0705	57	67	191	42.77	181	37.87
0803	12	11	208	33.53	199	33.30
0805	19	16	207	33.47	199	32.34
0806	11	10	186	47.36	211	21.10
1001	61	55	145	50.00	170	50.10
1003	79	82	181	39.10	185	39.19
1005	39	52	179	66.12	174	48.11

*Explanation of code number: Inbred strains are designated by two digit numbers as shown in Table 1. The code number for hybrids combines the parental two digit numbers into four digit numbers. The first two digits indicate the strain of the inbred mother, and the third and fourth digits indicate the strain of the inbred sire. For example, F_1 (0103) = F_1 (A/J♀ x Balb/c♂).

hybrids were related to each other, for example, F_1 0103 and F_1 0105 hybrids were half siblings; they had the same 01-A/J mother but different sires.

Inspection of Tables 1 and 2 did not reveal a significant difference between the exploration scores for females and males. The correlation of 0.834 between the two sets of scores was highly significant (42 degrees of freedom, $P < .001$). The overall mean for females did not differ from that for males; the average score for both sexes was 168. The identity of means and the high correlation between female and male scores enabled us to simplify the data. Instead of considering F_1♀ and F_1♂ means separately, their average was used in all computations. For example, for genotype F_1 0103 the average exploration score was $\overline{F}_1 = (143 + 132)/2 = 137.5$.

The data are presented again in Table 3. Entered in the left hand columns are the mean exploration scores for the parents of each hybrid. In the MP (for midparent) column are the averages of the parental scores, and in the F_1 column the average scores (♀ + ♂)/2, for F_1 hybrids. The correlation between the midparental values and the F_1 scores was computed and found to be 0.543 and significant (29 degrees of freedom, $P < .01$). Figure 2 presents this relation.

Table 3 shows that only 5 out of 31 groups of hybrid mice (0105, 0501, 0103, 0301, and 0511) scored below the midparent, and only one (511) below the lower scoring parent, LP. On the other hand, 21 groups scored higher than the higher scoring inbred parent, HP. Thus, overall, we can speak of heterotic inheritance of exploratory behavior. As a group, hybrid mice tended to explore more than their inbred parents.

This general relationship is also indicated in Figure 2. Shown is a scatter diagram in which the mean performance of each F_1 hybrid group, (♀ + ♂)/2, is plotted against the average performance of its midparent, (P♀ + P♂)/2. The diagonal line shown in Figure 2 represents what may be called the midparent line. An F_1 score that coincided with the midparent would be plotted on that diagonal, and F_1 groups that scored above their respective midparents would be indicated by data points above the line. As can be seen, most F_1 groups scored above the midparent line. They thus demonstrated what, in the discussion, will be referred to as "population heterosis."

Table 3 and Figure 2 were designed to make one further

Table 3. Exploratory behavior: Comparison of inbred parents with hybrid offspring.

	Genotype	*Dam*	*Sire*	*LP*	*MP*	*HP*	F_1	F_1-*HP*
				Parents not related				
	0105	132	146	132	139.0	146	138.5	− 7.5
	0106	132	165	132	148.5	165	153.5	−11.5
	0306	168	165	165	166.5	168	194.0	26.0
	0308	168	156	156	162.0	168	205.5	37.5
	0405	109	146	109	127.5	146	175.0	29.0
	0501	155	125	125	140.0	155	139.5	−15.5
	0502	155	176	155	165.5	176	189.0	13.0
	0504	155	118	118	136.5	155	152.0	− 3.0
	0508	155	156	155	155.5	156	192.5	36.5
	0509	155	182	155	168.5	182	192.0	10.0
	0510	155	172	155	163.5	172	192.5	20.5
	0601	161	125	125	143.0	161	153.0	− 8.0
	0603	161	152	152	156.5	161	183.5	22.5
	0604	161	118	118	139.5	161	187.0	26.0
	0803	144	152	144	148.0	152	203.5	51.5
	0805	144	146	144	145.0	146	203.0	57.0
	0806	144	165	144	154.5	165	198.5	33.5
	1005	167	146	146	156.5	167	176.5	9.5
	Mean	151.2	150.6	140.6	150.9	161.2	179.4	18.2
				Parents related				
	0103	132	152	132	142.0	152	137.5	−14.5
	0104	132	118	118	125.0	132	149.5	17.5
	0110	132	172	132	152.0	172	153.0	−19.0
	0301	168	125	125	146.5	168	143.5	−24.5
	0304	168	118	118	143.0	168	171.0	3.0
	0310	168	172	168	170.0	172	175.5	3.5
	0401	109	125	109	117.0	125	155.5	30.5
	0506	155	165	155	160.0	165	177.0	12.0
	0511	155	148	148	151.5	155	144.5	−10.5
	0605	161	146	146	153.5	161	175.5	14.5
	0705	181	146	146	163.5	181	186.0	5.0
	1001	167	125	125	146.0	167	157.5	− 9.5
	1003	167	152	152	159.5	167	183.0	16.0
	Mean	153.5	143.4	136.5	148.4	160.4	162.2	1.8
Overall	Mean	152.1	147.6	138.9	149.9	160.9	172.2	11.3

point. The 31 hybrid groups were subdivided into 18 groups whose parents had no blood ties, and 13 F_1 groups, which, according to the history of inbred strains given above, shared some ancestors. Figure 2 shows that the data points for hybrids whose parents are related lie

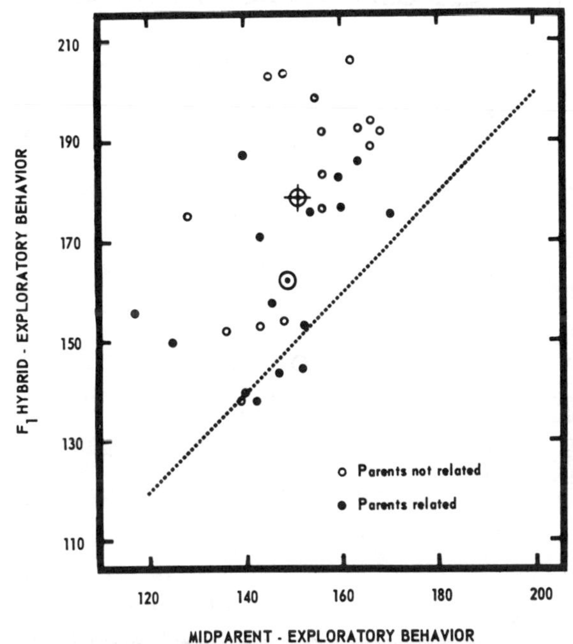

Fig. 2. Heterotic inheritance of exploratory behavior in mice. Relation between midparental score (P♀ + P♂)/2, and F_1 score (F_1♀ + F_1♂)/2. Shown are means for 18 groups of F_1 hybrids whose parents belonged to inbred strains derived from unrelated stock, and means for 13 F_1 groups whose inbred parents were related. The mean for "related hybrids" shown by a bull's-eye, differed significantly from the mean for "unrelated hybrids" shown by a cross. Note that most hybrids scored above the diagonal "midparent line."

closer to the midparent line than those for not related hybrids. And the last column of Table 3 shows that the average difference between the F_1 mean and the mean for the higher scoring parent, HP, was 18.2 for the not related "hybrids," and only 1.8 for "related" hybrids. These two averages differed at the .001 level of significance.

Other Behavior Genetic Studies

Elsewhere (Bruell, 1964) I have reported on the inheritance of spontaneous running in activity wheels in the same group of 4,000 mice as used here. Figure 3 summarizes the results of that study. We see that wheel-running is inherited in heterotic fashion, and that

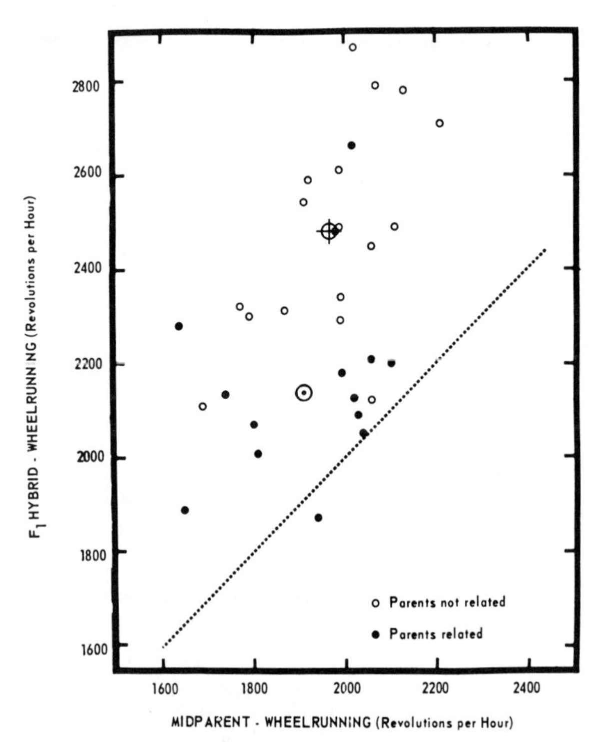

Fig. 3. Heterotic inheritance of wheel running in mice. Shown are the same 31 groups of F_1 hybrids as in Figure 2. Note that most hybrids scored above the diagonal "midparent line," and that again "unrelated" hybrids deviated more from the midparent than "related" hybrids. Means for related and unrelated hybrids are indicated by the bull's-eye and cross respectively.

again hybrids whose parents were related displayed less heterosis than those whose parents were unrelated.

Collins (1963, 1964) has studied avoidance conditioning in five inbred strains of mice (A/J, Balb/c, C3H, C57BL/10, DBA/1) and all 20 F_1 hybrids resulting from the systematic crossing of these strains. He showed that the mode of inheritance of learning in an avoidance conditioning situation is heterotic. Hybrids learned faster than their midparents.

In yet unpublished studies with the same 4,000 mice used in the present research, I found that hybrid mice climb down a pole on which they are placed somewhat faster than their midparents. They also emerge from a dark tunnel into a lighted open field more readily than their inbred parents. In both tests, then, the behavior measured is inherited in heterotic fashion. The situations but not the results just summarized have been described elsewhere (Bruell, 1962).

Inheritance of Serum Cholesterol Level

To illustrate intermediate inheritance, I have to turn to two physiological characters, serum cholesterol level and hematocrit values in mice. Serum cholesterol level was studied in the same 5 inbred strains and 20 F_1 hybrid groups as used by Collins (1963, 1964). The results of this study have been reported elsewhere (Bruell, 1963b) and are summarized in Figure 4. Each point in Figure 4 is based on 48 inbred animals and 24 hybrids. As can be seen, hybrids scored above and below the midparent, and the mean score for all hybrids, indicated by a cross in Figure 4, did not differ from

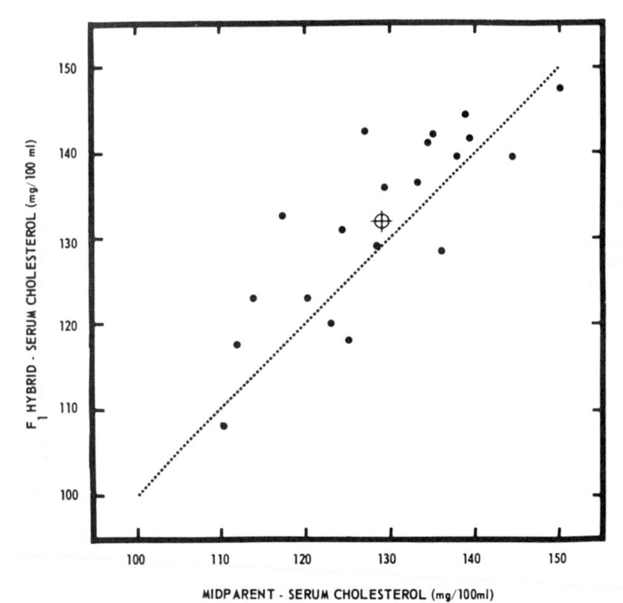

Fig. 4. Intermediate inheritance of serum cholesterol in mice. The mean for F_1 hybrids, indicated by the cross, does not deviate significantly from the mean of all midparents. The graph is based on data presented elsewhere (Bruell, 1963b).

the average of all midparents. Statistical analysis of the results (Bruell, 1963b) clearly indicated nonheterotic inheritance of serum cholesterol level in mice.

Inheritance of Hematocrit Percent

Figure 5 summarizes yet unpublished data on inheritance of hematocrit in mice. The term hematocrit or hematocrit percent refers to the relative proportions of red blood cells and serum in a sample of blood. The data shown in Figure 5 were obtained from the same five inbred strains and 20 F_1 hybrid groups as used in the serum cholesterol study. Again we see, and statistical analysis of the data confirms the impression, that in mice, on the average, inheritance of hematocrit is intermediate.

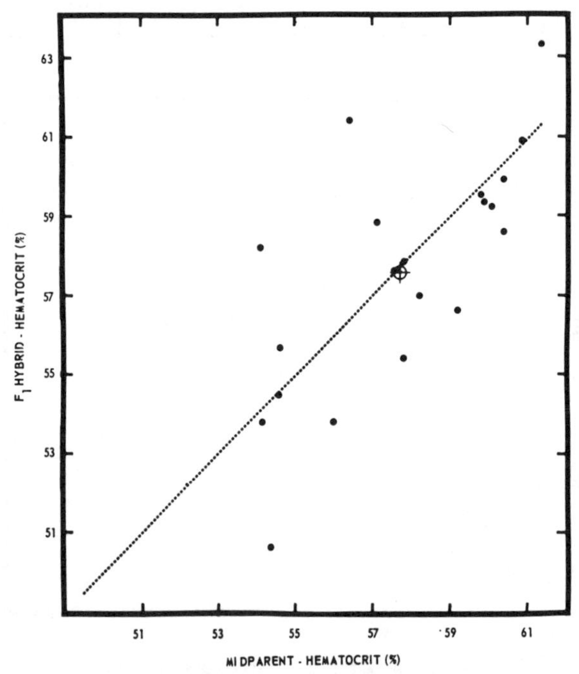

Fig. 5. Intermediate inheritance of hematocrit percent. The mean for F_1 hybrids did not differ from the mean for all midparents. The graph is based on unpublished original data.

In this section several examples of heterotic and intermediate inheritance of quantitative characters of mice were given. The remainder of this paper will deal with current theoretical views regarding intermediate and heterotic inheritance.

DISCUSSION

Two phenomena reported above stood out. First, we observed that one and the same trait, e.g., exploratory behavior, displayed intermediate inheritance in some strain crosses, and heterotic inheritance in others. Secondly, we found that different traits manifested different modes of inheritance. That is, if one disregarded single crosses and considered the average result of all strain crosses, some traits showed intermediate, and others showed heterotic inheritance. Thus, in broad outline, we will have to discuss two problems which I would like to call (1) the problem of single cross heterosis, and single cross intermediate inheritance; and (2) the problem of population heterosis, and population intermediacy. I will try to present current views concerning heterosis as I understand them. There exists no generally accepted theory of heterosis. Yet, as I read the record of theoretical discussions (Mather, 1949; Gowen, 1952; Cold Spring Harbor, 1955, 1959; Lerner, 1958; Falconer, 1960; Mayr, 1963), there exists a high degree of unanimity as to its probable causes. The reader who desires to gain a deeper understanding of quantitative inheritance and heterosis may want to study Falconer's (1960) *Introduction to Quantitative Genetics*, the most readable and explicit monographic treatment of the subject to date. And readers interested in evolutionary aspects of heterosis are directed to Mayr's (1963) recent treatise on evolution. It will be quite apparent that I have drawn heavily on ideas and concepts expounded in these two books.

Genetic theories of heterosis differ in details, but they all assume that complex quantitative characters are determined by many pairs of genes. There exists no wheel-running gene, or exploration gene, or pole-climbing gene; but a large number of gene pairs, collectively called a polygenic system, determine each of these complex quantitative traits. Each constituent gene pair of the system either moves the individual up or down the scale on which the quantitative character is measured, and the genotypic value of an individual is determined by the sum of all trait increasing and trait decreasing gene pairs he carries.

Coupled with this polygenic hypothesis is the notion that the single gene pairs making up the polygenic system display all the phenomena known from classical genetics, in particular, dominance and recessiveness. Consider two inbred strains P_1 and P_2, and assume that the phenotypic value of P_2 exceeds that of P_1, as shown in Table 4 and Figure 1. According to the polygenic hypothesis this must be due to the fact that the effects of trait increasing plus genes outweigh the effects of trait decreasing minus genes in P_2 more than they do in P_1. In Table 4, in extreme oversimplification of an actual situation, it is assumed that the quantitative trait under considera-tion is determined by gene pairs at four loci, *A, B, C,* and *D*. The genotypic value of an individual depends on the sum of the values of the four trait determining gene pairs he carries. The genotypic value of P_1 is −2, and that of P_2 is +2. Thus the value of the midparent, not shown in Table 4, is 0.

Table 4 indicates schematically five types of F_1 hybrids, which could result from a mating of P_1 to P_2. Since P_1 and P_2 carry differing alleles at four loci, four heterozygous gene pairs are created when their gametes join. In Table 4 it is assumed that in each of the heterozygous gene pairs one of the genes is dominant over the other. In case (a) all the trait decreasing minus genes are dominant over the

Table 4. Polygenic model of intermediate and heterotic inheritance.

	Parents		*F_1 hybrids*				
	P_1	*P_2*	*(a)*	*(b)*	*(c)*	*(d)*	*(e)*
A	+1	−1	−1	+1	+1	+1	+1
B	−1	+1	−1	−1	+1	+1	+1
C	−1	+1	−1	−1	−1	+1	+1
D	−1	+1	−1	−1	−1	−1	+1
Value	−2	+2	−4	−2	0	+2	+4

The midparental value, $(P_1 + P_2)/2$, is $(-2+2)/2 = 0$; thus, on a descriptive level, inheritance is intermediate in case (c), and heterotic in all other cases. The model, however, shows clearly that on the genotypic level the same genetic mechanism accounts for both intermediate and heterotic inheritance. The letters designating hybrids correspond to those shown in Figure 1.

trait enhancing plus genes, and in case (e) all trait increasing plus genes are dominant. In these two cases, the genotypic values of the hybrids deviate most from their midparent (Figure 1). Cases (b) and (d) are less extreme because, in these instances, at some loci the minus gene is dominant over the plus gene, and at other loci the plus gene is dominant over the minus gene. Case (c) represents the unique case in which the effects of minus genes which are dominant over plus genes is exactly balanced by the effects of plus genes which are dominant over minus genes. In this particular case the genotypic value of the F_1 hybrid corresponds to the value of the midparent. In essence then, according to the theory embodied in Table 4, the genetic mechanisms underlying intermediate inheritance are the same as those underlying heterotic inheritance.

At this point a possible source of misunderstanding must be removed. In Table 4, to simplify matters, all plus and minus gene pairs were assigned the same absolute value of one. Thus it must be stated explicitly that gene pairs affecting quantitative traits may have major, intermediate and minor effects; that is, some will affect the phenotype of an individual more, and others less. It is possible to deduce certain features of quantitative inheritance from the model just presented. Which set of trait-determining genes an individual draws from the gene pool is a matter of chance. The likelihood that two individuals would draw the same sample of genes is extremely small. Similarly, the likelihood that two inbred strains would carry the same set of genes determining a quantitative trait is quite remote. This, however, must not be taken to mean that two genotypically different strains must differ phenotypically. It should be obvious that different combinations of plus and minus genes can result in the same phenotype. Phenotypic identity in the same environment does not necessarily indicate genotypic identity. Borrowing and distorting a familiar term, we can say that in the case of quantitative traits we often will deal with genocopies.

A consequence of phenotypic similarity or identity of genotypically differing strains is that the phenotype of inbred parents cannot serve as a reliable guide to prediction of the phenotype of their hybrid offspring. The phenotype of the parents does not enable us to predict how they will "combine." The "combining ability" of inbred strains must be established empirically in each case. Even if we dealt with two pairs of inbred parents where

$P_1 = P_1'$, and $P_2 = P_2'$, the hybrids resulting from the cross $P_1 \times P_2$ could differ very much from the hybrids resulting from cross $P_1' \times P_2'$. Considering this we are not surprised to have found that one and the same trait in some strain crosses was inherited in an intermediate fashion, while in other crosses it showed varying degrees of heterosis. This is what could have been predicted from the theoretical model presented here, and this is what we observed.

Several variations and refinements of this theory have been proposed. The theory, as presented, explains intermediate and heterotic inheritance entirely in terms of dominance. Refinements of the theory, without denying the importance of dominance, point to other forms of intra-allelic and inter-allelic interaction as affecting mode of inheritance. Thus they assume that at some loci neither allele is dominant over the other, and that at such loci the genotypic value of the heterozygous gene pair is intermediate to that of the homozygous parental gene pairs. We would deal here with single-locus intermediacy, and such loci could account in part for intermediate inheritance. Other theories point to the well established fact that at some loci the genotypic value of the heterozygous gene pair exceeds that of either of the parental homozygotes. Such single-locus heterosis or overdominance, as it is commonly called, could account in part for heterotic inheritance. Finally, theories include epistasis, that is, interallelic interactions among the mechanisms which may contribute to heterotic inheritance. While all these mechanisms must be considered in a comprehensive theory of quantitative inheritance, they do not basically alter the simplified model illustrated in Table 4, and it is this model primarily that we will examine in more detail here.

Intermediate Inheritance as a Population Phenomenon

So far we have dealt with the possible results of single strain crosses of type $P_1 \times P_2$. We turn now to the statistical phenomena which are encountered when many inbred strains are crossed and when the resulting F_1 hybrids are compared with their parents. Under these conditions two phenomena can occur and have been observed by us. The average of all F_1 means can coincide with the average of all midparent values, or it may deviate significantly from it. In the latter case we will speak of "population heterosis," and in the former instance of "population intermediacy" or intermediate inheritance as a population phenomenon.

We will deal with intermediate inheritance first. Two examples of it were given above. We found that serum cholesterol level and hematocrit percent were inherited in intermediate fashion in mice. We have seen that in these two instances some F_1 hybrid groups showed intermediate inheritance and others negative or positive heterosis, so that the population of F_1 hybrids as a whole displayed intermediate inheritance. Hybrids as a group did not display "hybrid vigor," and inbreds, when compared with their hybrid offspring, were not "depressed"; they did not show "inbreeding depression" as far as serum cholesterol or hematocrit percent were concerned. With these observations in mind, let us speculate about attributes of the gene pool from which the founders of the inbred strains we dealt with might have drawn their genes.

Our observations lead us to postulate three characteristics of such a gene pool. We will assume that (1) the gene pool contained many plus (+) and many minus (–) genes; (2) that some of the genes were dominant (D), and others were recessive (R); and (3) that extreme minus or plus genes, whether dominant or recessive, were less frequent than genes with small negative or positive effects. In other words, disregarding the magnitude of genes, we assume that D+, D–, R+, and R– genes were equally represented in the gene pool. Figure 6a represents a gene pool with these three characteristics. If we clearly visualize such a pool, it is easy to see how intermediate inheritance as a population phenomenon follows from it.

Consider first single individuals drawing their genes from that pool. Since quantitative traits are based on many genes, it is unlikely that any one individual would draw only minus or plus genes, or only dominant or recessive genes from the pool. Thus extreme phenotypes would be rare, and their uncommonness would be a direct function of the number of genes determining the quantitative character under consideration. In spite, or because of the multitude of genes determining a trait, most individuals would resemble each other and approach closely the average phenotype of the population.

What would happen if such individuals were used for inbreeding, and if, subsequently, the resulting inbred strains were crossed? Two consequences can be listed. (1) In separate brother x sister lines different genes would become fixed, but each line or

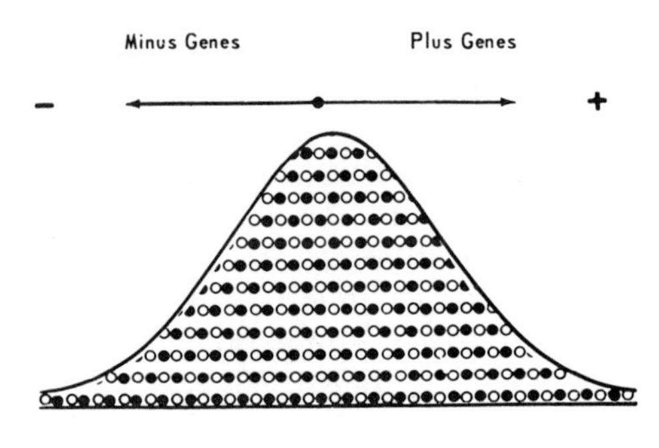

Neutral Traits

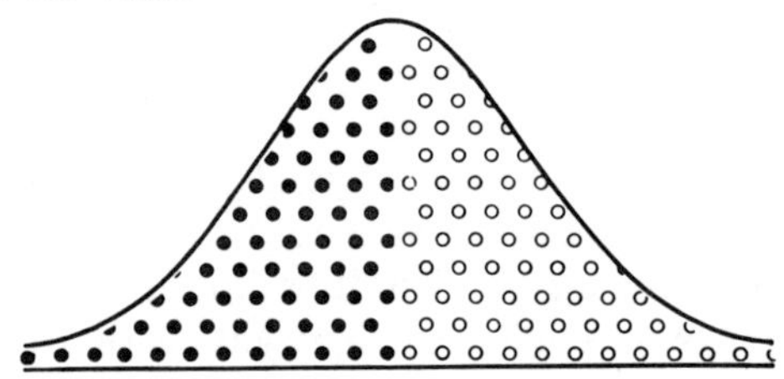

Selected Traits

Fig. 6. Models of Gene Pools. (6a) Neutral Traits Model represents pool of genes for quantitative trait which has not been subjected to selection. Dominant and recessive plus and minus genes are equally represented in the pool. Extreme trait-increasing or trait-decreasing genes are less frequent than genes with small effects. (6b) Selected Traits. Trait has adaptive value, and thus was exposed to selection. Dominant minus genes are eliminated from the pool. Most trait-decreasing genes are recessive, and most trait-increasing genes are dominant.

strain would get its share of D+, D–, R+, and R– genes. To be sure, because of errors of sampling, some strains would carry more D+ genes than others, or more D–, R+, or R– genes. And thus single strains would differ from each other and deviate in an upward or downward direction from the mean value of the base population from which the founders of the inbred strains were drawn. But the average value of all inbred strains would equal the mean value of the wild base population. Inbreeding would not lead to "inbreeding depression." (2) When such inbred strains were crossed, all hybrid genotypes shown in Table 4 would result. However, since most parent strains would transmit to their offspring some plus and some minus, some dominant and some recessive genes, the genotypes of hybrids would tend to resemble those represented under (b), (c), and (d) in Table 4. And the mean value of all F_1 hybrid groups would not differ from the average of all midparents. While single crosses would display negative or positive heterosis, in the population of F_1 hybrids as a whole inheritance would be intermediate.

Population Heterosis

In the preceding section we started with actual experimental observations of intermediate inheritance in a population of F_1 hybrids, and we inferred from it characteristics of the gene pool from which the genes controlling serum cholesterol level and hematocrit percent in mice may have been drawn. Let us repeat this procedure here when dealing with population heterosis. Several examples of it were given. We saw that inheritance of exploratory behavior, wheel running, avoidance conditioning, and other behavior traits was heterotic. We found that a population of F_1 hybrid groups deviated significantly from the average of all their midparents. As a group, hybrids scored above their midparents; they displayed what is commonly referred to as "hybrid vigor." By contrast, inbred strains as a group scored lower than their hybrid offspring; the inbred parent strains showed "inbreeding depression."

The data on exploratory behavior (Table 3, and Fig. 2), and wheel running (Fig. 3; and Bruell, 1964) permit us to make even more specific statements. They suggest that the degree of heterosis depends on the number of heterozygous gene pairs a hybrid carries. This conclusion is based on the following argument. Consider two quite unrelated inbred strains. The chances are that in the course of inbreeding they become homozygous for different alleles at most loci. When such strains are crossed, maximum heterozygosity will be achieved. Now think of two related inbred strains. To be related means to have a certain number of genes in common, and in the case of related inbred strains it means that the strains are quite likely to be homozygous for the same genes at some loci. If then such related inbred strains are crossed, the hybrid offspring will carry fewer heterozygous gene pairs than hybrids resulting from the crossing of unrelated strains. We found that "related hybrids" showed less heterosis than "unrelated hybrids," and we can attribute this to the differential number of heterozygous gene pairs possessed by related and unrelated hybrids.

What do these empirical findings tell us about the gene pool of the base population from which the inbred strains originated? In a single cross, according to the model presented in Table 4, a hybrid will score above the midparent if most of his plus genes are dominant over his minus genes. In other words, positive heterosis depends on a preponderance of D+ over D– genes, and in the extreme case illustrated by case (e) in Table 4, all dominant genes are D+, and all recessive genes are R–. If then in a series of strain crosses we observe positive heterosis of varying degrees, we can hypothesize two characteristics of the gene pool from which the founders of the inbred strains drew their genes. We can assume that (1) the gene pool contained mostly D+ and R– genes; and that (2) extreme D+ and R– genes were less frequent than D+ and R– with small positive and negative effects. A gene pool having these two characteristics is represented in Figure 6b.

Let us examine whether a gene pool with the characteristics shown in Figure 6b can account for population heterosis and inbreeding depression. To simplify discussion, let us consider genes at one locus only. Two types of alleles are found in the pool, namely, D+ and R– alleles. Let us designate D+ alleles by the capital letter A, and R– alleles by small a. And let us assume, as indicated in Figure 6b, that A and a occur with equal frequencies. Then, by random sampling, three genotypes will be generated in predictable proportions, namely, 1/4 AA, 1/2 Aa, and 1/4 aa.

Suppose that the genotypic value of $aa = -10$, and that the value of $AA = +10$. Because of dominance of A over a, the genotypic value of the heterozygous gene pair Aa will be +10 also. The contribution of these three gene pairs, occurring in the indicated proportions, to the mean value of the wild base population will be $(0.25)(-10) + (0.50)(+10) + (0.25)(+10) = +5$. What will happen if individuals are drawn at random from this base population and inbred? As a result of inbreeding only two genotypes will persist, namely, AA and aa homozygotes. They will be equally represented among inbred strains, so that their contribution to the average value of the population of inbred strains will be (0.50) (+10) + (0.50) (−10) = 0. In other words, as far as locus *A* is concerned, the average genotypic value of inbreds will be lower than the average genotypic value of a wild population containing homozygotes and heterozygotes. On the other hand, when the inbreds are crossed, 1/4 *AA*, 1/2 *Aa*, and 1/4 *aa* hybrid groups will result, and the average genotypic value of the hybrid groups will return to the average value of the wild base population. To summarize, the average value of inbred populations will be "depressed" when compared with the average value of hybrid populations. Or, looking at it from the vantage point of inbreds, hybrids on the average will be superior to them; they will display heterosis.

Note, however, that if we consider the situation at one locus only, single crosses of inbreds may result in hybrids whose genotypic value corresponds to the low genotypic value of *aa* homozygotes, and no F_1 hybrid will score above the highest scoring *AA* homozygote. In actual experimental work, however, we often encounter populations of F_1 hybrids where not a single hybrid resembles its lower scoring parent (e.g. Bruell, 1964), or where many hybrids score above their higher scoring parent (see Table 3), thus displaying what is commonly referred to as hybrid vigor. The phenomenon is readily explainable if we assume, as we did all along, that quantitative traits are determined by genes at several loci. Consider case (e) in Table 4. Inbred strains P_1 and P_2 both carry trait-decreasing homozygous R− genes and trait-increasing D+ genes. When P_1 and P_2 are crossed, the trait-reducing homozygous R− gene pairs carried by each parent are complemented by D+ genes carried by the other parent. Thus, in the hybrid, only the trait-raising D+ genes are expressed in the phenotype, and the hybrid when compared with his inbred parents displays hybrid vigor (Table 4, and Figure 1, case e); on the other hand, the parents show inbreeding depression. This, in a few words, is the essence of the so-called "complementary dominance theory" of hybrid vigor and inbreeding depression, and it is worth nothing that this theory makes assumptions about the gene pool of a population which correspond to those presented in Figure 6b. However, instead of speaking of D+ and R− genes, in the context of the complementary dominance theory, we usually speak of beneficial dominant and deleterious recessive genes.

Let us pause and summarize the salient points of this

discussion. We noted that some quantitative traits, e.g., serum cholesterol level and hematocrit percent in mice, are inherited in intermediate fashion if a population of F_1 hybrid groups is considered. And we found that other traits, e.g., exploratory behavior and wheel running in mice, displayed population heterosis. From this we inferred that genes controlling traits inherited in intermediate fashion must have been drawn from a different gene pool than genes controlling traits manifesting population heterosis. We then developed hypotheses regarding the differing characteristics of the two gene pools, and showed how the hypothesized features of the pools could account for the empirical findings. We now must go one step further in our inquiry and ask this question: granted that two kinds of gene pools exist, how did they come about? What was their evolution?

Evolutionary Considerations

It is probably fair to say that in treatments of quantitative genetics more pages have been devoted to heterotic than to intermediate inheritance. I have given "equal time" to both phenomena because, so it seems, both are the manifestations of the same genetic mechanisms and environmental forces. Discussion, however, may profitably proceed from what is accepted as likely by many to what is treated by few.

It is widely accepted that heterotic inheritance is characteristic of those traits which contribute to the fitness of organisms, and thus have been subjected to pressures of selection. When the complementary dominance hypothesis states that dominant genes are beneficial, and recessive genes, carried in double dose, are deleterious, it obviously refers to genes which increase or decrease the biological fitness of an organism; genes which either raise or lower the chances of an organism to reproduce successfully and to propagate its kind. Such plus and minus genes can be dominant or they can be recessive. All four types of genes, D+, D–, R+, and R– genes occur, and as such there is no reason why, when a gene mutates and a new allele arises, this allele should be an R– rather than D–, or D+ rather than R+. Why then are there more deleterious recessive R– genes than deleterious dominant D– genes? The answer is simple: D– genes, by virtue of being expressed in the phenotype, are rapidly eliminated by natural selection. On the other hand R– genes elude natural selection when carried in heterozygous state. Therefore we find in wild populations only few D– genes, while most wild populations are apt to be burdened by a heavy "mutational load"; they are likely to harbor many R– genes. And it is this imbalance between D– genes and R– genes which accounts for the twin phenomena of inbreeding depression and heterosis. The decreased vitality of inbreds and the vigor of hybrids are both a consequence of the natural selection which prevailed in the wild base population from which the founders of the inbred strains were drawn. Natural selection removed from the gene pool of the wild base population most D– genes, thus establishing a pool schematically represented by Figure 6b.

The foregoing considerations seem to imply that intermediate inheritance will be characteristic of quantitative traits which neither increase nor lessen the fitness of the organism possessing them, and thus traits which have not been subjected to selection. While some authors doubt that any character of an organism is absolutely neutral from an evolutionary point of view, there exist certainly traits which are for all practical purposes neutral or at least less contributing to fitness than others (Falconer, 1960; Mayr, 1963). Presumably such traits also depend on dominant and recessive genes which increase or decrease their phenotypic expression. However, because of the selective neutrality of such traits, the genes controlling them will all be preserved in the population: D– genes will have the same chance to persist as D+ genes, and R+ genes will not be favored over R– genes. The expected outcome of such circumstances is a gene pool represented by Figure 6a. An excellent and much more explicit presentation of similar ideas is contained in the last chapter of Falconer's (1960) book.

The essential point of this presentation is that population intermediacy and population heterosis can be understood only in terms of evolutionary processes, namely, an interaction between hereditary endowment of a population, that is, its gene pool, and environmental pressures. The gene pool is generated by random mutational processes, and it is shaped by selection. A trait that has not been subjected to selection reveals during inbreeding the random distribution of accidents of mutation. It shows intermediate inheritance, and the population mean remains constant during inbreeding and crossing. Similarly, a trait that was exposed to selection, that is, a trait whose gene pool was systematically culled by environmental forces discloses its evolutionary past during inbreeding. Its population mean decreases during inbreeding and increases during crossing. It manifests inbreeding depression and hybrid vigor.

Not essential to this presentation are the particular genetic mechanisms invoked. For example, to simply exposition I have chosen to discuss heterosis entirely in terms of the additive effects of dominance at many loci. However, there can be no doubt that other mechanisms enter the picture, for example, single-locus heterosis or overdominance. There is abundant evidence that heterozygous gene pairs exist which exceed in value both parental homozygotes. Such heterotic gene combinations could be called D++. If such D++ combinations exist, it can be argued that D–– gene combinations must arise also, and we are faced with the same problem as before. We have to explain why D++ combinations are observed rather frequently, and D–– combinations seldom, if at all. The preservation of D++ combinations in the population has been explained in evolutionary terms already (Mayr, 1963); the elimination of D–– combinations must be answered in the same terms. Thus population heterosis remains presumptive evidence for the operation of selection pressures, whatever the underlying genetic mechanisms, and intermediate inheritance of certain traits still suggests their selective neutrality.

Implications

The quantitative characters an experimenter chooses to study are arbitrary abstractions from the infinite number of observable attributes of organisms, and the measures he uses are no less arbitrary. Frequently one measures what is readily measurable in units of measurement which can be conveniently recorded. The data and theoretical considerations presented here suggest that, in spite of this arbitrary choice of characters, it should be possible to sort them into those which increase the fitness of an organism and those which are neutral from an evolutionary point of view. This could be done in breeding experiments of the kind described here. By applying to the results of such experiments the criteria developed above, it should be possible to distinguish between traits with and without adaptive value. Certainly, often we will not need to question nature in costly breeding tests since the adaptive value of a trait will be only too obvious. The results of the cholesterol study summarized above, however, should warn us not to be too sure too often. Based on current medical evidence and beliefs, one could have assumed that serum cholesterol level will be lower in hybrids than in inbred animals, but the results of the breeding test would have proved one wrong.

In behavioral research in particular it is often difficult to decide whether a trait has adaptive value or not. Consider, for example, susceptibility to audiogenic seizures (Fuller and Thompson, 1960), preference for alcohol (McClearn and Rodgers, 1961), or emotional defecation in a strange environment (Bruell, 1963a). It would be hard to say whether such traits possibly could have conferred a selective advantage on their bearers, and in case the traits actually were subjected to selection pressures, it would be hard to guess whether heterosis would be positive or negative. By conducting research of the type suggested here, however, and by thus broadening our base for generalization, we may in time discern a pattern: we may learn to spell out better than we can today the characteristics of behavior forms with and without evolutionary significance.

SUMMARY

Over 4,000 mice belonging to 13 inbred strains and 31 groups of F_1 hybrids were studied in two tests of behavior, namely, exploration of a strange environment, and spontaneous running in activity wheels. In these test situations the 31 hybrid populations outscored their inbred parents: they explored more and ran more in wheels. Thus they displayed "behavioral heterosis." Six hundred mice belonging to 5 inbred strains and 20 F_1 groups resulting from the systematic crossing of the inbreds were tested for serum cholesterol and hematocrit percent. In these physiological tests, hybrids did not differ from their parents. Hybrids tended to score midway between their inbred parents. Thus mode of inheritance was intermediate.

Current views regarding intermediate and heterotic inheritance were presented. It was hypothesized (1) that intermediate inheritance is characteristic of "neutral traits," that is, traits which do not confer a selective advantage on their bearers; and (2) that heterotic inheritance occurs only in traits which had been subjected to selection. The reasoning leading to the formulation of these hypotheses was presented in some detail. In concluding, it was suggested that determination of the mode of inheritance of characters may help one to distinguish between adaptive and selectively neutral traits.

REFERENCES

Bruell, J. H. 1962. Dominance and segregation in the inheritance of quantitative behavior in mice. p. 48-67. *In* E. L. Bliss, [ed.], Roots of behavior. Harper & Brothers, New York.

———. 1963a. Emotional defecation in mice, a territory marking response? Am. Psychol. 17:445.

———. 1963b. Additive inheritance of serum cholesterol in mice. Science 142:1664-1666.

———. 1964. Heterotic inheritance of wheel running in mice. J. Comp. Physiol. Psychol. (in press).

Cold Spring Harbor Symposia on Quantitative Biology. 1955. Population genetics: The nature and causes of genetic variability in populations. Vol. 20. Long Island Biological Assoc., Cold Spr. Harb., New York.

———. 1959. Genetics and twentieth century Darwinism. Vol. 24. Long Island Biological Assoc., Cold Spr. Harb., New York.

Collins, R. L. 1963. Genetics of avoidance conditioning in mice: A diallel study. Ph.D. Thesis. Western Reserve Univ.

———. 1964. Inheritance of avoidance conditioning in mice: A diallel study. Science 143:1188-1190.

Committee on Standardized Genetic Nomenclature for Mice. 1960. Standardized nomenclature for inbred strains of mice. Second listing, Cancer Research. 20:145-169.

Falconer, D. S. 1960. Introduction to quantitative genetics. The Ronald Press, New York.

Fuller, J. L., and W. R. Thompson. 1960. Behavior genetics. John Wiley and Sons, Inc., New York.

Gowen, J. W. (Ed.) 1952. Heterosis. Iowa State College Press, Iowa.

Lerner, M. I. 1958. The genetic basis of selection. John Wiley & Sons, Inc., New York.

Mather, K. 1949. Biometrical genetics. Methuen & Co., Ltd., London.

Mayr, E. 1963. Animal species and evolution. The Belknap Press of Harvard Univ. Press, Mass.

McClearn, G. E. and D. A. Rodgers. 1961. Genetic factors in alcohol preference of laboratory mice. J. Comp. Physiol. Psychol. 54:116-119.

Russell, E. S., and P. S. Gerald. 1958. Inherited electrophoretic hemoglobin patterns among 20 inbred strains of mice. Science 128: 1569-1570.

The Effect of Reciprocal Cross-Fostering on the Behaviour of Two Species of Rodents, Mus Musculus *and* Baiomys Taylori Ater

DAVID M. QUADAGNO

EDWIN M. BANKS

INTRODUCTION

In most species of rodents the young remain with the dam for a period of suckling and growth. According to Scott's critical period hypothesis, it is presumably during this period that the young learn certain socializing factors and species recognition cues that will influence their adult behaviour (Scott 1962). The hypothesis that there are periods in ontogeny during which the young organism is particularly sensitive to learning certain stimulus characteristics of the species has been advanced by numerous authors (Scott 1962; Moltz 1963; Sluckin 1965). The process by which the young organism attaches itself to the characteristics of the species was called 'imprinting' by Lorenz in his 'Kumpan' paper (Lorenz 1937). Imprinting as it will be used throughout this paper is defined as a process that occurs during a period in the life of the young animal when it is receptive to and learns certain cues by means of which a permanent attachment between the animal and its conspecifics is formed.

The most significant aspect of imprinting is the establishment of a stable preference which determines the class of objects to which filial and, frequently, sexual responses are addressed (Bateson 1966). Lorenz (1937) has stated that the biological function of imprinting is to enable animals to recognize their species rather than particular individuals. All of the available evidence from mammalian studies seems to indicate that the olfactory modality is used to a great extent in the imprinting process (Mainardi, Marsan & Pasquali 1965; Klopfer & Gamble 1966; Klopfer 1967).

One approach to the study of imprinting and its effect on later behaviour is the method of cross-fostering. Cross-fostering, i.e. fostering one species or strain on a different species or strain at birth, has been used to explore the effect of early experience on later behaviour in rodents (Denenberg, Hudgens & Zarrow 1964, 1966; Lagerspetz & Wuorinen 1965; Hudgens, Denenberg & Zarrow, 1967, 1968; Southwick 1968). The adult behaviours measured in the above studies included open field performance, social preference and aggressive behaviour.

These studies showed that cross-fostered animals were less active in the open field when compared to control animals raised by conspecifics. When placed in a test situation, where they could select between a conspecific or the foster species, cross-fostered animals spent more time in front of a chamber housing the foster species. In contrast, control animals spent more time in front of a chamber housing a conspecific. More fighting in pair encounters was found in control than in cross-fostered groups.

Hudgens et al. (1968) working with mice found that the procedure of intraspecific cross-fostering itself had no significant effect on the behaviours observed. The only difference between the fostered and control young was that fostered young had a higher survival incidence at the time of weaning than did pups reared by their own mothers.

Denenberg et al. (1966) and Hudgens et al. (1968) after manipulating such variables as pre- and post-weaning peer constitution and litter size concluded that the single, most powerful social variable affecting adult behaviour in mice was the mother.

Most previous studies employing reciprocal cross-fostering utilized two inbred strains of house mouse. Southwick (1968) found that the aggressive behaviour of young adult male mice of a passive strain (A/J) was significantly increased by fostering to females of a more aggressive strain (CFW). Fostering did not product significant changes in the aggressive behaviour of the CFW strain. Lagerspetz & Wuorinen (1965) found that young from an aggressive strain were significantly more aggressive than young from a non-aggressive strain regardless of the preweaning maternal care thus indicating that cross-fostering was without effect.

With the exception of Denenberg et al. (1966), who looked at the open field performance of cross-fostered males and females, all other cross-fostering studies excluded tests on cross-fostered females. Females were included in the present study because of their theoretical relevance. Knight, Robertson & Waddington (1956) stated that in the general case, selection for responses important in maintaining sexual isolation, and thereby minimizing hybridization, would be expected to act more strongly on females than males. Wastage of female gametes would thus be minimized. It might be anticipated that males and females would exhibit differential responsiveness to the cross-fostering procedure.

Mainardi et al. (1965) used males and females of the same strain of mice, *Mus musculus*, SWM/Mai; the young mice were reared by parents sprayed with commercial perfume. At maturity these animals were allowed to choose between two individuals of the opposite sex, one perfumed and one without perfume on its body. They found that female mice chose the perfumed conspecific whereas the male mice did not. They concluded, '. . . that olfactory stimuli are of paramount importance in defining the reproductive barriers in the mouse (in this case the only difference was an olfactory character; the subjects all belonged to the same strain)'. Mainardi et al. (1965) also suggested, 'the existence of a discriminating action that female mice, contrary to males, exercise in sexual selection.'

Marr & Gardner (1965) found that male and female rats reared by a dam that was rubbed daily with cologne preferred, in a social preference test, cologne-scented rats rather than rats not rubbed with cologne. The experimental rats were less responsive sexually, i.e. they mounted normal smelling rats less, and were more emotional, i.e. defaecated more and moved less in an open field situation when compared to control rats. These authors did not distinguish between males and females except in the sexual test situation.

Kalkowski (1967) found no significant differences in the ability of male and female house mice to distinguish odours of specific individuals. The test animal was conditioned to prefer certain individuals' odours by the use of electric shock. Kalkowski concluded that 'the efficiency of identification by smell of species-partners remains basically on the same level in males and females.' This author also stated 'that between the sexes no statistically significant differences were found in their ability to discriminate other specimens whether they were animals of the same or different sex . . .'. Kalkowski's study did not control for the oestrous state of the female.

The present study also differs from all previous research in its experimental design, with the exception of Hudgens et al. (1967). In other studies cross-fostered animals were paired with other cross-fostered animals, and only the presence or absence of fighting was noted. Also control animals were paired with other control animals, and again, only the presence or absence of fighting was noted. The scores of the cross-fostered animals were then compared with the scores of the control animals. Hudgens et al. (1967) paired rat-reared mice with mouse-reared mice and noted the presence or absence of fighting behaviour. They found that 44 per cent of the thirty-six pairs fought at least once. In every case of a fight the mouse-reared member of the pair was noted to be the aggressor.

In the present study reciprocal cross-fostering was between a highly inbred strain of house mouse, *Mus musculus*, C57BR/cdJ and a wild-caught population of the pygmy mouse, *Baiomys taylori ater* (Blossom and Burt).

Cross-fostered animals were paired with control animals and numerous behavioural criteria were observed and recorded. The behaviour of the cross-fostered animals was then compared to the behaviour of the control animals when the control animals were paired with each other. Therefore, changes in behaviour due to cross-fostering were readily compared with a pattern previously established by pairing two control animals. The goal of this study was to determine the effect of reciprocal cross-fostering on behaviour in tests of social preference, open field, pair encounters and mating for both sexes from two unrelated species.

METHODS

Subjects

The two species studied were the pygmy mouse and the inbred laboratory mouse, C57BR/cdJ. The pygmy mice were trapped in Cochise Co., Arizona during the summer of 1967, and the house mice came from Jackson Laboratory in Bar Harbor, Maine. Both were bred in our laboratory. *Baiomys* were mated to minimize inbreeding and only their first two generations of laboratory progeny were studied.

Baiomys is polyoestrous (Blair 1941) and breeds throughout the year in the field (Raun & Wilks 1964) and in the laboratory (Blair 1941). Blair (1941) reported that sexual maturity is reached at approximately 60 days and gestation lasts 20 days. Weaning occurs at 22 days and the average litter size is 2.7 (range, 1 to 5) according to Blair (1941). Packard (1960) reported an average litter size of 2.48 (range, 1 to 4). In our laboratory the average litter size was 2.85 (range, 1 to 5). The young *Baiomys* remain attached to the female's teats during the day but are detached in the evening while the female feeds. We have observed that the young cannot be removed from the female's teats without force. The young are born with incisors erupted. The house mice were highly inbred and selected, in part, for adaptability to laboratory life, whereas the pygmy mice were wild-caught.

Procedure

Conspecific males and females were paired and when the female was visibly pregnant, approximately 15 days, she was placed in a clean 35 x 20 x 15 cm metal cage that contained wood shavings and cotton. The female was left undisturbed until parturition. The young were assigned to one of four treatment groups at 48 hr (± 12 hr) after birth (Table I).

Cross-fostering eighty-one *Mus* and fifty-eight *Baiomys* pups yielded twenty *Mus* and twenty-one *Baiomys* alive at weaning. All litters were reduced to three. The control litters contained three conspecific sibs being raised by their biological dam, while the cross-fostered litters contained one cross-fostered pup being raised by

Table I. Summary of treatment conditions and distribution of subjects.

Subjects	*Dam*	*Sibs*	*Groups*
Mus	*Mus*	*Mus*	Control *Mus* $N = 24$♀♀ + 24♂♂
Mus	*Baiomys*	*Baiomys*	Cross-fostered *Mus* $N = 10$♀♀ + 10♂♂
Baiomys	*Baiomys*	*Baiomys*	Control *Baiomys* $N = 21$♀♀ + 24♂♂
Baiomys	*Mus*	*Mus*	Cross-fostered *Baiomys* $N = 11$♀♀ + 10♂♂

a foster dam with two of her own pups. For example, the cross-fostered *Baiomys* group contained one *Baiomys* pup and two *Mus* pups being raised by a *Mus* dam. The sex ratio of the litters was not controlled because the *Baiomys* dams usually had only three pups per litter. In the control *Mus* group the litter size was randomly reduced to three pups. Occasionally four pups were born to a dam in the *Baiomys* control group. When this occurred one of the pups was randomly removed.

The *Baiomys* pups were pried loose from their biological dam by means of a blunt dental probe. This procedure took approximately 20 s to perform. The control *Baiomys* were not exposed to the same treatment. All cross-fostered animals were placed in litters of approximately the same age (± 24 hr).

The litters remained undisturbed until the pups were 21 days old. At this time the litters from all four groups were weaned, weighed and each animal was then placed individually into a small metal cage (25 x 17.5 x 15 cm) that contained wood shavings and a piece of cotton. All four groups were fed Purina Mouse Breeder Chow and water ad libitum. Lettuce, apple slices and wild bird feed were provided once per week. A light cycle of 13L : 11D and temperature regime 22 ± 1°C was maintained in the animal rooms. Each of the four treatment groups was housed in a separate room. The individual cages were placed next to each other so that each animal was exposed to acoustic and olfactory stimuli from neighbouring cages.

When the animals in all four groups reached 65 days of age, a series of tests was initiated as follows.

Open Field Test

Starting at 65 days of age all subjects were tested for 3 min a day for three consecutive days in an open field. The open field arena was a circular field, 105 cm in diameter. The floor was plywood and marked into 5-cm square grids, except around the edges. The 'squares' around the edges varied in size. The field was enclosed by a galvanized metal wall 20 cm in height. Illumination measured 409.03 lumen per m^2 in the arena and was provided by a 100-W bulb suspended 87 cm above the arena. Each subject was removed from its cage, carried in a covered container to the arena, and then released in its centre. The total number of 5-cm squares entered, the number of 'squares' around the edge entered, the number of faecal boluses defaecated, and the total number of escapes attempted were scored. The 60 cm^2 area located in the centre of the field was designated as the 'centre squares'. All tests were run between 11.00 and 13.00 hours. The subjects were weighed on the 1st day of open field testing after the test was completed.

Social Preference Test

At 75 to 80 days of age all animals were tested for social preference in a Y-shaped maze constructed of Plexiglas (Fig. 1). The air flow through the apparatus was 45 m per min. The Y-maze was located in a room that contained both gerbils (*Meriones*) and *Baiomys.*

The stimulus animals located in the last chambers were always females in dioestrus as judged by vaginal smears. Thus test males and females from all four groups were given a choice between a dioestrous female *Baiomys* and a dioestrous female *Mus*. All female test animals used in the social preference test were in dioestrous condition. The test animals were placed in the Y-maze for two ½-hr trials. During each trial the following data were recorded manually: latency until the test animal entered chamber adjacent to conspecific, time spent in chamber adjacent to foster species and time spent in darkened neutral area (single passageway or either arm). The stimulus animals were alternated between the right and left chambers after each test was completed. The control and cross-fostered *Mus* groups were tested between 15.00 and 17.00 hours, whereas the control and cross-fostered *Baiomys* groups were tested between

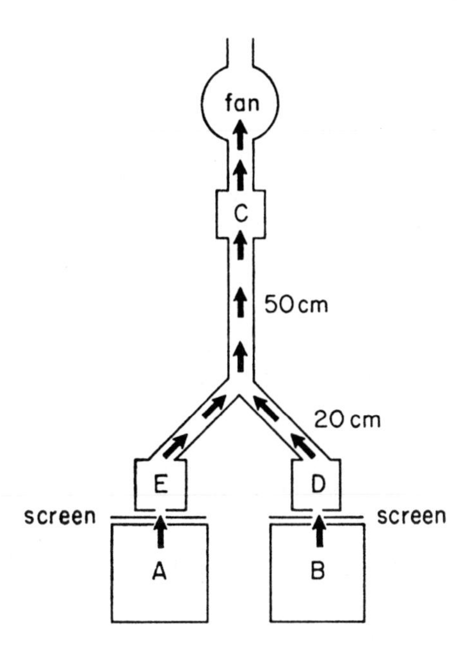

Fig. 1. Diagram of Y-shaped maze used in social preference test. Odours of females located in chambers A and B were presented simultaneously to the test animal who was initially located in C (starting box). The test animal scored a choice by entering the antechamber to either A or B.

17.00 and 20.00 hours under red light. It was determined in a pilot study that *Mus* and *Baiomys* were most active in late afternoon and in early evening respectively.

Pair Encounters

The pair encounter arena was a glass observation cage 35 x 20 x 25 cm high. It had wood shavings on the bottom. At 100 to 115 days of age all animals were placed in 15-min pair encounters. At this age all of the females exhibited oestrous cycles and all males had scrotal testes. A twenty-channel event recorder was used to record quantitatively numerous behavioural elements for each animal in the pair encounter (Table II). All pair encounters were staged between 16.00 and 17.00 hours.

Table II. Behavioral elements analysed in 15-min encounters.

Social and maintenance behaviour
1. Frequency of approaches toward each other made by both animals
2. Latency to initial contact
3. Animal initiating contact
4. Frequency of encounters (physical contacts) between animals
5. Duration of physical contact with each other (s)
6. Duration of allogrooming by both animals–allogrooming includes nasal, oral or vibrissal contact with any part of the other animal (s)
7. Frequency with which each animal avoided the other animal–avoidance is a collection of withdrawal movements following contact with the other animal, e.g., running away, turning over, etc.
8. Duration of autogrooming by both animals–autogrooming includes self-licking, scratching with hindleg, or rubbing forelegs over head and face (s)

Exploratory behaviour
1. Frequency of elongate (investigatory) postures by both animals
2. Duration of elongate posture by both animals (s)

Sexual behaviour
1. Frequency of attempted mounts–from position behind female, male raises forelegs, attempts to mount, but is unsuccessful
2. Frequency of mounts–male approaches from behind, clasps pelvic region of female with forelegs. Both hindfeet of male are in contact with ground
3. Frequency of times lordosis occurred
4. Frequency of intromissions

Agonistic behaviour
1. Duration of tail rattling by both animals (s)
2. Duration of hind leg bracing–the hind leg is extended and braced against the wall of the arena (s)
3. Frequency of upright threats and biting
4. Frequency of escape leaps by both animals–the animals attempt to jump out of the arena

All subjects were weighed and given the opportunity to interact with conspecifics as well as with the foster species. To elicit sexual behaviour males were paired with oestrous females. Test females in dioestrus were paired with other dioestrous females. The order of these four pairings for each subject was determined from a table of random numbers.

Sexual Behaviour Test

Between 110 and 120 days of age the control and cross-fostered *Mus* males and females were paired with conspecifics of opposite sex. When the test animal was a male it was presented with a sexually experienced female *Mus* in which behavioural oestrus had been induced with 0.035 mg of oestradiol benzoate followed 48 hr later with 0.1 mg of progesterone. Eight to 10 hr after the progesterone injection, the injected females were placed with a stud male *Mus* that usually mounted within 5 min. Those females exhibiting lordosis to the stud male were then paired with the test males. The test male was paired with the injected female for a ½-hour encounter in a small arena (35 x 20 x 25 cm high). Table III lists the behavioural measures recorded.

Table III. Behavioural elements recorded during sexual tests.

A. When the test animal was a male the following information was recorded:
1. Latency to the first mount or attempted mount
2. Frequency of mounts or attempted mounts
3. Latency to the first intromission
4. Frequency of intromissions
5. Latency of first ejaculation
6. Frequency of ejaculations

B. When the test animal was a female the following information was recorded:
1. Latency to the first lordosis
2. Frequency of lordosis

When the test animal was a female she was judged to be in natural oestrus by the vaginal smear technique and was placed with a sexually experienced male that had sired four or more litters. The test female and experienced male were together for 12 hr beginning at 21.00 hours and ending at 09.00 hours. They were placed in a small arena (35 x 20 x 25 cm high), and time-lapse photography was utilized to record the behaviour. One frame per min was exposed during the 12 hr that the animals were together. The frames were later analysed with a time and motion projector and the behavioural measures listed in Table III were recorded. Latency to first lordosis was computed by recording the first frame showing the female in the lordosis position. Frequency of lordosis was computed by recording the number of frames that showed the female in lordosis. There were no observations in which the female was in the lordosis position for two consecutive frames. No sexual behaviour tests were performed on *Baiomys* for reasons to be cited in the discussion. Statistical procedures other than those indicated in reporting the results were also applied to all data: factor analysis, computation of correlation coefficients and analysis of variance. None of these provided additional insight in the interpretation of the data.

RESULTS

Success at Cross-fostering

The *Mus* accepted foster *Baiomys* pups 36.20 per cent of the time, whereas 24.69 per cent of the time the *Baiomys* dams accepted the foster *Mus* pups. These differences were not statistically significant. The attempts made at cross-fostering were fifty-nine *Baiomys* to *Mus* and eighty-two *Mus to Baiomys.* The survival rate of the control *Mus* and *Baiomys* was 83 per cent and 96 per cent, respectively. In the majority of cases when cross-fostering was unsuccessful the dam

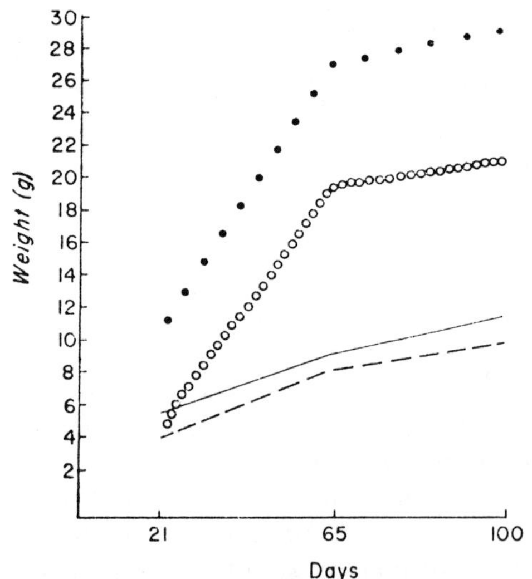

Fig. 2. Combined weights of males and females from all four groups. Solid circles, control *Mus*; open circles, cross-fostered *Mus*; solid line, control *Baiomys*; broken line, cross-fostered *Baiomys*.

killed the foster pup. In all other unsuccessful cases the foster pups were ignored, and they starved to death.

Body Weight

When the body weights of the cross-fostered *Mus* and *Baiomys* were measured at 21, 65 and 100 days, both groups weighed less than the controls (Fig. 2). A *t*-test showed no significant difference in body weights when the control and cross-fostered *Baiomys* groups were compared at 21 and 65 days, however a difference significant at the 0.05 level was found at 100 days. The control and cross-fostered *Mus* groups were significantly different in body weights at 21, 65 and 100 days with *P* values of 0.001, 0.001 and 0.01, respectively. In each of the four groups the weights of the males and females were combined.

Open Field Behaviour

The open field performance for all four groups is summarized in Table IV. These data are the mean sum of total activity, number of squares entered in the centre of the field and faecal boluses for 3 successive days testing in the open field.

Both the male and female cross-fostered *Baiomys* showed an increase in total activity (ambulation) scores in the open field when compared to controls. This difference was not significant for the females. Both the cross-fostered male and female *Mus* showed a significant decrease in activity in the open field when compared to controls.

Social Preference Test

The results of the social preference test are presented in Table V. The values presented in the table are the mean sums for the two 30-min trials in the Y-maze. The column labelled 'per cent time adjacent to conspecific' was computed from the total time spent with both stimulus animals.

The cross-fostered *Mus* males and females spent significantly less time than controls adjacent to a conspecific. The *Baiomys* male and female reacted differently to cross fostering; the females spent significantly less time than controls adjacent to a conspecific, males did not differ significantly from controls.

Table IV. Summary of open field performance.

Group	*Mean total no. squares entered*		*Mean no. squares in centre entered*		*Mean no. faecal boluses*	
CB♂♂	848.45 (± 64.60)		83.65 (± 15.71)		7.31 (± 0.96)	
		***		NS		***
CFB♂♂	1776.10 (± 417.34)		137.80 (± 35.20)		13.00 (± 1.14)	
CB♀♀	899.64 (± 58.61)		82.31 (± 11.36)		8.89 (± 1.08)	
		NS		*		NS
CFB♀♀	999.00 (± 172.98)		142.20 (± 52.81)		7.20 (± 1.22)	
CM♂♂	1861.57 (± 117.33)		508.86 (± 56.97)		4.14 (± 0.97)	
		*		**		*
CFM♂♂	1558.42 (± 53.62)		366.85 (± 32.97)		1.33 (± 0.37)	
CM♀♀	1786.21 (± 72.32)		553.52 (± 44.86)		3.40 (± 0.68)	
		***		***		NS
CFM♀♀	1300.50 (± 88.81)		278.75 (± 33.42)		3.25 (± 1.22)	

SE of means is in parentheses. The *P* values were obtained from values of *t* computed from the difference between two means. NS not significant; *$P<0.05$; **$P<0.005$; and ***$P<0.001$. Control *Baiomys* group (CB); cross-fostered *Baiomys* group (CFB); control *Mus* group (CM); cross-fostered *Mus* group (CFM).

Pair Encounters

The results of the 15-min pair encounters are summarized in Table VI. Only differences in behaviours significant with a *t*-test at the 0.05 level are reported. When control animals were paired with cross-fostered animals only the scores of the latter were used in the analysis of behavioural changes.

All of the cross-fostered groups showed behaviour patterns indicating that they were reacting more positively to the foster species than to conspecifics. In this context an animal is said to be reacting more positively to another when it showed an increase in these behaviours: frequency of approaches, number of encounters, duration in seconds of physical contact, and duration of allo-grooming. An animal is said to be reacting negatively to another when it showed an increase in: frequency of avoidance behaviour number of fights and threats, tail rattling, leg bracing and number of escape leaps.

Table V. Summary of social preference test data.

Group	*Latency (s) to initial choice*		*Initial choice (per cent time)*	*Per cent time adj. to conspecific*		*Total time (s) in neutral area*	
CB♂♂	35.41 (± 5.70)	*	Conspecific–78.19*	66.59 (± 2.78)	NS	2483.73 (± 130.27)	NS
CFB♂♂	111.43 (± 60.10)		Foster species–75.81*	67.35 (± 4.93)		2897.20 (± 202.60)	
CB♀♀	15.38 (± 4.48)	*	Conspecific–78.60*	64.88 (± 3.68)	**	2307.60 (± 143.80)	***
CFB♀♀	64.40 (± 30.31)		Foster species–50.00 NS	42.68 (± 5.88)		3477.20(± 57.20)	
CM♂♂	8.15 (± 0.82)	NS	Conspecific–58.31 NS	56.45 (± 1.22)	***	1735.85 (± 37.10)	
CFM♂♂	6.78 (± 1.00)		Foster-species–58.53 NS	41.32 (± 1.14)		1608.85 (± 40.48)	
CM♀♀	10.37 (± 0.69)	*	Conspecific–66.00*	56.22 (± 0.85)	***	1922.04 (± 52.28)	*
CFM♀♀	5.93 (± 0.70)		Foster species–52.11 NS	35.33 (± 0.96)		1728.25 (± 40.26)	

SE of means is in parentheses. The P values were obtained from values of t computed from the difference between two means, with the exception for initial choice where P values were obtained from χ^2 analysis with Yates' correction factor. NS not significant; *$P<0.05$**$P<0.001$; and ***$P<0.001$. Control *Baiomys* group (CB); cross-fostered *Baiomys* group (CFB); control *Mus* group (CM); cross-fostered *Mus* group (CFM).

Table VI. Comparisons of 15 min encounters between cross-fostered and control animals in the four pairings.

Behavioural elements (when paired with:)	*Mus* (females)			*Mus* (males)			*Baiomys* (females)			*Baiomys* (males)		
	Cross-fostered mean (±SE)	Control mean (±SE)	Probability level	Cross-fostered mean (±SE)	Control mean (±SE)	Probability level	Cross-fostered mean (±SE)	Control mean (±SE)	Probability level	Cross-fostered mean (±SE)	Control mean (±SE)	Probability level
1. *Mus* males												
Allogrooming (s)							13·60 (± 4·11)	0·00 (± 0·00)	0·01			
Approaches				62·71 (±13·37)	15·37 (± 4·89)	0·01	47·20 (± 11·54)	4·33 (± 2·09)	0·01	65·57 (±14·58)	6·33 (± 3·04)	0·001
Avoidances	19·80 (± 3·24)	8·09 (± 1·08)	0·001				2·20 (± 0·48)	15·16 (± 2·76)	0·01	6·14 (± 1·51)	22·55 (± 5·36)	0·05
Autogrooming (s)							141·00 (± 16·12)	18·00 (± 1·03)	0·001			
Elongate postures							14·00 (± 4·42)	2·00 (± 0·89)	0·05			
Elongate posture (s)				52·71 (± 9·23)	124·25 (±18·26)	0·01	67·00 (± 21·18)	2·00 (± 0·76)	0·01			
Encounters	32·71 (± 3·00)	51·00 (± 4·39)	0·05	52·00 (± 7·04)	29·25 (± 7·26)	0·05	79·80 (± 21·09)	14·00 (± 4·05)	0·01	62·58 (±11·87)	14·77 (± 5·45)	0·01
Leg bracing (s)										0·85 (± 0·71)	60·11 (±12·61)	0·001
Physical contact (s)							224·00 (± 64·51)	29·16 (± 8·03)	0·01	147·42 (±28·30)	52·12 (±18·79)	0·01
2. *Mus* females												
Allogrooming (s)				65·60 (±15·92)	214·72 (±30·66)	0·01	42·06 (± 17·14)	5·00 (± 1·50)	0·05	15·00 (± 2·55)	67·32 (±13·06)	0·01
Approaches				64·20 (±11·06)	46·00 (±28·65)	0·05						
Avoidances							4·20 (± 1·11)	12·00 (± 2·04)	0·01			
Elongate postures	34·40 (± 3·41)	19·33 (± 2·31)	0·01									
Escapes							0·02 (± 0·20)	21·16 (± 5·98)	0·05			
Fights							0·00 (± 0·00)	4·83 (± 0·79)	0·001	0·00 (± 0·00)	5·00 (± 0·85)	0·001
Leg bracing (s)							7·00 (± 0·31)	3·83 (± 0·90)	0·05	4·16 (± 3·22)	66·00 (±18·07)	0·01
Mounts and attempts				34·40 (± 7·67)	4·63 (± 1·85)	0·001						
Physical contact (s)				134·00 (±22·82)	279·45 (±37·87)	0·05	385·40 (±103·74)	101·83 (± 8·90)	0·05			
Trail rattling							0·00 (± 0·00)	4·00 (± 0·81)	0·01			
3. *Baiomys* males												
Allogrooming (s)	97·80 (±26·55)	30·40 (±14·09)	0·05	85·28 (±20·45)	16·44 (±11·40)	0·01	2·16 (± 0·54)	56·00 (± 3·57)	0·001			
Approaches	22·20 (± 0·86)	16·43 (± 2·11)	0·05	52·85 (± 8·85)	27·22 (± 2·85)	0·01	4·16 (± 0·41)	8·77 (± 0·66)	0·001			
Avoidances							16·83 (± 5·13)	4·33 (± 0·76)	0·05			
Elongate posture (s)	39·20 (± 7·73)	77·31 (± 5·95)	0·01	32·42 (± 6·01)	87·91 (±12·53)	0·05						
Encounters				46·85 (± 5·45)	11·44 (± 5·79)	0·001				12·20 (± 2·39)	21·66 (± 0·91)	0·01
Fights							1·50 (± 0·50)	0·00 (± 0·00)	0·01	4·22 (± 0·87)	0·33 (± 0·15)	0·05
Mounts and attempts				30·42 (±11·30)	0·00 (± 0·00)	0·01						
Physical contact (s)	278·20 (± 6·15)	43·00 (±22·32)	0·001	149·57 (±30·53)	39·77 (±20·07)	0·01				478·20 (±34·26)	273·33 (±15·92)	0·001
Tail rattling (s)							2·26 (± 0·52)	0·00 (±0·00)	0·001			
4. *Baiomys* females												
Allogrooming (s)	89·00 (± 9·60)	26·71 (± 2·16)	0·001	72·50 (±19·61)	21·20 (± 6·15)	0·05	0·00 (± 0·00)	34·28 (± 5·50)	0·001			
Approaches	54·33 (±11·05)	24·25 (± 3·47)	0·05	76·28 (±12·06)	26·61 (± 3·50)	0·05						
Avoidances										21·14 (± 7·00)	3·28 (± 0·47)	0·05
Autogrooming (s)				19·75 (± 1·31)	1·40 (± 0·81)	0·001	28·00 (± 3·79)	48·14 (± 0·48)	0·01	45·85 (± 5·85)	72·42 (± 7·76)	0·05
Elongate postures				10·75 (± 4·46)	25·80 (± 3·91)	0·05	3·00 (± 0·94)	0·28 (± 0·18)	0·01			
Elongate posture (s)							11·00 (± 3·47)	1·14 (± 0·73)	0·01	6·00 (± 2·71)	24·42 (± 7·21)	0·05
Encounters							1·20 (± 0·20)	4·57 (± 0·29)	0·001			
Escapes							73·00 (± 8·22)	11·00 (± 0·21)	0·001	12·83 (± 4·78)	2·28 (± 1·61)	0·05
Fights							12·00 (± 3·79)	0·00 (± 0·00)	0·01			
Leg bracing (s)							19·00 (± 6·00)	0·00 (± 0·00)	0·01	6·85 (± 1·66)	21·42 (± 4·01)	0·01
Mounts and attempts				16·00 (± 5·36)	0·00 (± 0·00)	0·01						
Physical contact							1·80 (± 0·43)	695·00 (±15·43)	0·001			
Tail rattling (s)							5·00 (± 1·58)	0·00 (± 0·00)	0·01	4·43 (± 1·44)	0·00 (± 0·00)	0·01

Sexual Behaviour Test

The control and cross-fostered female *Mus* did not significantly differ in their latency to first lordosis and in the number of times they exhibited lordosis. The control and cross-fostered male *Mus* did not significantly differ in any of the behavioural measures analysed in the sexual test.

DISCUSSION

Body Weight

Hudgens et al. (1967, 1968) and Denenberg et al. (1966) found that rat-reared mice weighed more at weaning than mouse-reared mice. A possible explanation for our findings that the cross-fostered animals were lighter in weight than the control animals is that *Mus* and *Baiomys* are in different taxonomic families, Muridae and Cricetidae respectively, and may have different nutritional requirements. There is also a large size differential between *Baiomys* and *Mus*; adult *Baiomys* average approximately 12 g, whereas *Mus* average approximately 26 g. It is likely that the quantity of milk supplied by a *Baiomys* dam was not within the range normally provided to a *Mus* pup. The two species studied previously, *Rattus* and *Mus*, are more closely related, being in the same family, and may have similar nutritional requirements. Further, rat-reared mice may have received more milk than they would normally, thus accounting for their larger size.

Open Field Behaviour

Both male and female cross-fostered *Baiomys* showed an increase in activity scores in the open field when compared to control *Baiomys* (Table IV). This difference was not significant for the females. Both male and female cross-fostered *Mus* showed a decrease in activity and defecation scores in the open field when compared to control *Mus* groups (Table IV).

The effects of cross-fostering on *Baiomys* and *Mus* are clear: Open field activity increased in *Baiomys* and decreased in *Mus.*

Moreover, the cross-fostered animals showed activity levels similar to those of the foster species. The control *Mus* showed activity levels that were higher than those of the control *Baiomys*, and the fostered *Baiomys* displayed increased activity levels. Conversely, the control *Baiomys* showed activity levels that were lower than those of the control *Mus*, and the fostered *Mus* decreased their activity levels (Table IV). This trend is suggestive of some post-natal factor(s) operating during the nursing-suckling period. It has been established that rats manipulated in infancy will generally be more active and will defaecate less when tested in an open field as adults than non-handled animals. (Denenberg 1966; Levine et al. 1967; Ader 1968). Ressler (1962) described a difference in the amount of maternal handling provided by the mothers of two strains of *Mus musculus.* It is conceivable that the changes in activity levels observed in the cross-fostered *Mus* and *Baiomys* could be the result of differential handling by the dams. It was previously mentioned that the *Baiomys* pups attached to the teats of the *Baiomys* dam and remained attached, except during the evenings, until weaning occured at approximately 20 days. It was evident that the *Baiomys* dams did not handle or manipulate their pups to the same extent as the *Mus* dams. Thus the increased handling by the *Mus* dams could account for the increased activity of the cross-fostered *Baiomys,* and the decreased handling by the *Baiomys* dams could account for the decreased activity of the cross-fostered *Mus*.

Social Preference Test

The cross-fostered male and female *Mus* spent significantly less time adjacent to a conspecific than did controls. The cross-fostered male and female *Baiomys* differed in that the females spent significantly less time adjacent to the conspecific than did the controls, whereas the males did not differ significantly from their controls. It is evident that the cross-fostered female *Baiomys* had been influenced in their social preference by their early experience. The cross-fostered female *Mus* showed a stronger preference for the foster species than did the cross-fostered male *Mus*. These findings support Mainardi et al. (1965) who concluded that females learn species recognition in the nest but males do not. This conclusion was based on the results of a social preference test similar to the one used in this study.

Observations of rodent sexual behaviour suggest that males do not show very much discrimination when attempting to mount. Males will mount other males of the same and different species, and they will also mount con- as well as hetero-specific females. The females, if in oestrus, will accept a conspecific male but will avoid a male of another species. Work with amphibians and birds has shown a similar pattern. In a breeding pond containing several different species, the male frog will indiscriminately clasp a male or female. If the female is a receptive conspecific, the sexual behaviour patterns continue. However, if the clasped animal is a male or a receptive female of a different species a struggle typically ensues until the clasping male releases the struggling animal (Capranica 1965).

Selander & Giller (1961) stated that '... the absence of demonstrable hybridization between two species of Grackles (*Cassidix mexicanus* and *C. major*) in their zone of sympatry indicates the existence of an effective biological isolating mechanism.' They suggested that '... the only line of defense against hybridization appears to be ethological.' They contend that females have the selective role in mating and distinguish between males of the two species largely on the basis of their behavioural differences, both at the time of nest site selection and at the time of mating. According to these authors, males show no obvious preference for females of their own species and seem unable to distinguish between them. Females seem to select homospecific mates on the basis of major differences in the displays and vocalizations of the males.

Thus the evidence from certain species of frogs, birds and rodents indicates that males do not discriminate to the same degree as females.

If imprinting is the mechanism leading to discrimination capability, mouse females would be expected to imprint more strongly than males to species characteristics to which they are exposed during the nursing-suckling period.

Pair Encounters and Sexual Behaviour Tests

In addition to the changes in social preference of most of the cross-fostered groups, their behaviour in the pair encounters indicated that they were reacting more positively, as previously defined, to the foster species than to conspecifics (Table VI). The cross-fostered *Mus* males showed many behavioural changes in the pair encounters when compared to the control *Mus* males (Table VI). When paired with male or female conspecifics, cross-fostered *Mus* males allogroomed less and spent less time in physical contact than did the control *Mus* males. However, when paired with *Baiomys* males and females the cross-fostered *Mus* males allogroomed more, approached more and spent more time in physical contact than did their controls.

It was also noticed that the cross-fostered *Mus* males attempted to mount and mounted the male and female pygmy mice. At no time did their controls behave in a similar manner. Also the cross-fostered male *Mus* attempted to mount and mounted a female conspecific more than did their controls. This seems to indicate that these males were more receptive to stimuli related to sexual behaviour than were the control *Mus* males. The scope of sexual responsiveness of the cross-fostered male *Mus* has been widened to accommodate the *Baiomys* while still maintaining responsiveness to *Mus* females. There was no significant difference in the measures of sexual behaviour between control and cross-fostered *Mus* males when they were presented with oestrous-induced *Mus* females.

Clearly, the cross-fostered male *Mus* were greatly affected in many of their social behaviours by their early experience with a *Baiomys* dam and *Baiomys* pups. However, they were not affected in their sexual behaviour with conspecifics. This might imply that social behaviours such as allogrooming and approach and avoidance behaviours are labile, but that sexual behaviours are more fixed and less subject to early experimental modifications.

The cross-fostered *Mus* females were not as affected as were similarly treated males. When paired with *Mus* males and females the cross-fostered female *Mus* showed more avoidance behaviour and had fewer encounters than did their controls (Table VI). When paired with *Baiomys* males and females, the cross-fostered female *Mus* allogroomed more, approached more and spent more time in physical contact than did their controls. The results indicate that both cross-fostered and control *Mus* females respond in the same way to an experienced male *Mus* when the females were in natural oestrus. There was no significant difference in the number of times lordosis occurred or in latency of first lordosis. Social behaviours such as allogrooming, and approach and avoidance behaviour were affected, but sexual behaviours were not. This indicates, as in cross-fostered males, that allogrooming and approach and avoidance behaviours are labile and subject to change due to early experience.

When paired with *Baiomys* males and females, cross-fostered male *Baiomys* had fewer contacts, fought more, attempted more escapes, avoided more and tail rattled more than did their controls (Table VI).

We were unsuccessful in inducing oestrus in pygmy mice by the use of exogenous oestrogen and progesterone despite the use of many different combinations of dosages and time intervals. Therefore no sexual tests were performed with the control and cross-fostered male *Baiomys*. It was evident that the cross-fostered male *Baiomys* were reacting more positively toward the foster species than to conspecifics. An extremely interesting change was noted in scores of aggression that occurred in the cross-fostered male *Baiomys* depending upon with whom they were paired. When with *Baiomys* males they fought more than controls, but when with *Mus* females they fought less than the controls (Table VI). The cross-fostered female *Baiomys* displayed similar behaviours. Thus the cross-fostered male and female *Baiomys* interacted non-aggressively with the species that reared them, but fought with conspecifics.

When paired with *Baiomys* males and females the cross-fostered female pygmy mice allogroomed less, approached less, tail rattled more, avoided more, leg braced more, had fewer encounters, and spent less time in physical contact than did their controls (Table VI). When paired with *Mus* males and females the cross-fostered female *Baiomys* allogroomed more, had more encounters, spent more time in physical contact, attempted to escape less and fought more than did their controls (Table VI). The cross-fostered *Baiomys* were reacting more positively toward the foster species than toward conspecifics. Lordosis was not observed when the cross-fostered and control female *Baiomys* were in natural oestrus, and thus no sexual tests were performed.

Differences in handling by the dams could account for the differences in activity levels observed in the cross-fostered *Mus* and *Baiomys*, but they very likely do not account for changes in such social behaviours as allogrooming, approach and avoidance behaviour, mounting behaviour, social preference and aggressive behaviour. Convincing support is to be found in the differential character of the behaviours observed. Allogrooming has not merely increased in all of the four types of pair encounters, but the duration scores of allogrooming are dependent upon who the partner is. Thus a cross-fostered animal allogroomed a member of the foster species more than it allogroomed a conspecific. This same pattern has been observed for many other behaviours (Table VI). Another example of the differential aspect of the observed behaviours was the incidence of fighting. A cross-fostered animal fought less when with a member of the foster species than when with a conspecific. Approach behaviour also showed this differential response, cross-fostered animals approaching members of the foster species more than they approached conspecifics. If a simple increase in activity were responsible for the observed behaviours, then cross-fostered *Baiomys* should always approach more regardless with which partner they were paired. Such was not the case in the pair encounters.

The present study has shown that the procedure of cross-fostering to a different species at birth has not affected the ability of the cross-fostered male and female *Mus* to mate with a conspecific. Cross-fostering has affected many other social behaviours such as allogrooming, aggressive behaviour and approach-avoidance behaviour. This implies that, in mice, sexual behaviour may be firmly fixed by the genotype and that it is released by the presence of a conspecific. Other social behaviours are more labile and easily changed by manipulating the early experience of these rodents.

Precisely how the observed changes in the social behaviours of the cross-fostered animals were brought about is not known. One may speculate with Mainardi et al. (1965) and Marr & Gardner (1965) that imprinting has occurred during the nursing-suckling period and that pheromones relevant to social behaviours are learned in the nest. Under ordinary circumstances the young animal is reared by a conspecific to which it imprints. In the present experiment the cross-fostered pups imprinted to the foster species and, as adults, reacted more positively to the foster species than to conspecifics. The only stimulus inputs to the developing foster pups were those provided by the foster dam and her pups.

SUMMARY

1. Four treatment groups were used: two control groups, *Baiomys* pups reared by *Baiomys* dams and *Mus* pups reared by *Mus* dams: two experimental groups, *Mus* and cross-fostered *Baiomys* pups reared by *Mus* dams, and *Baiomys* and cross-fostered *Mus* pups reared by *Baiomys* dams. The adult behaviours of control animals were compared to those of experimental conspecifics.

2. The open field total activity scores of cross-fostered *Baiomys* were greater than those of control *Baiomys*. The open field total activity scores of cross-fostered *Mus* were lower than those of control *Mus*. It is suggested that differential handling by the dams might account for this difference.

3. In a social preference test control *Mus* and *Baiomys* spent more time in a chamber adjacent to a conspecific. Both cross-fostered male and female *Mus* spent more time in a chamber adjacent to a *Baiomys*. However, the cross-fostered female *Mus* showed a stronger preference for the foster species than did the cross-fostered *Mus* males and cross-fostered male *Baiomys* spent more time adjacent to a conspecific. Thus the results from the social preference tests indicated that females were more affected by cross-fostering than males.

4. The behaviours of animals from control groups differed from those of the cross-fostered groups when pair encounters were staged between conspecifics and between *Baiomys* and *Mus*. Some of the differences involved measures of fighting and grooming behaviour, number of attempted mounts and approach and withdrawal behaviour.

5. Pair encounters revealed that the cross-fostered animals were reacting more positively to the foster species than to conspecifics.

6. Cross-fostered animals were profoundly influenced in open field performances, social preferences (with the exception of the male cross-fostered *Baiomys*) and social behaviours as a result of being cross-fostered to a different species at birth. The cross-fostered animals established, presumably through learning, new social relationships with the foster species.

7. Cross-fostered male and female *Mus* did not lose their ability to mate with a conspecific. This implies that sexual behaviour

in this species is less susceptible to change due to early experience than other social behaviours such as fighting, allogrooming, and approach and avoidance behaviours.

REFERENCES

Ader, R. (1968). Effects of early experience on emotional and physiological reactivity in the rate. *J. comp. physiol. Psychol.*, **66**, 264-268.

Bateson, P. P. (1966). The characteristics and context of imprinting. *Biol. Rev.*, **41**, 177-220.

Blair, W. F. (1941). Observations on the life history of *Baiomys taylori subater. J. Mammal.*, **22**, 378-383.

Capranica, R. R. (1965). *The Evoked Vocal Response of the Bullfrog*, p. 110. Cambridge: M.I.T. Press.

Denenberg, V. H. (1966). Stimulation in infancy, emotional reactivity, and exploratory behavior. In: *Biology and Behavior: Neurophysiology and Emotion* (Ed. by D. C. Glass). New York: Russel Sage Foundation.

Denenberg, V. H., Hudgens, G. A. & Zarrow, M. X. (1964). Mice reared with rats: modification of behaviour by early experience with another species. *Science, N.Y.*, **143**, 380-381.

Denenberg, V. H., Hudgens, G. A. & Zarrow, M. X. (1966). Mice reared with rats: effects of mother on adult behavior patterns. *Psychol. Rep.*, **18**, 451-456.

Hudgens, G. A., Denenberg, V. H. & Zarrow, M. X. (1967). Mice reared with rats; relations between mother's activity level and offspring's behavior. *J. comp. physiol. Psychol.*, **63**, 304-308.

Hudgens, G. A., Denenberg, V. H. & Zarrow, M. X. (1968). Mice reared with rats: Effects of preweaning and postweaning social interactions upon adult behaviour. *Behaviour*, **30**, 259-275.

Kalkowski, W. (1967). Olfactory bases of social orientation in the white mouse. *Folia Biol.*, **16**, 69-87.

Klopfer, P. H. (1967). Is imprinting a cheshire cat? *Behav. Sci.*, **12**, 122-129.

Klopfer, P. H. & Gamble, J. (1966). Maternal "imprinting" in goats: the role of chemical senses. *Z. Tierpsychol.*, **23**, 588-592.

Knight, G. R., Robertson, A. L. & Waddington, C. H. (1956). Selection for sexual isolation within a species. *Evolution*, **10**, 14-22.

Lagerspetz, K. & Wuorinen, K. (1965). A cross-fostering experiment with mice selectively bred for aggressiveness and non-aggressiveness. *Rep. Psychol. Inst. Univ. Turku.*, **17**, 1-6.

Levine, S., Haltmeyer, G., Karas, G. & Denenberg, V. H. (1967). Physiological and behavioral effects of infantile stimulation. *Physiol. Behav.*, **2**, 55-59.

Lorenz. K. (1937). Companionship in bird life: fellow members of the species as releasers of social behaviour. *Auk,* **54**, 245-273.

Mainardi, D., Marsan, M. & Pasquali, A. (1965). Causation of sexual preferences of the house mouse. The behavior of mice reared by parents whose odour was artificially altered. *Atti Soc. Ital. Sci. nat. Museo Civ. Milano,* **104**, 325-338.

Marr, J. N. & Gardner, L. E. (1965). Early olfactory experience and later social behavior in the rat: preference, sexual responsiveness, and care of the young. *J. genet. Psychol.,* **107**, 167-174.

Moltz, H. (1963). Imprinting: An epigenitic approach. *Psychol. Rev.,* **70**, 132-138.

Packard, R. L. (1960). Speciation and evolution of the pygmy mice, Genus *Baiomys. Univ. Kansas Publ. Mus. nat. Hist.,* **9**, 579-670.

Raun, G. G. & Wilks, B. J. (1964). Natural history of *Baiomys taylori* in Southern Texas and competition with *Sigmodon hispidus* in a mixed population. *Texas J. Sci.,* **16**, 28-49.

Ressler, R. H. (1962). Parental handling in two strains of mice reared by foster parents. *Science, N.Y.,* **137**, 129-130.

Scott, J. P. (1962). Critical periods in behavioral development. *Science, N.Y.,* **138**, 949-958.

Selander, R. K. & Giller, D. R. (1961). Analysis of sympatry of great-tailed and boat-tailed grackles. *Condor,* **63**, 29-86.

Sluckin, W. (1965). *Imprinting and Early Learning.* Chicago: Aldine Pub. Co.

Southwick, C. H. (1968). Effect of maternal environment on aggressive behavior of inbred mice. *Commun. behav. Biol.,* **1**, 129-132.

SUGGESTIONS FOR FURTHER READING

Bliss, E. L. (Ed.) *Roots of behavior.* New York: Hafner, 1968.
*Fuller, J. L. The genetics of behaviour. In E. S. E. Hafez (Ed.), *The behaviour of domestic animals.* London: Balliere 1969. Pp. 45-64.
Hirsch, J. *Behavior genetic analysis.* New York: McGraw-Hill, 1967.
Manosevitz, M., Lindzey, G., & Thiessen, D. D. *Behavioral genetics: Methods and research.* New York: Appleton-Century-Crofts, 1969.

* Introductory reviews.

V BEHAVIOR DEVELOPMENT AND EFFECTS OF EARLY EXPERIENCE

The question of how a given behavior has evolved (its phylogeny) may be answered in part by studying different species—the comparative method. Further insight is gained by following its development (or ontogeny). To what extent, for instance, is a given behavior dependent upon experience for its development? Some birds, such as the Junco, will develop a normal song if raised in social isolation and even if they are deaf. Others, such as the chaffinch, must be exposed to the song of an adult during a critical period early in life; later in life, as in white-crowned sparrows, they may even acquire a local dialect. Some bird species show an innate preference for their own species song; others, such as the bullfinch, do not. It is through such isolation or deprivation studies, and by giving subjects experience at certain stages of development, that the degree of dependence upon experience can be determined. Environmental (or experiential) influences may have their optimal effect during a critical or sensitive period early in life, as shown in the song development studies of birds. Imprinting in birds and socialization in dog pups and human infants develop at this critical period. If social experiences are eliminated by raising the animal alone during this period, it may never develop close social relationships.

Developmental studies may be focused upon a longitudinal life-history approach, with development divided into arbitrary stages (such as neonatal, transitional, socialization, juvenile, and adult in the dog). Behavior then may be correlated with the particular life style and social relationships of the organism at a given stage of development. One interesting finding of such longitudinal studies is the identification of infantile behaviors that persist into adulthood in a different motivational or situational context (e.g., infantile food-soliciting signals seen in the adult as appeasement or greeting gestures).

Another general approach of the ethologist and developmental psychobiologist may be termed the "programmed life-history" method. By providing the organism with specific experience at selected stages of development, researchers can determine the consequences of such experience as the organism matures. The later consequences of early maternal deprivation, handling stress, castration, or rearing in an enriched complex environment, for example, can be followed. In such studies researchers must control rigorously what "experiences" the animal in question is receiving under the life-history program. It is, however, impossible to prevent proprioceptive and kinesthetic feedback; for although the organism can be virtually isolated from its external environment by isolation rearing, it cannot be isolated from itself. In some experiments, this aspect of self-stimulation feedback has been investigated. Thus, some birds, if deafened early in life, do not develop a normal song, while other species are able to; the development of hand-eye coordination may be blocked when an animal is reared with an "Elizabethan" collar and is therefore unable to see its forelimbs.

Some hypothetical schemas of developmental patterns are shown in Figure 1. Type A represents a genetically programmed behavior that matures independent of experience or environmental input (E), although self-stimulation feedback may be necessary. In all developmental patterns, the relationship between structure and function holds true; in the absence of function, the underlying neural structure may atrophy, so that function may be regarded as vital for the maintenance and often for the maturation of structure. The developmental pattern of type B is dependent upon environmental (or experiential) input for maturation to proceed normally, the E input occurring at a critical period. In type C, the E input may modify the direction or rate of development (broken line), but development is not dependent upon such input; this pattern is exemplified by the sensitive-period phenomenon, where handling stress at a vulnerable time early in life influences subsequent

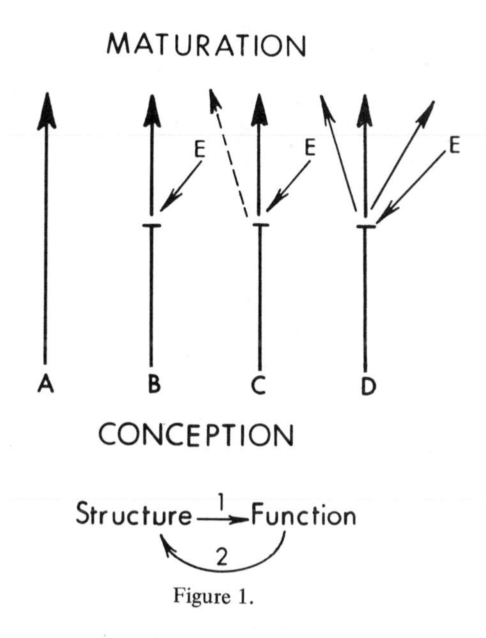

Figure 1.

maturation. The behavioral phenotype may be thus altered. In type D the pattern of development is experientially modifiable, flexible, and multidirectional (i.e., highly adaptive). This represents the most variable and advanced developmental pattern, exemplified by the broad and variable repertoires of the primates (Mason, 1968).

Some of the interrelated developmental issues that might be advantageously studied include stages or levels of organization; dependence or independence of experience for continued development at different ages; developmental stability and flexibility (i.e., modifiability of the developing behavioral phenotype); critical and sensitive periods underlying the development of certain behaviors; latent or delayed consequences of prior experience; genetic-environmental patterning and fitness or adaptability to different environments. Further analysis of these phenomena will provide us with pertinent information on development, plasticity, and adaptability of brain and behavior, susceptibility of the genotype, and modifiability of the phenotype. It may also ultimately enable us to develop the potentials latent in our own species.

This broad and ramifying area of research has been brought

together in three major reviews included in this chapter. The first reading is a classic ethological study of the development of displays in the junglefowl. This study by Kruijt demonstrates the usefulness of the purely observational method of tracing development of behavior patterns to their earliest unintegrated forms.

The Development of Ritualized Displays in Junglefowl

J. P. KRUIJT

The courtship of the adult male Junglefowl is characterized by the performance of several intricate and highly stereotyped display activities, specific to the species. When *waltzing*, for example, the male sidles toward the female with the primary feathers of the outer wing fanned downward toward the ground. As the male proceeds to circle the female, the outer foot scrapes through the extended feathers. The sudden approach of the male and the sharp rasp of foot against feathers function as signals which induce the female to crouch, a movement to which the male may respond by mounting and copulation.

A second feature of male display is *tidbitting*. In this the male scratches for and pecks at food, takes it in the bill, and bows up and down while producing a rapidly repeated call. Females often approach a tidbitting male and eat the food which is dropped by him. Thus, this display serves to attract the female and to maintain a bond with her.

Another very striking display is *cornering*, performed by the male under shrubs or at other concealed places. In unplanted pens it is usually oriented to corners. While cornering, the male assumes a half-crouched posture, scratches and stamps with his legs, makes peculiar zigzagging movements with his head and produces a low purring sound. Females often approach the cornering male and make nesting movements at the place chosen by the male. This suggests

From *Philosophical Transactions of the Royal Society of London*, B. Vol. 251, pp. 479-484, 1966.

that cornering can be considered as a signal serving the selection of the nest site.

All these displays are ritualized in the ethological sense: they serve as signals in the communication between individuals and have become adapted during evolution to this function. By comparing the displays of closely related species, it is possible to arrive at a picture about the probable changes that must have taken place during the evolution of such signals.

To find out which factors contributed to the evolution of such signals, and how, is an important biological problem. But equally important is the question of how ritualized displays develop ontogenetically, that is, in the life of the individual. Is it necessary for a bird to see the example of his parents or siblings before he can produce the displays characteristic for his species? Is practice necessary before the full-fledged display occurs? In many cases it appears that this is not so. Ethologists have therefore often used the term 'innate' for species-specific displays, in order to indicate that their ontogeny is not influenced by conditioning, imitation, or similar learning processes. But, in addition, 'innate' sometimes carried the connotation that the development of behaviour takes place entirely without regard to external conditions, provided these conditions were sufficiently favourable for the animal to stay alive. This way of thinking has probably obscured and discouraged a more fertile approach toward ontogenetic problems.

Recently, however, Lorenz (1961) has pointed out that 'innate' should be taken to mean that the ontogeny takes place–not independently of *all* external conditions–but independently of those with respect to which the behaviour in question has been adapted during evolution. Thus, if an animal develops a behaviour pattern when raised in isolation from conspecifics, and if this pattern is clearly adapted to the function of communication between individuals, then, according to Lorenz, such a pattern should be called innate. To take a concrete example, if a male Junglefowl raised in isolation waltzes for the female the first time he encounters one, waltzing should be considered innate.

But if waltzing is innate in this sense, the only thing we learn by applying the term is that social experience is *not* necessary for its development. With this statement, no light at all is thrown on the nature of *positive factors* underlying the development of this pattern.

Furthermore, we remain ignorant about the role of the other external factors to which an isolated animal is exposed. The ontogenetic question is not answered by pointing out which factors are not necessary; what we need to know is which factors–internal as well as external–are of importance for the development of the state in which waltzing is produced by the male. That genetic factors are of importance is obvious, but of little help, since these factors are localized in the chromosomes and bear no immediate resemblance to the behaviour.

Although the term 'innate' may have some merit when applied to evolutionary questions (cf. Lorenz 1961; Wickler 1965), its usefulness for ontogenetic questions is extremely limited. Instead of classifying the behaviour patterns into the categories innate and not-innate, it appears to be much more promising to investigate how behaviour develops, and to keep an open mind about the possible influence of external conditions in guiding the development of behaviour.

As a first step in this approach I have studied the development of social behaviour in small groups of incubator-hatched chicks, raised without a mother-hen. In this paper some of the conclusions will be mentioned; for details the reader is referred to a previous paper (Kruijt 1964). I shall limit myself to the male courtship patterns described above.

By observing the chicks from hatching to sexual maturity it became clear that their social behaviour develops in a regular and predictable sequence, starting at a simple level of organization and becoming gradually more complex. At first, social behaviour is limited to mutual attachment, but gradually, aggressive behaviour, fleeing, and copulatory behaviour are added in this order. Each of these groups of patterns can occur more or less in isolation of the others early in development; but later, simultaneous activation of several is the rule. This gives rise to complex interactions between simultaneously activated systems, as a result of which new patterns start to emerge; these can be considered as 'ambivalent' or 'displaced.'

The courtship displays of the male do not occur in complete form until the stage in which copulatory behaviour is performed, but most of the components of these displays develop much earlier and are then shown during fighting. This suggests that the courtship displays are mainly due to conflicting tendencies of the male to attack the female and to flee from her. The fact that these displays accompany copulatory behaviour so frequently, suggests that conflicts between attack and escape are facilitated by activation of a tendency to copulate with the female.

Of the three displays described earlier, cornering is more dependent on activation of copulatory behaviour than waltzing or tidbitting. The latter two can be shown when the male has no tendency to copulate, but they are more likely to occur as the male's tendency to copulate increases—as judged by his inclination to mount a crouching female. Cornering, on the other hand, is nearly always associated with a strong tendency to copulate; in other words, in the absence of a tendency to copulate, cornering is nearly never shown. Yet, most or perhaps even all components of all displays (included cornering) appear to be expressions of agonistic conflicts, i.e. conflicts between aggression and escape. Therefore, it appears that a strong tendency to copulate can facilitate agonistic conflicts that do not occur normally when the tendency to copulate is absent or weak.

Although this picture throws some light on the causation of the courtship displays of the male, it does not yet show which factors underlie their development. But if the courtship displays are due to complicated interactions between the tendencies to attack, to flee and to copulate, then it will be necessary to study which factors underlie the development of these types of behaviour.

As a next step, therefore, we may ask to what extent the development of these tendencies depends on social experience. To this end a number of males were raised in visual isolation from conspecifics starting on the day of hatching. The behaviour of these males is rather variable, but all develop certain abnormalities which are absent in group-raised males, even if the latter are kept in prolonged isolation at later periods of their life. The following results were obtained.

Many of the isolated males showed excessive fleeing behaviour at some time during the first month of their life. Apparently this behaviour was often aroused by events occurring outside the cage, such as the approach of a human being. Fleeing from outside disturbances of course also occurs in group-raised birds, but in this case fleeing stops soon after the disturbing factor disappears. Isolated males, however, would often continue for long periods after the disappearance of outside disturbances. In other instances no outside inducement was observed at all, but it sometimes seemed that the bird was trying to flee from parts of its own body, especially the tail.

Sooner or later all isolated males start to fight with their own tail. While raising his neck-hackles, the cock turns round and round his own axis, attempts to kick with his legs in the direction of his tail, and pecks viciously at the base of the tail-feathers. Often tail-fighting is initiated when something happens outside the cage, e.g. when humans approach. In alternation with tail-fighting the male may run around the cage while looking backward, as if he were fleeing from his own tail. Once tail-fighting has developed, isolated males usually start to be aggressive toward humans as well.

One of the isolated males even developed copulatory behaviour in the absence of conspecifics. This male often pecked at loose feathers scattered about the cage. Often he would pick one up and perform the copulatory pattern while keeping the feather in the bill.

These observations show that aggressive and fleeing behaviour and, more exceptionally, copulatory behaviour, can develop in the absence of normal social experience; but in the absence of social companions, these types of behaviour show abnormalities especially with regard to the releasing and directing external factors.

The next question which may be raised is whether aggressive, fleeing, and copulatory tendencies are ever aroused simultaneously in isolated males. In other words, do conflicts occur, and how are they expressed?

I mentioned earlier that isolated males may alternate their tail-fighting with behaviour which appears to be an attempt to flee from their own tail. But, moreover, tail-fighting is often interspersed with bouts of tidbitting and the male may waltz around his own axis. In group-raised males these displays are mainly due to a conflict between aggressive and fleeing behaviour. The most parsimonious explanation seems to be that similar conflicts can occur in males raised in isolation, although in this case the conflicting tendencies are aroused by quite different external factors.

Further support for this idea can be derived from the fact that cornering occurs only rarely in isolated males. As discussed earlier, this display is shown by normal males when agonistic and copulatory behaviour are all activated simultaneously and strongly. Most isolated males, however, never showed copulatory behaviour while alone in their cage. The kind of conflicts that produce cornering were usually not arising in these birds and this explains why this display occurred so rarely.

Cornering was also very rare in the isolated cock which copulated with feathers. Again this is understandable since this male attacked humans or his own tail but not loose feathers. Simultaneous activation of agonistic and copulatory behaviour probably never occurred to the same extent in this male as in normal birds where these types of behaviour are elicited by one and the same external object, the social companion.

Thus, this picture leads to the conclusion that Junglefowl males develop ritualized displays both when raised in a group and when raised in isolation, provided the external conditions arouse the conflicts which are necessary to produce displays. Even without social companions the external conditions apparently give many opportunities for such conflicts to arise.

Two further conclusions follow. First, it appears that the development of escape and aggressive behaviour is possibly governed by quite unspecific conditions. I shall return to this conclusion later. Secondly, once aggression and escape are developed, and simultaneously aroused, they interact more or less automatically in such a way that a display, in species-specific form, is performed. This suggests that the processes underlying these interactions are mainly under internal control, and occur independently of the nature of the external factors which gave rise to the conflict.

This should not be taken to mean that the resulting sequences of behaviour are always the same whether the male was raised in isolation or in a group. I sometimes got the impression that the behaviour of isolated males is more erratic and less predictable than that of normal males. This may be due to the fact that the external factors which elicit aggressive and escape behaviour in an isolated male do not allow the type of mutual interactions that are possible between social companions. For example, a male cannot chase away his own tail nor can he flee from it.

Some further observations were made on the behaviour of isolated males toward females. Three males raised in isolation from hatching to the age of 6 to 9 months were subsequently tested with females. All three males copulated successfully after a few encounters, but their behaviour was abnormal. Instead of showing the normal amount of courtship, they often pursued the female frantically. Their attempts to mount were often misoriented and interspersed with aggressive behaviour directed toward their own tail.

Of eleven males isolated until the age of 10 to 16 months only two eventually copulated successfully when subsequently tested with females. The unsuccessful males either ignored or attacked the female. Thus, the ability to copulate is usually lost after prolonged isolation. But this is not true if group-raised males are isolated at later age; other males were raised in male groups and isolated at the age of 2½ months for a period of 13 or 14 months. These males achieved successful copulation after few encounters with females. Their behaviour did not differ from that of group-raised males at the age of 4 months, the age at which they start to perform complete copulatory behaviour.

Recent experiments indicate that prolonged isolation after the age of 6 weeks has the same effect as isolation from hatching, but copulatory ability is not affected if the isolation started at the age of 9 weeks. Apparently, experience gained during social contacts with other males before the age of 9 weeks brings about a change in the organization of the male's behaviour with the result that copulatory ability can develop and be preserved during long periods of isolation after this age. But as mentioned above, males deprived of social experience from hatching can also perform copulatory behaviour, provided contact with the female occurs before the age of 10 months. The final conclusion therefore is that although copulatory ability can develop without early social experience, it cannot be maintained in this case over long periods of isolation. It appears that males which have passed this sensitive period develop abnormal fixations which are difficult or impossible to change.

Waltzing and tidbitting were performed by some of the males in the presence of females, but cornering was always absent or rare. That the female released display at all is not surprising if one considers the fact that these displays were performed in response to very unspecific external factors in general. To an isolated male a female is probably just another object out of a large class of objects which can elicit agonistic behaviour.

More surprising is the fact that isolated males if not older than 10 months were able to copulate. This suggests that copulatory behaviour is released by properties which are more or less unique to the female and can only rarely be released by the external conditions in which a socially deprived male lives.

The variability in the behaviour of isolated males may be due to the fact that many of the disturbances around the cage were not under our control. At present we are starting experiments in which we try to control the environment of an isolated chick much more precisely. One example demonstrating the difficulties in this approach may be mentioned briefly.

Since isolated males attack their own tail, it occurred to us that experience with nearby moving objects gained in early life is possibly an important factor in the development of aggressive behaviour. This was also suggested by the observation that isolated chicks several weeks of age may start to fight with the heating lamp which was attached with flex to the ceiling of their cage. We wondered what would happen if the lamp was attached in such a way that it could no longer move. It was found that isolated chicks raised in this situation had little inclination to fight the lamp, but instead, some of them attacked their transparent drinking bottle, often exactly at the moment that air bubbles floated toward the surface.

This observation suggests an important conclusion: in the absence of social stimulation other external factors are probably influencing the development of aggressive behaviour, and these factors may be very unspecific and difficult to control.

Now, if this is true, then it is also possible that some of these factors are contained in the social experience which group-raised birds gain during their development. If, for example, experience with moving objects influences the development of aggressive behaviour, then it seems quite possible that isolated males can obtain such experience by interacting with their tail, although in normal development the social companions provide the experience. It is, therefore, not possible to conclude that social experience is unimportant if behaviour develops without it. At most we can conclude that such experience is not necessary; but this statement gives very little insight, and should not distract from the real ontogenetic problems.

In summary, it may be said that the ritualized courtship displays of Junglefowl depend for their occurrence on simultaneous activation of agonistic and copulatory behaviour. If the latter are developed, the displays follow more or less automatically and without social experience, although their orientation in socially deprived birds is often abnormal. The interactions between agonistic and copulatory tendencies which produce the displays seem to be mainly under internal control.

The development of agonistic and copulatory behaviour can also take place without social experience. This does not mean that external conditions have no influence at all, but possibly very unspecific conditions are sufficient. For further insight into the development of social behaviour it will therefore be necessary to control the external conditions very precisely, even the unspecific ones.

REFERENCES

Kruijt, J. P. 1964 Ontogeny of social behaviour in Burmese Red Junglefowl. *Behaviour* (Suppl.), No. 12.

Lorenz, K. 1961 Phylogenetische Anpassung und adaptive Modifikation des Verhaltens. *Z. Tierpsychol.* **18**, 139-187.

Wickler, W. 1965 Über den taxonomischen Wert homologer Verhaltensmerkmale. *Naturwissenschaften* **52**, 441-444.

Imprinting in Birds and Primates

ERIC A. SALZEN

I. INTRODUCTION

The term imprinting was used by Lorenz (1937) for the process of rapid development of social attachments in precocial birds, *i.e.*, the fixation of the class of objects to which social responses, both present and future, are directed and confined. The reviews of Fabricius (1962), Hinde (1961, 1962), Salzen (1962), Sluckin & Salzen (1961) and the book by Sluckin (1965) follow the original concept of imprinting as a process in which innate social responses that can be elicited by and directed to a wide variety of objects come to be elicited by and directed to only the class or classes of objects experienced in a limited neonatal period. Thus imprinting is a process of goal or object acquisition and *not* response acquisition. The responses are innate and the goal objects are learned. In 1963 Hinde was able to say that most workers now regard imprinting as not involving just supra-individual learning, that the sensitive period is by no means clearly marked, that the irreversibility of imprinting had been overestimated, and that it is not clear to what extent imprinting as studied in the context of the following response of the newly hatched bird affects later behaviour. Nevertheless, some workers still employ these distinctions. Thus the critical period concept is still used by Fabricius (1964), by Schutz (1965) who recognises a second critical period for sexual imprinting, and by Hess (1964) who would have us accept separate periods for social, environmental and food imprinting.

It is not surprising, therefore, that when explicit attempts are made to apply the concept of imprinting to mammalian development considerable confusion and argument arise. Furthermore, when making this comparison between birds and mammals Hinde (1961) has pointed out that ". . . it is essential to remember that: (a) the basic structure of the telencephalon of birds is very different from that of mammals; (b) the synapsid and diapsid reptiles, from which mammals and birds arose, have been distinct since at least the Permian; and (c) parental care has evolved independently in the two groups. Similarities in behaviour, therefore, are not very likely to indicate similarities in underlying mechanisms. Nevertheless, the development of the human mother-child relationship bears many similarities to the analogous process in birds".

Gray (1958) has suggested that imprinting occurs in humans and that the smiling response is the motor equivalent of the following response. Ambrose (1963) has criticised some of Gray's statements and applied his own, somewhat rigid, view of imprinting to the smiling response and social attachment in infants. Less formal comparisons of imprinting in birds and the development of social attachments in mammals have been made by numerous writers. Outstanding are the works of Scott (1962) and Schneirla (1965). These less formal comparisons follow the view expressed by Hinde (1963) that it is ". . . not useful to ask whether imprinting occurs in mammals or not, or whether the learning which accompanies smiling is or is not imprinting." Instead one should ask questions of the kind posed by Hinde, such as "Do mammals learn to follow strange objects?" "Does this have to occur within a sensitive period?" and "Does it influence later sexual behaviour?"

The purpose of the present paper is to make a detailed comparison of this kind between the behaviour patterns of the domestic chick as revealed in studies on imprinting and the behaviour of infant Rhesus monkeys as revealed by the studies of Harlow and co-workers on the development of affectional systems. The behaviour descriptions for the chick are to be found primarily in papers by Collias (1952), Guiton (1959, 1961), Hess & Schaefer (1959), Jaynes (1956, 1957, 1958a, b) and Salzen (1962). The descriptions for the monkey are to be found in Harlow (1959, 1960a, b, 1961, 1962, 1963), Harlow & Harlow (1962), Harlow & Hansen (1963) and Harlow & Zimmerman (1958a, b).

In making a comparison between birds and mammals it is important to examine the biological bases of the structures and functions concerned, for these two classes of vertebrates have had a separate origin among the reptiles and have had a separate evolution for about 150 million years. Yet, as Hinde (1963) has pointed out, ". . . birds and mammals are faced with many of the same problems in their ontogeny and we can expect them to show the same sorts of characteristics of behaviour as a result of convergence produced by natural selection". Fundamental similarities may exist through their common vertebrate sensory and nervous systems. The relevance of this to behaviour has been formulated by Sherrington (1947), chiefly on the basis of his studies with mammalian reflex systems. Thus Sherrington distinguishes between contact and distance receptors. Contact receptors are the body receptors for touch, temperature, pain, pressure and chemical stimulation and they mediate local body movements in response to local stimulation. They also are the receptors for final or consummatory actions, *e.g.* swallowing. Distance receptors represent highly sensitive contact receptors developed for hearing, vision and olfaction and have far greater receptive ranges and fields. They mediate total body movements and postures in the form of reactions precurrent to the consummatory actions elicited by contact stimulation. It is important to note that both birds and primates rely heavily on vision and hearing rather than on olfaction for distance reception and that both also rely on vision for spatial and object discrimination. Both have skin receptor systems involving free nerve endings and encapsulated sense corpuscles with some similar kinds, though the functions of such endings have been studied primarily in man only (Portmann, 1961). In both cases the epidermal appendages, feathers or hairs, may play a part in contact reception via their movement in relation to nerve endings at their bases.

II. REACTIONS OF NEONATAL CHICKS AND MONKEYS TO OBJECTS

In the absence of warmth and contact the newly or recently hatched chick shows struggling movements and distress calling. If able to walk it will do so and will approach moving objects or, in their absence, static ones. On achieving contact with an object the chick pushes its head beneath and crawls under the object with characteristic nestling movements and pleasure calls. The distress and pleasure or contentment calls have been described by Collias & Joos (1953) and by Hess & Schaefer (1959). Once beneath the object the chick may turn so that its head is peeping out. If the object is small the chick will push against it. If adequate contact is not achieved the chick will adjust its position. Finally it will stay beneath or alongside the object and quieten and sleep. If the object moves away the chick will follow it giving the well known approach and following responses. I have observed that if the object is cold the chick becomes restless and active once more. However, most objects provide some warmth in that they act as insulators and draught screens.

The young infant Rhesus also seems to require warmth and contact. After the first day it may show a "following response" by moving after a cloth that has been in contact with its face and then been drawn away. When placed on its back such a monkey will show righting movements, but if given something to clasp and contact such as a piece of cloth or an object it will remain quiescent and no righting occurs (Harlow, 1960a; Mowbray & Cadell, 1962). Solitary infants provided only with a diaper pad spend much time in contact with the pad. If left with an object such as a cloth covered roll of wire-mesh (Harlow, 1960a) the young monkey apparently ends up in contact with it and stays with it, either snuggled up in contact with its base or, if able to climb, clinging to the roll with ventral body surface in full contact. An object that fails to give adequate contact will be deserted, so that Harlow's monkeys stayed on cloth mother surrogates rather than on uncovered wire mesh mothers (1961).

Is contact or warmth important for attachment?

The importance of contact in the attachment behaviour of chicks is shown by the fact that chicks will spend time with an object that provides contact even though they have to leave it at intervals to get food and warmth. Sluckin & Salzen (1961) found that single chicks would follow and stay with an intermittently moving box in a runway but would go at intervals to food, water and to a heated chamber. The fact that the latter could also provide some contact highlights the importance of movement in attracting chicks to objects. In the absence of moving objects, however, chicks may show attachment to static ones. Thus, I have reported (1966 a, b) that solitary chicks have become attached to their water reservoirs, the only tall objects in their cages, and that such chicks spend much time sitting alongside the reservoirs in preference to sitting over a heated area of the cage floor. As these chicks became increasingly independent of heat, they spent more time beside the reservoirs.

In the case of the monkey, Harlow (1960a) has reported that although heating pads were provided for the first 15 days the monkeys would still leave them at times for the cloth covered mother surrogate and that with age more time was spent on the mothers. Harlow (1960a) also experimented with a wire mother equipped with a heater. In this case, for the first 15-20 days the monkeys would go to either the unheated cloth mothers or to the heated wire mothers if both were present. Some even preferred the heated mother, but after 15-20 days they all went to and stayed with the unheated cloth mothers. The important point is that although the chick and the monkey may spend time with a source of heat they ultimately desert such a source in favour of an object that provides more contact stimulation.

Are food and water factors in attachment?

It is a well-known characteristic of imprinting in precocial birds that it is independent of food reinforcement (Hinde, 1961) and this seems true of domestic chicks if the numerous imprinting studies with them are considered. I found (1966a, b) that isolated chicks that became attached to their water reservoirs would distress call when the reservoirs were removed from the cage and give pleasure calls when the reservoirs were replaced. Similar behaviour did not occur when their food troughs were removed. One of these chicks failed to learn to drink from its water reservoir and had to be provided with a dish of water for drinking, yet it showed the same attachment behaviour to its reservoir as did the other chicks. It is clear, then, that this attachment was not due to food or water reinforcement.

Harlow (1960a) has tested the same point in the infant monkey and has found that a solitary monkey will spend its time on a cloth mother rather than on a wire mother even when the latter is the only source of food. Furthermore, there seems to be no greater time spent on a cloth mother that provides food than on one that does not. Harlow (1961) also used two coloured cloth mothers with different faces and showed that although monkeys preferred the one that provided food this preference disappeared by 100 days. Thus for food, as for temperature, it would seem that any attachment based on such needs is not enduring.

What happens if there are no objects available for contact?

A chick placed in a bare chamber tends to spend time in a corner. Sluckin (personal communication) has placed single ducklings in an empty circular chamber and noted that they spent time against a particular part of the wall, usually where there was some blemish which the bird tended to increase by its pecking. Harlow (1960a) reports that in the first 10-15 days the infant Rhesus will move to the wall of its empty cage and on contacting the wall with its face will show nose rubbing due to the head turning or rooting response. Another behaviour that may occur is a self-contacting pattern in which the monkey sits and clasps itself and remains hunched and rocking.

Can siblings provide contact comfort for one another?

It is well known that chicks huddle together and show nestling movements in which one pushes its head under another chick and tries to crawl under. Imprinting to siblings has been reported by Guiton (1959), Sluckin & Salzen (1961) and was suggested as a factor in socialization by Collias (1952). If two infant monkeys are reared in an empty cage they spend much time clasping each other, and Harlow (1960a) reports that such behaviour is extremely enduring. Harlow & Harlow (1962) have reported similar huddling together in four infant Rhesus reared together.

What is the effect of delaying the presentation of objects for contact attachment?

If chicks are reared for 7 days in isolation without objects and are then exposed to a moving object they show some fear reactions but very quickly come to approach and follow the object

(Salzen, 1962; see also Bateson, 1964). Harlow (1960a) has found that when isolate-reared monkeys were exposed to a mother surrogate at 250 days they showed fear for 48 hours, especially to the cloth mother's face, but that contact attachment to the cloth mother developed although the time spent on the mother was only about half that spent by monkeys reared with such a mother. In both the chick and the monkey it is not certain to what extent these late attachments can become equivalent to the early ones. In birds Hess (1959) has claimed that such delayed exposures do not result in imprinting while Sluckin & Salzen (1961) and Salzen (1962) have suggested that given sufficient exposure and confinement with the object subsequent social responses should be indistinguishable from similar attachment relationships set up immediately after hatching. Harlow (1959) found that although his isolate-reared monkeys developed contact attachment to the cloth mother and not to a wire mother after exposure at 250 days they failed to show any preference of this kind after a second period of separation from the mothers. It is possible that a longer exposure period before this separation is required to produce a lasting preferential attachment. However, Rosenblatt *et al.* (1961) have shown very clearly in the case of the cat that difficulties of forming attachments later in development may be due to the formation of conflicting stimulus response patterns or to the failure to acquire appropriate ones to meet the later situations. Thus kittens taken at various times from the mother and reared alone in a brooder with a self-feeder had difficulty in adapting to suckling a real mother at a later date, especially if removed to the brooder late in the litter period. Conversely, if first reared in a brooder none had much difficulty in adjusting to suckling in the brooder after a period with a real mother regardless of the time at which they were first removed from the brooder. Rosenblatt *et al.* suggest that this is because the brooder situation remains unchanged during the absence of the kitten, whereas the mother-litter situation changes. This factor of the changing and complex stimulus-response requirements and characteristics of social situations during development can explain much of the data on the effects of social deprivation on later sexual and social behaviour that Harlow & Harlow (1962) report for their monkeys.

III. THE ROLE OF CONTACT REINFORCEMENT IN IMPRINTING

The important thing to note at this point is that *at first* the chick and the monkey will approach and contact *any object*. This is very well known for the chick. In the case of the monkey, Harlow (1960a) deliberately provided his preferred cloth mothers with faces that produced fear in 70-80 day monkeys. These faces had no such effect on the newborn monkeys who would accept any cloth mother regardless of its face or colour. Harlow (1961) has written "Initially, visual and contactual exploration are positive to all objects that are not actually painful; in other words, all, or almost all, stimuli elicit approach responses, and the larger, stronger, brighter and more mobile the stimuli, the stronger the approach responses". This could well have been written for the chick. It is as though there is no innate schema, or at least only a very broad and non-specific schema of visual stimulation for the release of approach and following behaviour in the neonate. However, objects do differ in their capacity to keep the infant monkey in contact, so that Harlow's monkeys would not stay with a wire mother. Clearly the monkey is born with a requirement for a particular pattern of contact stimulation and does not rest until it is achieved. Perhaps it should be noted that Harlow (1960a) found that visual solidity provided by a solid terry-towelling surface inside a wire mother, and olfactory stimulation provided by soaking this towelling with the infant's urine failed to make the wire mother permanently attractive. In the case of the chick Sluckin *et al.* (1966) have performed an experiment modelled on Harlow's studies. Solitary chicks were reared each with two boxes into which they could and did crawl. One box had a smooth lining and the other in each pair had a rough lining. The chick's preferences were tested by separating each chick from its boxes for a brief period, and recording which box each chick returned to on removal of the separating screen. The chicks showed a tendency to return to the smooth lined boxes rather than to the rough lined ones. If reared with only one type of box and then given a separation test, most returns to the familiar box were made by chicks with smooth lined boxes. This suggests that the chick is hatched with a particular contact requirement and, what is more important, this requirement is not easily changed by experience. It is interesting that Harlow (1959) reared monkeys with wire mothers only and that such monkeys failed to obtain emotional comfort from them in a fear situation. Monkeys reared with cloth mothers were much less disturbed when with their cloth mothers in such a situation. The inference is that the development of a lasting social attachment to an object requires that the object provide an adequate contact stimulus pattern.

Such a conclusion may appear reasonable for the monkey but it has been persistently stated that no reinforcement other than the visual presence of the object is required in imprinting in birds (Thorpe, 1956; Hinde, 1962). Unfortunately most of the studies of imprinting use the rather special situation defined by Moltz (1960). Usually this involves first eliciting approach and following responses with one object, then isolating the bird for a short period, sometimes as short as 24 hours, and frequently in the dark (Hess, 1957), and finally making a test of approach and following responses to the same object either alone or with a second previously unseen object in a simultaneous choice situation. It is doubtful if one can regard such experiments as testing social attachment in the way that Harlow's tests do. Further, we can rarely be sure that the chicks are unable to contact the objects. There is no doubt that striking a chick with an object increases the intensity of approach and following responses and produces pleasure calls. Observations of this kind led Kovach & Hess (1963) to test the effect of electric shock on following in chicks. Shock generally interfered with following but at 14 and 18 hours moderate amounts produced better following. Once again comparison with studies of the Rhesus monkey is illuminating. Harlow (1960a) equipped a cloth mother with air nozzles that would blast the young monkey with the result that it clung more tightly than ever. Such a mother, however, did not provide comfort in a subsequent fear situation. It is still not clear in the case of the chick whether shock affects subsequent attachment to the object.

Returning to the question of the role of contact in imprinting in chicks it must be noted that in some studies chicks have been imprinted without following or contacting the object (Baer & Gray, 1960; Collins, 1965; Moltz *et al.*, 1960; Thompson & Dubanoski, 1964). Thompson & Dubanoski report that the imprinting that occurred in the absence of following was relatively slight. Smith (1962) and Smith & Bird (1963) were unable to detect significant effects on approach responses in chicks allowed to crawl under or contact the stimulus source. What may be happening in so many of these studies, however, is that the initial approach and following behaviour is being elicited and, because of the relatively short period spent in isolation between exposure and subsequent testing (rarely more than five days), these original responses occur again on re-presentation of the object. In other words it could be that contact reinforcement is necessary for fixation of a social attachment, *i.e.*, for imprinting, but not for the persistent performance of approach and following by the 'unattached' chick to a perceptually learned familiar stimulus pattern. The possibility and mechanism of such perceptual learning will be considered later. I have also treated the question of contact reinforcement, social attachment and environmental learning more fully elsewhere (1966b).

The mere presence, without contact, of the imprinting object can serve as a goal and reward for behaviour in the chick. Thus Campbell & Pickleman (1961) have shown that chicks will run a T-maze in order to follow their imprinting object in a runway, though it is not clear whether they could contact the object as well as follow it. Perhaps better evidence is that of Peterson (1960) who has shown that ducklings will peck a key in order to view their imprinting object moving in a runway. In the case of the monkey, Harlow (1959) has used a Butler type viewing apparatus and has shown that surrogate-reared monkeys will work to see their cloth mother as much as to see a real monkey, but a wire mother produces no more responding than occurs to an empty room. Monkeys reared with no mother showed equal rates of responding to cloth and wire mothers and a higher rate to a real monkey. Thus, in the monkey too, the sight of the mother surrogate can serve as a reward for lever pressing activity. In both the chick and the monkey, however, it could be said that the objects had acquired their reinforcing properties secondarily. Thus it is clear that only the cloth mother which had provided contact comfort became reinforcing in this way. It should be remembered that approach behaviour to the sight of the mother surrogate or imprinting object is frequently subject to intermittent reinforcement since successful contact is by no means always achieved. This is true of most maternal care situations, as Gerwirtz (1961) has pointed out in his excellent learning analysis of the development of social attachment. He has also suggested that contact reinforcement may play an important role in conditioning the visual reinforcing stimuli and has emphasized the fact that the intermittent nature of such reinforcement would make the secondary reinforcing stimuli highly resistant to extinction (see also Zimmerman, 1957).

IV. FEAR BEHAVIOUR IN CHICKS AND MONKEYS

Most workers on imprinting agree that, at the close of the so-called sensitive period, fear behaviour becomes manifest. Many feel that it is the development of fear that prevents chicks from becoming imprinted to new objects. In two papers (1962, 1966a) I have given experimental evidence in favour of the opposite view, that imprinting results in fear behaviour toward non-imprinting objects. In any event, fear of new objects develops rapidly in chicks after the first day and attachments to mother surrogates or siblings are usually developed sufficiently for discrimination to occur by that time (Sluckin & Salzen, 1961). In the Rhesus monkey (Harlow, 1960a) fear responses develop from 20-40 days and attachment to cloth mothers, in terms of the time spent upon them, is clearly established from about 20 days. Discrimination of the mothers' faces does not appear until about 45 days.

Sluckin & Salzen (1961) have described how chicks kept singly and for some hours with an intermittently moving object spend much time following the object but ultimately tend to spend time in a warm chamber and give up following. If a strange object is then introduced into the runway or if movements or noises are made such chicks immediately rush to the object and resume following with distress calls giving place to pleasure calls. It is important to note that the chicks did not go to the warm chamber when disturbed in this way. I have already mentioned the study (1966a) in which solitary caged chicks became attached to their water reservoirs. When strange objects or chicks were introduced into the cages of such chicks they would dash to their water reservoir, push against it and stay by it. From there they would watch and perhaps ultimately come out and approach and explore peck the strange intruding object. Candland *et al.* (1963) have also shown that chicks reared with other chicks and/or manipulable objects will go to the familiar chick or object when disturbed by a fear stimulus in the form of an unfamiliar moving object. The presence of the social companion has long been known to alleviate fear and has been demonstrated frequently for chicks (Guiton, 1959; Salzen, 1962, 1963a).

Harlow (1960a) has described what happened when his surrogate reared monkeys were placed in an arena with strange objects. They immediately dashed to the cloth mother and clung to her. Their fear appeared to subside when in contact with the mother. They did not go to familiar heater pads even when the cloth mother was not present. When on the cloth mother they soon began to watch the fear object and many finally left the mother, approached and explored the object. Once again the chick and the monkey data seem to coincide. Further, once the chick has a familiar moving object and is well experienced, the substitution of another and different moving object causes flight and distress (Sluckin & Salzen, 1961). Harlow (1962) reared one monkey with a cloth mother that had a smooth round face. At 90 days it was given two mothers with ornamental faces and it quickly learned to twist the heads round so as to bring the smooth round backs to the front. The implication is that with sufficient exposure the monkey comes to discriminate details of the surrogate's visual appearance. Clearly in the monkey as well as the chick (Gray & Howard, 1957) social attachment processes may involve learning the individual as well as the species.

Harlow (1960) has also reared monkeys with two cloth mothers of different colours and with different faces. Only one provided food, yet by 80-90 days the monkeys spent their time equally on them and subsequently either mother provided comfort in the fear tests. This, besides confirming that nursing is not an essential factor in social attachment, parallels the suggestion (Salzen, 1962) that imprinting to more than one object may occur in birds. Thus Hinde *et al.* (1956) were able to train coots and moorhens to follow several models.

What happens if the mother surrogate is absent in a fear provoking situation?

The monkey rushes about, throws itself on the floor, clutches its head and body (self-contacting?) and screams. Harlow (1959) reports that wire mother reared monkeys were even more disturbed, even with the wire mother present. The self-contacting behaviour is significant in that it provides some of the stimulation normally obtained from the mother surrogate and apparently highly effective as a tranquillizer (see also Mason & Green, 1962). Imprinted chicks in a similar situation may freeze or rush about and squeal. They may then search with distress calls, jump at the walls, and may push into a corner where some contact and quiescence may be achieved.

Harlow (1959) also describes the fear behaviour of monkeys that have been reared with a padded crib plus cloth mother and a padded crib only. The former spent more time in the crib than on the mother during rearing, yet in the fear situation they went to the mother. The crib-only reared monkeys did go to their cribs and did obtain some emotional support when in the fear situation. Somewhat comparably, if isolate chicks are reared in a cage with a heated chamber they will retreat to the chamber when strange objects are introduced into the cage.

What is the reaction to loss of the mother surrogate or imprinting object?

Chicks give distress calls and searching behaviour and change to pleasure calling and approach with contacting when the object is restored. This was the response pattern shown by isolate chicks on removal and return of water reservoirs to which they had become attached (Salzen, 1966a, b). Similarly in the monkey, Harlow (1960a) has reported that solitary monkeys became attached to their diapers so that when these were removed for cleaning the monkeys showed distress by their expression and even by beating their heads on the cage walls. "When the diapers were returned the monkeys would put their thumbs in their mouths, the diaper against their faces, and close their eyes in utter ecstasy".

V. ATTACHMENT AND LATER SOCIAL BEHAVIOUR

Studies of the effects of early isolation on later social behaviour of birds would suggest that such birds integrate surprisingly quickly and easily after their period of isolation (Baron & Kish, 1960; Waller & Waller, 1963). There is some evidence (Collias, 1962; Baron *et al.*, 1962; Weidmann, 1958) that such birds may not be entirely normal in their social behaviour, but more studies of this problem in birds are required. Harlow & Harlow (1962) report that two monkeys raised in isolation for 2 years simply crouched or fled in fear of other monkeys and after 2 years of social caging they still showed an abnormal fear of other monkeys. Monkeys similarly isolated for the first six months only had failed to develop normal social defence reactions after eight months of regular periods of social experience. Monkeys raised for 80 days with cloth mothers seem to be able to develop satisfactory social behaviour subsequently. More recently Harlow (1965) has confirmed these findings with 16 monkeys reared in total isolation.

Harlow & Harlow (1962) found that infant monkeys reared in single cages developed abnormal patterns of behaviour. They sat and stared, circled the cages repetitively, clasped their heads and rocked for long periods. They often developed habits of pinching particular areas of the body, or even chewing such parts. The approach of a human often set off this self-aggression (see also Cross & Harlow, 1965). One is reminded of the description by Kruijt (1962) of Burmese red junglefowl cockerels reared in isolation. They passed through a phase of strong escape behaviour, running madly about the cage, dashing into corners and often screaming. Such fits could last for hours. Kruijt got the impression that they were escaping from their own seen bodies, especially their legs and perhaps tails. I have also noticed escape behaviour in isolate chicks after about 2 weeks of age. Kruijt also reports that subsequently his cockerels went through a phase in which they showed aggressive behaviour directed to their tails and, later, to human beings. When finally placed with a hen these cocks showed excessive aggression. It is a common observation that when isolate reared chicks are placed together they show abnormally severe pecking of one another. Socially reared ones develop learned adjustments which are thus lacking in the isolates. Harlow & Harlow (1962) also found this tendency to more vicious aggressive behaviour in their previously isolated monkeys. A group of such monkeys showed severe fighting before dominance relations were established, after which normal social grooming appeared. Surrogate reared monkeys were equally deficient in their social behaviour though they were not so aggressive.

Harlow & Harlow (1962) have also shown that infant-infant interaction may be sufficient experience for normal social and sexual behaviour but that mother-infant interactions undoubtedly also influence such subsequent behaviour. Domestic chicks are normally reared, nowadays, in age-mate flocks with apparently normal adult social and sexual behaviour. One is left with the feeling that for both the chick and the monkey the later effects of varying periods of isolation at varying ages may be best understood and analysed in the manner suggested by Rosenblatt *et al.* (1961), *i.e.* in terms of the changing situation and its required stimulus-response patterns during the course of development.

VI. ATTACHMENT AND SEXUAL BEHAVIOUR

What has been said for social behaviour may also be said for sexual behaviour and it remains only to present some of the relevant facts for chicks and monkeys. The evidence that imprinting determines the object of sexual behaviour in birds is not unequivocal. Some studies have failed to show any clear effect (Goodwin, 1948; Wood-Gush, 1958) while others have shown at least some influence of early experience on later choice of sex partner (see review of such works by Schutz, 1965). The work of Schutz (1965) is the most recent and comprehensive evidence in favour of such effects in ducks; Schein (1963) gives evidence for the turkey, and Bambridge (1962) and Guiton (1961, 1962) for the chicken. I have made a critical review of much of this evidence (1966a) and have suggested an explanation more compatible with the approach of Rosenblatt *et al.* (1961) by laying emphasis on the part played by avoidance due to strangeness of non-imprinting objects in preventing sex responses towards them. For the present, therefore, we may concentrate on comparable data for the chick and the monkey.

Harlow's studies have involved totally and partially isolated monkeys and ones reared with surrogate mothers. According to Harlow & Harlow (1962) monkeys reared in partial isolation (*i.e.* could see and hear but could not make body contact with other monkeys) for 2 years failed to show normal sexual behaviour even after as much as 7 years of subsequent social caging. Some approach and display has occurred in these monkeys but incorrect orientation and fighting prevent successful mating (see also Mason, 1960). Surrogate reared ones similarly have failed to show normal sexual behaviour. However, it should be noted that recently Meier (1965) has reported that his partially isolated monkeys have subsequently been successful in breeding. Kruijt (1962) found that his isolate reared cockerels failed to show successful copulations. Some courted the females but when the female crouched they would pay no attention, or walk away, or continue to waltz, or attack her by kicking or pecking. These cocks persisted in this behaviour even after extensive experience with females. Only two birds were successful, one tested at a younger age (9 months) and the other after making disoriented attempts and after being caged with a female for one week. It is interesting that one cockerel was seen to copulate on the ground with a feather held in his beak. It could be that these cockerels had developed a tendency to direct sex behaviour to their tails, just as they had directed their escape and aggressive behaviour to their tails. This would explain their behaviour of mounting hens the wrong way round. I have found that isolate chicks persistently presented with a hand may go through a sequence of escape, changing to aggression to the hand. Androgen injected isolate chicks similarly tested also showed some aggression and then strong sex responses to the hand (1966a). Both in the chick and the monkey the isolate reared individual seems to come to the test situation with the wrong response patterns–fear at first, unrestrained aggression as fear subsides, and inadequate bodily interactions in sex or social behaviour. These are the features present in Harlow's isolate reared monkeys who become mothers and fail to respond appropriately to their infants, to whom they show indifference or even abuse (Harlow & Hansen, 1963). Once again the analysis of Rosenblatt *et al.* (1961) seems apposite, both to sexual and maternal behaviour. It only remains to complete the comparison between chick and monkey by pointing out that the infant monkey's response to an abusive abnormal mother is to redouble its efforts to contact her, just as does the chick when struck with the imprinting object.

VII. ATTACHMENT BEHAVIOUR IN THE HUMAN INFANT

A few comments on the comparable behaviour and attachment processes in the human infant may be worthwhile although the subject does not need extensive reviewing because of the contributions to the subject in Foss (1961, 1963). In one of these contributions Gewirtz (1961) has given an analysis of social motivation and attachment in the human that parallels much of what has been said in the present paper. He has pointed out that smiling, laughter, glances, stares, reaching, manipulating, and vocalizing, can all bring reinforcement and proximity of the caretaker and that maintaining contact with the object is the key to the learning in social attachment. As these responses develop they appear to be released at first by a wide range of stimuli. In many cases, *e.g.* smiling, there seems to be a progression from contact and kinaesthetic release to auditory and finally visual release. Smiling at first occurs in response to a variety of sounds but soon comes to be particularly strongly elicited by the human voice (Wolff, 1963). There is evidence that the first smile to visual stimuli can be elicited by non-specific black and white contours (Ahrens, 1954) or even a flashing light (Salzen, 1963b). Such evidence is contrary to the claim by Spitz & Wolf (1946) that a face like configuration is essential for smiling; a claim still accepted in recent contributions (*e.g.* Schaffer, 1963). It would seem that as in the chick the first social responses are elicited by very elemental forms of visual stimulation. Very quickly, however (5th-11th week), social smiling comes to be restricted to the human face and, rather more slowly (6th-16th month), preferentially to particular human faces. At the same time fear and withdrawal responses to unfamiliar faces may develop. Throughout this time there is plenty of opportunity for these specific stimulus patterns to acquire secondary reinforcing properties through their intermittent association with handling, rocking and nursing and their accompanying contact and kinaesthetic reinforcement. It is, of course, well known that rocking can quieten a distressed infant. Yet kinaesthetic stimulation is not vital for attachment in the monkey, for Harlow (1960a) has found that although the infant monkey at first spends much time on a rocking plane crib, it subsequently comes to spend as much time on a static one. Kinaesthesis may be more important in the human since most cultures provide the infant with continuous contact in the form of clothing. One wonders whether the surprising proportion of infants that dislike physical contact in the form of cuddling, hugging and kissing (Schaffer, 1963) is due to this fact. It is interesting that when such contact becomes acceptable it is frequently in the form of cheek contact, the most likely form to be experienced between the infant and parent. In any event there remains the study by Brackbill (1958) in which smiling rates in infants were affected by rewarding smiles by picking up and petting the infant. Further she demonstrated that intermittent reinforcement resulted in greater resistance to extinction of the smiling response. Much earlier, Dennis (1935) reared two infants so that the adult's voice was not associated with smiling aroused by other agencies including handling and contact. Under these conditions the human voice never aroused smiling.

Recently there has been a move to emphasise the role of distance receptors in the formation of social attachments (Rheingold, 1961; Schaffer, 1963; Schaffer & Emerson, 1964) and evidence for this view has been marshalled by Walters & Parke (1965). It is doubtful whether the evidence adequately allows for the possibility of early acquisition of secondary reinforcing properties by visual and auditory stimulation through association with contact and kinaesthetic stimulation. Such secondary reinforcing properties would account for attachments to people other than the actual caretaker. Since human infants have to be cleaned and fed it is difficult to see how such a possibility can be adequately controlled for. At present I feel that we must rate the evidence on the role of contact and distance reception provided by Harlow's studies above that available for the human.

VIII. THE ESTABLISHMENT OF DISTANCE PERCEPTION

When this has been said, there is still the possibility of a process distinct from the social attachment or fixation process, namely the development of a familiar perceptual world based on distance stimulation and the behavioural responses to changes in this familiar world. Rheingold (1961) has studied this process in the human infant. The infant responds to visual stimuli of light and dark, to contour and complexity, and above all to change or movement – in short ". . . to temporal and spatial changes in stimulation" a phrase used by Rheingold and also by myself when reporting (1963b) an infant smiling to a flashing light. These are the same stimuli that attract the newly hatched chick. Rheingold proceeds to say that the infant shows the orienting reflex of Pavlov to such stimulation. In the case of the chick I have used (1962, 1966b) Sokolov's (1960) neuronal model hypothesis for the orienting reflex to explain similar responses to this stimulation. Rheingold points out that smiling, brightening of face, bodily activity and vocalization may also occur and that she has observed these in response to a ray of sunshine or a wallpaper pattern, and to a rattle. She accepts the notion, therefore, that the human infant responds to the human adult simply as a particularly effective stimulus among a complex of stimuli. I have also expressed this view (1963b) and in a joint paper (Sluckin & Salzen, 1961) employed the notion of Gibson (1959) that animate stimuli are, by their nature as deforming surfaces, peculiarly effective in eliciting responses in the neonate. I should like to suggest that one of the distinguishing features of animate or social environmental stimuli is that they move independently of the infant's movements, whereas the inanimate environment typically shows response-produced movements only. The study by Held & Hein (1963) has shown in the cat how important the latter may be for the development of normal depth perception. It would seem highly likely that experience of non-response produced movement stimulation will be crucial for the development of behaviour directed to independently moving objects, *i.e.* for the acquisition of appropriate social perceptions and response patterns.

However, I cannot agree with Rheingold's (1961) assumption that the orienting patterns of behaviour which include smiling are expressions of delight, at least not when first elicited. It seems to me that this is an anthropocentric conclusion. Rather we need to look at the nature of the smiling response. Ambrose (1960) has made an excellent analysis of this and has considered the possibility that smiling is ritualized low intensity laughing while laughing itself is an ambivalent movement. In brief Ambrose suggests the possibility that laughing is a combination of crying (a fear/anger response involving expiration) and simultaneous pleasure responses (relief involving inspiration). The result is the ha-ha-ha of laughing. Ambrose gives a detailed analysis of this pattern. I should like to suggest that laughing does occur when fear is first aroused and then is suddenly relieved. If smiling is regarded as low intensity laughing it should occur in similar circumstances. Van Hooff (1962) has suggested that the "grin face" found in apes and monkeys indicates a tendency to flee and may be related to human smiling. Both may serve as appeasement displays and reduce attack tendencies in social partners. In the human infant smiling seems to occur at the sudden presentation of stimuli, especially familiar ones. Hence there may be a first sudden fear or arousal followed by the relief of recognition. Hence smiling of this kind should appear in infants only as they acquire familiar perceptions. One might expect, therefore, the progression of smiling in response to changing stimulation first to touch and kinaesthesis, then to sounds and finally to sights. Furthermore, it is just this type of reaction, *i.e.* recognition relief following fear arousal through sudden new stimulation, that could come to serve and be developed as a greeting signal in social behaviour. Reinforcement of this kind of reaction would involve contact stimulation from the familiar social object and such reinforcement would ensure the further development of the greeting response. In this way the smile as an ambivalent response becomes transformed to the smile as a social response. Yet smiling as an ambivalent response may still occur in non-social situations involving mild fear or arousal followed by relief or recognition. Hence the confusion that follows if smiling is treated as a single response pattern.

We can see that non-social smiling and orienting behaviour to non-social stimulation are related to the formation of perceptions of the distant environment. As indicated previously the development of such perceptions may well be independent of conventional reinforcements and even of the contact/kinaesthetic reinforcements used to explain the development of social attachments. It is important to distinguish between the perception and the attachment. Attachment in the sense tested by Harlow with his monkeys may well require contact reinforcement for its establishment, while perceptions in the sense of recognisable and known stimulus patterns of distance reception may not require reinforcement of any kind. I would suggest that the phenomena of environmental stimulation dealt with by Rheingold (1961) and Schaffer (1963) and Walters & Parke (1965) involve development of perceptions in the latter sense. In a recent paper (1966b) I have considered this phenomenon of environmental learning in the neonate and have used the neuronal model hypothesis modified from that of Sokolov to account for this kind of development of perceptions through the distance receptors. In the same paper I have considered some of the evidence concerning the role of contact reinforcement in social attachment and have concluded that satisfactory evidence of such attachment in the absence of adequate contact stimulation has yet to be found.

SUMMARY

Birds and Primates might be expected to have some similar behaviour patterns because they have some similarities in the nature and organization of their distance and contact receptors. An analysis of the reactions of newly-hatched chicks and neonatal monkeys to objects reveals many similarities and suggests that the contact provided by objects is an important factor influencing these reactions. Further similarities are evident in the behaviour of neonatal chicks and monkeys which are reared without objects either alone or in small groups, and in the behaviour of these infants when they are subsequently presented with objects or placed in small groups. The behaviour of neonates towards large objects is analysed into approach responses mediated by distance receptor systems and contacting responses mediated by contact receptor systems. It is suggested that contact reinforcement is required for the establishment of enduring social attachments and for distance perceptions to become secondary reinforcers for social behaviour. Available data on the role of contact reinforcement in imprinting are reviewed.

The fear behaviour of chicks and infant monkeys is compared. There are similarities in their fear responses to strange objects both when tested alone and when tested in the presence of imprinting objects to which they have developed social attachments. In both chicks and monkeys fear of the unfamiliar object or situation is alleviated by the presence of the imprinting object.

The social and sexual behaviour of chickens and monkeys that have been reared in isolation is briefly described and the similarities of their abnormal and inadequate responses are indicated. Normal social and sexual behaviour is prevented by fear, aggression, and lack of acquired stimulus-response adjustments to an active social partner.

A similar analysis of social attachment in the human infant is presented and it is suggested that contact stimulation is necessary for such attachment but not for the establishment of distance perceptions of a familiar environment. The smiling response is treated as an ambivalent fear/relief response involving recognition of familiar distance stimulation. Social smiling differentiates from this ambivalent response through reinforcement by the social partner.

The paper is based on available published experimental studies of neonatal birds and Primates and is intended to provoke new analysis and further studies rather than to provide a definitive analysis of the behaviour of neonates.

REFERENCES

Ahrens, R. (1954). Beitrag zur Entwicklung des Physiognomie und Mimikerkennens. Z. exp. angew. Psychol. 2, p. 414-454 and 599-633.

Ambrose, J. A. (1961). The smiling and related responses in early human infancy: an experimental and theoretical study of their course and significance. Unpublished doctoral dissertation, Univer. of London.

——— (1963). The concept of a critical period for the development of social responsiveness in early human infancy. In: Foss, B. M. (Ed.), Determinants of infant behaviour II. London, Methuen, p. 201-225.

Baer, D. M. & Gray, P. H. (1960). Imprinting to a different species without overt following. Percept. mot. Skills 10, p. 171-174.

Bambridge, R. (1962). Early experience and sexual behavior in the domestic chicken. Science 136, p. 259-260.

Baron, A. & Kish, G. B. (1960). Early social isolation as a determinant of aggregative behavior in the domestic chicken. J. comp. physiol. Psychol. 53, p. 459-463.

———, ——— & Antonitis, J. J. (1962). Effects of early and late social isolation on aggregative behavior in the domestic chicken. J. genet. Psychol. 100, p. 355-360.

Bateson, P. P. G. (1964). Changes in chicks' responses to novel moving objects over the sensitive period for imprinting. Anim. Behav. 12, p. 479-489.

Brackbill, Y. (1958). Extinction of the smiling response in infants as a function of reinforcement schedule. Child Develpm. 29, p. 115-124.

Campbell, B. A. & Pickleman, J. R. (1961). The imprinting object as a reinforcing stimulus. J. comp. physiol. Psychol. 54, p. 592-596.

Candland, D. K., Nagy, Z. M. & Conklyn, D. H. (1963). Emotional behavior in the domestic chicken (White Leghorn) as a function of age and developmental environment. J. comp. physiol. Psychol. 56, p. 1069-1073.

Collias, N. E. (1952). The development of social behavior in birds. Auk 69, p. 127-159.

Collias, N. E. (1962). Social development in birds and mammals. In: Bliss, E. L. (Ed.), Roots of behavior. New York, Harper, p. 264-273.
——— & Joos, M. (1953). The spectographic analysis of sound signals of the domestic fowl. Behaviour 5, p. 175-187.
Collins, T. B. (1965). Strength of the following response in the chick in relation to degree of "parent" contact. J. comp. physiol. Psychol. 60, p. 192-195.
Cross, H. A. & Harlow, H. F. (1965). Prolonged and progressive effects of partial isolation on the behavior of Macaque monkeys. J. exp. Res. Pers. 1, p. 39-49.
Dennis, W. (1935). An experimental test of two theories of social smiling in infants. J. soc. Psychol. 6, p. 214-223.
Fabricius, E. (1962). Some aspects of imprinting in birds. Symp. zool. Soc. Lond. 8, p. 139-148.
——— (1964). Crucial periods in the development of the following response in young nidifugous birds. Z. f. Tierpsychol. 21, p. 326-337.
Foss, B. M. (Ed.) (1961). Determinants of infant behaviour. London, Methuen; Idem, II (1963).
Gewirtz, J. L. (1961). A learning analysis of the effects of normal stimulation, privation and deprivation on the acquisition of social motivation and attachment. In Foss, B. M. (Ed.), Determinants of infant behaviour. London, Methuen, p. 213-299.
Gibson, J. J. (1959). Perception as a function of stimulation. In: Koch, S. (Ed.), Psychology: a study of a science. Study I. Conceptual and systematic. Vol. I. Sensory, perceptual and physiological formulations. New York, McGraw-Hill, p. 456-501.
Goodwin, D. (1948). Some abnormal fixations in birds. Ibis 90, p. 45-48.
Gray, P. H. (1958). Theory and evidence of imprinting in human infants. J. Psychol. 46, p. 155-166.
——— & Howard, K. I. (1957). Specific recognition of humans in imprinted chicks. Percept. mot. Skills, 7. p. 301-304.
Guiton, P. (1959). Socialisation and imprinting in brown Leghorn chicks. Anim. Behav. 7, p. 26-34.
——— (1961). The influence of imprinting on the agonistic and courtship responses of the brown Leghorn cock. Anim. Behav. 9, p. 167-177.
——— (1962). The development of sexual responses in the domestic fowl in relation to the concept of imprinting. Symp. zool. Soc. Lond. 8, p. 227-234.
Harlow, H. F. (1959). Love in infant monkeys. Scient. American 200, p. 68-74.
——— (1960a). Affectional behavior in the infant monkey. In: Brazier, M. A. B. (Ed.), The central nervous system and behavior. New York, J. Macy Jr. Foundation, p. 307-357.
——— (1960b). Primary affectional patterns in primates. Amer. J. Orthopsychiat. 30, p. 676-684.

Harlow, H. F. (1961). The development of affectional patterns in infant monkeys. In: Foss, B. M. (Ed.), Determinants of infant behaviour. London, Methuen, p. 75-88.
——— (1962). Development of affection in primates. In: Bliss, E. L. (Ed.), Roots of behavior. New York, Harper, p. 157-166.
——— (1963). The maternal affectional system. In: Foss, B. M. (ed.), Determinants of infant behaviour II. London, Methuen, p. 3-29.
——— (1965). Total social isolation: effects on Macaque monkey behavior. Science, 148, p. 666.
——— & Harlow, M. K. (1962). Social deprivation in monkeys. Scient. American, 207, p. 137-146.
———, ——— & Hansen, E. W. (1963). The maternal affectional system of rhesus monkeys. In: Rheingold, H. L. (Ed.), Maternal behavior in mammals. New York, Wiley, p. 254-281.
——— & Zimmermann, R. R. (1958). Affectional responses in the infant monkey. Science 130, p. 421-432.
——— & ——— (1958). The development of affectional responses in infant monkeys. Proc. Amer. Phil. Soc. 102, p. 501-509.
Held, R., & Hein, A. (1963). Movement-produced stimulation in the development of visually guided behavior. J. comp. physiol. Psychol. 56, p. 872-876.
Hess, E. H. (1957). Effects of meprobamate on imprinting in waterfowl. Ann. N.Y. Acad. Sci. 67, p. 724-732.
——— (1959). Imprinting. Science 130, p. 133-141.
——— (1964). Imprinting in birds. Science, 146, p. 1128-1139.
——— & Schaefer, H. H. (1959). Innate behavior patterns as indicators of the "critical period," Z. f. Tierpsychol. 16, p. 155-160.
Hinde, R. A. (1961). The establishment of the parent-offspring relation in birds, with some mammalian analogies. In: Thorpe, W. H. & Zangwill, O. L. (Eds.), Current problems in animal behaviour. Cambridge, University Press, p. 175-193.
——— (1962). Some aspects of the imprinting problem. Symp. zool. Soc. Lond. 8, p. 129-138.
——— (1963). The nature of imprinting. In: Foss, B. M. (Ed.), Determinants of infant behaviour II. London, Methuen, p. 227-233.
———, Thorpe, W. H., & Vince, M. A. (1956). The following response of young coots and moorhens. Behaviour 9, p. 214-242.
Hooff, J. A. R. A. M. van (1962). Facial expressions in higher primates. Symp. zool. Soc. Lond. 8, p. 97-125.
Jaynes, J. (1956). Imprinting: the interaction of learned and innate behavior. I. development and generalization. J. comp. physiol. Psychol. 49, p. 201-206.
——— (1957). Imprinting: the interaction of learned and innate behavior. II. the critical period. J. comp. physiol. Psychol. 50, p. 6-10.

Jaynes, J. (1958a). Imprinting: the interaction of learned and innate behavior. III. practice effects on performance, retention and fear. J. comp. physiol. Psychol. 51, p. 234-237.

——— (1958b). Imprinting: the interaction of learned and innate behavior. IV. generalization and emergent discrimination. J. comp. physiol. Psychol. 51, p. 238-242.

Kovach, J. K. & Hess, E. H. (1963). Imprinting: effects of painful stimulation upon the following response. J. comp. physiol. Psychol. 56, p. 461-464.

Kruijt, J. P. (1962). Imprinting in relation to drive interaction in Burmese red junglefowl. Symp. zool. Soc. Lond. 8, p. 219-226.

Lorenz, K. Z. (1937). The companion in the bird's world. Auk 54, p. 245-273.

Mason, W. A. (1960). The effects of social restriction on the behavior of rhesus monkeys. I. free social behavior. J. comp. physiol. Psychol. 53, p. 582-589.

——— & Green, P. C. (1962). The effects of social restriction on the behavior of rhesus monkeys. IV. responses to a novel environment and to an alien species. J. comp. physiol. Psychol., 55, p. 363-368.

Meier, G. W. (1965). Other data on the effects of social isolation during rearing upon adult reproductive behaviour in the rhesus monkey (*Macaca mulatta*). Anim. Behav. 13, p. 228-231.

Moltz, H. (1960). Imprinting: empirical basis and theoretical significance. Psychol. Bull. 57, p. 291-314.

——— Rosenblum, L. & Stettner, L. J. (1960). Some parameters of imprinting effectiveness. J. comp. physiol. Psychol. 53, p. 297-301.

Mowbray, J. B. & Cadell, T. E. (1962). Early behavior patterns in rhesus monkeys. J. comp. physiol. Psychol. 55, p. 350-357.

Peterson, N. (1960). Control of behavior by presentation of an imprinted stimulus. Science 132. p. 1395-1396.

Portmann, A. (1961). Sensory organs: skin, taste and olfaction. In: Marshall, A. J. (Ed.), Biology and comparative physiology of birds. New York, Academic Press, Vol. II. p. 37-48.

Rheingold, H. L. (1961). The effect of environmental stimulation upon social and exploratory behaviour in the human infant. In: Foss, B. M. (Ed.), Determinants of infant behaviour. London, Methuen, p. 143-171.

Rosenblatt, J. S., Turkewitz, G. & Schneirla, T. C. (1961). Early socialization in the domestic cat as based on feeding and other relationships between female and young. In: Foss, B, M. (Ed.), Determinants of infant behaviour. London. Methuen, p. 51-74.

Salzen, E. A. (1962). Imprinting and fear. Symp. zool. Soc. Lond. 8, p. 199-218.

——— (1963a). Imprinting and the immobility reactions of domestic fowl. Anim. Behav. II. p. 66-71.

——— (1963b). Visual stimuli eliciting the smiling response in the human infant. J. genet. Psychol. p. 51-54.

Salzen, E. A. (1966). The interaction of experience, stimulus characteristics and exogenous androgen in the behaviour of domestic chicks. Behaviour 26, p. 286-322.

——— (1966). Imprinting and environmental learning. In: Aronson, L. R., Lehrman, D. S., Rosenblatt, J. S. & Tobach, E. (Eds.), Development and evolution of behavior. New York, Freeman, Vol. I. (in press).

Schaffer, H. R. Some issues for research in the study of attachment behaviour. In: Foss, B. M. (Ed.), Determinants of infant behaviour II. London, Methuen, p. 179-199.

——— & Emerson, P. E. (1964). The development of social attachments in infancy. Monogr. Soc. Res. Child. Developm. 29, No. 3, Ser. No. 94.

Schein, M. W. (1963). On the irreversibility of imprinting. Z. f. Tierpsychol. 20, p. 462-467.

Schneirla, T. C. (1965). Aspects of stimulation and organization in approach/withdrawal processes underlying vertebrate behavioral development. In: Lehrman, D. S., Hinde, R. A. & Shaw, E. (Eds.), Advances in the study of behavior. New York, Academic Press, Vol. I. p. 1-74.

Schutz, F. (1965). Sexuelle Prägung bei Anatiden. Z. f. Tierpsychol. 22, p. 50-103.

Scott, J. P. (1962). Critical periods in behavioral development. Science 138, p. 949-958.

Sherrington, C. S. (1947). The integrative action of the nervous system. New Haven, Yale University Press (2nd ed.).

Sluckin, W. (1965). Imprinting and early learning. London, Methuen.

——— & Salzen, E. A. (1961). Imprinting and perceptual learning. Quart. J. exp. Psychol. 13, p. 65-77.

———, Taylor, K. F. & Taylor, A. (1966). Approach of domestic chicks to stationary objects of different texture. Percept. mot. Skills 22, p. 600-702.

Smith, F. V. (1962). Perceptual aspects of imprinting. Symp. zool. Soc. Lond. 8, p. 171-191.

——— & Bird, M. W. (1963). The relative attraction for the domestic chick of combinations of stimuli in different sensory modalities. Anim Behav. II. p. 300-305.

Sokolov, E. M. (1960). Neuronal models and the orienting reflex. In: Brazier, M. A. B. (Ed.), The central nervous system and behavior. New York. Josiah Macy Jr. Foundation. Transactions of the third conference, p. 187-276.

Spitz, R. A. & Wolf, K. M. (1946). The smiling response: a contribution to the ontogenesis of social relations. Genet. Psychol. Monogr. 34, p. 57-125.

Thompson, W. R. & Dubanoski, R. A. (1964). Imprinting and the "law of effort". Anim. Behav. 12, p. 213-218.

Thorpe, W. H. (1956) Learning and instinct in animals. London, Methuen.

Waller, P. F. & Waller, M. B. (1963). Some relationships between early experience and later social behavior in ducklings. Behaviour 20, p. 343-363.

Walters, R. H. & Parke, R. D. (1965). The role of the distance receptors in the development of social responsiveness. In: Lipsitt, L. P. & Spiker, C. C. (Eds.), Advances in child development and behavior. New York, Academic Press, Vol. 2, p. 59-96.

Weidmann, U. (1958). Verhaltensstudien an der Stockente (*Anas platyrhynchos* L.) II. Versuche zur Auslösung und Prägung der Nachfolge und Anschluss-reaktion. Z. f. Tierpsychol. 15, p. 277-300.

Wolff, P. H. (1963). Observations on the early development of smiling. In: Foss, B. M. (Ed.), Determinants of infant behavior II. London, Methuen, p. 113-138.

Wood-Gush, D. G. M. (1958). The effect of experience on the mating behaviour of the domestic cock. Anim. Behav. 6, p. 68-71.

Zimmerman, D. W. (1957). Durable secondary reinforcement: method and theory. Psychol. Rev. 64, p. 373-383.

Play in Mammals

CAROLINE LOIZOS

SYNOPSIS

Problems faced in studying animal play are discussed, and some generally held views examined. Play in animals has generally been thought to be without function. This attitude has possibly arisen from a false analogy with the use of the word as it applies to human behaviour, where play is opposed to work. Animals do not work and therefore cannot be said to play, at any rate in the human sense of the word. It is suggested that it might be a more fruitful approach to start with the assumption that animal play does have survival value, in view of the time and energy spent in play by, in particular, the carnivores and the primates. Much behaviour has been classified as play simply because it was imperfectly understood: the category needs definition. Some play patterns are possibly remnants of phylogenetically ancient behaviour that have become freed through a change in the environment from their original adaptive functions.

Some of the motivating conditions necessary for the occurrence of play are discussed, including the apparent need for the animal to be free of conflicting physiological and environmental pressures. Play invitations are mentioned, and the fact that priority is given to the play signal over other conflicting and equally strong signals.

Current theories of the causation and function of play are treated briefly. Observers have tended to regard as play all behaviour performed while the young animal's primary needs were being taken care of by its adult conspecifics; but although young animals may be playing, they may equally well be performing at maximum efficiency for their

From *Symp. Zool. Soc. Lond.*, 1966, 18, 1-9.

particular level of development. Behaviour must not be called play simply because it appears inefficient. Practice is generally regarded to be the primary function of play, but it has yet to be shown that animals prevented from playing are less efficient as adults than those that play. This is not to deny that practice is certainly one of the incidental benefits of play, but it is not necessary to play in order to practice. The same objection is offered to the other main theory of the function of play: that is, that it provides the animal with vital information about the environment. It clearly does, but so does everything the animal engages in; it certainly is not necessary to play in order to gain information about the environment, since the animal may simply explore.

Theories of the causation of play have stated that it arises from the overflowing of surplus energy; that it is its own motivation in that it is "fun", "is enjoyed purely for its own sake", is "self-rewarding activity." The surplus energy hypothesis is shown to be an insufficient explanation for play, and the self-rewarding hypotheses are not considered to be explanations at all.

The actual behaviour that is called play is then looked at, and a comparison made of the motor patterns occurring in play with the same motor patterns occurring in their originally motivated contexts. Differences between the two are shown to consist of the economy with which the pattern is performed, or the efficiency in terms of its function in its original context. Lack of economy arises in several ways, amongst them exaggeration, repetition, reordering of the sequence, and breaking up of the sequence by insertion of apparently unrelated activities.

Since many of these characteristics are also shared by ritualized behaviour, the similarity between the two is discussed. Current research is concerned with precise distinction between them.

The main problem in studying animal play has resulted from a basic misconception in the approach, arising purely from our use of the word *play*. Play is an exclusively human concept used of activity that is other than, or even opposed to work. By analogy the word has come to be applied to behaviour in animals which cannot be seen to have any immediate biological end, any obvious survival value. Bierens de Haan's (1945) statement that "animal play is useless" is fairly typical of this attitude. The implication is simply that animal play cannot be serious, since if it were, if it had a function, it would not be play.

But for animals, of course, it is different. Since they do not work, at any rate in our sense of the word, they cannot really be said to play—in our sense of the word. The problem is not solved by thinking of an alternative word for play. The fact that even an untrained observer may be quite accurate in determining when an animal is playing suggests that somewhere in the complex of behaviour called play there is a fundamental similarity with the same kind of activity in human beings. What this similarity might consist of will be suggested later.

It is probably more useful to change the direction of approach. Instead of saying that human play appears to be without survival value and that therefore the same must be true of animal play, let us assume that animal play *has* survival value and that it has possibly become divorced from its original function, or functions, by the time it occurs in human beings—at any rate adult human beings. I think it would be rash to assume that it does not have survival value in animals, is not in this sense serious, since amongst other things the amount of time and energy spent in play by, for instance, the carnivores or the primates, would surely put these animals at a disadvantage if their play were totally without function.

Of course there are examples of animal behaviour that have been regarded as play simply because they were imperfectly understood. Beach (1945) quotes an instance in which various fishes had been observed to leap over free-floating objects in the water, such as sticks and reeds. This was considered to have no practical value and was therefore called play, until Breder (1932) suggested that what the fish were doing was using the sticks to scrape encrustations of ectoparasites from their undersides. It would be interesting to speculate on what might happen to this behaviour were the species to rid itself permanently of these particular parasites. It is quite possible that the habit of leaping over floating objects in the water would remain, and ethologists in the next century would certainly be tempted to call it play once more. Tembrock (1960) has pointed out that in the Arctic fox (*Alopex lagopus*) certain behaviour which now appears only in playful contexts probably originally had specific adaptive value in a particular earlier environment; when freed of the necessity to perform this particular function, perhaps through a change in the environment, such behaviour could be incorporated freely into the repertoire of play patterns. Thus it is likely that some play consists of the vestiges of phylogenetically very old behaviour; in some cases it may be no more than a trace, but in others complete sequences may have become "fossilized" and preserved whole. One cannot do more than make informed guesses about the origins of some play patterns. On the other hand, there are probably many more instances of what we now think of as play that will turn out to have quite specific and other functions, since the concept has, certainly until very recently, always been used as the wastepaper basket of imperfectly understood animal behaviour.

For the moment it might be useful to approach play in a roundabout way, in terms of some of the conditions necessary for its occurrence, and some of the features which invariably accompany it. There are motivating conditions which are necessary for the occurrence of play, though as they consist almost entirely of the absence of other conflicting sources of motivation, they cannot be said in any way to be sufficient. As far as can be told, play only occurs when the animal is free of environmental pressures such as heat, cold, wet and the presence of predators; and free of physiological pressures such as the need for food, drink, sleep or a sexual partner. Thus play is often most characteristic of young animals, whose needs are taken care of by their parents, and of animals in captivity for whom the same functions are served by their guardians. Again, however, this is only part of the story, since there is some evidence from observation of zoo animals (Morris, 1964) that there exists a positive need to engage in certain types of play. Play probably does not occur solely as the result of the absence of conflicting drives.

Play also appears to be voluntary, in that as far as one can tell an animal cannot be made to play by means of specific kinds of deprivation or reinforcement. Schiller (1957) reported that ". . . with no incentive the chimpanzee displayed a higher variety of handling objects than under the pressure of a lure which they attempted to obtain." In his case, the attempt to direct play by reinforcing the animals for this behaviour resulted in its inhibition.

However, those animals which do play may be encouraged to play by the presentation of suitable stimuli in a suitable manner. Moreover, they may be *invited* to play by a conspecific, or even a member of another species, as for example often happens with humans and domestic animals. A mother cat lying on her side and twitching the tip of her tail on which her kittens will pounce might well be an example of such a play invitation. This kind of invitation–what Altmann (1962) called metacommunication, or a signal about the quality of the communication which is to follow–may be seen in many mammals. Cats and dogs both have preliminary play movements, play intention movements in fact, which consist of a half-crouch with forelegs extended stiffly combined with wide-open eyes and ears pricked forward. Brownlee (1954) has described this phenomenon in domestic cattle. It occurs most noticeably in chimpanzees and other primates, but at that level on the phylogenetic scale the signal area has been reduced to the face, and a special facial expression indicating a playful mood is sometimes used as a kind of shorthand for the full motor play invitation. Similarly with humans: if one is punched quite hard by somebody with a broad grin on his face one will at least hesitate before interpreting it as an aggressive act. The interesting thing in this situation is that given the choice of two conflicting signals to attend to, the one that is always given priority is the one announcing that this is play, even though the punch may have been hard enough to hurt. Play signals seem to be very powerful and unambiguous. One can observe young chimpanzees putting up with treatment from each other that is rough enough to cause pain, provided it has been made clear at the outset that they are playing.

Current theories of the causation and function of play will now be treated briefly, before its actual motor characteristics are discussed. The most generally accepted theory of the function of play is to consider it as practice for adult activity (Pycraft, 1912; Mitchell, 1912; Groos, 1898). The main problem with this approach is that no clear distinction has been drawn between playful and serious behaviour in the young of any particular species. During the infancy and adolescence of many mammals it is possible to see immature forms of behaviour patterns which will appear in their complete form and appropriate context in adult life. In the young animal this kind of behaviour does not appear to serve the same biological ends that it does in maturity, and consequently observers have tended to regard as play all behaviour performed while the young animal's primary needs were being taken care of by its adult conspecifics. Now often these immature forms of adult behaviour are performed in a characteristically playful manner (what that might mean will be discussed later). But equally often such behaviour is performed with the greatest possible degree of efficiency for whatever level of development the animal is at *at that point*. Thus, a kitten can and often does chase bits of paper and string and so on in a playful manner; but it may equally well deal with them in a way that would have meant instant death to a mouse. In the same way, a fight between young chimpanzees may be quite as seriously intended as one between two adults, but the effects are obviously less drastic. It is a mistake, therefore, to regard as play all chase behaviour by a kitten, either because it is a kitten or because the pursued object is inedible; and the same principle holds for all young animals.

Nevertheless it is a widely held view that the animal that plays–or practises–will become more expert, and thereby have a selective advantage over the animal that does not (Groos, 1898). None of this is to deny that practise or rehearsal of many forms of behaviour is likely to improve the efficiency with which they are performed in adult life. But it has yet to be shown that it is the *playful* execution of these particular patterns in infancy or childhood that is crucial to their later perfection, as opposed to their *serious* execution at whatever level of maturity at which the animal is then operating. Quite simply, it is not necessary to play in order to practise: there is no reason why the animal should not just practise. Certainly social interactions involving play within the peer group in rhesus monkeys have been shown by Harlow (1962) to be crucial for the full development of adult social behaviour. But the precise role of each of play's component parts–vision, smell, sound, physical contact, movement and any combination of these factors–has yet to be isolated and defined.

As well as this, to regard play as practise for adult function does not account for the fact that adults as well as infants play in most mammalian species in which play occurs at all. They may certainly play less, but they still play. The fact that they play does not of course prevent the same behaviour in infants from serving as preparation of some kind; but as an explanation of function this must be enlarged to account for the persistence of, for example, play-wrestling in the adult cat.

The same objection is offered to the other major theory of the function of play; that it provides the animal with a constant stream of vital information about every feature of the environment with which it comes into contact. Again, it is simply not necessary to play in order to learn about the environment. The animal could explore as in fact some mammals that do not appear to play certainly do; for example, the rat. Of course it is inevitable that during play an animal will be gaining additional knowledge about what or who it is playing with, but if this is the major function of play one must wonder why the animal does not use a more economical way of getting hold of this information.

The earliest attempt to account for the causation of play, especially as seen in the young, suggested that it represented the release or overflowing of abundant energy which had no other immediate outlet. A modern parallel to this theory is that of "vacuum" activity, which occurs when a particular response has not been released for some time, and eventually occurs in the apparently total absence of any specific releasing stimulus. However, there are clear motoric differences between playful and vacuum activity, which led Lorenz (1956) to propose a distinction between them.

Tolman suggested that under certain conditions men and lower animals have a need to redress a state of physiological imbalance produced by the presence of abundant energy by achieving a complementary state of mild fatigue. Beach (1945), however, considered this to be simply a "variation . . . in modern dress" of the surplus energy hypothesis. He points out that interpretation of the energy expended in a particular action as surplus simply depends on whether you consider the behaviour under observation to be playfully, or otherwise motivated. In any case, as Groos (1898) pointed out, young animals can be seen to lie panting and exhausted after a bout of play and suddenly resume the game with apparently equal vigour. Although play is most likely to occur when the animal is not exhausted, so also is non-playful activity. So again, although energy may be a necessary condition for play, it has not been shown to be sufficient.

Play has sometimes been accounted for by stating that it is "fun" (Bierens de Haan, 1952), "expresses a joy of living" (Pycraft, 1912), "is enjoyed purely for its own sake" (Tinkelpaugh, 1942), or, more recently, is "self-rewarding activity" (Morris, 1962). Bolwig (1963) describes the motivating condition for play as one of joy and goes on to describe joy as a condition which motivates increased activity. "Postures of aggression and retreat never become complete, and non-aggressive movements are frequently exaggerated. In other words, joy is a condition which induces play actions." All these statements may at the moment be the most useful shorthand way we have of describing the apparent effect of accompanying certain motor patterns; but their use as an explanation of that same behaviour is unjustified and not at all useful.

However, before causation and function can be discussed to any great effect, it is necessary to consider the actual behaviour that is going to be classed as play. One of its immediately noticeable characteristics is that it is behaviour that adopts for its purposes patterns that appear in other contexts where they achieve immediate and obvious ends. When these patterns appear in play they seem to be divorced from their original motivation and are qualitatively distinct from the same patterns appearing in their originally motivated contexts. Lorenz (1956) points out that although in play fighting movements occur which are only seen at the peak of intensity in a serious fight, the next moment the animal demonstrates that such specific motivation is lacking by switching to behaviour seen in defensive or grooming, or other unrelated situations. Thus a *reordering* of the original sequence is one way in which play differs from the source of its motor patterns. All the other ways in which it differs are of economy, or degree; and it is here that we come back to a statement made earlier, about the fundamental similarity to the observer between human and animal play. This similarity lies in the exaggerated and uneconomical quality of the motor patterns involved. Regardless of its motivation or its end-product, this is what all playful activity has in common; and it is possible that it is all that it has in common, since causation and function could vary from species to species. Beach puts this more strongly: ". . . no single hypothesis can be formulated to explain all forms of play in every animal species".

These are some of the ways in which motor patterns may be altered and elaborated upon when transferred to a playful context.

1. The sequence may be *reordered*.
2. The individual movements making up the sequence may become *exaggerated*.
3. Certain movements within the sequence may be *repeated* more than they would usually be.

4. The sequence may be broken off altogether by the introduction of irrelevant activities, and resumed later. This could be called *fragmentation.*
5. Movements may be both *exaggerated and repeated.*
6. Individual movements within the sequence may never be completed, and this incomplete element may be repeated many times. This applies equally to both the beginning of a movement (the *intention element*) and to its ending (the *completion element*).

In every case, during play, the performance of the movements from which the play is derived is uneconomical, and therefore would be inefficient in terms of the original motivating context. It might, of course, be possible to consider that it is the exaggerated movements of play that are refined and economized, and used in chasing, wrestling, biting, jumping, chewing and so on, instead of the reverse process. However, since the patterns of aggression and defense occur in the phylogenetic scale long before unequivocal behaviour makes its appearance, it seems fair to assume that the "original" context–in this case at any rate–is that of aggression. Aggression is also of course more basic to survival. The same is true of most other motor patterns that are employed in play: investigation of objects occurs both phylogenetically and for purposes other than play. It follows that just as patterns of fight, flight, sexual and eating behaviour and so on are species-specific, so will the play behaviour making use of these same patterns be species-specific.

One final point remains to be made. It is clear that the motor differences between a pattern used in play and the same pattern occurring in its original context are not exclusive to play. Ritualized behaviour shares many of the characteristics described as typical of play; and social play clearly contains a strong element of ritualization. Morris (1956a) quotes the following examples of some of the ways in which basic patterns can be modified–or ritualized–to form signals: (a) threshold lowering; (b) development of rhythmic repetition; (c) differential exaggeration of components; (d) omission of components; (e) change in sequence of components; (f) changes in component co-ordination; (g) increases or decrease in speed of performance; (h) change in vigour of movements.

Although Morris (1956b) has shown that the sequence of events in a highly ritualized piece of behaviour such as the stickleback's courtship dance is not nearly as rigid as it was once considered to be, it is suggested that the most likely area in which the precise differences between play and other forms of ritualized behaviour will be isolated is that of relative rigidity in the ordering of the sequence. It may be that play has no formalized sequence of events, such that action A will always be followed by actions B, C or D. In play, depending upon the feedback from the object or the social partner, A may be followed with equal likelihood by B or by Z; anyway by a far greater range of responses than are seen in other forms of ritualized behaviour. In short, it is suggested that in play the number of combinations or permutations of the available motor patterns is greater than in almost any other form of behaviour.

Research on play at the London Zoo is now concerned with precise analysis and comparison of the motor patterns involved with the same motor patterns occurring in their originally motivated contexts. It is hoped that this may help to answer the above questions, and to disentangle the essential qualities that make much play instantly recognizable to professional and casual observers alike.

REFERENCES

Altmann, S. A. (1962). Social behavior of anthropoid primates: analysis of recent concepts. *In* "Roots of Behavior" (E. L. Bliss, ed.), pp. 277-286. Harper & Bros., New York.

Beach, A. F. (1945). Current concepts of play in animals. *Am. Nat.* **79**, 523-541.

Bierens de Haan. (1952). The play of a young solitary chimpanzee. *Behaviour* **4**, 144-156.

Bolwig, N. (1963). Facial expression in primates. *Behaviour* **22**, 167-192.

Breder, C. M. (1932). On the habits and development of certain Atlantic Synentognathi. *Pap. Tortugas Lab.* **28** (1), 1-35.

Brownlee, A. (1954). Play in domestic cattle in Britain: an analysis of its nature. *Br. vet. J.* **110**, 46-68.

Groos, K. (1898). "The Play of Animals." Chapman and Hall, London.

Harlow, H. H. and Harlow, M. K. (1962). Social deprivation in monkeys. *Sci. Am.* **207**, 136-146.

Lorenz, K. Z. (1956). Plays and vacuum activity in animals. *In* "Symposium. L'Instinct dans le comportement des animaux et de l'homme," pp. 633-645. Masson, Paris.

Mitchell, P. C. (1912). "The Childhood of Animals." Frederick A. Stokes, New York.

Morris, D. (1956a). "Typical intensity" and its relation to the problem of ritualization. *Behaviour* **11**, 1-12.
Morris, D. (1956b). The function and causation of courtship ceremonies in animals (with special reference to fish). *In* "Symposium. L'Instinct dans le comportement des animaux et de l'homme," pp. 261-286. Masson, Paris.
Morris, D. (1962). "The Biology of Art," pp. 144. Methuen, London.
Morris, D. (1964). The response of animals to a restricted environment. *Symp. zool. Soc. Lond.* No. 13, 99-118.
Pycraft, W. P. (1912). "The Infancy of Animals." Hutchinson, London.
Schiller, P. H. (1957). Innate motor action as a basis of learning manipulative patterns in the chimpanzee. *In* "Instinctive Behaviour" (C. H. Schiller, ed.), pp. 264-287. International Universities Press, New York.
Tembrock, G. (1960). Spielverhalten und vergleichende Ethologie. Beobachtungen zum Spiel von *Alopex lagopus. Z. Saugetierk.* **25**, 1-14.
Tinkelpaugh, O. L. (1942). *In* "Comparative Psychology," 2nd ed. (F. A. Moss, ed.). Prentice-Hall, New York.

Neurobehavioral Development and the Genotype-Environment Interaction

M. W. FOX

ABSTRACT

Several research areas, notably those of psychology, physiology, and ethology, are reviewed in order to construct an interdisciplinary picture of problems and concepts pertaining to neurobehavioral development. Genetic factors, pre- and post-natal experiences and environmental influences which may affect ontogeny and modify the behavioral phenotype are reviewed. Development is considered as a series or continuum of genotype-environment interactions, and the effects of self-stimulation, experiential deprivation, enrichment, and "handling" are discussed. Ontogenetic phenomena, such as heterochronous patterning, induction and canalization, socialization, exploration and motivation, and the relationship between ontogeny and phylogeny of behavior are detailed to expose the dynamic and intrinsic complexities of neurobehavioral development and of the genotype-environment interaction.

INTRODUCTION

The intention of this paper is to consider some major issues in developmental neurobiology, namely, the role played by stimulus-independent and stimulus-dependent processes in the development of the nervous system and of behavior, and the complexities and ramifications of genotype-environment interactions.

From *The Quarterly Review of Biology*, 1970, 45, 131-147. Reprinted by permission.

As early as 1895 Roux (cited by Riesen, 1966) recognized two phases in the development of the central nervous system (CNS): an initial period of intrinsic growth and self differentiation which is followed by a period of growth *dependent upon* functional activity. Similarly Thorpe (1964), in reviewing ethological studies, stated that maturation precedes practice and learning. It is not clear, however, whether experience or "exercise" is essential for a given neural system or behavior pattern to be functional or overtly manifest. For example, Cruze (1935) showed that pecking accuracy in chicks improved after hatching as a result of *both* maturation and experience, experience prior to final maturation thereby being demonstrated contrary to Thorpe's assertion. Spalding (1873) raised swallows in cages that prevented wing-movements. Despite this treatment they apparently flew as well as controls; experience prior to final maturation therefore was not essential for the development of the neural system controlling the pattern of flight behavior. Conclusions somewhat similar to those of Cruze were drawn by Fox, Inman, and Glisson (1968) in studying the effects of visual deprivation on the structural and functional development of the visual cortex of the dog; although development was retarded by such treatment, neuronal development and myelinization were relatively well advanced in the visual cortex. Thus, some degree of maturation, independent of exercise or stimulation, had occurred. Comparable effects were found after bilateral enucleation (see also Riesen, 1966). The possibility of non-specific afferent connections from the reticular formation providing some form of endogenous stimulation to a visual cortex deprived of exogenous stimulation (by blindfolding or removal of the eyes) cannot be ruled out. Bioelectric activity in the form of evoked potentials is clearly present in the visual cortex following auditory stimulation in blinded dogs.

Crain, Bornstein, and Peterson (1968) have shown that in vitro development of nervous tissue is unaffected by blocking agents such as curare; the normal ontogeny of bioelectric activity proceeds at the normal rate. Such findings are reminiscent of Carmichael's (1927) observations that salamander larvae anesthetized during early ontogeny were later able to swim as well as controls when the drug (chloretone) was withdrawn.

Self-stimulation, via proprioceptive feedback following a single movement or during continuous activity in embryos, may have an important function, not in organizing fixed action patterns, but in insuring normal musculo-skeletal development. This feedback probably develops some time after spontaneous motility is observed, at the time when reflexive or evoked activity can be elicited by light (cutaneous) or deeper (proprioceptive) external stimulation of the embryo. From this phase of effector-affector integration at the segmental level of the spinal cord, subsequent integration occurs at higher levels of the developing and integrating nervous system until complex coordinated action patterns emerge (Sedlacek et al., 1961), and individuation (Humphrey, 1964) and inhibition (Tuge, 1961) of relevant and non-relevant components develop. Hamburger (1963) has discussed the possible role of these phenomena in the embryogenesis of activity in the chick. Experiments in his laboratory (Hamburger et al., 1965; Hamburger, Wenger, and Oppenheim, 1966) have shown that spontaneous activity develops prior to evoked activity, even in isolated segments of the locomotor system, and that around the 17th day of incubation a diffuse integrative phenomenon involving the entire nervous system occurs, much in the same way as shown by Fox (1966) in nonprecocial mammals after birth.

Held and Hein (1963) have conclusively demonstrated that deprivation of all non-visual feedback or reafferent "experiences" in kittens severely disrupts their later visually guided exploratory behavior. Reafferentation and associations within and between different modalities may therefore play an important role in the organization and acquisition (learning) of more complex activities in later life. Rats blinded early in life perform poorly on a spatial auditory discrimination task compared to those that have had prior visual experiences (Spigelman and Bryden, 1967) and yet, paradoxically, rats blinded early in life perform better on a simple auditory discrimination than those blinded later in life.

EXPERIENTIAL DEPRIVATION

It is often difficult to separate the roles of maturation processes and experiential influences in the development of a particular neural system or behavior pattern. The isolation or deprivation experiment is a useful technique (see Lorenz, 1965), although "non-specific" effects such as excessive arousal on emergence from isolation (Fox, 1967) may be misleading and even produce paradoxical effects;

Lindsley et al. (1964) found that dark-raised monkeys responded to a light being turned on in the same way that normal monkeys respond when a light is turned off. Excessive arousal in dogs emerging from isolation interferes with their problem-solving ability (Fox and Stelzner, 1966) and with their ability to perceive or respond appropriately to painful stimuli (Melzack and Scott, 1957). Other "non-specific" effects, which may contaminate attempts to investigate a given sensory system or behavior pattern, include masking or repression of certain response patterns due to lack of stimulation or reinforcement; these patterns may simply disappear or "mature out" or become linked with an abnormal stimulus or releaser. Kovach and Kling (1967), for example, found that kittens raised by stomach tube were later unable to nurse from the mother, a clearly demonstrated "interference" phenomenon. Also, because of the deprivation treatment, the animal may adapt and show some ontogenetic shift or change in development–immature patterns such as contactual circling and rooting response in pups (Fox and Stelzner, 1967) or new, often bizarre, patterns may even develop (e.g., stereotypies–Fox, 1966).

Isolation may not only disrupt maturation of a particular neural system (or behavior pattern), but may also impair the structuro-functional integration of one system or action pattern with others. For example, Held and Bauer (1967) and Hein and Held (1967) have shown that placing a collar around the neck of a newborn monkey or neonate kitten to prevent the animal from seeing its forelimbs prevents the development and integration of eye-forelimb associations so that visually guided movements of the forelimbs are absent when the collar is first removed. Piaget (Piaget and Inhelder, 1969), Gesell (1945), and others have also emphasized the subtle integration of hand and arm movements with head movements in the human infant, and subsequent integration of a "hand-eye" schema which controls visually guided reaching.

EXPERIENTIAL ENRICHMENT AND "HANDLING"

In contrast to the isolation or deprivation experiment, the enrichment and handling techniques have provided some insights into the neuro-ontogeny of behavior. "Enrichment" may consist of uni- or multi-modality stimulation (Denenberg, 1964, 1968; Bennett et al.,

1964). Handling (essentially causing a transient lowering of body temperature in neonatal animals) and "gentling" (petting) in somewhat older animals result in dramatic changes in neuro-endocrine systems, in CNS development, and in subsequent behavior (Morton, 1968). The optimum or sensitive periods for such treatment may lie within discrete periods of integration–of the adrenal with the pituitary and of the gonads with the pituitary in early life (Levine and Mullins, 1966); of the sensory and motor systems (Hein and Held, 1967) and of the sensory cortical analyzers, association areas, and limbic regions in later life (Hebb, 1949; Bronson, 1965).

One of the most remarkable ontogenetic findings is that early experience (handling or stressing in early life, i.e., indirect neuro-endocrine influences, or direct neuro-endocrine influences by hormonal injection or removal of a particular endocrine gland) may result in profound changes in later behavior. The early effects apparently set or "tune" the developing neuro-endocrine system (Levine and Mullins, 1966) so that in later life, the threshold and duration of emotional and stress reactions and temporal patterning of certain behavior patterns (e.g., sexual) are altered.

External stimuli to which an organism is exposed early in life (and which the organism is mature enough to perceive even if it cannot respond) may sensitize the organism to respond appropriately and preferentially to the same or to a similar stimulus in later life (as in imprinting and sexual selection) or effect a type of latent or exposure learning (Gibson and Gibson, 1955). Gottlieb (1968) has shown how the external auditory stimuli provided by the avian mother to the embryo within the shell during the last few days of incubation may result in auditory imprinting. This effect may be facilitated by some degree of selective auditory perception for conspecific vocalizations (i.e., perceptual filter mechanism–Marler, 1961). These handling effects may be transmitted across generations (= non-genetic transmission of information–Denenberg and Rosenberg, 1967; Ressler, 1966) and are phylo-ontogenetically akin to acculturation; the genotype, however, must be susceptible to such effects (Joffe, 1965; Levine and Broadhurst, 1963). Such non-genetic transmission of the effects of handling the pregnant rat on her offspring have been conclusively demonstrated by cross-fostering them onto non-handled mothers, breeding them, and comparing subsequent offspring with those of control subjects. Postnatal effects are also of significance in the perpetuation and dissemination of environmental influences on behavior and emotional reactivity via mother-infant, infant-mother, and infant-infant interactions. Such interacting variables do constitute a severe methodological problem, and hand-raising in isolation incubators (which in itself can introduce many variables outlined earlier) may be necessary.

ONTOGENETIC SEQUENCES: HETEROCHRONOUS MATURATION

A number of behavior patterns (and underlying neural systems) are already fully formed at birth in various species. Varying degrees of practice or conditioning may be required to lock or shape the action pattern to a particular stimulus or releaser (as in bottle and breast feeding in the human infant). Hailman (1967) has elegantly studied such processes in the ontogeny of the bill-oriented pecking response of gull-chicks to the parent. Once this "locking" has occurred, a change of stimulus (e.g., switch from breast to bottle) may temporarily or permanently disrupt the release of the original pattern (e.g., "frustration" reactions in the human infant). Piaget (see Flavell, 1963; Piaget and Inhelder, 1969) has discussed such phenomena in the human infant in terms of accommodation and assimilation, and more complex learning phenomena associated with centration and decentration. In order to perceive and process new information, the infant progresses through several cognitive stages of development. According to Piaget, perception and processing improves as a consequence of two processes, namely, accommodation and assimilation, or the restructuring of existing conceptual schemata as new schemas are constructed. Between these stages of development are periods of stability or centration at which times accommodation and assimilation are purportedly limited; training therefore has little influence on development until decentration occurs (Flavell, 1963). Such concepts are in close accord with those of developmental psychobiologists who recognize ontogenetic shifts to new patterns and ontogenetic limitations in the degree of plasticity and adaptability at any given age. Tinbergen (1968) has discussed these processes from the ethologist's view in terms of conceptual models or schemata, templates, or "sollwertes," where schema may be built upon schema during ontogeny, along lines similar to Piaget's. Klopfer and Hailman (1967) stress that in certian behavior patterns in which a stimulus perference is evident at birth, experience has little effect in modifying the response; if, however, the initial preference is more general, rapid conditioning takes place (as in food-pecking preferences in gull chicks–Hailman, 1967). A number of "preformed" (ethologically innate or genetically programmed) patterns can be elicited at birth; only recently have the underlying structural-functional relationship of the CNS been studied in some instances (Anokhin, 1964). The presence of precociously matured patterns (such as the food-locating responses in non-precocial mammals–Fox, 1966) reflects the evolutionary selection processes that insure that the organism will be able to adapt to its particular environmental niche at birth (Fig. 1). Such phylogenetically programmed patterns which "presuppose" what the environmental requirements will be at birth (Anokhin, 1964), or in Schneirla's terminology, represent an environmental-situational structuring of genetically programmed development, may undergo limited ontogenetic change postnatally and then subsequently "mature out," disappearing from the animal's repertoire or becoming integrated with later emerging patterns. Stimulus specificity is often remarkable and may in some cases be due to selective heterochronous maturation of the CNS, and/or to prenatal conditioning or exposure learning (as in species-preferences for vocalizations in birds–Anokhin, 1964; Gottlieb, 1968).

One phenomenon of behavioral maturation, which as yet has received little rigorous investigation, is the patterning or sequencing of various stages of development: the emergence and subsequent regression, submergence, or integration of early action patterns (such as rooting and thigmotactic and thermotactic approach) with patterns emerging later (such as visually guided approach); and of neonatal contactual and care-soliciting (brood care) patterns with later intraspecific social behavior patterns. In some instances in spite of adequate reinforcement (i.e., little change in external releasers) a phylogetically pre-fixed ontogenetic shift occurs; sucking, for example, gives way to lapping and chewing. If, however, such reinforcement is suboptimal, the ontogenetic shift (to a new pattern) may occur earlier. Pups fed by stomach tube can be weaned onto solid food much earlier than those still sucking on the mother

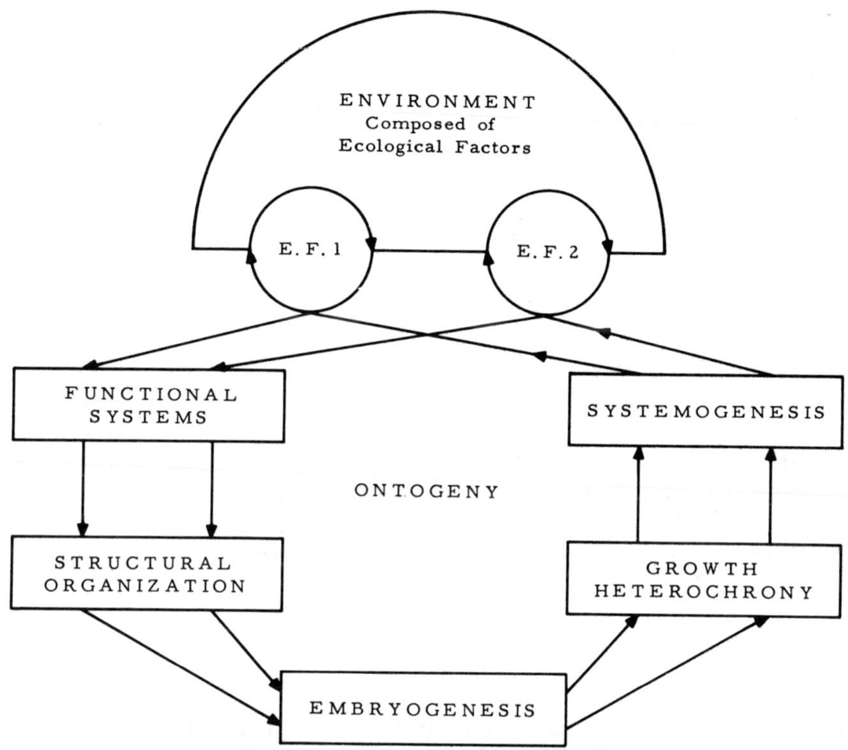

Fig. 1. Relation of systemogenesis in evolutionary development of functional adaptation to environment. E. F. 1 and E. F. 2 represent ecological factors in the environment (after Anokhin, 1964).

(personal observations). Frequently the ontogenetic shift is not due entirely to maturation but to a change in the stimulus-releasing qualities; alternative stimulation may be sought (meat is preferred to milk in a carnivore at the time of natural weaning). In social situations, the earlier patterns may be inhibited: for example, the mother dog begins to punish the infants when they attempt to nurse. She no longer reflexively stimulates them to urinate, for they have now developed voluntary control and the pups now urinate and defecate together at a specific area outside the nest. A number of neonatal patterns apparently may "mature out" (reflexive urination, sucking) or become submerged or integrated with patterns developing later (inguinal contact inhibition; Fox, 1968b). The apparently lost neonatal pattern may reappear in later life in two forms: (1) when neural inhibition by higher CNS structures is lost, as in pathological reappearance of such patterns with lesions of these inhibitory structures (Paulson and Gottlieb, 1968); or (2) as submissive and appeasement gestures having the effect of remotivating an aggressor (Schenkel, 1967) during agonistic encounters and in courtship in many mammals and birds.

An intriguing characteristic of some action patterns–notably the survival-promoting neonatal responses associated with food location and ingestion, avoidance of pain and maintenance of body temperature–is that at birth they are well developed and are characterized by a high degree of stereotypy and are difficult to fatigue or habituate (Wells, 1958). Their response threshold, however, shifts in accordance with the state of the animal–be it hungry or satiated–and as such they represent a distinct class of neonatal behavior patterns that have some characteristics of simple reflexes and can similarly be subsequently integrated into more complex behavior patterns and persist throughout adult life.

INDUCTION AND CANALIZATION

It is possible that a process akin to embryonic tissue and organ induction occurs in neuro-behavioral ontogeny. At genetically predetermined periods in ontogeny, the maturation of one system triggers the development of another (or "tunes" it as in the gonadal setting of the hypothalamus) and eventually these systems become integrated. Their integration may then provide the induction stimulus for the development of further systems (or components of a behavior pattern, see Fig. 2). Thus an ontogenetic progression of reciprocally interwoven components emerges in accordance with the changing life history and adaptation requirements of the organism. The sudden onset or appearance of a particular response pattern implies such a process, where the integration of now-maturated components provides the necessary induction for the appearance of a new response pattern. The timing of such events in the organism's life history may be synchronized with environmental influences and so represent critical periods, according to Scott (1962) and King (1968). The fact that these genetically predetermined events occur at

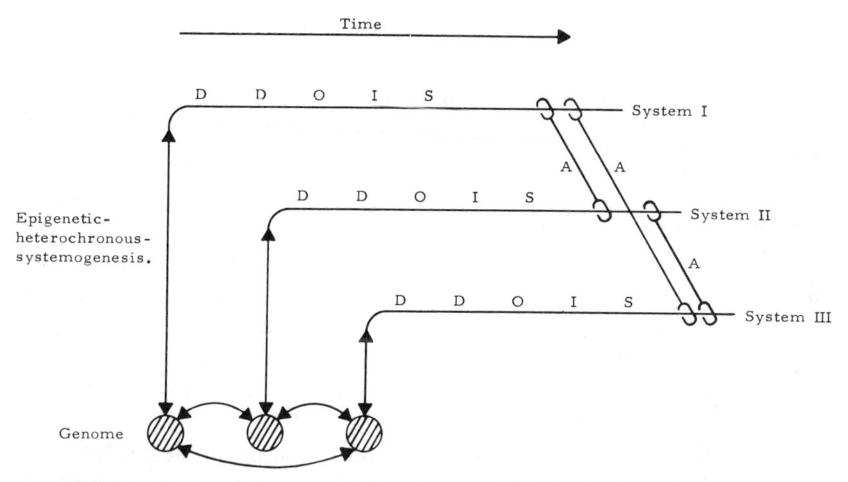

Fig. 2. Ontogeny in three hypothetical neural systems showing their heterochronous rates of maturation. The appearance of new responses or perceptual and cognitive abilities late in development may be due to delayed maturation of one system or of associations between systems. The rate and timing of development through integration of components within a system and its subsequent specialization may occur at a specific time in the animal's life cycle in accordance with socio-ecological conditions (i.e., canalization and critical period; see discussion). The letters D, D, O, S, and A represent sequential ontogenetic processes of development, differentiation, organization, integration, specialization, and association.

a time when optimal environmental influences are in effect, suggests that systemogenesis is structured in accordance with the environment or the situation (Anokhin, 1964); King (1968) appropriately describes this as a canalization phenomenon. He relates the process of phenotypic "buffering" to critical period phenomena and states:

> The degree of this buffering of a developmental pathway or the degree of canalization varies for each character. Some behavior characters are more canalized than others, and we tend to group them under such categories as taxes or instincts. Along this continuum, other characters show varying degrees of vulnerability to genetic and environmental modification. Often thresholds occur, which may be symmetrical or asymmetrical. If they are symmetrical, too little stimulation in infancy could have the same effect as too much stimulation, while within certain ranges, variations in stimulation would have no appreciable effect (p. 58).

The ontogeny of bird song (reviewed in Marler and Hamilton, 1966; and by Thorpe, 1961) presents numerous phenomena which may be operating in other systems of behavior. Not only does the auditory system of *adults* of some species show a selective sensitivity or preference for conspecific audio-frequency (Anokhin, 1964), but *young birds* show a selection preference for the conspecific song. Although some species develop relatively normal song patterns following auditory deafferentation (Konishi, 1963, 1965), auditory feedback while singing is essential for other species. Exposure to conspecific song early in life, prior to the onset of singing in the chaffinch, for example, provides sufficient experience (i.e., without exercise or in the absence of actual singing) for normal song patterns to develop. This period of sensitivity prior to the onset of singing may be restricted to a critical period, and in some species, selectivity or preference for conspecific song may also be operating as a result of either perceptual filtering (selective auditory reception) or ecological or social factors. This latter point (socio-ecological "filtering") is exemplified by the young male bullfinch, which by virtue of the proximity of its father, acquires its species specific song, but if raised experimentally by a foster-species, will instead develop the foster species' song. Such mimetic learning is seen in many parasitic birds which acquire the song of the host early in life, while other parasitic species, such as the European cuckoo, in contrast remain "resistant" as fledglings and retain their own species song. Thus, a complex interaction between an innate susceptibility (which provides the basis for the elaboration of a song template and which in turn facilitates the development of a species-typical song pattern), environmental influences in the form of exposure learning, feedback stimulation (reafferentation) while singing, and acculturation or acquisition of a "local dialect" can occur in some species (Marler and Tamura, 1964) while other avian species show a lesser dependence upon such interacting ontogenetic influences.

SOCIALIZATION, FILIAL ATTACHMENTS AND EXPLORATION

The age at which an organism develops sufficient sensory and motor abilities to interact more fully with its socio-environmental milieu, represents an important critical period (Scott, 1962; Fox, 1966).

This may occur slightly before hatching or birth in precocial reptiles, birds, or mammals, or after a more prolonged period of postnatal development in non-precocial species.

Scott (1962) observes:

> Both growth and behavioral differentiation are based on organized processes. This suggests a general principle of organization: that once a system becomes organized, whether it is the cells of the embryo that are multiplying and differentiating, or the behavior patterns of a young animal that are becoming organized through learning, it becomes progressively more difficult to reorganize the system. That is, organization inhibits reorganization. Further, organization can be strongly modified only when active processes of organization are going on, and this accounts for critical periods of development (p. 957).

King (1968) has also emphasized this point and states:

> A critical period is that period in development during which the probability of a behavior pattern being emitted and the probability of it being reinforced by the environment are greatest. . . . Complexity is added by the fact that many responses develop simultaneously, interact and reinforce each other, and at the same time the environment provides a spectrum of stimuli and reinforcers. This complexity results in a population of probability curves for both the behavior and the reinforcers (p. 62).

Raising in isolation or with an alien species may drastically modify filial relationships and social preferences in non-precocial birds and mammals (Fox and Stelzner, 1967; Klinghammer, 1967). The neurological events underlying the onset of this critical period of socialization have been studied extensively in the domesticated dog (Fox, 1970). The first signs of neocortical myelinization in the primary (sensory) cortical areas, a relatively mature EEG (Fox, 1967), and auditory and visual evoked potentials are detectable (Fox, 1968a) towards the fourth postnatal week. Neurologically, and in terms of neocortical neuronal and spinal cord development the organism attains maturity at this time (Fox, 1964; Fox, Inman, and Himwich, 1966, 1967). Subsequently, myelinization of the major association areas occurs (Fox, 1967). Thus, in accordance with Hebb's (1949) hypothesis, the critical period for socialization as defined by Scott (1962) also includes a critical phase for learning (akin to imprinting in precocial species) and for exploration of the environment. During this time, when sensory-sensory and sensory-motor associations are formed, histological studies reveal that the major association areas of the neocortex are undergoing myelinization as would be predicted on the basis of Hebb's hypothesis.

One fundamental difference between precocial and non-precocial animals is that the latter, having a more protracted infancy, are generally more exploratory or neophilic. Those organisms having the most highly evolved CNS are confined primarily to the non-precocial group and in accordance with Hebb's hypothesis, have a higher ratio of association cortex to primary sensory cortex than do other animals. What makes such young organisms so exploratory early in life? Possibly a lack of internal inhibition (cf. the immaturity of the frontal lobes–Luria, 1961) and lower arousal threshold, together with a short attention span (thus negating stimulus fixations) may insure that the organism will randomly and repeatedly investigate its environment. Also habituation is slow, so that novel stimuli will evoke repeated interactions. Indeed this lack of habituation and internal inhibition may give the advantage to the young organism over the adult in certain problem solving situations (Vince, 1961).

In the absence of exogenous stimulation, endogenous or interneural activity, in the form of spontaneous coded impulses, may facilitate the establishment of genetically determined neural circuits, prior to their activation by or involvement with external stimuli. These problems have been discussed by Hamburger (1963) and Decker and Hamburger (1967) in regard to the functional role of spontaneous motility in the chick embryo and by Roffwarg, Muzio, and Dement (1966) in relation to the importance of activated or REM sleep in the fetus and neonate. The spontaneous motility observed in mammalian and avian embryos in the absence of exogenous stimulation is a phenomenon which probably has more to do with integrating structure and function at different levels of the peripheral and central nervous system, than with specific action patterns in the animal's behavior repertoire. Similarly we may postulate that the predisposition of young animals to manipulate, explore, and play with novel exogenous stimuli, and with conspecifics, may have an organizing function in determining the subsequent stimulus preferences, response thresholds, and temporal patterning of behavior. The organism experiences (or exposes itself to) an optimal level of stimulation in concordance with its arousal level or motivational need to explore and manipulate. This will be considered subsequently in terms of perceptual-motor homeostasis and the effects of increments or decrements of experience during ontogeny. This initial predisposition to respond to qualitative (Oppenheim, 1968) or quantitative (Schneirla, 1965) aspects of the environment may result in immediate reinforcement (contact comfort, food reward, arousal of parasympathetic and de-arousal of sympathetic systems) or in some type of experience early in life which will subsequently influence the development of S-R relationships. Such relationships established early in life may contribute immeasurably to the subsequent organization of behavior, including imprinting and socialization processes and stimulus preferences in terms of food (Burghardt and Hess, 1966), mate (Klinghammer, 1967), and even habitat (Wecker, 1963; Klopfer and Hailman, 1965).

One highly significant ontogenetic finding is that prior exploratory (or social) experiences facilitate subsequent exploratory and social interactions (Sackett, 1965; Fox and Spencer, 1969). Animals denied or given restricted opportunities during early life manifest preferences and response intensities which reflect their prior experiences. Thus an isolation-raised animal has a marked preference for a relatively barren, asocial environment. Sackett (1965) postulated a process of paced increments of environmental complexity; thus an organism receiving little experience or input early in life will subsequently show a preference for low input or minimal complexity. It is intriguing that animals raised under varying degrees of complexity tend to select out and to interact socially with conspecifics having been raised under similar conditions (Sackett, 1968). Fuller (1967) concluded that the mass fear response of isolation-raised dogs which is seen on emergence from isolation represents an "overload" effect. Without perceptual filtering to block out irrelevant from relevant stimuli (on the basis of prior experience) the organism avoids contact and withdraws into its isolation quarters. These reactions imply a behavioral regulation of cortical input, i.e., a perceptual homeostasis. Thompson and Heron (1954), on the other hand, thought that their isolation-raised dogs behaved like immature animals, in that they showed a high interaction frequency with various novel stimuli. Thus, without prior associations, their behavior was adapted to provide them with input and information (as in an immature, but normally raised animal). The fear response and withdrawal observed by Fuller could be the result of reactive inhibition (as a result of the particular breed-genotype studied) which blocked exploration in spite of a high level of arousal or central excitation. Krushinski (1962) has also shown that genotype-environment interactions can influence the effects of isolation rearing; innately more timid dogs are more fearful on emergence from isolation. These breed differences in mature dogs emerging from isolation suggest that the nervous typology (active and passive defensive behavior–Krushinski, 1962) in part influences the direction of effect that early experience will have. Thus, an isolation-raised "outgoing" type would tend to behave like a normal but younger dog on emergence into a novel environment; it would explore intensively, in contrast to the brief exploration characteristic of adults (Fuller and Clark, 1968; Fox and Spencer, 1969).

With similar experiences during early life (or with programmed life histories), young organisms are, to some extent, behaviorally similar, but differences between individuals appear with increasing age. The early similarities of the direction, rate, and patterning of development in a given species imply a common genotype-environment interaction, so that phenotypically, some uniformity is evident. Individual differences within a given species in the absence of contributory environmental or experiential differences are indicative of genetic peculiarities attributable to sex or a greater range of heterozygosity within a given population. In the Pavlovial sense, the emergence of individual differences later in life represents individuation of nervous typology as a consequence of concatenated genotype-environmental interactions or the effect of experience coupled with later occurring (genetically programmed) developmental changes in brain and behavior, such as the onset of mature sexual activity, courtship patterns, recognition of another's territory and defense of one's own, and care of young. Behavioral or emotional differences between individuals may be minimized if subjects are raised in an enriched, amenable environment and given paced increments of experience (i.e., environmental buffering of the genotype). For example, an innately timid dog if carefully handled and gradually exposed to stimuli of increasing novelty and complexity during early life may develop some adaptation and compensate to some extent for its inherited susceptibility to over-react to novel stimuli.

This buffering effect closely parallels Mayr's (1963) notion of phenotypic uniformity, as a result of homologous environmental influences; the genotype is "buffered." In contrast, experiential deprivation does not allow such a "buffering" effect, so that on behavioral characteristics, animals of different nervous typology or genotype, and so deprived, can be more readily identified. However, a dramatic alteration in the environment of *normally* raised dogs, can facilitate the identification of different innate characteristics, and such manipulations are used in Pavlovian studies to evaluate the individual nervous typology of experimental animals.

The fact that innately "out-going" isolation-raised dogs (i.e., having little internal inhibition) resemble immature dogs points up an interesting ontogenetic phenomenon—that of reactive inhibition or fearfulness of the strange or unfamiliar. In young organisms, parasympathetic-approach processes predominate, but with increasing age sympathetic-withdrawal processes emerge (Schneirla, 1965). Similarly, in conditioning, positive conditional reflexes can be elaborated prior to negative conditional responses (Volokhov, 1959). It would appear that this reactive inhibition, which normally develops at a set time within the critical period of socialization, is minimal in young organisms; such lack of internal inhibition therefore facilitates exploration early in life, and attachments to conspecifics. The later appearing "fear period" also tends to consolidate earlier established socio-emotional attachments. The perseverance and generalization of fearfulness (or of reactive inhibition) may be determined primarily by the genotype, genotype-environment interactions having differential effects in organisms exposed to the same environment but having different genotypes. In precocial animals, the onset of this period is more abrupt and heralds the termination of the period of imprintability; in the human infant it appears at around 9 months of age and in the dog at 8 weeks of age (Fox and Stelzner, 1967).

ONTOGENETIC AND PHYLOGENETIC INTER-RELATIONSHIPS

In the present discussion, phylogenetic factors influencing development are interpreted as being the gene complex or genome which has been acquired through the evolutionary processes of selection and mutation, and which provides the blueprint for neuro-behavioral development. Ontogenetic factors, both intrinsic and extrinsic, play an integral role in development; the effects of the more recently acquired genes (in Mayr's terminology, see later) or those genes affecting ontogeny later in life may be more susceptible to exogenous environmental influences acting on the epigenetic system (see also Waddington, 1961) than those genes which influence development earlier in ontogeny. These genes, or rather the effects of such genes that come into play late in development, are regarded in this discussion as the intrinsic or endogenous ontogenetic factors which may be affected by extrinsic environmental influences. The time of onset of their effects may be delayed, as with the onset of sexual activity at the time of puberty, for example (although some earlier "hormonostat" setting in neonatal life, part of a complex epigenetic sequence, occurs in some rodent species–Levine and Mullins, 1966). Environmental influences, such as stress or handling (Morton, 1968), may influence the onset of sexual activity, while more precise timing may be triggered by endogenous circadian or cyclic activity with or without an external stimulus such as sunlight (Marler and Hamilton, 1966).

Roux's two phases of CNS development (an early period of intrinsic growth and self-differentiation, followed by a period of growth dependent upon functional activity) can now be equated with the early phylogenetically regulated phase of development and the later ontogenetic phase, where endogenous and exogenous influences act to mold development (see also Skinner, 1966). So we speak of early "plasticity" and "adaptability" of both the nervous system (Tucker and Kling, 1967) and of behavior (Kovach and Kling, 1967) operating *in addition* to phylogenetically more fixed programming which has been selected through evolution, and which contributes to the species-specificity of brain and behavior development. The later sequences of ontogeny may be more variable between individuals of the same species, and between different strains (or subspecies) of the same species (King, 1968). The interrelationships between ontogeny and phylogeny (Fig. 3) are such that phylogeny regulates ontogeny, but ontogeny may subsequently modify phylogeny, as emphasized by Garstang (1921) who states that "ontogeny not only recapitulates phylogeny, but also creates it." Ontogeny also determines what is experienced at a given age or

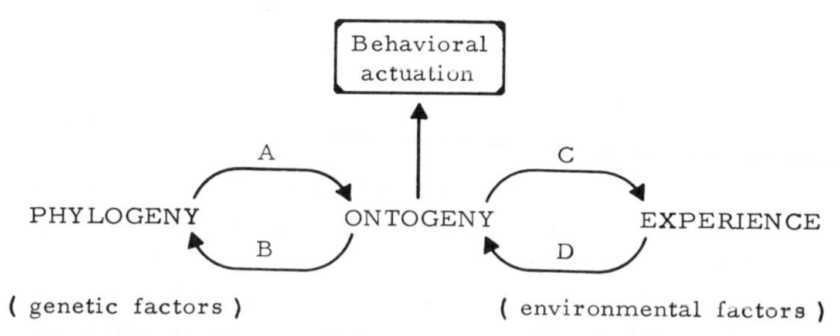

Fig. 3. Interrelationships between genetic and environmental factors. Through reciprocal interaction, genetic and environmental factors can influence ontogeny. Ontogeny, in turn, can influence phylogeny via selection (B) as a result of environmental influences (D). These interactions result in behavioral actuation, or the expression of the overt behavior phenotype. A, phylogeny influences ontogeny: selection, adaptation, situation structuring; B, ontogeny influences phylogeny: selection, adaptation; C, ontogeny influences type of environmental experiences (e.g., too immature to perceive; also critical periods); D, experience influences ontogeny: may accelerate, disrupt, reorganize; also endocrine effects via handling.

what environmental influences can affect the developing organism. It may be too immature to respond to visual or auditory stimuli but can perceive thermal, tactile, and olfactory stimuli, which may later influence stimulus preferences and the type of reaction in later life. For example, the neonate rat perceives, or at least responds to, changes in body temperature as a result of handling (Morton, 1968), and such reactions can have profound effects on development and subsequent behavior and neuro-endocrine responses. Rats exposed to odors early in life show later a sexual and social preference for conspecifics sharing the same odor (Marr and Gardner, 1965). Receptor-effector limitations at a particular stage of ontogeny may act as a type of filter in regulating what the animal experiences (or can perceive and respond to) at a given age; thereby fashioning an umwelt (perceptual environment) which changes qualitatively and quantitatively as the organism's perceptual, emotional, and motor capacities mature.

We must not lose sight of the fact, however, that many fixed action patterns, such as those associated with sexual behavior, can be elicited by "non-specific" stimuli or induced by hormones prior to puberty in many animals (e.g., Andrew, 1966). With maturity, these fixed action

> patterns are subsequently organized into temporal sequences within a specific motivational context, in relation to more specific stimuli or releasers.

Stimulus preferences, response specificity, and generalization emerge as a result of genetic and experiential influences. Experience may modify ontogeny, and the various modifications possible have been reviewed earlier in this paper. Through these interrelationships, it becomes clear how environmental influences operate in the development of organisms, and how complex are the factors which contribute to the expression or actuation of behavior (Fig. 3).

The CNS does not simply develop in a straight caudo-cephalad progression; heterochronous patterning of ontogeny is seen, in accordance with the phylogenetic program of development which anticipates the adaptive needs of the organism in relation to its environment. CNS development anterior to the posterior commissure is caudo-cephalad (Yakovlev and Lecours, 1967; Fox, unpubl., 1970), at which level different myelinization cycles in the limbic, association cortex, and hypothalamic regions can be identified. Development caudal to the posterior commissure follows the general embryogenic cephalo-caudal direction of maturation. This phenomenon in part accounts for the profound effects that early experiences may have on subsequent behavior. This is because development and integration of later maturing neural structures are more extensively affected by influences early on in development, than by similar influences later in life after these structures are mature and integrated. Bronson (1965; Fig. 4) has discussed the relationship between the level of CNS development at a given age and the type of experiential influences (handling, social attachments, and environmental complexity or enrichment) that can literally "get through" and affect the organism (i.e., critical or sensitive periods). Three major periods can be identified, namely an initial period when the developing neuroendocrine system can be influenced (Levine and Mullins, 1966), an intermediate period when emotional and social reactions can be modified (Scott, 1962), and a later period when learning abilities can be affected by exposing the animal to an experientially enriched or deprived environment (Bennett et al., 1964). It should be added that there are more dramatic repercussions as a result of manipulations earlier in life than later in life. For

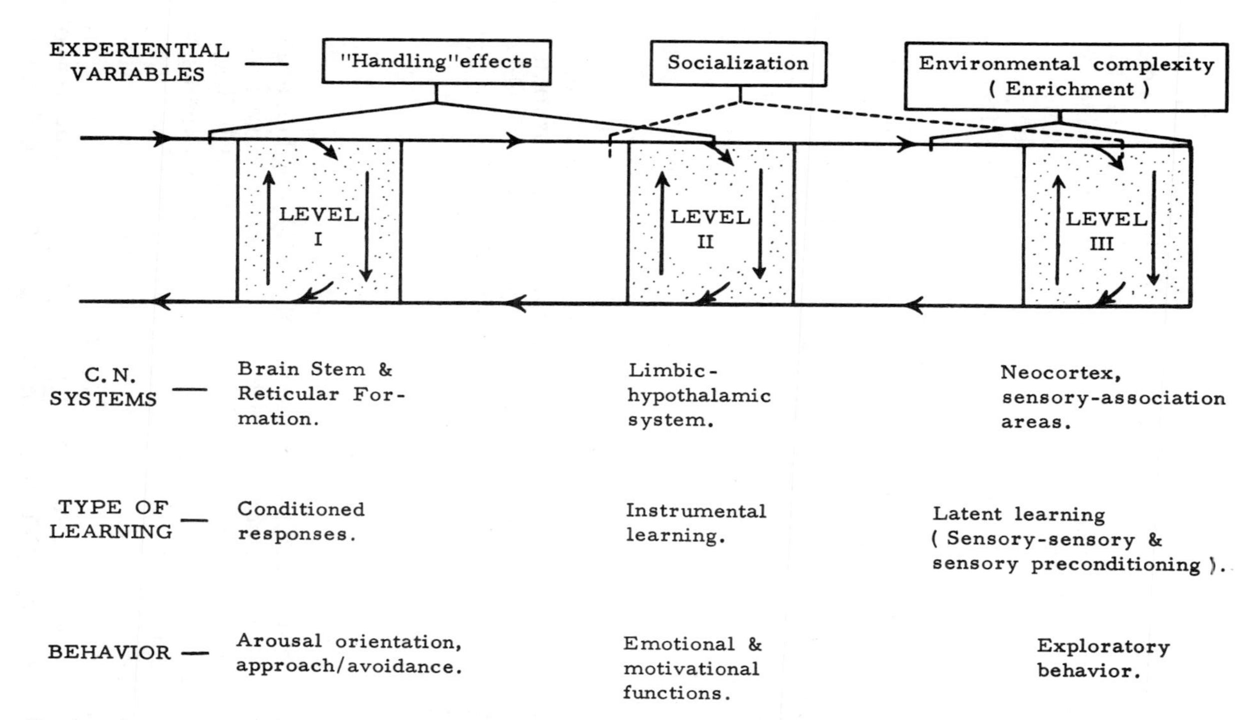

Fig. 4. Ontogenetic integration of CNS. As the CNS develops, the integrative process at various levels can be correlated with the type of learning and behavior possible, and the experiential variables that can affect development (after Bronson, 1965).

example, handling influences emotionality which in turn influences learning abilities (Morton, 1968).

In apparent contradiction of the fact that experimentally induced disruptions in the normal sequence of ontogeny have a more profound effect if instigated early in ontogeny instead of later, it has been shown that CNS lesions may be compensated for if made early in life (Tucker and Kling, 1967). This phenomenon of plasticity of the developing brain in early life may be due to synaptic reorganization which is possible prior to maturation and integration of cortico-subcortical and cortico-cortical connections.

Mayr (1963) postulated that the degree of modification of the phenotype is in itself genetically controlled and that phenotypic stability (and uniformity) in spite of great genetic variability is brought about by developmental flexibility (so that the gene pool is protected or "buffered" from selection processes). Mayr also suggests that the longer a gene is part of the genotype, the more completely it becomes part of the epigenetic system and the earlier its pleiotropic effects will play a role in ontogeny. Hirsch (1963) has emphasized the important role played by meiosis of gametes, which results in the individual being endowed with unique gene combinations from the parents. However, ontogenetic patterns follow a strikingly similar sequence in different individuals of the same species, which could be explained in terms of Waddington's developmental canalization or Mayr's hypothesis of the recency of the gene being incorporated into the genotype and the time in development when its pleiotropic effects operate.

CONCLUSIONS

Altman (1966) distinguishes three models of neural programming or patterning of behavior which have been discussed in this paper: (1) fixed morphogenetic programming which occurs without individual experience and is, in general, impervious to alterations by experience; (2) modifiable epigenetic programming, which consists of essentially inborn components but which also necessitates individual experience for its proper realization; and (3) acquired transactional programming in which new schemata of behavior are formed on the basis of individual experience, with minimal employment of inborn elements.

In these three models we see varying increments of environmental influence on the genotype which emphasizes the point that species uniformity is not necessarily entirely genetically determined but is also influenced by the socio-environmental milieu and the type of ecology (and cultural influences in man).

The various processes associated with development and subsequent attainment of mature structure and function reviewed in this paper, present a complex picture (Fig. 5). Future research will reveal more precisely the chronological sequences of development, the interaction between different neural and endocrine systems, and the existence of sensitive and critical periods when environmental factors can influence structuro-functional integration.

> Sensitive and critical periods may be differentiated on the grounds that experiences during a critical period are essential for further development while during a sensitive period experiences may influence ontogeny but are not necessarily essential for further development.

Such information will provide us with a deeper understanding of evolutionary (phylogenetic) and ontogenetic processes (genotype-environment interactions to produce the phenotype). We may also come to know the potentials and limitations of genotype-environmental interactions during development and how much or how varied stimulation at different ages should be to promote optimal conditions for development within the genetic capacities of the organism. We may argue that there is little point in studying the development of animal forms lower than the highest primates, because man is evolving almost independent of biological inheritance by transmission of non-genetic information (or acculturation) from one generation to the next. This phenomenon certainly accounts for our accelerating evolution, but this evolution is based upon phylogeny and ontogeny. It is to our advantage, therefore, to study ontogenetic and phylogenetic processes in lower forms where basic biological phenomena common to many species can be identified and experimentally manipulated independent of acculturation. It may also enable us to shape and improve our own development for, as emphasized by Teilhard de Chardin, education in its broadest sense represents biological accumulation, and heredity represents an information-transfer process shaped by prior environmental influences, where the cultural milieu acts as a mold or matrix for development.

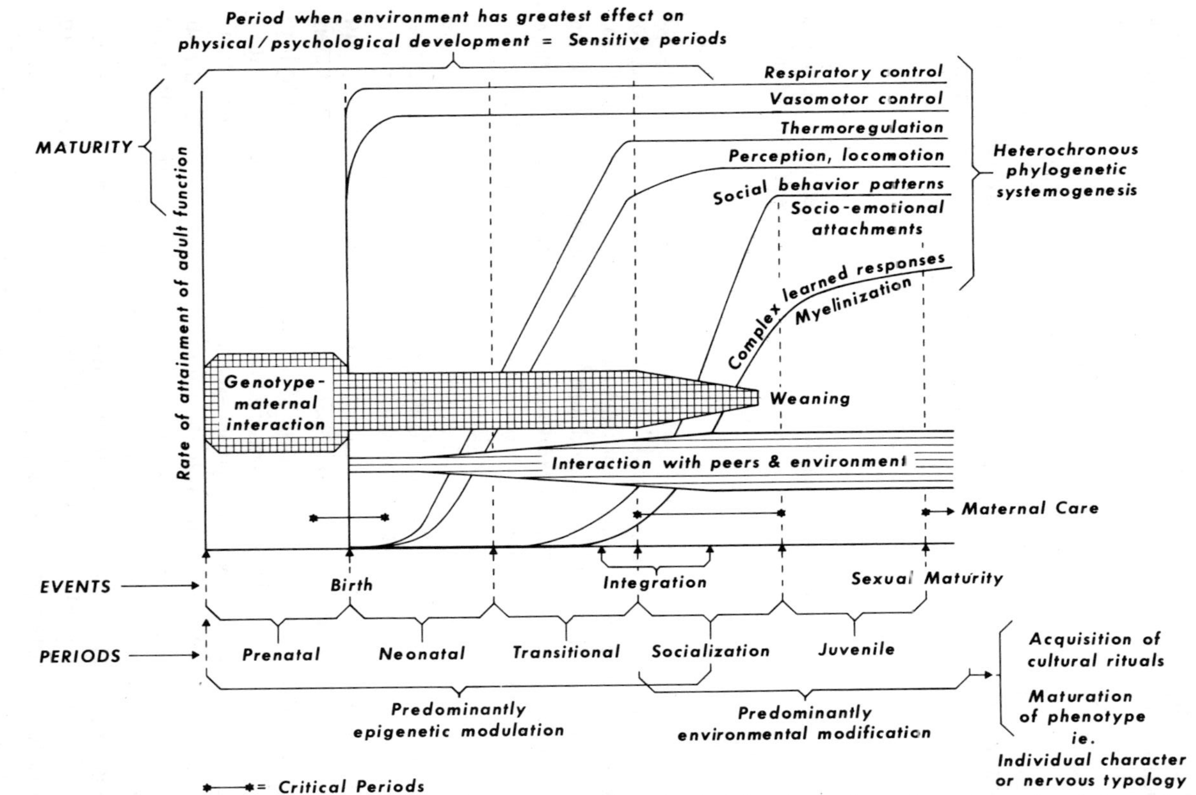

Fig. 5. Schema of developmental phenomena in a non-precocial animal. This schema shows the ontogenetic relations of various developmental phenomena: sensitive periods (Denenberg, 1968), critical periods and socialization (Scott, 1962), epigenetic modulation (Waddington, 1961), integration period (Fox, unpubl.; 1970), heterochronous phylogenetic systemogenesis (Anokhin, 1964).

SUMMARY

Studies concerned with neuro-behavioral ontogeny in various species are reviewed and an attempt is made to bring together the concepts of several disciplines to provide a framework for future studies in this field.

Several variables which may influence the ontogeny of behavior and of the nervous system have been reviewed under the general concept of genotype-environment interaction. Distinction is made between precocial and non-precocial animals, namely those which are mature or immature at birth, for their degree of maturity to some extent determines what they can experience (or perceive) both qualitatively and quantitatively, how they can respond, and to what extent experiences can influence subsequent development. Experience, either prenatal or postnatal, includes such factors as endogenous stimuli or self-stimulation, handling, and experimental manipulation of the neuro-endocrine system; and in later life, qualitative and quantitative differences in environmental complexity, and experiences afforded through play, exploration and socialization. These various categories of experience are discussed in relation to the continuum of genotype-environment interactions during various stages of ontogeny. Organization and integration of the nervous system and of action patterns into complex behavior patterns are effected by both genetic and experiential influences.

The degree of neural and behavioral development at a given age is in part determined by phylogenetic programming and by prior experiences, the latter being a function of what can be experienced or perceived and responded to. Experience at a given age may modify subsequent neural and behavioral development and consequently determines what the organism experiences or how it perceives and responds later in life. The direction, perseverance or degree of modification may also be determined by the genotype, the interaction of such variables until maturation or stabilization of the phenotype is discussed, and a multidisciplinary schema of neurobehavioral development constructed.

REFERENCES

Altman, J. 1966. *Organic Foundations of Animal Behavior*. Holt, Rinehart & Winston, New York.

Andrew, R. J. 1966. Precocious adult behavior in the young chicken. *Animal Behav*., 14: 485-500.

Anokhin, P. K. 1964. Systemogenesis as a general regulator of brain development. In W. A. Himwich and H. E. Himwich (eds.), *Progress in Brain Research, Vol. 9, The Developing Brain*, p. 55-86. Elsevier, Amsterdam.

Bennett, E. L., M. C. Diamond, M. R. Rosenzweig, and D. Krech. 1964. Chemical and anatomical plasticity of brain. *Science*, 146: 610-619.

Bronson, G. 1965. The hierarchical organization of the central nervous system: implications for learning processes and critical periods in early development. *Behavioral Science*, 10: 7-25.

Burghardt, G. M., and E. H. Hess. 1966. Food imprinting in the snapping turtle, *Chelydra serpentina. Science*, 151: 108-109.

Carmichael, L. 1927. A further study of development of behavior in vertebrates experimentally removed from the influence of external stimulation. *Psychol. Rev.*, 34: 34-47.

Crain, S. M., M. B. Bornstein, and E. R. Peterson. 1970. Development of functional organization in cultured fetal CNS tissues during chronic exposure to bioelectric blocking agents. In L. Jilek and S. Trojan (eds.), *Ontogenesis*, p. 19-25. Symposium Neuroontogeneticum, XII, Scientific Conference. Charles Univ. Press, Prague.

Cruze, W. W. 1935. Maturation and learning in chicks. *J. Comp. Psychol*., 19: 371-409.

Decker, J. D., and V. Hamburger. 1967. The influence of different brain regions on periodic motility of the chick embryo. *J. Exp. Zool*., 165: 371-384.

Denenberg, V. H. 1964. Critical periods. Stimulation input and emotional reactivity: a theory of infantile stimulation. *Psychol. Rev*., 71: 335-351.

__________ . 1968. A consideration of the usefulness of the critical period hypothesis as applied to the stimulation of rodents in infancy. In G. Newton and S. Levine (eds.), *Early Experience and Behavior*, p. 142-167. C. C Thomas, Springfield.

Denenberg, V. H., and K. M. Rosenberg. 1967. Nongenetic transmission of information. *Nature*, 216: 549.

Flavell, J. H. 1963. *The Developmental Psychology of Jean Piaget*. Van Nostrand, Princeton.

Fox, M. W. 1964. The ontogeny of behavior and neurologic responses in the dog. *Animal Behav*., 12: 301-310.

__________ . 1966. Neuro-behavioral ontogeny. A synthesis of ethological and neurophysiological concepts. *Brain Research*, 2: 3-20.

Fox, M. W. 1968a. Neuronal development and ontogeny of evoked potentials in the auditory and visual cortex of the dog. *Electroenceph. Clin. Neuro-physiol.*, 24: 213-226.

__________ . 1968b. Ontogeny of inguinal approach and presentation in canids and foxes. *Am. Zool.*, 2: 746. (Abstr. # 62)

__________ . 1970. *Integrative Development of Brain and Behavior*. Univ. Chicago Press.

Fox, M. W., and J. Spencer. 1960. Development of exploratory behaviour in the dog. *Develop. Psychobiol.*, 2: 68-74.

Fox, M. W., and D. Stelzner. 1966. Behavioural effects of differential early experience in the dog. *Animal Behav.*, 14: 273-281.

__________ , and __________ . 1967. The effects of early experience on the development of inter- and intra-species social relationships in the dog. *Animal Behav.*, 15: 377-386.

Fox, M. W., O. Inman, and S. Glisson. 1968. Age differences in central nervous effects of visual deprivation in the dog. *Develop. Psychobiol.*, 1: 48-54.

Fox, M. W., O. Inman, and W. A. Himwich. 1966. The postnatal development of neocortical neurons in the dog. *J. Comp. Neurol.*, 127: 199-206.

__________ , __________ , and __________ , 1967. The postnatal development of the spinal cord of the dog. *J. Comp. Neurol.*, 130: 233-240.

Fuller, J. L. 1967. Experiential deprivation and later behavior. *Science*, 158: 1645-1652.

Fuller, J. L., and L. D. Clark. 1968. Genotype and behavioral vulnerability to isolation in dogs. *J. Comp. Physiol. Psychol.*, 66: 151-156.

Garstang, W. 1921. The theory of recapitulation: A critical restatement of the biogenetic law. *J. Linnean Soc.*, London, 35: 81.

Gesell, A. 1945. *The Embryology of Behavior*, Harper, N.Y.

Gibson, J. J., and E. J. Gibson. 1955. Perceptual learning: differentiation or enrichment? *Psychol. Rev.*, 62: 32-41; 447-450.

Gottlieb, G. 1968. Prenatal behavior of birds. *Quart. Rev. Biol.*, 43: 148-174.

Hailman, J. P. 1967. *The Ontogeny of an Instinct*. E. Brill. Leiden.

Hamburger, V. H. 1963. Some aspects of the embryology of behavior. *Quart. Rev. Biol.*, 38: 342-365.

Hamburger, V., E. Wenger, and R. Oppenheim. 1966. Motility in the chick embryo in the absence of sensory input. *J. Exp. Zool.*, 162: 133-160.

Hamburger, V., M. Balaban, R. Oppenheim and E. Wenger. 1965. Periodic motility of normal and spinal chick embryos between 8 and 17 days of incubation. *J. Exp. Zool.*, 159: 1-14.

Hebb, D. O. 1949. *Organization of Behavior*. John Wiley, New York.

Hein, A., and R. Held. 1967. Dissociation of the visual placing response into elicited and guided components. *Science*, 158: 390-392.

Held, R., and A. Hein. 1963. Movement produced stimulation in the development of visually guided behavior. *J. Comp. Physiol. Psychol.*, 56: 872-876.

Held, R., and J. A. Bauer, Jr. 1967. Visually guided reaching in infant monkeys after restricted rearing. *Science*, 155: 718-720.

Hirsch, J. 1963. Behavior genetics and individuality understood. *Science*, 142: 1436-1442.

Humphrey, T. 1964. Some correlations between the appearance of human fetal reflexes and development of the nervous system. In D. P. Purpura and J. P. Schade (eds.), *Growth and Maturation of the Brain*, p. 93-136. Elsevier, N.Y.

Joffe, J. M. 1965. Genotype and prenatal and premating stress interact to affect adult behavior in rats. *Science*, 150: 1844.

King, J. A. 1968. Species specificity and early experience. In G. Newton and S. Levine (eds.), *Early Experience and Behavior*, p. 42-64. C. C Thomas, Springfield.

Klinghammer, E. 1967. Factors influencing choice of mate in altricial birds. In H. W. Stevenson, E. H. Hess, and H. L. Rheingold (eds.), *Early Behavior*, p. 5-42. John Wiley, New York.

Klopfer, P. H., and J. P. Hailman. 1965. Habitat selection in birds. In D. S. Lehrman, R. A. Hinde, and E. Shaw (eds.), *Advances in the Study of Behavior*, p. 279-303. Academic Press, New York.

———, and ———. 1967. *An Introduction to Animal Behavior. Ethology's First Century*. Prentice-Hall, Englewood Cliffs.

Konishi, M. 1963. The role of auditory feedback in the vocal behavior of the domestic fowl. *Z. Tierpsychol.*, 20: 349-367.

———. 1965. Effects of deafening on song development in American robins and blackheaded grossbeaks. *Z. Tierpsychol.*, 22: 584-599.

Kovach, J. K., and A. Kling. 1967. Mechanisms of neonate sucking behaviour in the kitten. *Animal Behav.*, 15: 91-101.

Krushinski, I. V. 1962. *Animal Behavior.* Consultant Bureau, New York.

Levine, S. and P. L. Broadhurst. 1963. Genetic and ontogenetic determinants of adult behavior in rats. *J. Comp. Physiol. Psychol.*, 56: 423-428.

Levine, S., and R. F. Mullins. 1966. Hormonal influences on brain organization in infant rats. *Science*, 152: 1585-1592.

Lindsley, D. B., R. H. Wendt, D. F. Lindsley, S. S. Fox, J. Howell, and W. R. Aday. 1964. Diurnal activity, behavior and EEG responses in visually deprived monkeys. *Ann. N.Y. Acad. Sci.*, 117: 564-587.

Lorenz, K. 1965. *Evolution and the Modification of Behavior*. Univ. of Chicago Press, Chicago.

Luria, A. R. 1961. *Speech and the Regulation of Behavior*. Pergamon Press, Oxford.

Marler, P. 1961. The filtering of external stimuli during instinctive behavior. In W. H. Thorpe and O. L. Zangwill (eds.), *Current Problems in Animal Behaviour*, p. 150-166. Cambridge Univ. Press, London.

Marler, P., and W. J. Hamilton III. 1966. *Mechanisms of Animal Behavior.* John Wiley, New York.

Marler, P., and M. Tamura. 1964. Culturally transmitted patterns of vocal behavior in sparrows. *Science*, 146: 1483-1486.

Marr, J. N., and L. E. Gardner, Jr. 1965. Early olfactory experience and later social behavior in the rat: preference, sexual responsiveness and care of young. *J. Genet. Psychol.*, 107: 167-174.

Mayr, E. 1963. *Animal Species and Evolution*. Harvard Univ. Press, Cambridge.

Melzack, R., and T. H. Scott. 1957. The effects of early experience on the response to pain. *J. Comp. Physiol. Psychol.*, 50: 155-161.

Morton, J. 1968. Effects of early experience on behavior. M. W. Fox (ed.), *Abnormal Behavior in Animals*, p. 261-292. W. B. Saunders, Philadelphia.

Oppenheim, R. 1968. Color preferences in the pecking response of newly hatched ducks. (*Anas platyrhynchos*). *J. Comp. Physiol. Psychol.*, 66 (Part 2): 1-17.

Paulson, G., and G. Gottlieb. 1968. Developmental reflexes: the reappearance of foetal and neonatal reflexes in aged patients. *Brain*, 91: 37-52.

Piaget, J., and B. Inhelder. 1969. *The Psychology of the Child*. Basic Books, N.Y.

Ressler, R. H. 1966. Inherited environmental influences on the operant behavior of mice. *J. Comp. Physiol. Psychol.*, 61: 264-267.

Riesen, A. H. 1966. Sensory deprivation. In E. Stellar and J. M. Sprague (eds.), *Progress in Physiological Psychology*, p. 117-147. Academic Press, New York.

Roffwarg, H. P., J. N. Muzio, and W. C. Dement. 1966. Ontogenetic development of the human sleep-dream cycle. *Science*, 152: 604-619.

Sackett, G. P. 1965. Effects of rearing conditions upon the behavior of Rhesus monkeys (*Macaca mulatta*). *Child Develop.*, 36: 855-868.

__________ . 1968. Abnormal behavior in laboratory-reared Rhesus monkeys. In M. W. Fox (ed.), *Abnormal Behavior in Animals*, p. 293-331. W. B. Saunders, Philadelphia.

Schenkel, R. 1967. Submission: its features and functions in the wolf and dog. *Am. Zool.*, 7: 319-330.

Schneirla, T. C. 1965. Aspects of stimulation and organization in approach/withdrawal processes underlying vertebrate behavioral development. In D. S. Lehrman, R. A. Hinde, and E. Shaw (eds.), *Advances in the Study of Animal Behavior*, Vol. 1, p. 1-74. Academic Press, New York.

Scott, J. P. 1962. Critical periods in behavioral development. *Science*, 138: 949-958.

Sedlacek, J., M. Svehlova, M. Sedlackova, J. Marsala, and J. Kapras. 1961. New results in the ontogenesis of reflex activity. In P. Sobotka (ed.), *Functional and Metabolic Development of the Central Nervous System*, p. 167-179. Charles Univ. Press, Prague.

Skinner, B. F. 1966. The phylogeny and ontogeny of behavior. *Science*, 153: 1205-1213.

Spalding, D. 1873. Instinct: with original observations on young animals. *Macmillan's Mag.*, 27: 282-293. [Reprinted in *Anim. Behav.*, 2: 1-11, 1954.]

Spigelman, M. N., and M. P. Bryden. 1967. Effects of early and late blindness on auditory spatial learning in the rat. *Neuropsychologia*, 5: 267-274.

Thompson, W. R., and W. Heron. 1954. Exploratory behavior in normal and restricted dogs. *J. Comp. Physiol. Psychol.*, 47: 77-82.

Thorpe, W. H. 1961. *Bird-Song.* University Press, Cambridge.

———. 1964. *Learning and Instinct in Animals.* Methuen & Co., London.

Tinbergen, N. 1968. On war and peace in animals and men. *Science*, 160: 1411-1418.

Tucker, T. J., and A. Kling. 1967. Differential effects of early and late lesions of frontal granular cortex in the monkey. *Brain Res.*, 5: 377-389.

Tuge, H. 1961. Comparative study of ontogenetic development of unconditioned and conditioned reflexes. In P. Sobotka (ed.), *Functional and Metabolic Development of the Central Nervous System*, p. 147-154. Charles Univ. Press, Prague.

Vince, M. A. 1961. Developmental changes in learning capacity. In W. H. Thorpe and O. L. Zangwill (eds.), *Current Problems in Animal Behavior*, p. 234-251. University Press, Cambridge.

Volokhov, A. A. 1959. Comparative-physiological investigation of conditioned and unconditioned reflexes during ontogeny. *J. Higher Nerv. Activity*, 9: 49-60.

Waddington, C. H. 1961. Genetic assimilation. In E. W. Caspari and J. M. Thoday (eds.), *Advances in Genetics*, 10: 257-293. Academic Press, New York.

Wecker, S. C. 1963. The role of early experience in habitat selection by the prairie deer mouse. *Ecol. Monogr.*, 33: 307-325.

Wells, M. J. 1958. Factors affecting reactions to *Mysis* by newly hatched *Sepia. Behaviour*, 13: 96-111.

Yakovlev, P. I. and R. A. Lecours. 1967. Myelogenetic cycles of regional maturation of the nervous system. In A. Minkowski (ed.), *International Conference on Regional Maturation of the Nervous System*, p. 1-42. Blackwell, London.

SUGGESTIONS FOR FURTHER READING

Aronson, L. R., Tobach, E., Lehrman, D. C., & Rosenblatt, J. S. (Eds.) *Development and evolution of behavior*. San Francisco: W. H. Freeman, 1970.

Bliss, E. L. (Ed.) *Roots of behavior*. New York: Hafner, 1968.

Denenberg, V. H. Critical periods, stimulus input, and emotional reactivity: A theory of infantile stimulation. *Psychology Review*, 1964, **71**, 335-351.

*Denenberg, V. H. The effects of early experience. In E. S. E. Hafez (Ed.), *The behaviour of domestic animals*. London: Balliere, 1969.

Fox, M. W. *Integrative development of brain and behavior in the dog*. Chicago: University of Chicago Press, 1971.

Glass, D. C. (Ed.) *Environmental influences*. New York: Rockefeller University Press, 1968.

Harlow, H. F. Development of affection in primates. In E. L. Bliss (Ed.), *Roots of behavior*. New York: Hafner, 1962. Pp. 157-166.

Harlow, H. F., & Harlow, M. K. Social deprivation in monkeys. *Scientific American*, 1962, **207**, 136-146.

Joffe, J. M. *Prenatal determinants of behaviour*. New York: Pergamon Press, 1969.

Newton, G., & Levine, S. (Eds.) *Early experience and behavior*. Springfield Ill.: C. C. Thomas, 1968.

*Scott, J. P. *Early experience and the organization of behavior*. Monterey, California: Brooks/Cole, 1968.

*Welker, W. I. An analysis of exploratory and play behavior in animals. In D. W. Fiske & S. R. Maddi (Eds.), *Functions of varied experience*. Homewood, Ill.: Dorsey Press, 1961. Pp. 175-226.

*Introductory reviews.

VI COMPARATIVE PSYCHOLOGY OF LEARNING

Thorpe in his book *Learning and Instinct in Animals* defines learning as a process that manifests itself by adaptive changes in individual behavior as a result of experience. Learning is therefore both a process and an adaptive function. He gives the following basic classification of different types of learning: *habituation*, *classical conditioning*, trial-and-error or *operant* (instrumental) *conditioning*, *latent learning*, *insight learning*, *imprinting* (discussed in the previous chapter). These various types of learning will be covered subsequently in the readings of Maier and Maier. Latent learning, however, receives scant attention; and little work has been done in this area. A well-fed rat, for example, will explore a maze and at a later time, when hungry, will run through the maze with greater accuracy to reach food at the end than another rat that has not had such prior exposure. The first experience in the maze, although not rewarding, did influence subsequent performance in the maze; hence the synonymous term to this phenomenon, *exposure learning*.

We can add *observational* (or imitative) *learning* to this list, a class of learning that again has not been extensively studied but is certainly one of the most common kinds of advanced learning for the acquisition of skills and of cultural traditions in the higher primates.

There have been numerous studies on learning in male laboratory rats and in invertebrates—planarians, cockroaches, and the like; but few studies have dealt with *comparative* aspects of learning.

A major problem in comparing the learning abilities of two or more different species lies in the fact that they may be "specialists," particularly adept in one learning task over another. A squirrel, for example, who hides nuts for the winter may be a better place-learner when reinforced by food than a rat. A rat, which by nature is skilled at learning its home range of complex runways, would perform better in a maze than a squirrel. Another central problem is one of motivation: Are the different species equally motivated under the same test conditions?

Maier and Maier (1970) point out many difficulties in learning studies. Increased running speed in a maze, for example, may not indicate learning if the animal makes more actual errors. The subject may respond to other cues, such as odor trails or kinesthetic cues in the maze, which catch the investigator unawares if he does not control for them. The laboratory setting may not be optimal for learning to take place; how closely does it match the subject's natural environment? Is the animal afraid and not sufficiently "shaped" to the test conditions? Are extraneous odors or high-frequency sounds affecting the study? Is the subject a nocturnal animal that would be best tested at night or in a simulated night-time environment? Is the experiment designed with regard to the subject's sensory abilities (albino rats, for example, perform poorly on visual problems)? Is the animal sufficiently motivated to perform? How many trials should be given and at what interval (since overtraining can cause interference with acquisition)?

One of the pioneers in the study of comparative learning abilities is M. E. Bitterman; his paper gives a good survey of the comparative approach in species such as earthworms, cockroaches, fish, turtles, pigeons, and rats. At a higher phylogenetic level, the reading by Warren focuses mainly on the learning abilities of various primate species and also of squirrels, raccoons, and cats; he also provides many examples of studies on other vertebrates, including fish, birds, and rodents.

In the first reading, from Maier and Maier, which provides a concise review of the various classes of learning, the section on learning in invertebrates has been omitted. For such information, and also for an excellent introduction to comparative animal behavior, the reader is referred to their text *Comparative Animal Behavior* (Monterey, California: Brooks/Cole, 1970).

This chapter should provide a useful link for the student who, in learning the techniques of the comparative psychologist, will also have the perspective of the ethologist from the earlier readings. In this way he may avoid one of the pitfalls of "behaviorism"; namely, of running a battery of learning or performance tests on an animal that he has never looked at in the ethological sense. The tests given might be totally inappropriate or inadequate for the species in question; and the actual attributes and skills of this species may be neither recognized nor tested by the investigator who never really looks at his animal.

Experience I: Learning

R. A. MAIER

B. M. MAIER

HABITUATION

Habituation can be defined as a developing tendency *not* to respond to certain stimuli that originally evoked some sort of a response. In other words, an animal exposed repeatedly to the same stimulus may lose sensitivity to it for a period of time. Habituation is an important factor in the conservation of an animal's time and energy, since it reduces the probability of false positive responses, i.e., making responses to stimuli that have no functional significance.

Habituation is similar in some respects to phenomena such as sensory adaptation and muscular fatigue. However, habituation lasts for relatively long periods of time (24 hours or more in some cases); sensory adaptation generally lasts only a few seconds. Habituation can be differentiated from muscular fatigue in that the habituated response decrement is specific only to a particular stimulus; decrement attributed to muscular fatigue occurs in response to a variety of stimuli.

Among bilaterally symmetrical invertebrates, habituation seems to be well established. The earthworm *Lumbricus* shows a diminution of responsiveness to both tactual and electrical stimuli. This appears to be true habituation, since these responses are independent; i.e., repeated stimulation by touch does not reduce sensitivity to electrical stimulation (both touch and electrical sensitivity are mediated by tactual receptors). The habituation is apparently not specific to the immediate area of stimulation; adjacent areas of the integument also show reduced responsiveness. The degree of loss in sensitivity is proportional to the distance from the habituated area of stimulation (Kuenzer, 1958).

Habituation may last for a relatively long period of time in some arthropods. Spiders (*Cyclosa*), which drop to the ground at the first vibrations from a tuning fork, gradually inhibit their response to this stimulus. Once habituation is well established, it may last for several days (Peckham & Peckham, 1887).

Toads seem to habituate to certain types of cues associated with feeding. If a visual stimulus (prey) is presented to a toad in the same area of the visual field but the toad is unable to obtain the prey, the turning movement of the toad's head toward the stimulus diminishes. However, the response quickly reappears if the toad is stimulated in another part of the visual field (Eikmanns, 1955).

Among certain birds, habituation seems to be involved in the differentiation of predators from friendly birds. Laboratory investigations indicate that ducklings give a crouching response to any object overhead. After a period of time, the response to objects seen frequently, e.g., leaves or friendly birds, habituates. On the other hand, hawks are seen infrequently and the response never habituates. Thus as the result of selective experience, the crouching response occurs in the presence of hawks but not in response to familiar, friendly birds (Melzack, Penick, & Beckett, 1959).

Habituation could prove nonadaptive if it occurred readily to all stimuli, including stimuli that occasionally signaled danger. In at least some cases, animals exhibit a resistance to habituation to such stimuli. For example, sparrows fail to habituate to an owl or a model of an owl; this failure occurs even in hand-reared varieties in which other experiential variables have apparently been controlled (Nice & ter Pelkwyk, 1941).

In mammals, emotional responses typically habituate after the animal has been repeatedly exposed to a certain type of stimulation. A laboratory rat placed in a small box freezes, urinates, and defecates excessively; after a period of time, these emotional responses significantly decrease.

At least in certain mammals, there seems to be habituation

within the nervous system. For example, if a cat is subjected to clicks repeated at intervals of 2 seconds, the clear burst of neural activity in its cochlear nucleus disappears after the first few presentations of the stimulus. The habituation seems to be specific to a particular frequency; other frequencies will evoke the initial burst of activity. A critical neural area for the habituation process appears to be the midbrain reticular system; cats with destruction of this system fail to habituate to the sound (Jouvet & Hernandez-Peon, 1957; Hernandez-Peon & Brust-Carmona, 1961).

CLASSICAL CONDITIONING

Classical conditioning involves a sort of stimulus substitution. A previously neutral stimulus, when paired several times with a stimulus that normally evokes a response, begins to elicit the response. For example, a piece of meat (an unconditioned stimulus) normally produces salivation in a dog. If a bell is sounded several times at the same time the meat is presented, the sound of the bell alone will soon evoke salivation. The bell is then said to have become a conditioned stimulus. Thus classical conditioning is a process of developing a conditioned response through association with an unconditioned stimulus. In the natural state, this type of learning may be involved in the development of sensitivity to cues associated with positive reinforcement (e.g., food) or aversion (e.g., unpleasant taste). A bird may try to eat an unpleasant-tasting butterfly. Soon the mere appearance of the butterfly evokes aversion.

Conditioning usually proceeds slowly, and, even when it has been well established, conditioned responses tend to occur somewhat inconsistently. Ordinarily, any stimulus that is well above threshold (but not too intense) may serve as a conditioned stimulus (CS). However, there are several limitations on the types of stimuli that may serve as the unconditioned stimulus (US). In the first place, a US must consistently elicit a response. Second, the US must not be subject to rapid adaptation or habituation. Third, a US seems to be most effective if it evokes a broad response (a response having several components). A US that evokes several autonomic responses is more effective than one that evokes a single, discrete response (Ratner & Denny, 1964).

When a CS is presented several times in the absence of a US

(which may be considered as a reinforcer), the conditioned response (CR) typically becomes weaker and, finally, fails to occur. This failure of the CR to be elicited by the CS is known as extinction. Although similar to habituation, extinction refers to the failure of a conditioned, or learned, response to occur; habituation refers to the failure of an unlearned response to occur.

Classical conditioning has been established in a large number of vertebrates (Thorpe, 1963; Yaremko, Boice, & Thompson, 1969). The characteristics of conditioning are basically similar in these animals, although different stimuli and responses have been utilized.

Many of the basic principles of conditioning were developed in conjunction with studies of salivation in the dog (Pavlov, 1927, 1928). In these studies, a phenomenon known as higher-order conditioning was identified. Higher-order conditioning involves a series of steps. First, a CR, such as salivation, is established to a CS, such as a bell (first-order conditioning). Second, a neutral stimulus, such as a light, is paired with the bell for a series of trials during which the US (food) is omitted; a salivary response that is evoked by the light alone is called a second-order conditioned response. Higher-order CRs would be established by pairing a neutral stimulus with a CS of the preceding order.

Using food as the US and salivation as the CR, it has not been possible to develop more than second-order conditioning. However, when shock is used as the US, and leg flexion as the CR, conditioning can be carried out to the fifth order (Finch & Culler, 1934).

Higher-order conditioning does not seem to be restricted to mammals; it has also been established (in an instrumental conditioning paradigm) with fish. Goldfish trained to respond to a disk (CS) for a food reward were able to learn to approach the disk when an olfactory CS (amylacetate) was presented (Sanders, 1940).

Many of the responses amenable to conditioning are autonomic responses that are not always directly observable. For example, fish (*Mugil*) show a progressive increase in respiratory rate when either a light or a tone is used as a US (Kellogg & Spanovick, 1953); similarly, changes in skin temperature of dogs can be conditioned to a metronome CS when shock is used as a US (Chambers & Fuller, 1958).

Conditioning can be established in very young vertebrates.

Monkeys between 2 and 14 days old can be conditioned to make avoidance movements to a tone paired with shock (Mason & Harlow, 1958). In some cases, conditioning can take place in an embryo; a leg-twitch response has been conditioned in an embryo chick as early as 7 days before hatching. This response may persist after hatching under optimal conditions, i.e., if the animal remains isolated in a dark environment (Hunt, 1949).

Finally, at least some types of conditioning can apparently be established in vertebrates without brains. Both frogs and dogs whose brains have been destroyed are able to establish certain conditioned responses (Rensch & Franzisket, 1954; Shurrager & Culler, 1940). Apparently, some conditioning can take place entirely in the spinal cord.

INSTRUMENTAL LEARNING

Instrumental learning refers to the development of responses that bring about some kind of reinforcement, e.g., a positive incentive or the removal of a negative stimulus. In the laboratory, these responses often consist of lever pressing or locomotion from one area to another. Instrumental learning differs from classical conditioning in that in the former the animal actively does something to bring about reinforcement, i.e., is instrumental in eliciting reinforcement; in classical conditioning, the animal is relatively passive, waiting, in essence, for the CS and the US to appear. However, there are obvious similarities between instrumental and classical conditioning. Notably, both seem to be dependent upon reinforcement for their development, and both tend to extinguish in the absence of reinforcements.

A great deal of research has been done on instrumental learning in vertebrates. Four topics have received particular attention: general comparative aspects of instrumental learning, the role of reinforcement, the role of RNA, and brain mechanisms related to instrumental learning.

The type of response that is easiest for an animal to learn is related to structural specializations and patterns of behavior in the natural state. For example, pecking responses are relatively easy to train in most birds, and manipulatory responses in most primates.

Even though it is structurally possible, it is extremely difficult to train birds to manipulate objects with their feet, or primates to make pecking-like movements with their jaws.

Sometimes, even after an instrumental response has been learned, basic unlearned patterns of behavior will interfere with the expression of this response. For example, pigs can easily learn to pick up large wooden coins and drop them in a large "piggy bank" for a food reward. But after a period of time (usually several weeks) the pigs begin to drop the coins, root them, pick them up, toss them into the air, root them again, and so on. It appears that the rooting behavior, characteristic of the unlearned feeding response, interferes with the learned response pattern (Breland & Breland, 1961).

Avoidance learning is often tested in a shuttle-box arrangement (a box with two compartments). A light or sound is presented a few seconds before the animal is shocked; in order to escape the shock, the animal must run (shuttle) into the next compartment. If the animal is faced with a uniformly colored shuttle box (e.g., all black) and must learn to escape by going first to one side and then the other, learning is relatively slow. However, if the compartments are distinctive and the animal always escapes by going to one side (a definite "safe" region), learning usually takes place in two or three trials (Denny, Koons, & Mason, 1959). The results of shuttle-box studies are quite similar for fish, toads, birds, and mammals (Behrend & Bitterman, 1963; Crawford & Langdon, 1966).

As noted earlier, animals may learn different things in the same avoidance experiment. For example, cats were placed in a box (one at a time) with a rat and shocked. In a test situation, some of the cats avoided the box, but not the rat; others avoided rats, but not the box; still others avoided neither a rat nor the box singly, but avoided the combination rat-in-a-box (Kuo, 1930).

When psychologists began to systematically study learning, it was generally assumed that there were relatively few reinforcers, e.g., food, water, and, on occasion, sex. However, it now appears that there are a very large number of variables that can serve as reinforcers for learning. The following are just some examples of these: the opportunity for male Siamese fighting fish to fight (Simpson, 1968); an area of high temperature for lizards (Vance, Richardson, & Goodrich, 1965); availability of sand for mice (King & Weisman, 1964); electrical brain stimulation for dolphins (Lilly & Miller,

1962); and an opportunity for monkeys to manipulate a puzzle (Butler, 1953).

Generally speaking, all reinforcers have the same effect–to increase the probability of the occurrence of a response. In most vertebrates, the magnitude of the reinforcement is not related to speed of learning; animals learn an instrumental response about as rapidly with a small reinforcement as with a large one. However, magnitude of reinforcement does seem to be related to speed of extinction. Thus goldfish that have been trained with a large reinforcement extinguish slower (show more resistance to extinction) than fish trained with a small reinforcement (Gonzalez & Bitterman, 1967). These results are predictable if it is assumed that strength of response (measured in terms of resistance to extinction) is related to magnitude of reinforcement.

In mammals, just the opposite kind of effect is found. Large reinforcers (over a period of 75 trials) tend to produce faster rates of extinction than small reinforcers (Armus, 1959). This finding can best be explained if it is assumed that large reinforcers create relatively large "expectancies." The failure of a large reinforcement to appear during the extinction trials has a greater contrast effect–in terms of the animal's expectancies–than the failure of a small reinforcement to appear; as a result, the animal stops responding sooner (Denny & Adelman, 1955).

Learning may occur even if a reinforcement is not given for each response (partial reinforcement). Some responses may be learned when the reinforcement ratio is 1:100 or less. A series of studies have compared the effects of partial reinforcement on various vertebrate groups. In fishes, partially reinforced responses extinguish faster than consistently reinforced responses (Wodinsky & Bierman, 1959, 1960). As in the paradigm involving magnitude of reward, this is predictable if it is assumed that strength of response is related to number of reinforcements.

In turtles, a clear-cut difference between extinction of partially and consistently reinforced responses is not found. There is no significant difference between extinction rates of partially and consistently reinforced animals (Eskin & Bitterman, 1961; Gonzalez & Bitterman, 1962).

Birds and mammals show an effect opposite to that of fishes: partially reinforced responses extinguish slower than consistently reinforced ones (Ratner & Denny, 1964). As in the experiments involving mammals' responses to magnitude of reward, the "expectancy" explanation seems to be appropriate.[1]

There are a number of studies involving instrumental learning in vertebrates that suggest that RNA is involved in the retention or memory of a response. For example, when goldfish were injected with puromycin—an antibiotic known to block RNA-mediated protein synthesis—within one hour after having learned an instrumental avoidance response in a shuttle box, they lost this response. However, fish that did not receive the injection, or received the injection more than an hour after the training sessions, retained the response. These findings suggest that RNA affects the fixation of a learned response (Agranoff & Davis, 1967).

There is also evidence that RNA is related to instrumental learning in rats. Animals treated with RNA derived from yeast learned an avoidance response more rapidly and retained it longer than untreated controls (Cook et al., 1963). Furthermore, animals injected with RNA extracted from the brains of other rats trained on an instrumental learning problem learned the problem faster than controls, i.e., rats injected with RNA from untrained rats (Babich et al., 1965).

A follow-up study suggests that the "transfer" effect is quite specific. One group of rats was trained on a problem involving an approach to a food cup, with a click serving as the discriminative stimulus; a second group was trained on an identical problem except that a flashing light served as the discriminative stimulus. RNA extracted from these groups was then injected into two test groups. The test group receiving RNA from the click-trained group tended to react to the click most readily; the test group receiving RNA from the light-trained group tended to respond to the light most readily (Jacobson et al., 1965).

In summary, there seems to be considerable support for the conclusion that RNA is related to memory in vertebrates (as well as planaria). However, it should be pointed out that other investigators have reported a failure to replicate some of these findings (Luttges et

[1] The differences between higher and lower animals in regard to the effects of partial reinforcement seem to appear consistently only among vertebrates. Some invertebrates fail to show the presumably primitive effects seen in fishes (Yaremko & Kimmel, 1969).

al., 1966). Therefore at least some of the conclusions should be regarded as tentative.

It is difficult to evaluate the role of the nervous system in instrumental learning. If, after brain lesions, an animal fails to learn a response or shows deficits of some kind, it may be due to some change in motivation, sensory capacity, or attention, and not a loss of learning capacity per se. Furthermore, destruction in one area of the brain may cause deficits in other areas, which remain unidentified. However, certain general conclusions seem justified. There appear to be several areas of the mammalian brain involved in instrumental conditioning–the frontal cortex, the thalamus, the hypothalamus, and the cingulate gyrus of the limbic system (Thompson, 1959; Doty et al., 1959; Thompson, 1963). In the limbic system, there seems to be a differentiation of areas that function in passive and active avoidance conditioning. For example, cats with anterior cingulate lesions are unable to learn passive avoidance responses, e.g., refraining from eating; cats with posterior cingulate lesions are unable to learn active avoidance responses, e.g., escape from a shuttle box (McCleary, 1961).

In conclusion, it appears that more neural areas are involved in instrumental learning than in classical conditioning. Furthermore, certain higher brain centers of mammals seem to have become associated with instrumental learning.

MAZE LEARNING

Maze learning may be considered as a special type of instrumental learning; an animal is required to go directly to a goal area that is not visible or apparent from the starting area. "Correct" responses are positively reinforced; "incorrect" responses may be either unrewarded or negatively reinforced. The simplest mazes have the shape of a *T* or *Y* and involve only one choice point. More choice points can be obtained by adding more *T*s or *Y*s. In the natural state, maze-learning ability is probably related to an ability to locate objects or landmarks.

In lower vertebrates, maze-learning ability is related to locomotion. For example, larval salamanders learn faster than adults, probably because the adults are more inert (Kuntz, 1923). Similarly, toads learn mazes faster than frogs; the slow, walking gait of toads appears to be more suitable for mazes than the frog's jumping pattern (Franz, 1927).

Among reptiles, turtles appear to be the most proficient at learning mazes. *Chelopus guttatus* was able to learn both a four- and six-blind maze (Yerkes, 1901). The slow, steady gait of the turtle is presumably advantageous for this type of task.

It is interesting to note that temperature is a factor of importance in the maze learning of certain reptiles. Thus the desert iguana (*Dipsosaurus dorsalis*) fails to learn a simple maze at 22°C but successfully learns it at 27°C and 32°C (Krekorian, Vance, & Richardson, 1968). Perhaps neural efficiency is reduced at suboptimal temperatures in these cold-blooded animals.

Bird maze learning is typically slow, but retention is often very good. For example, pigeons did not show any improvement in a six-blind maze until the sixtieth trial; however, retention was 100% after 6 weeks (Hunter, 1911). Slight variations in experimental procedure tend to interfere greatly with performance of birds in maze-type tasks (Diebschlag, 1940). It appears that, like arthropods, birds have difficulty generalizing what they have learned in a maze situation.

The behavior of mammals in mazes appears to be more flexible than that of birds or lower vertebrates. The typical mammal appears to make "vicarious trials," visually scanning alternatives at choice points (Tolman, 1932). Furthermore, in contrast to birds, mammals are relatively undisturbed by variations in experimental procedure. Finally, mammals such as rats seem to be capable of learning a maze by either attending to the location of the goal box in relation to other cues or by attending to the sequences of responses, e.g., going right, then left (see Figure 1). If there are prepotent extra-maze cues, e.g., distinctive, visual patterns or arrangements of lights in the room where the maze is located, the animal tends to learn the place of reward. On the other hand, if there are few extra-maze cues, i.e., white sheets hung all around that occlude visual cues, the animal relies on learning a series of responses (Gleitman, 1963).

Individual rats often have a preference for a particular kind of maze cue. For example, some rats consistently utilize proprioceptive cues, and others react primarily to visual cues. However, most

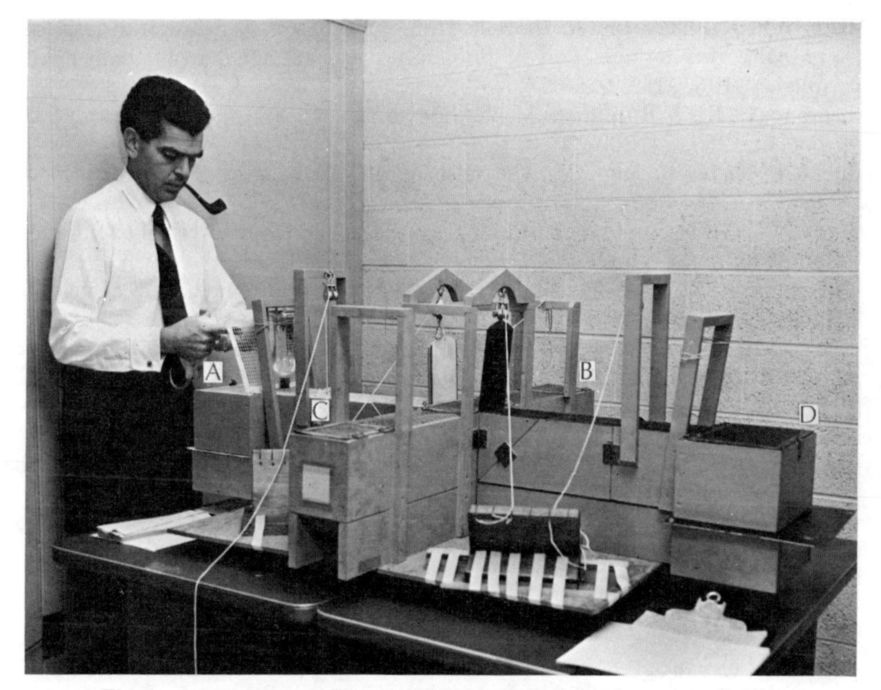

Fig. 1. A cross maze. The rat may be trained to go from *A* to *B*. If the rat is then started at *D*, a choice of *B* indicates that the rat picked a certain place; a choice of *C* indicates that the rat learned to turn left.

rats are able to respond to both sets of cues and shift from a visual to a spatial "hypothesis" or vice versa (Krechevsky, 1932). If one type of cue is eliminated, they apparently rely on the other. Thus rats that have had proprioceptive impulses eliminated by hemisections of the spinal cord can still learn mazes (Lashley & Ball, 1929; Ingebritzen, 1932).

REFERENCES

Agranoff, B. W., & Davis, R. E. Further studies on memory formation in the goldfish. *Science*, 1967, 158, 523.

Armus, H. L. Effect of magnitude of reinforcement on acquisition and extinction of a running response. *J. exp. Psychol.*, 1959, 58, 61-63.

Babich, F. R., Jacobson, A. L., Bubash, S., & Jacobson, A. Transfer of response to naive rats by injection of ribonucleic acid extracted from trained rats. *Science*, 1965, 149, 656-657.

Behrend, E. R., & Bitterman, M. W. Sidman avoidance in the fish. *J. exp. Anal. Behav*., 1963, 54, 700-703.

Breland, K., & Breland, M. The misbehavior of organisms. *Amer. Psychol.*, 1961, 16, 681-684.

Butler, R. A. Discrimination learning by rhesus monkeys to visual-exploration motivation. *J. Comp. physiol. Psychol.*, 1953, 46, 95-98.

Chambers, R. M., & Fuller, J. L. Conditioning of skin temperature changes in dogs. *J. comp. physiol. Psychol.*, 1958, 51, 223-226.

Cook, L., Davidson, A. B., Davis, D. J., Green, H., & Fellows, E. J. Ribonucleic acid: Effect on conditioned behavior in rats. *Science*, 1963, 141, 268-269.

Crawford, F. T., & Langdon, J. W. Escape and avoidance responding in the toad. *Psychonom. Sci.*, 1966, 6, 115-116.

Denny, M. R., & Adelman, H. M. Elicitation theory: I. An analysis of two typical learning situations. *Psychol. Rev*., 1955, 62, 290-296.

Denny, M. R., Koons, P. B., & Mason, J. E. Extinction of avoidance as a function of the escape situation. *J. comp. physiol. Psychol.*, 1959, 52, 212-214.

Diebschlag, E. Überden Lernvorgang bei der Haustaube. *Z. vergl. Physiol.*, 1940, 28, 67-104.

Doty, R. W., Beck, E. C., & Kooi, K. A. Effect of brain-stem lesions on conditioned responses of cats. *Exp. Neurol.*, 1959, 1, 360-385.

Eikmanns, K. H. Verhaltenphysiologische Untersuchungen über den Beutefang und das Bewegungssehen der Erdkröte. *Z. Tierpsychol.*, 1955, 12, 229-253.

Eskin, R. M., & Bitterman, M. E. Partial reinforcement in the turtle. *Quart. J. exp. Psychol.*, 1961, 13, 112-116.

Finch, G., & Culler, E. Higher order conditioning with constant motivation. *Amer. J. Psychol.*, 1934, 36, 596-602.

Franz, V. Zur tierpsychologischen Stellung von *Rana temporaria u. Bufo calamita. Biol. Zbl.*, 1927, 47, 1-12.

Gleitman, H. Place-learning. *Sci. Amer.*, 1963, 209 (4), 116-122.

Gonzalez, R. C., & Bitterman, M. E. Partial reinforcement effect in the goldfish as a function of amount of reward. *J. comp. physiol. Psychol.*, 1967, 64, 163-167.

Gonzalez, R. C., & Bitterman, M. E. A further study of partial reinforcement in the turtle. *Quart. J. exp. Psychol.*, 1962, 14, 109-112.

Hernandez-Peon, R., & Brust-Carmona, H. Functional role of subcortical structures in habituation and conditioning. In J. F. Delafresnaye (Ed.), *Brain mechanisms and learning*. Council for International Organ. of Medical Sciences Symp., Oxford, 1961. Pp. 393-412.

Hunt, F. L. Establishment of conditioned responses in chick embryos. *J. comp. physiol. Psychol.*, 1949, 42, 107-117.

Hunter, W. S. Some labyrinth habits of the domestic pigeon. *J. anim. Behav.*, 1911, 1, 278-304.

Ingebritsen, O. C. Maze learning after lesions of the spinal cord. *J. comp. Psychol.*, 1932, 14, 279-294.

Jacobson, A. L., Babich, F., Bubash, A., & Jacobson, A. Differential-approach tendencies produced by injection of RNA from trained rats. *Science*, 1965, 150, 636-637.

Jouvet, M., & Hernández-Péon, R. Mécanismes neurophysiologiques concernant l'habituation, l'attention et le conditionnement. *Electroenceph. clin. Neurol-physiol.*, 1957, 39, Suppl. 6.

Kellogg, W. N., & Spanovick, P. Respiratory changes during the conditioning of fish. *J. comp. physiol. Psychol.*, 1953, 46, 124-128.

King, J. A., & Weisman, R. G. Sand digging contingent upon bar pressing in deermice (*Peromyscus*). *Anim. Behav.*, 1964, 12, 446-450.

Krechevsky, I. "Hypotheses" versus "chance" in the pre-solution period in sensory discrimination learning. *Calif. U. Publ. Psychol.*, 1932, 6, 27-44.

Krekorian, C. O., Vance, V. J., & Richardson, A. M. Temperature-dependent maze learning in the desert iguana, *Dipsosaurus dorsalis. Anim. Behav.*, 1968, 16, 429-436.

Kuenzer, T. Zur physiologischer Untersuchungen über das Zuken des Regenwurms. *Z. Tierpsychol.*, 1958, 15, 31-49.

Kuntz, A. The learning of a simple maze by the larva of *Ambystoma tigrinum. Univ. Iowa Studies in Nat. Hist.*, 1923, 10, 27-35.

Kuo, Z. Y. The genesis of the cat's responses to the rat. *J. comp. Psychol.*, 1930, 11, 1-35.

Lashley, K. S., & Ball, J. Spinal conduction and kinaesthetic sensitivity in the maze habit. *J. comp. Psychol.*, 1929, 9, 71-105.

Lilly, J. C., & Miller, A. M. Operant conditioning of the bottle-nose dolphin with electrical stimulation of the brain. *J. comp. Physiol. Psychol.*, 1962, 55, 73-79.

Luttges, M., Johnson, T., Buck, C., Holland, J., & McGaugh, J. An examination of "transfer of learning" by nucleic acid. *Science*, 1966, 151, 834-837.

Mason, W. A. & Harlow, H. F. Formation of conditioned responses in infant monkeys. *J. comp. physiol. Psychol.*, 1958, 51, 68-70.

McCleary, R. A. Response specificity in the behavioral effects of the limbic system lesions in the cat. *J. comp. physiol. Psychol.*, 1961, 54, 605-613.

Melzack, R., Penick, E., & Beckett, A. The problem of "innate fear" of the hawk shape; an experimental study with mallard ducks. *J. comp. physiol. Psychol.*, 1959, 52, 694-698.

Nice, M. M., & Pelkwyk, J. J. ter. Enemy recognition by the song sparrow. *Auk*, 1941, 58, 195-214.

Pavlov, I. P. *Conditioned reflexes* (Trans. by G. V. Anrep). London: Oxford Univ. Press, 1927.

Peckham, G. W., & Peckham, E. G. Some observations on the mental powers of spiders. *J. Morph.,* 1887, 1, 383-419.

Ratner, S. C., & Denny, M. R. *Comparative psychology*. Homewood, Ill.: Dorsey Press, 1964.

Rensch, B., & Franzisket, L. Lang audauernde bedingte Reflexe bei Rückenmarksfröschen. *Z. vergl. Physiol.*, 1954, 36, 318-326.

Sanders, F. K. Second-order olfactory and visual learning in the optic tectum of goldfish. *J. exp. Biol.*, 1940, 30, 412-425.

Shurrager, P. S., & Culler, E. Conditioning in the spinal dog. *J. exp. Psychol.*, 1940, 26, 133-159.

Simpson, M. J. A. The display of the Siamese fighting fish, *Betta splendens. Anim. Behav. Monogr.*, 1968, 1, 1-73.

Thompson, R. Thalamic structures critical for retention of an avoidance conditioned response in rats. *J. comp. physiol. Psychol.*, 1963, 56, 261-267.

Thompson, R. Learning and retentiveness in brain-damaged rats. *J. comp. physiol. Psychol.*, 1959, 52, 501-505.

Thorpe, W. H. *Learning and instinct in animals*. (2nd Ed.) Cambridge: Harvard Univ. Press., 1963.

Tolman, E. C. *Purposive behavior in animals and men.* New York: Appleton-Century-Crofts, 1932.

Vance, V. J., Richardson, A. M., & Goodrich, R. B. Brightness discrimination in the collared lizard. *Science*, 1965, 147, 758-759.

Wodinsky, J., & Bitterman, M. E. Partial reinforcement in the fish. *Amer. J. Psychol.*, 1959, 72, 184-199.

Wodinsky, J., & Bitterman, M. E. Resistance to extinction in the fish after extensive training with partial reinforcement. *Amer. J. Psychol.*, 1960, 73, 429-434.

Yaremko, R. M., Boice, R., & Thompson, R. W. Studies of classical and avoidance conditioning of the nicitating membrane in frogs and toads. *Psychonom. Sci.*, 1969, in press.

Yaremko, R. M., & Kimmel, H. D. Two procedures for studying partial reinforcement effects in classical conditioning of the planarian. *Anim. Behav.*, 1969, 17, 40-42.

Yerkes, R. M. Formation of habits in the turtle. *Pop. Sci. Month.*, 1901, 58, 519-525.

Experience II: Higher Processes

R. A. MAIER

B. M. MAIER

Some animals exhibit abilities more complex than those discussed in the previous chapter. Besides being able to make substitutions or selections from immediately available alternatives, which characterizes simple learning, they are also able to generalize broad characteristics of the situation, acquire information, extract a principle, and sometimes integrate elements that were not experienced in temporal or spatial contiguity. These higher processes enable an animal to find unique solutions to problems that arise in complex, changing environments. There have been many attempts to measure and compare the higher processes of animals.[1] However, comparative studies have been replete with difficulties. As in the case of comparative learning studies, differences in performance on various tasks may reflect such factors as motivation, sensory capacities, and ability to perform motor movements, rather than reflecting differences in higher processes. Furthermore, it is often difficult to separate performance based on complex, unlearned behavior or simple learning from performance that reflects higher processes. For example, the use of a tool such as a stick may result from a type of instrumental learning that may be described as

[1] Some of the early studies of higher processes referred to this ability as intelligence (Thorndike, 1911). However, the term "intelligence" has taken on too much excess meaning from its widespread use with humans and therefore cannot advantageously be applied to subhuman animals.

trial-and-error learning, or it may reflect a higher process referred to as insight.[2]

Because of these difficulties in distinguishing higher processes, several categories of studies are not included in this chapter. However, six types of problems—observational learning, probability learning, discrimination-reversal learning, learning-set formation, concept formation, and reasoning and insight—come close to satisfying the definition of higher processes and allow for systematic comparisons of groups of animals. These are discussed in the following sections.

OBSERVATIONAL LEARNING

Observational learning requires that one animal (the observer) duplicate, in some way, an act performed by a second animal (the demonstrator). This type of learning appears to be a somewhat higher ability than instrumental learning. Instrumental learning involves sensitivity to a particular stimulus (or stimuli); observational learning involves not only sensitivity to stimuli, but the translation of information into specific action, i.e., the duplication of some aspects of the model's sequence of activities.

Visual observational learning is well documented in mammals, particularly cats, monkeys, and chimps. For example, cats that have served as observers while other cats were trying to get out of problem-boxes consistently learned solutions to this problem faster than cats that did not have an opportunity to observe. Furthermore, the cats learned faster if they observed all trials by the demonstrator as it learned the problems than if they watched only the skilled trials (Herbert & Harsh, 1944). Apparently, prolonged observation was beneficial, even when this included observation of errors.

These findings suggest that the activity of the demonstrator may simply enhance certain aspects of the stimulus situation rather than provide a model that is directly copied (Crawford & Spence, 1939). However, studies with monkeys indicate that some observa-

[2] Trial-and-error behavior is exhibited when an animal is first placed in a problem situation; first one set of responses is made, then another, and so on. A solution may eventually result from "stumbling" upon the correct response.

tional learning includes more than stimulus enhancement. When a monkey watches a second monkey perform in a series of discrimination problems, the observer does not always choose the same object as the demonstrator; if the demonstrator chooses the wrong object in a two-choice problem the observer typically chooses the other object. In other words, the observer tends to utilize information gained during the demonstration (Darby & Riopelle, 1959).

Some of the most complex types of observational learning have been demonstrated by a chimpanzee named Viki that was raised in the home of two psychologists. Viki imitated a number of household routines, including the putting on of lipstick. She was also able to perform many imitations on the command: "Do this," including the imitation of an act shown in a photograph of herself (Hayes & Hayes, 1952).

Visual observational learning can apparently take place in several ways: (1) the action of a demonstrator may function as a cue to the location of a reward; (2) the action of the demonstrator may enhance certain aspects of the stimulus situation; (3) the demonstrator's performance may provide pertinent "information"; and (4) the demonstrator's actions may be copied directly. Observational learning seems to be more highly developed in apes and monkeys than in lower mammals.

PROBABILITY LEARNING

Probability learning problems require that an animal maximize his gains, or number of reinforcements, on a discrimination-type task. On this type of problem, cross-species comparisons are relatively easy, and systematic comparisons can be made.

A probability learning problem consists of a two-choice situation. An animal is randomly rewarded for the choices he makes. For example, one choice may be rewarded 70% of the time and the other choice, 30% of the time. Maximal gain can be expected if the animal makes 100% of his responses to the choice most often rewarded (in this case, the 70% choice).

Two general types of responses are found to these problems—maximizing gains (responding nearly 100% to one choice) and matching probabilities (responding approximately 70% of the time to one choice and 30% to the other). Presumably, if an animal maximizes its gains, it is doing something akin to building expectancies of reinforcement based on probabilities. On the other hand, if an animal matches the probabilities of reinforcement for the two choices, it may be assumed that the animal is responding in a somewhat automatic way to frequency of reinforcement. In other words, maximizing gains seems to be related to higher processes.

Two types of probability learning problems can be presented. On "spatial" problems, the animal is maximally rewarded for responding to a stimulus in a particular spatial position (e.g., on the left side). In this case, the stimuli are similar on both sides of the discrimination apparatus. On "visual" problems, the animal is maximally rewarded for responding to a particular stimulus regardless of spatial position (the two stimuli differ significantly from each other). The visual problem is generally more difficult for an animal to learn than the spatial one.

Representative mammals–rats, cats, and monkeys–maximize on both visual and spatial problems, thereby demonstrating some superiority over lower vertebrates (Bitterman, 1965; Schweikert & Treichler, 1969). It is interesting to note that lesions in the cortex of a rat result in a loss of this superiority; lesioned animals match probabilities on the visual problem (Gonzalez, Roberts, & Bitterman, 1964). Apparently, mammals without an intact cortex function in a fashion similar to that of lower vertebrates.

In conclusion, studies of probability learning suggest that vertebrates differ systematically in their ability to express higher processes as defined in terms of maximizing gains. However, it should be kept in mind that certain procedural variations will disrupt the superior performance of mammals. Under high motivational conditions, rats "match" probabilities (Weitzman, 1967). This finding is consistent with studies of human problem solving that show loss of variability and ability to solve complex problems under stress or high motivation (Maier, 1955).

DISCRIMINATION REVERSAL

Discrimination-reversal problems are essentially series of discrimination tasks. An animal is first trained to make a discrimination, e.g., black from white, and rewarded for responses to black. Then the situation is reversed, with white serving as the positive stimulus. A series of reversals such as this are presented, and the ability of an animal to reduce the number of trials required to learn the discrimination after each reversal is measured.

As in the case of probability learning, both spatial and visual problems can be presented. On the spatial problems, the animal must shift from making a response to the left to making a response to the right; on the (more difficult) visual problem, the animal must shift a response from one stimulus to the other.

Presumably, a tendency to reduce trials necessary for learning after each reversal reflects an ability to respond to the situation as a whole. In other words, the animal carries over some information or expectancy from one discrimination task to another–an ability included in the definition of higher processes. However, a failure to reduce the number of trials suggests that the animal is responding in a more primitive fashion, i.e., responding to the discrimination task after each reversal as if it were a new task to be learned.

Birds (pigeons and chickens) and mammals (mature rats and monkeys) show progressive improvement on both spatial and visual reversal problems (Bullock & Bitterman, 1962; Bacon et al., 1962; Fischer, 1966; Cole, 1951). Thus there appears to be a systematic improvement in flexibility–as defined by the reversal problem–from lower to higher vertebrates.

There is also some evidence of superior performance in primates as compared with lower mammals. After a series of discrimination-reversal tasks, rhesus monkeys are consistently able to respond correctly on the second trial after a reversal; subprimates do not seem to be able to respond at this level (Riopelle, 1960). This correct response on the second trial (the first trial providing the critical information, i.e., which choice is correct) implies an ability to utilize optimally the information supplied by the task situation.

As in many of these problems, factors besides higher processes are involved in obtaining solutions to reversal problems. For example, frustration resulting from the fact that the previously correct stimulus is now incorrect seems to interfere with performance. Thus the tranquilizer chlorpromazine improves the rat's performance on reversal problems, presumably because it reduces the effects of the frustration (Gonzalez & Ross, 1961).

LEARNING SETS

Learning sets are similar to discrimination-reversal problems in that animals are tested on their ability to show improvement over a series of problems. For example, Problem 1 may involve a number of trials during which the animal learns to choose object *A* over object *B*; Problem 2, object *C* over object *D*; Problem 3, object *E* over object *F*, etc. For higher processes to be demonstrated, the animal must be able to solve each succeeding task in a fewer number of trials. That is to say, the animal must show that he has learned "how to learn" efficiently. If, after a number of problems, an animal makes a correct response on Trial 2 and succeeding trials (Trial 1 having provided the critical information), he will have maximally utilized the information, i.e., solved the learning set (Harlow, 1949).

As in the case of discrimination-reversal problems, there are

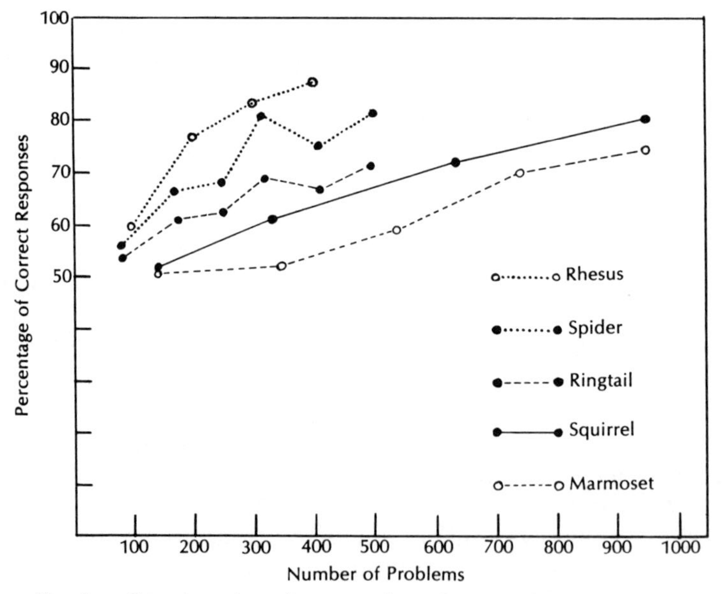

Fig. 1. Learning-set performance in various species of monkeys. (Modified from Riopelle, A. J., "Complex Processes." In R. H. Waters, D. A. Rethlingshafer, and W. E. Caldwell (Eds.), *Principles of Comparative Psychology*. Copyright 1960 by McGraw-Hill, Inc. Used by permission of McGraw-Hill Book Company.)

systematic differences in ability to solve learning sets. Rats and lower vertebrates have not demonstrated any ability to reduce the frequency of errors on the second trial of a new task; cats show improved performance after a large number of tasks; and monkeys show improvement after fewer tasks. There are also differences between species of monkeys that correspond to the complexity of their brains. Thus primitive marmosets exhibit the worst performance; New World spider monkeys are intermediate in performance; and the highly developed rhesus monkeys exhibit the best performance (see Figure 1).

In rhesus monkeys, lesions of the frontal cortex interfere with learning-set performance. Since these lesions do not affect discrimination ability, it may be assumed that this deficit is due to something other than a visual impairment. One factor of importance may be loss of flexibility; animals that have difficulty with learning sets have preferences or aversions for certain stimuli, which may interfere with their performance; i.e., they tend to keep choosing the same stimulus, regardless of the reward. Obviously, optimal performance requires that the animal utilize information provided in the first trial and reject any natural preference or aversion (Riopelle, 1960).

CONCEPT FORMATION

Concept formation involves the acquisition of a common response to dissimilar stimuli; i.e., the animal must develop a response to a class of objects or events.

One test of concept formation involves a complex visual concept. Animals must respond to various visual stimuli varying in form and complexity and representing an abstraction of the presented material–or a concept of it. For example, racing pigeons have been trained to respond to the presence or absence of humans in photographs for a food reward (Hernstein & Loveland, 1964).

One of the most basic tests of concept formation is the oddity problem. In each of a series of tasks, three stimuli are presented to the animal; two of these stimuli are similar and the third one differs from the others in some significant way. The animal must choose the odd stimulus. The oddity problem has been solved by canaries, rats, and chimpanzees (Pastore, 1954; Wodinsky et al., 1953; Nissen & McCulloch, 1937). Other things being equal, primates seem to have less difficulty than other animals with this type of problem.

Primates are also able to solve more complex types of oddity problems. For example, rhesus monkeys are able to respond correctly to an oddity problem in two dimensions–odd form when the stimuli are presented against one background and odd color when the stimuli appear against another background (Harlow, 1943). (See Figure 2.) In one case, in which training and testing took place over a three-year period, a chimpanzee was able to solve an oddity problem involving five dimensions (Nissen, 1951).

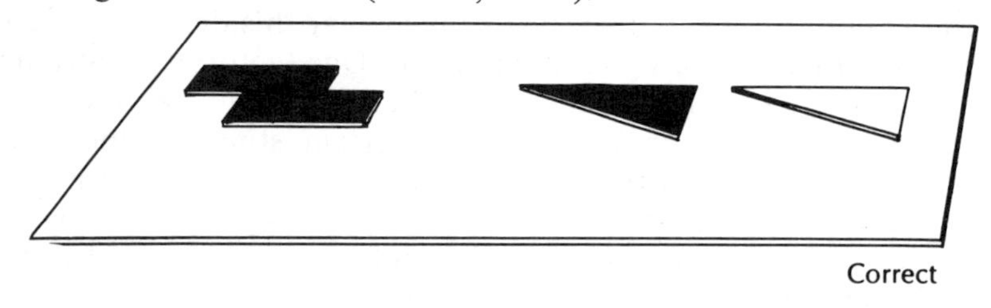

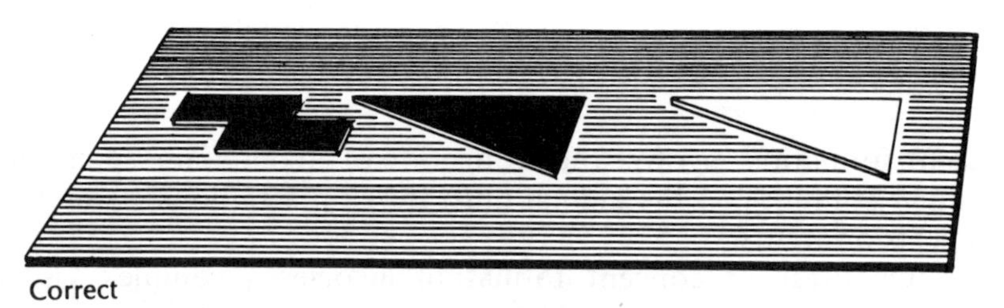

Fig. 2. A two-dimensional oddity problem: odd color correct on light tray; odd form correct on dark tray.

Finally, on a somewhat different type of problem, two chimpanzees apparently developed some basic number concepts. After an extensive period of training, these animals were able to recognize numbers and "write" them in binary form. That is, they were able to match "on" and "off" lights with the binary representation of decimal numbers (see Figure 3). The test material

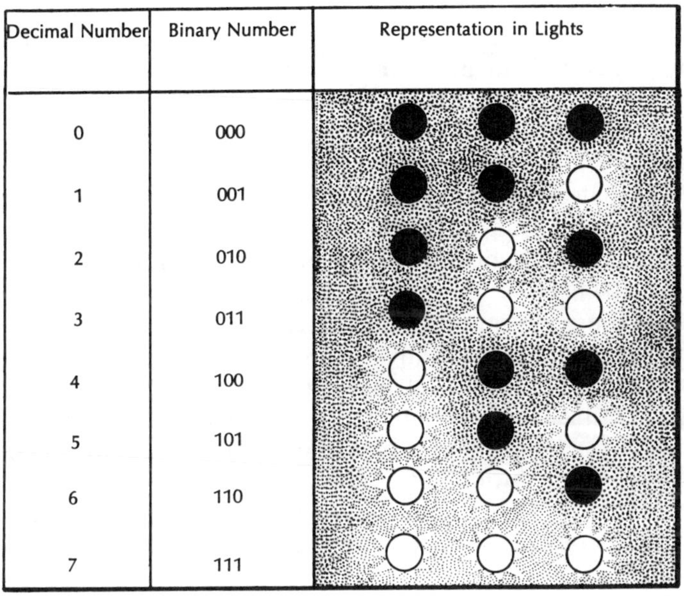

Decimal Number	Binary Number	Representation in Lights
0	000	● ● ●
1	001	● ● ○
2	010	● ○ ●
3	011	● ○ ○
4	100	○ ● ●
5	101	○ ● ○
6	110	○ ○ ●
7	111	○ ○ ○

Fig. 3. The binary representation of numbers mastered by chimpanzees. (Modified from "Arithmetic Behavior in Chimpanzees" by Charles B. Ferster.

consisted of presenting various numbers (0-7) of triangles to the animal and requiring him to represent the number of triangles with his three lights (Ferster, 1964).

INSIGHT

Problems that test reasoning ability and insight require a combination of two or more separate experiences into a reward-securing act. The operation of chance factors such as those involved in blind trial-and-error behavior must be ruled out with a reasonable degree of certainty.

Insight involves the sudden appearance of a correct response and, on succeeding problems, the immediate solution to the problem without apparent trial-and-error behavior. This ability implies some sort of comprehension or overview of the problem. Insight is typically measured on problems that require the use of an instrument. Some of the problems that have been used in comparative studies are the patterned-string test, the stick-and-hoe test, and the box-stacking test.

The patterned-string test, which is a type of spatial-relations problem, requires that an animal pull a string in order to obtain a food reward. The "correct" string is placed parallel to or crossed with other strings that do not lead to a reward. One advantage of this test is that the position of the strings can be varied so that a solution by simple trial-and-error is highly unlikely. Immediate solutions to both parallel- and crossed-string patterns have been reported for monkeys, gorillas, and chimpanzees (Klüver, 1933; Riesen et al., 1953; Finch, 1941). Apparently, a high level of perceptual capability is required for solution of these problems. Thus performance improves with age up to and beyond puberty in rhesus monkeys, even when experiential factors are controlled (Mason & Harlow, 1961).

Primates are also able to use a stick or hoe to reach for or rake in food that is placed out of their immediate reach. More complicated problems require the use of a shorter stick to obtain a longer stick that will reach the food. This variation has been mastered by cebus monkeys and chimpanzees. It is most difficult for them if the hoe is placed some distance from the food, and easiest if the food can be obtained by simply pulling on the hoe (Köhler, 1925).

When presented with a problem involving food hung from the ceiling out of their reach, chimpanzees are able to place a box or pile several boxes beneath the food and climb up onto the boxes where they can reach the food. As many as four boxes have been stacked on top of each other. The sudden appearance of the solution suggests that the chimps' behavior reflected insight rather than a trial-and-error solution (Köhler, 1925).

In conclusion, it appears that certain mammals exhibit reasoning and insight. Insight is most easily demonstrated in apes, but is also apparent in monkeys and rats. It should not be concluded, however, that other animals are incapable of insight. Failure on instrumentation problems may result from motor or sensory problems related to manipulation and not from lack of insight. For example, early reports indicated that gibbons (*Hylobates*) were quite inferior to other apes in problem solving (Yerkes & Yerkes, 1929). However, when gibbons are presented with a string-pulling problem in which the strings are elevated so that they do not lie on a flat surface, they solve the problem easily. Apparently, elevated strings are more suitable to the anatomy and sensory capacities of these animals and are more consistent with the objects found in their natural, arboreal environment than instruments lying on a flat surface (Beck, 1967).

Another difficulty in interpreting instrumentation problems is related to previous experience. Chimpanzees that have never had experience with sticks fail to use sticks to obtain food (Birch, 1945). If adult animals are captured and tested—as was the case with Köhler's chimps—it is difficult to assess the importance of early experience in the use of instruments.

HIGHER PROCESSES IN THE NATURAL STATE

There are several additional difficulties in evaluating the role of higher processes in behavior patterns observed in an animal's natural state. It is virtually impossible to tell whether a particular behavior observed in the wild is the result of trial-and-error learning or some sort of insight. Anecdotal evidence is particularly likely to be misleading because untrained observers have a tendency to read inappropriate motives into behavior patterns. For example, an observer may claim that an animal is trying to communicate with humans when it vocalizes and makes eye-to-eye contact with the human. Furthermore, untrained observers tend to be biased in their reports of behavior, sometimes emphasizing examples of "intelligent"-looking behavior and leaving out examples of stereotyped behavior.[3]

However, there is some evidence for the use of higher processes in primate feeding and defensive behavior. In certain societies, the experience of an indivual member seems to affect the

[3] Reports of intelligence in dolphins, which have appeared in a number of popular scientific journals and in at least one text on animal behavior, are a good example of the misuse of anecdotal evidence. Unpublished research on dolphins at Point Mugu, California, has failed to support any claim of intelligence comparable to that of primates.

eating habits of the group. If one member of a baboon group happens to kill and eat meat, the other members tend to become meat eaters (Eimerl & DeVore, 1965).

Extensive field studies have been conducted on the feeding of the Japanese monkey *Macaca fuscata*. The origin of the habit of washing sweet potatoes before eating was observed, as was its gradual transference to other monkeys in the group and, eventually, extensively throughout the island. The habit started with one female, was copied first by two infants, and then gradually imitated by more and more monkeys (Miyadi, 1964).

Finally, monkeys' and apes' use of sticks as defensive weapons appears to be an example of instrumentation. It is interesting to note that only animals that live in relatively open forest areas or savannas have been observed to use weapons; members of the same species that live in dense forests (where throwing objects is impractical) do not seem to use implements (Kortlandt & Kooij, 1963).

The observations of relatively well-developed higher processes in monkeys and apes (and, of course, man) raise the question: why did this ability develop to such an extent in higher primates and not in other groups of animals? Two factors seem to be of major importance. First, it is necessary to have a brain with a considerable potential before such abilities can be expressed. Primates have good vision and motor ability, capabilities which are associated with a well-developed cerebral cortex. Second, higher processes must be of some selective advantage. The primates that came out of the trees and spent relatively large amounts of time on the ground were not structurally adapted for terrestrial existence. They could not defend themselves against predators or obtain food so easily as animals that had evolved on the ground. For these primates, higher processes, which facilitated such activities as defense and feeding, were of considerable selective advantage. Consequently, primates that spent considerable time on the ground (e.g., rhesus monkeys, chimpanzees, and man) developed higher processes to a greater degree than their counterparts that remained in the trees.

REFERENCES

Bacon, H. R., Warren, J. M., & Schein, M. W. Non-spatial reversal learning in chickens. *Anim. Behav.*, 1962, 10, 239-243.

Beck, B. B. A study of problem solving by gibbons. *Behaviour*, 1967, 28, 95-109.

Birch, H. G. The relation of previous experience to insightful problem solving. *J. comp. physiol. Psychol.*, 1945, 38, 295-317.

Bitterman, M. R. Phyletic differences in learning. *Amer. Psychol.*, 1965, 20, 396-410.

Bullock, D. H., & Bitterman, M. E. Probability-matching in the pigeon. *Amer. J. Psychol.*, 1962, 75, 634-639.

Cole, J. A study of discrimination reversal in monkeys. *J. comp. physiol. Psychol.*, 1951, 44, 467-472.

Crawford, M. P., & Spence, K. W. Observational learning of discrimination problems by chimpanzees. *J. comp. Psychol.*, 1939, 27, 133-147.

Darby, C. L., & Riopelle, A. J. Observational learning in the rhesus monkey. *J. comp. physiol. Psychol.*, 1959, 52, 94-98.

Eimerl, S., DeVore, I., & the Editors of Time-Life Books. *The primates.* New York: Time, 1965.

Ferster, C. B. Arithmetic behavior in chimpanzees. *Sci. Amer.*, 1964, 210, 98-106.

Finch, G. The solution of patterned string problems by chimpanzees. *J. comp. Psychol.*, 1941, 32, 83-90.

Fischer, G. J. Discrimination and successive reversal learning in chicks that fail to imprint and ones that imprint strongly. *Percept. Mot. Skills*, 1966, 23, 579-584.

Gonzalez, R. C., Roberts, W. A., & Bitterman, M. E. Learning in adult rats with extensive cortical lesions made in infancy. *Amer. J. Psychol.*, 1964, 77, 547-562.

Gonzalez, R. C., & Ross, S. The effects of chlorpromazine on the course of discrimination-reversal learning in the rat. *J. comp. physiol. Psychol.*, 1961, 54, 645-648.

Harlow, H. F. Solution by rhesus monkeys of a problem involving the Weigl principle using the matching-form-sample method. *J. comp. Psychol.*, 1943, 36, 217-227.

Harlow, H. F. The formation of learning sets. *Psychol. Rev.*, 1949, 56, 51-65.

Hayes, K. J., & Hayes, C. Imitation in a home raised chimpanzee. *J. comp. physiol. Psychol.*, 1952, 45, 45-459.

Herbert, M. J., & Harsh, C. M. Observational learning by cats. *J. comp. Psychol.*, 1944, 37, 81-95.

Hernstein, R. J., & Loveland, D. H. Complex visual concept in the pigeon. *Science*, 1964, 146, 549-551.

Klüver, H. *Behavior mechanisms in monkeys*. Chicago: Univ. Chicago Press, 1933.

Köhler, W. *The mentality of apes*. New York: Harcourt, 1925.

Kortlandt, A., & Kooij, M. Protohominid behaviour in primates. (Preliminary communication.) *Symp. Zool. Soc. London*, 1963, 10, 61-88.

Maier, N. R. F. *Psychology in industry*. Boston: Houghton Mifflin, 1955.

Mason, W. A., & Harlow, H. F. The effects of age and previous training on patterned-string performance of rhesus monkeys. *J. comp. physiol. Psychol.*, 1961, 54, 704-709.

Miyadi, D. Social life of Japanese monkeys. *Science*, 1964, 143, 783-786.

Nissen, H. W. Analysis of a complex conditional reaction in chimpanzees. *J. comp. physiol. Psychol.*, 1951, 44, 9-16.

Nissen, H. W., & McCulloch, T. L. Equated and non-equated stimulus situations in discrimination learning by chimpanzees. I. Comparison with unlimited response. *J. comp. Psychol.*, 1937, 23, 165-189.

Pastore, N. Discrimination learning in the canary. *J. comp. physiol. Psychol.*, 1954, 47, 389-390.

Riesen, A. H., Greenberg, B., Granstron, A. S., & Fantz, R. L. Solutions of patterned string problems of young gorillas. *J. comp. physiol. Psychol.*, 1953, 46, 19-22.

Riopelle, A. J. Complex processes. In R. H. Waters, D. A. Rethlingshafer, & W. E. Caldwell (Eds.), *Principles of comparative psychology*. New York: McGraw-Hill, 1960. Pp. 208-249.

Schweikert, G. E., & Treichler, F. R. Visual probability learning and reversal in the cat. *J. comp. physiol. Psychol.*, 1969, 67, 269-272.

Thorndike, E. L. *Animal intelligence*. New York: Macmillan, 1911.

Weitzman, R. A. Positional matching in rats and fish. *J. comp. physiol. Psychol.*, 1967, 63, 51-59.

Wodinsky, J. Varley, M. A., & Bitterman, M. E. The solution of oddity-problems by the rat. *Amer. J. Psychol.*, 1953, 66, 137-140.

Yerkes, R. M., & Yerkes, A. W. *The great apes*. New Haven: Yale, 1929.

Phyletic Differences in Learning

M. E. BITTERMAN

One way to study the role of the brain in learning is to compare the learning of animals with different brains. Differences in brain structure may be produced by surgical means, or they may be found in nature—as when the learning of different species is compared. Of these two approaches the first (the neurosurgical approach) has been rather popular, but the potentialities of the second still are largely unexplored. Students of learning in animals have been content for the most part to concentrate their attention on a few closely related mammalian forms, chosen largely for reasons of custom and convenience, which they have treated as representative of animals in general. Their work has been dominated almost from its inception by the hypothesis that the laws of learning are the same for all animals—that the wide differences in brain structure which occur in the animal series have a purely quantitative significance.

The hypothesis comes to us from Thorndike (1911), who more than any other man may be credited with having brought the study of animal intelligence into the laboratory. On the basis of his early comparative experiments, Thorndike decided that however much animals might differ in "what" they learned (which could be traced, he thought, to differences in their sensory, motor, and motivational properties), or in the "degree" of their learning ability (some seemed able to learn more than others, and more quickly), the principles which governed their learning were the same. Although Thorndike's hypothesis was greeted with considerable skepticism,

From *American Psychologist*, **20**, 1965, 396-410.

experiments with a variety of animals began to turn up functional similarities far more impressive than differences, and before long there was substantial disagreement only as to the *nature* of the laws which were assumed to hold for all animals. As acceptance of the hypothesis grew, the range of animals studied in experiments on learning declined—which, of course, was perfectly reasonable. If the laws of learning were the same everywhere in the animal series, there was nothing to be gained from the study of many different animals; indeed, standardization offered many advantages which it would be foolish to ignore. As the range of animals declined, however, so also did the likelihood of discovering any differences which might in fact exist.

It is difficult for the nonspecialist to appreciate quite how restricted has been the range of animals studied in experiments on animal learning because the restriction is so marked: the novelty of work with lower animals is such that two or three inexpressibly crude experiments with a flatworm may be better publicized than a hundred competent experiments with the rat. Some quantitative evidence on the degree of restriction was provided about twenty years ago by Schneirla, whose conclusion then was that "we do not have a comparative psychology." Schneirla's analysis was carried further by Beach (1950), who plotted the curves which are reproduced in Figure 1. Based on a count of all papers appearing between 1911 and 1948 in the *Journal of Animal Behavior* and its successors, the *Journal of Comparative Psychology*, and the *Journal of Comparative and Physiological Psychology*, the curves show how interest in the rat mounted while interest in submammalian forms declined. By the '30s, a stable pattern had emerged: about 60% of papers on the rat, 30% on other mammals (most primates), and 10% on lower forms. The set of points at the extreme right, which I have added for the decade after 1948, shows no change in the pattern. What we know about learning in animals we know primarily from the intensive study of a small number of mammalian forms.

How widespread is the acceptance of Thorndike's hypothesis by contemporary theorists and systematists may be judged from a set of writings recently assembled by Koch (1959). Skinner is quite explicit in his assumption that which animal is studied "doesn't matter." When due allowance has been made for differences in sensory and motor characteristics, he explains, "what remains of . . .

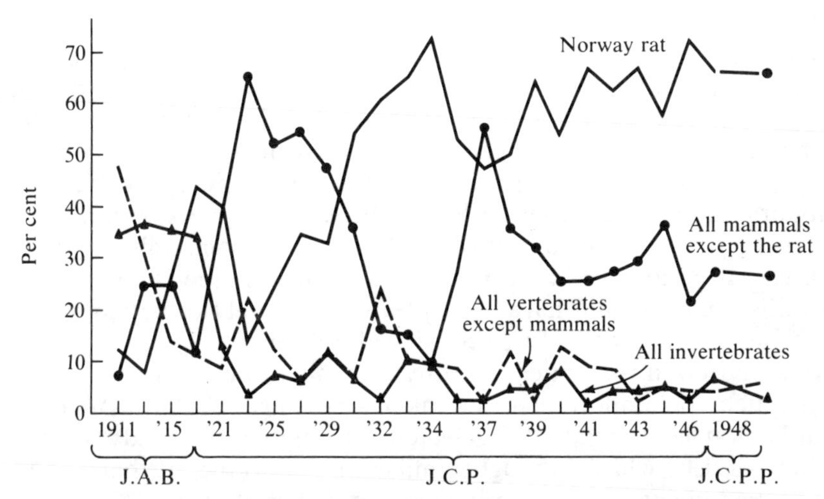

Fig. 1. Percentage of papers dealing with animals in each of four categories which appeared between 1911 and 1948 in the *Journal of Animal Behavior*, the *Journal of Comparative Psychology*, and the *Journal of Comparative and Physiological Psychology* (Beach, 1950). (The points at right, for the decade after 1948, were added by me.)

behavior shows astonishingly similar properties" [Koch, 1959, p. 375]. Tolman, Miller, Guthrie, Estes, and Logan (representing Hull and Spence) rest their perfectly general conclusions about the nature of learning on the data of experiments with a few selected mammals–mostly rat, monkey, and man–skipping lightly back and forth from one to another as if indeed structure did not matter, although Miller "does not deny the possibility that men may have additional capacities which are much less well developed or absent in the lower mammals" [Koch, 1959, p. 204]. Harlow alone makes a case for species differences in learning, pointing to the unequal rates of improvement shown by various mammals (mostly primates) trained in long series of discriminative problems, but he gives us no reason to believe that the differences are more than quantitative. While he implies clearly that the capacity for interproblem transfer may be absent entirely in certain lower animals–in the rat, he says, it exists only in a "most rudimentary form" [Koch, 1959, p. 505]–submammalian evidence is lacking.

Although I have been considering thus far only the work of the West, I do not think that things have been very different on the other side of the Curtain. The conditioning has been "classical" rather than "instrumental" in the main, and the favored animal has been the dog rather than the rat, but the range of animals studied in any detail has been small, at least until quite recently, and the principles discovered have been generalized widely.

The results of the experiments which I shall now describe support quite another view. I began these experiments without very much in the way of conviction as to their outcome, although the formal attractions of the bold Thorndikian hypothesis were rather obvious, and I should have been pleased on purely esthetic grounds to be able to accept it. I was convinced only that the hypothesis had not yet received the critical scrutiny it seemed to warrant, and that it was much too important to be taken any longer on faith. With the familiar rat as a standard, I selected for comparative study another animal–a fish–which I thought similar enough to the rat that it could be studied in analogous experiments, yet different enough to afford a marked neuroanatomical contrast. I did not propose to compare the two animals in terms of numerical scores, as, for example, the number of trials required for (or the number of errors made in) the mastery of some problem, because such differences would not necessarily imply the operation of different learning processes. I proposed instead to compare them in terms of *functional* relations–to find out whether their performance would be affected in the same way by the same variables. Why I chose to begin with certain variables rather than others probably is not worth considering–the choice was largely intuitive; whatever the reasons, the experiments soon turned up some substantial differences in the learning of fish and rat. I shall describe here two of those differences, and then present the results of some further experiments which were designed to tell us what they mean.

One of the situations developed for the study of learning in the fish is illustrated in Figure 2. The animal is brought in its individual living tank to a black Plexiglas enclosure. The manipulanda are two Plexiglas disks (targets) at which the animal is trained to strike. The targets are mounted on rods set into the needle holders of phonograph cartridges in such a way that when the animal makes contact with one of the targets a voltage is generated across its cartridge. This voltage is used to operate a set of relays which record the response and control its consequences. The targets are illumina-

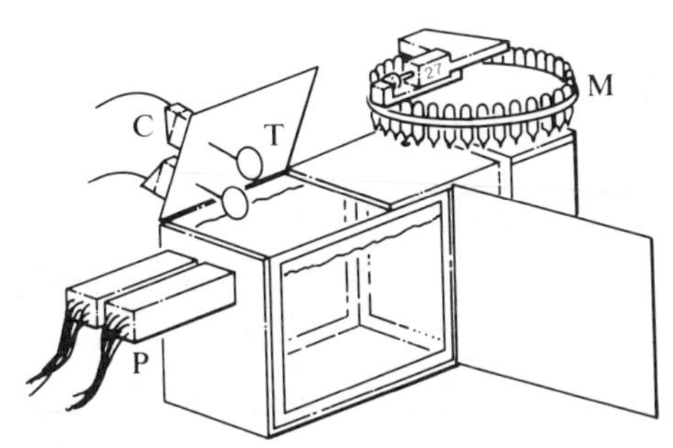

Fig. 2. A situation for the study of discrimination in the fish. (T, targets which are lowered into the water as the cover of the enclosure is brought down; C, phonograph cartridges which hold the targets and register contacts with them; P, projectors for projecting various stimuli on the targets; M, live worm dispenser.)

ted with colored lights or patterns projected upon them from behind; on any given trial, for example, the left target may be green and the right one red, or the left target may show a triangle and the right one a circle. The reward for correct choice is a *Tubifex* worm discharged into the water through a small opening at the top of the enclosure–the worm is discharged from an eyedropper whose bulb is compressed by a pair of solenoid-operated jaws. When a worm is dropped, a magazine light at the rear of the enclosure is turned on for a few seconds, which signals that a worm has been dropped and provides some diffuse illumination which enables the animal to find it. All of the events of training are programmed automatically and recorded on tape.

I shall talk about two kinds of experiments which have been done in this situation. The first is concerned with *habit reversal.* Suppose an animal is trained to choose one of two stimuli, either for a fixed number of trials or to some criterion level of correct choice, and then the positive and negative stimuli are reversed; that is, the previously unrewarded stimulus now is rewarded, and the previously rewarded stimulus is unrewarded. After the same number of trials as were given in the original problem, or when the original criterion has been reached in the first reversal, the positive and negative stimuli are reversed again–and so forth. In such an experiment, the animal typically shows a dramatic improvement in performance. It may make many errors in the early reversals, but as training proceeds it reverses more and more rapidly.

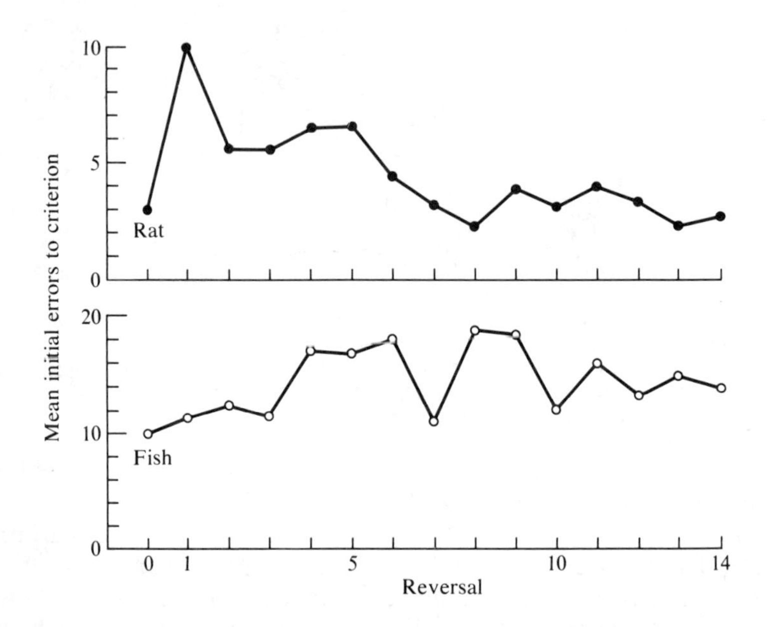

Fig. 3. Spatial habit reversal in fish and rat.

In Figure 3, the performance of a group of African mouthbreeders is compared with that of a group of rats in a series of spatial reversals. (In a spatial problem, the animal chooses between a pair of stimuli which differ only with respect to their position in space, and reinforcement is correlated with position, e.g., the stimulus on the left is reinforced.) The apparatus used for the rat was analogous to the apparatus for the fish which you have already seen. On each trial, the animal was offered a choice between two identically illuminated panels set into the wall of the experimental chamber. It responded by pressing one of the panels, and correct choice operated a feeder which discharged a pellet of food into a lighted food cup. The fish were trained in an early version of the apparatus which you have already seen. For both species, there were 20 trials per day to the criterion of 17 out of 20 correct choices, positive and negative positions being reversed for each animal whenever it met that criterion. Now consider the results. The upper curve of the pair you see here is quite representative of the performance of rats in such a problem–rising at first, and then falling in negatively accelerated fashion to a low level; with a little more training than is shown here, the animals reverse after but a single error. The lower curve is quite representative of the performance of fish in such a problem–there is no progressive improvement, but instead some tendency toward progressive deterioration as training continues.

How is this difference to be interpreted? We may ask first whether the results indicate anything beyond a quantitative difference in the learning of two animals. It might be contended that reversal learning simply goes on more slowly in the fish than in the rat–that in 10 or 15 more reversals the fish, too, would have shown progressive improvement. In fact, however, the training of fish has been carried much further in later experiments, some animals completing more than 150 reversals without any sign of improvement. I invite anyone who remains skeptical on this point to persist even longer in the search for improvement.

Another possibility to be considered is that the difference between fish and rat which is reflected in these curves is not a difference in learning at all, but a difference in some confounded variable–sensory, motor, or motivational. Who can say, for example, whether the sensory and the motor demands made upon the two animals in these experiments were exactly the same? Who can say whether the fish were just as hungry as the rats, or whether the bits of food given the fish were equal in reward value to those given the rats? It would, I must admit, be a rare coincidence indeed if the conditions employed for the two animals were exactly equal in all of these potentially important respects. How, then, is it possible to find out whether the results obtained are to be attributed to a difference in learning, or to a difference in sensory, or in motor, or motivational factors? A frank critic might say that it was rather foolish to have made the comparison in the first place, when a moment's thought would have shown that it could not possibly have any meaningful outcome.

I do not, of course, know how to arrange a set of conditions for the fish which will make sensory and motor demands exactly equal to those which are made upon the rat in some given experimental situation. Nor do I know how to equate drive level or reward value in the two animals. Fortunately, however, meaningful comparisons still are possible, because for *control by equation* we may substitute what I call *control by systematic variation*. Consider, for example, the hypothesis that the difference between the curves which you see here is due to a difference, not in learning, but in degree of hunger. The hypothesis implies that there is a level of hunger at which the fish *will* show progressive improvement, and, put in this way, the hypothesis becomes easy to test. We have only to vary level of hunger widely in different groups of fish, which we know well how to do. If, despite the widest possible variation in hunger, progressive improvement fails to appear in the fish, we may reject the hunger hypothesis. Hypotheses about other variables also may be tested by systematic variation. With regard to the question of reversal learning, I shall simply say here that progressive improvement has appeared in the rat under a variety of experimental conditions–it is difficult, in fact, to find a set of conditions under which the rat does not show improvement. In the fish, by contrast, reliable evidence of improvement has failed to appear under a variety of conditions. I think that the burden of proof now rests with the skeptic. Until someone produces positive results, I shall assume that the fish is incapable of progressive improvement, and that we have come here upon a difference in the learning of fish and rat.

Experiments on *probability learning* also have given different results for rat and fish. Suppose that we train an animal in a choice situation with a ratio of reinforcement other than 100:0; that is, instead of rewarding one alternative on 100% of trials and the other never, we reward one alternative on, say, a random 70% of trials and the other on the remaining 30% of trials, thus constituting what may be called a *70:30 problem*. Under some conditions, rat and fish both "maximize" in such a problem, which is to say that they tend always to choose the more frequently reinforced alternative. Under other conditions–specifically, under conditions in which the distribution of reinforcements is exactly controlled–the rat continues to maximize, but the fish "matches," which is to say that its distribution of choices approximates the distribution of reinforcements: In a 70:30 problem it chooses the 70% alternative on about 70% of trials and the 30% alternative on the remaining trials.

Figure 4 shows some sample data for a visual problem in which the discriminanda were horizontal and vertical stripes. In the first stage of the experiment, response to one of the stripes was rewarded on a random 70% of each day's twenty trials, and response

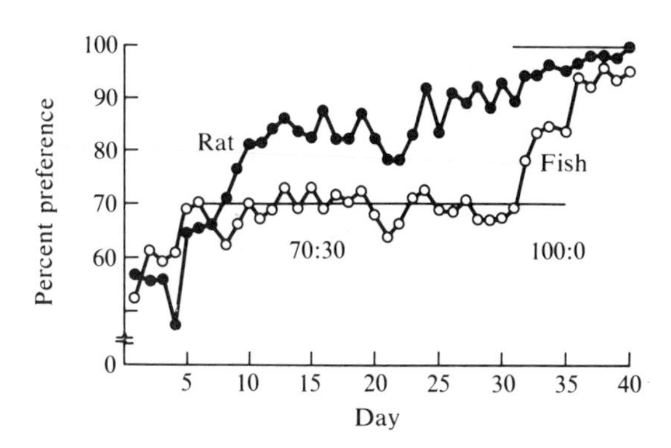

Fig. 4. Visual probability learning in fish and rat.

to the other stripe was rewarded on the remaining 30% of the trials–a 70:30 problem. In the second stage of the experiment the ratio of reinforcement was changed to 100:0, response to the 70% stripe of the first stage being consistently rewarded. The curves shown are plotted in terms of the percentage of each day's responses which were made to the more frequently rewarded alternative. The fish went rapidly from a near-chance level of preference for the 70% stimulus to about a 70% preference, which was maintained from Day 5 until Day 30. With the beginning of the 100:0 training, the preference shifted rapidly upward to about the 95% level. The preference of the rats for the more frequently reinforced stimulus rose gradually from a near-chance level at the start of the 70:30 training to about the 90% level on Day 30. In the ten days of 100:0 training, this preference continued to increase gradually, as it might have done irrespective of the shift from inconsistent to consistent reinforcement. Some further evidence of the close correspondence between choice ratio and reward ratio, which is easy to demonstrate in the fish, is presented in Figure 5. The upper portion shows the performance of two groups of mouthbreeders; one trained on a 100:0 and the other on a 70:30 confounded (black-white) problem, and both then shifted to the 0:100 problem (the less frequently rewarded alternative of the first phase now being consistently rewarded). The lower portion shows what happened when one group then was shifted to 40:60 and the other to 20:80, after which both were shifted to 50:50.

Two characteristics of these data should be noted. First, the

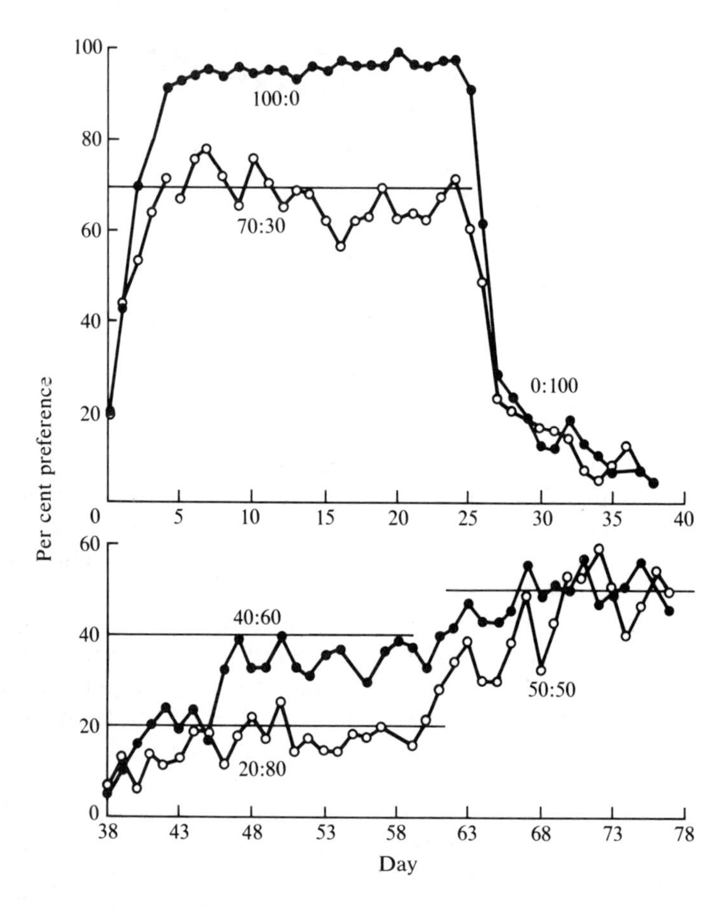

Fig. 5. Probability matching in the fish.

probability matching which the fish curves demonstrate is an individual, not a group phenomenon—that is, it is not an artifact of averaging. All the animals in the group behave in much the same way. I make this obvious point because some averaged data which have been taken as evidence of matching in the rat are indeed unrepresentative of individual performances. Second, the matching shown by the fish is random rather than systematic. The distribution of choices recorded in the 70:30 problem looks like the distribution of colors which might be obtained by drawing marbles at random from a sack of black and white marbles with a color ratio of 70:30—that is, no sequential dependency is to be found in the data. While the rat typically maximizes, it may on occasion show a correspondence of choice ratio and reward ratio which can be traced to some systematic pattern of choice, like the patterns which are displayed in analogous experiments by human subjects.

Here then, are two striking differences between rat and fish. In experiments on habit reversal, the rat shows progressive improvement while the fish does not. In experiments on probability learning, the fish shows random matching while the rat does not. These results suggest a number of interesting questions, of which I shall raise here only two: First, there is the question of how the two differences are related. From the point of view of parsimony, the possibility must be considered that they reflect a single underlying difference in the functioning of the two animals–one which has to do with adjustment to inconsistent reinforcement. Inconsistency of reinforcement certainly is involved in both kinds of experiment, between sessions in reversal learning and within sessions in probability learning. It also is possible, however, that the results for reversal learning reflect one functional difference and the results for probability learning quite another. A second question concerns the relation between the observed differences in behavior and differences in brain structure. We may wonder, for example, to what extent the cortex of the rat is responsible for its progressive improvement in habit reversal, or for its failure to show random matching. In an effort to answer such questions we have begun to do some experiments, analogous to those which differentiate fish and normal rat, with a variety of other animals, and with rats surgically deprived in infancy of relevant brain tissues.

I shall describe first some results for extensively decorticated rats. The animals were operated on at the age of 15 or 16 days in a one-stage procedure which resulted in the destruction of about 70% of the cortex. The experimental work with the operates, like the work with normals, was begun after they had reached maturity–at about 90 days of age. From the methodological viewpoint, work with a brain-injured animal is perfectly equivalent to work with a normal animal of another species, and rats operated in our standard fashion are treated in all respects as such, with systematic variation employed to control for the effects of sensory, motor, and motivational factors. The substantive relation of the work with decorticated rats to the work with normal animals of different species is obvious: We are interested in whether extensive cortical damage will produce in the rat the kinds of behavior which are characteristic of precortical animals, such as the fish, or of animals with only very limited cortical development.

The results for decorticated rats emphasize the importance of the distinction between spatial and visual problems. In a pure spatial problem, you will remember, the two alternatives are identical except for position in space, and reinforcement is correlated with position, e.g., the alternative on the left is reinforced. In a pure visual problem, the two alternatives are visually differentiated, each occupying each of the two positions equally often, and reinforcement is correlated with visual appearance—e.g., the green alternative is reinforced independently of its position. The behavior of the decorticated rat is indistinguishable from that of the normal rat in spatial problems, but in visual problems it differs from the normal in the same way as does the fish.

The criterion-reversal performance of a group of decorticated rats trained in a spatial problem is shown in Figure 6 along with that of a group of normal controls. There were 20 trials per day by the correction method, and the criterion of learning was 17 out of 20

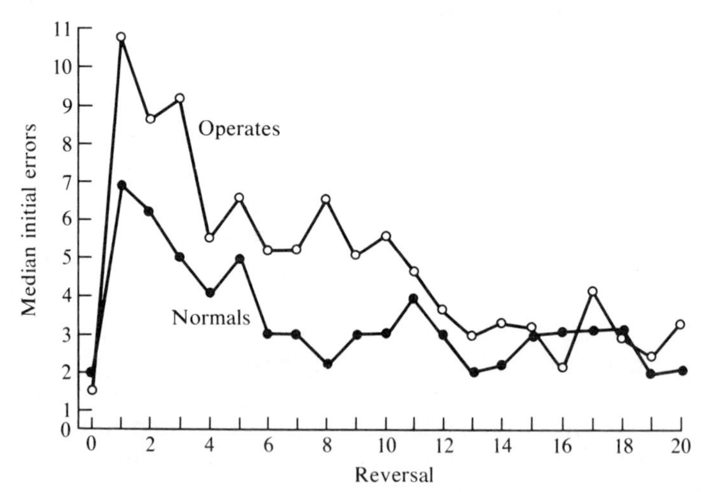

Fig. 6. Spatial habit reversal in normal rats and in rats extensively decorticated in infancy.

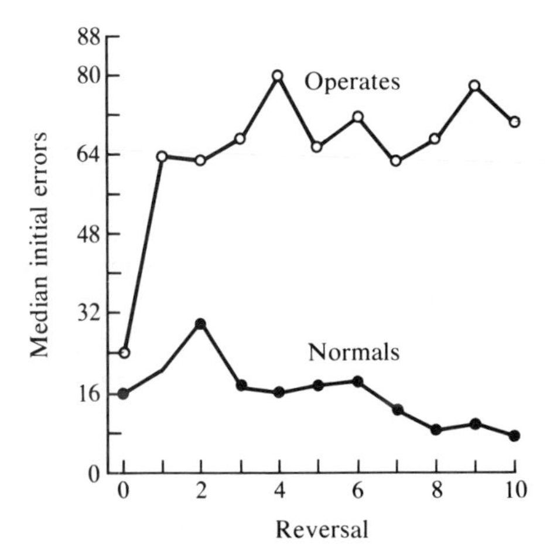

Fig. 7. Visual habit reversal in normal rats and in rats extensively decorticated in infancy.

correct choices. As you can see, the performance of the two groups was very much the same in the original problem. In the first 10 reversals the operates made more errors than did the normals, but (like the normals) they showed progressive improvement, and in the last 10 reversals, there was no difference between the two groups. The results for two additional groups, decorticated and normal, trained under analogous conditions in a visual problem (a brightness discrimination) are plotted in Figure 7. Again, the performance of normals and operates was much the same in the original problem. In the subsequent reversals, the error scores of the normal animals rose at first and then declined in characteristic fashion, but the error scores of the operates rose much more markedly and showed no subsequent tendency to decline.

In spatial probability learning the performance of the operates was indistinguishable from that of normals, but in visual probability learning the operates showed random matching. In the 70:30 problem, the operates came to choose the 70% stimulus on about 70% of trials (the mean was 71.7%); in the 50:50 problem they chose the two stimuli about equally often (the mean preference for the former 70% stimulus was 53.7%). No sequential dependencies could be found in their behavior. By contrast, the normal animals tended to maximize in the 70:30 problem. The two whose preferences came closest to 70% adopted rigid position habits (CP) in the 50:50 problem while one of the others also responded to position, and two continued in the previously established preference. In both spatial experiments, then, the decorticated rats behaved like normal rats, while in both visual experiments they behaved like fish.

These results are compatible with the hypothesis that the cortex of the rat is responsible in some measure for its progressive improvement in habit reversal and for its failure to show random probability matching, at least in visual problems. They are compatible also with the hypothesis that the behavioral differences between fish and rat which appear in the two kinds of experiment are reflections of a single functional difference between the two species. The latter hypothesis is contradicted, however, by some results for the pigeon which I shall now describe. I need not go into any detail about the experimental situation, because it is a fairly familiar one. Suffice it to say that the Skinnerian key-pecking apparatus was adapted for discrete-trials choice experiments directly analogous to those done with fish and rat. The bird, in a darkened enclosure, pecks at one of two lighted keys, correct choice being rewarded by access to grain. Contingencies are programmed automatically, and responses are recorded on tape.

In experiments on habit reversal, both visual and spatial, the pigeon behaves like the rat; that is, it gives clear evidence of progressive improvement. Shown in Figure 8 is the criterion-reversal performance of a group of pigeons trained in a blue-green discrimination. There were 40 trials per day to the criterion of 34 correct choices in the 40 trials, with positive and negative colors reversed for each animal whenever it met that criterion. The results look very

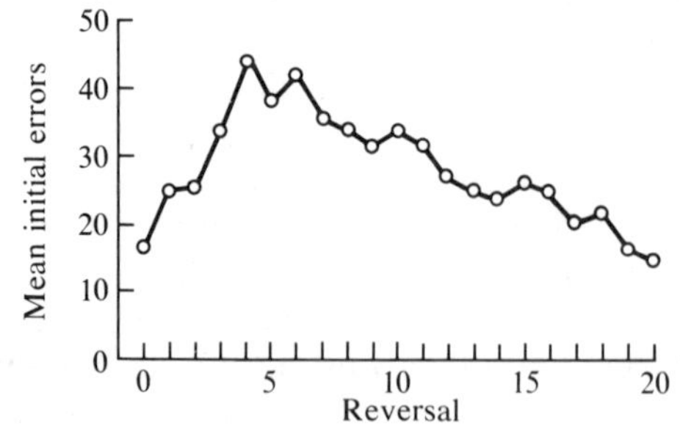

Fig. 8. Visual habit reversal in the pigeon.

much like those obtained in analogous experiments with the rat: There is an initial increase in mean errors to criterion, followed by a progressive, negatively accelerated decline. Now what can we say of the behavior of the pigeon in experiments on probability learning? The pigeon shows random matching only in visual problems; in spatial problems it tends to maximize.

The results for the pigeon, then, are in a sense intermediate between those for the rat and for the fish. Like the rat, the pigeon shows progressive improvement in habit reversal, but, like the fish, it shows random probability matching–in visual problems if not in spatial ones. One conclusion which may be drawn from these results is that experiments on habit reversal and experiments on probability learning tap somewhat different processes. If the processes were the same, any animal would behave either like the fish, or like the rat, in both kinds of experiment. We have, then, been able to separate the processes underlying the two phenomena which differentiate fish and rat by a method which might be called *phylogenetic filtration*. It is interesting, too, that the visual-spatial dichotomy which appeared in work with the decorticated rat appears again in the probability learning of the pigeon. In experiments on habit reversal, the pigeon behaves like a normal rat; in experiments on probability learning, the pigeon behaves, not like a fish, but like an extensively decorticated rat.

Now let me show you some comparable data for several other species. Being very much interested in the reptilian brain, which is the first to show true cortex, I have devoted a good deal of effort to the development of a satisfactory technique for the study of learning in the painted turtle. As in our latest apparatus for monkey, rat, pigeon, and fish, the turtle is presented with two differentially illuminated targets between which it chooses by pressing against one of them. Correct choice is rewarded with a pellet of hamburger or fish which is rotated into the chamber on a solenoid-driven tray. Some experiments on habit reversal now under way in this situation have yielded the data plotted in Figure 9. One group of turtles was trained on a spatial problem (both targets the same color) and another group on a visual problem (red versus green). There were twenty trials per day, with reversal after every four days. As you can see, progressive improvement has appeared in the spatial problem, but not in the visual problem. Some experiments on probability

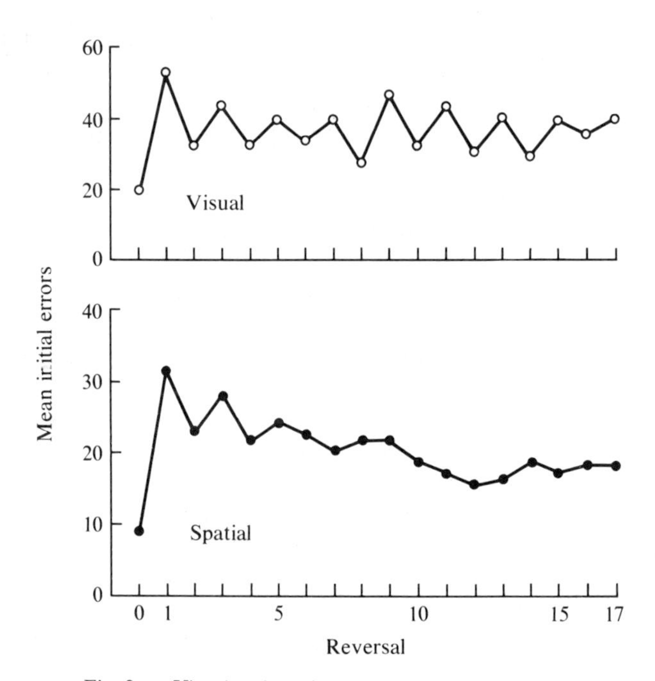

Fig. 9. Visual and spatial habit reversal in the turtle.

learning also are under way in this situation. In spatial problems, only maximizing and nonrandom matching (reward following) have been found, but in visual problems, random matching has begun to appear. This pattern of results, you will remember, is exactly that which was found in decorticated rats. Insofar as performance in these tests is concerned, then, extensive decortication in infancy turns rats into turtles.

I come now to some work with invertebrates. A Y maze was used with the cockroach. The motive utilized is shock avoidance: Ten seconds after the animal is introduced into the starting box, shock is turned on, and remains on, until the animal enters the goal box, which is its home cage; if the animal reaches the goal box in less than ten seconds, it avoids shock entirely. Choices are detected objectively by photocells, but complete automation is not possible, because no satisfactory alternative to handling the animal has been found. The results of an experiment on spatial probability learning in the cockroach, which was patterned after those done with verte-

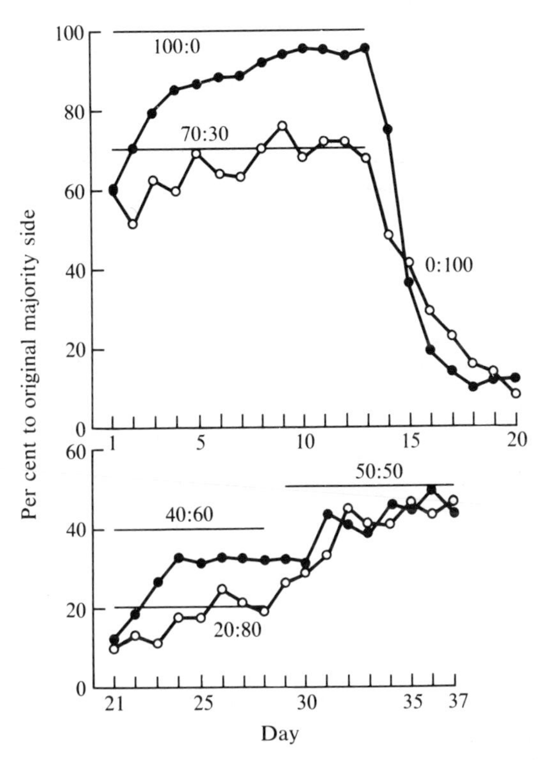

Fig. 10. Spatial probability matching in the cockroach.

brates, are plotted in Figure 10. Like the fish–but *unlike any higher vertebrate*–the cockroach shows random matching under spatial conditions. The results of an experiment on spatial habit reversal in the cockroach are plotted in Figure 11. Three groups of animals were given ten trials per day–one group reversed each day, another group reversed every four days, and a control group never reversed during the stage of the experiment for which data are plotted. Although the four-day group showed no significant improvement (its curve hardly declines at all beyond the first point, which is for the original problem), the daily group did show significant improvement (its curve declining in much the same way as that of the control group). What does this result mean? Have we found in the primitive cockroach a capability which does not exist in the fish? A

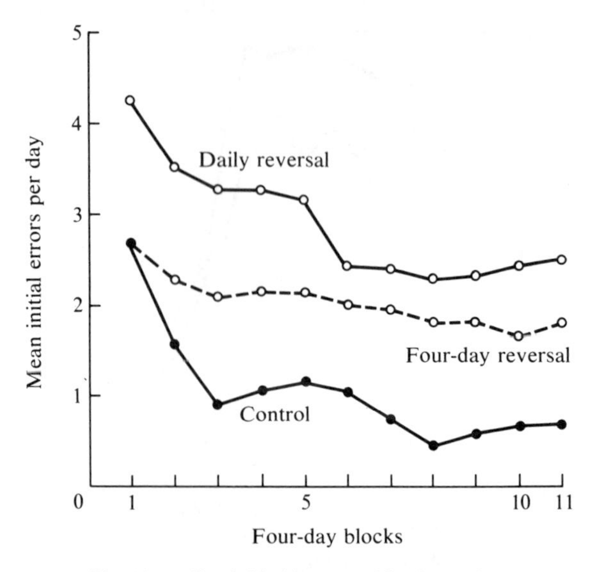

Fig. 11. Spatial habit reversal in the cockroach.

consideration of some results for the earthworm will help to answer this question.

A T maze was developed for the earthworm. The stem of the maze is bright, warm, and dry, and the animal occasionally is shocked in it. A correct turn at the choice point carries the animal to its dark, moist, cool, shock-free home container, while an incorrect turn is punished with shock from a metal door which converts one arm of the maze into a cul. When the animal is shocked for contact with the door, a sensitive relay in the circuit is energized, thereby providing an objective index of error. This technique, again, is a crude one by vertebrate standards, but it seems to give reliable results. Some sample data on spatial habit reversal are plotted in Figure 12. The worms were given five trials per day and reversed every four days. Note that the mean number of errors rose in the first reversal, and thereafter declined progressively, the animals doing better in the fourth and fifth reversals than in the original problem. In a further experiment, however, this improvement was found to be independent of reversal training per se and a function only of general experience in the maze: A control group, trained always to the same side while an experimental group was reversed repeatedly, did not

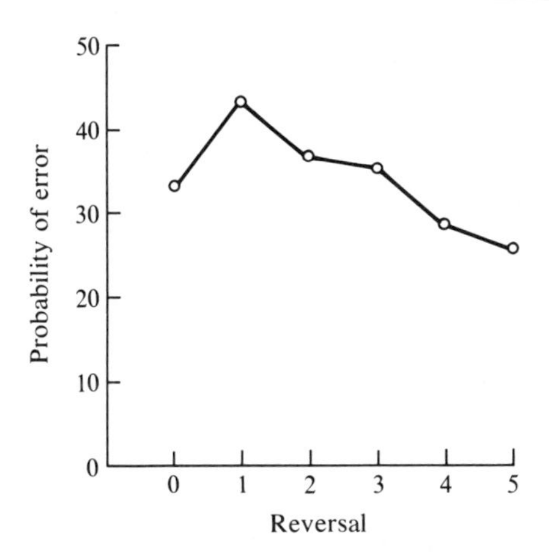

Fig. 12. Spatial habit reversal in the earthworm.

differ from the experimental group when eventually it, too, was reversed. This test for the effects of general experience is feasible in the earthworm, because the turning preferences which it develops do not persist from session to session. The analysis of the progressive improvement shown by the cockroach is, however, a more difficult matter, and I must be content here simply to state the opinion that it reflects, as in the earthworm, not an improvement in reversal capability, but an improved adjustment to the maze situation. The course of that general improvement is traced by the curve for the control group, which parallels that of the daily group. Nonspecific improvement probably is not as evident in the vertebrate data because general adjustment to the experimental situation proceeds rapidly and is essentially completed at the end of pretraining.

The results of these experiments on habit reversal and probability learning in a variety of animals are summarized in Table 1. Spatial and visual problems are categorized separately because they give different results. The rows for all the subjects except one are ordered in accordance with the conventional scale of complexity–monkey at the top and earthworm at the bottom. The only subject whose place in the table is not based on preconceived complexity is the decorticated rat, whose placement (with the turtle, between the pigeon and the fish) is dictated by experimental outcomes. The differences between fish and rat which provided

Table 1. Behavior of a variety of animals in four classes of problem which differentiate rat and fish expressed in terms of similarity to the behavior of one or the other of these two reference animals.

	Spatial problems		*Visual problems*	
Animal	*Reversal*	*Probability*	*Reversal*	*Probability*
Monkey	R	R	R	R
Rat	R	R	R	R
Pigeon	R	R	R	F
Turtle	R	R	F	F
Decorticated rat	R	R	F	F
Fish	F	F	F	F
Cockroach	F	F	–	–
Earthworm	F	–	–	–

Note. F means behavior like that of the fish (Random probability matching and failure of progressive improvement in habit reversal). R means behavior like that of the rat (maximizing or nonrandom probability matching and progressive improvement in habit reversal). Transitional regions are connected by the stepped line. The brackets group animals which have not yet been differentiated by these problems.

points of departure for the subsequent work with other organisms also provide a frame for reference for reading the table: R means that the results obtained in a given kind of experiment with a given subject are like those for the rat (that is, progressive improvement in habit reversal and failure of random matching), while F means that the results obtained are like those for the fish (that is, random matching and failure of progressive improvement). It should be understood that these entries are made with varying degrees of confidence. Where there are no data, there are no entries, but an entry is made even where, as in the case of the turtle, the data are yet fragmentary and incomplete. All entries are based on data from my laboratory, except those for reversal learning in the monkey, which are based on the literature.

The table is an orderly one. In each column there is a single transition from F to R as the scale of subjects is ascended, although the point of transition varies from column to column, suggesting a certain functional independence: Rat-like behavior in spatial problems of both kinds appears first in decorticated rat and turtle, rat-like behavior in visual reversal learning appears first in pigeon, and rat-like behavior in visual probability learning appears first in rat. The eight subjects fall into four different groupings: monkey and rat in one; pigeon in a second; turtle and decorticated rat in a third; fish, cockroach, and earthworm in a fourth. Monkey and rat fall into the same grouping because they are not differentiated by these experiments when all failures of random probability matching are classified as R. The data for the two mammals do, however, show different kinds of sequential dependency in experiments on probability learning, reward following in the rat giving way in the monkey to the opposite strategy (avoiding the rewarded alternatives of the preceding trial). It is interesting to note that this new strategy of the monkey has been manifested thus far only with respect to the spatial locus of reward, even when the alternatives have been visually distinct. This finding fits the generalization suggested at other points in the table: that as we ascend the phyletic scale new modes of adjustment appear earlier in spatial than in visual contexts.

It is of some interest to ask whether R modes of adjustment are in any sense more effective than F modes, and for habit reversal, at least, the answer is clear. Progressive improvement is on its face a superior adjustment, representing a flexibility that cannot help but be of value in an animal's adjustment to changing life circumstances. The answer for probability learning is less clear, although it can be said that maximizing produces a higher percentage of correct choice than does matching. In a 70:30 problem, for example, the probability of correct choice is .70 for maximizing but only .58–(.70 x .70) + (.30 x .30)–for matching. Nonrandom matching is no more successful than random matching by this criterion, but we know that in human subjects it is the outcome of an effort to find a principle that will permit 100% correct choice; the hypotheses tested reflect the observed reward ratio, and they produce a corresponding choice ratio. To the degree that nonrandom matching in infrahuman subjects is based on an emerging hypothetical or strategic capability, it represents a considerable functional advance over random matching.

The table does, of course, have certain obvious limitations. Clearly, I should like to be able to write *bird* rather than *pigeon*, I should like by *fish* to mean more than *mouthbreeder*, and so forth. It will be interesting to discover how representative of their classes are the particular species studied in these experiments–whose choice was dictated largely by practical considerations–and to extend the comparisons to other classes and phyla. I can say, too, that the behavioral categories used in the table almost certainly will need refining; already the R-F dichotomy is strained by the data on probability learning (with R standing for maximizing, for near maximizing, and for nonrandom matching of several different kinds), while better techniques must be found for isolating the various constituents of progressive improvement in habit reversal. The uncontaminated linear order which now appears in the table, while undeniably esthetic, is rather embarrassing from the standpoint of the far-from-linear evolutionary relationships among the species studied; non-linearities are perhaps to be expected as the behavioral categories are refined and as the range of tests is broadened.

Whatever its limitations, the table is useful, I think, not only as a summary of results already obtained, but as a guide to further research. Almost certainly, the order in the table will permit us to reduce the amount of parametric variation which must be done before we are satisfied that some phenomenon for which we are looking in a given animal is not to be found.

REFERENCES

Beach, F. A., 1956. The snark was a boojum, *Amer. Psychol.*, 5, 115-124.

Koch, S., 1959. *Psychology: A Study of a Science.* Vol. 2. *General Systematic Formulations, Learning, and Special Processes*. New York: McGraw-Hill.

Thorndike, E. L., 1911. *Animal Intelligence*. New York: Macmillan.

Primate Learning in Comparative Perspective

J. M. WARREN

I. INTRODUCTION

In what ways does learning in primates differ from learning in other vertebrates? This chapter reviews the experimental data regarding learning by primate and nonprimate species with the objective of answering that question.

The review is doubly selective. It considers only those problems on which both primates and representatives of some other vertebrate taxon have been tested. Thus, there will be very little to say about maze learning since primates are seldom tested in mazes, and nothing at all to say about the Weigl oddity problem (see Chapter 5 by French), because no nonprimate has solved it.

II. CONDITIONING

A. Acquisition of Conditioned Responses

1. CLASSICAL CONDITIONING. The rate of conditioning varies markedly within the same species, even within the same organism, as a function of many experimental conditions. For example, macaque monkeys (*Macaca* spp.) learned to make anticipatory movements to a tone associated with shock after 10 paired presentations of tone

followed by shock (Harris, 1943), but consistent eyelid closure was not observed after 300 combinations of light (CS) and air puff (UCS) in some of the rhesus monkeys (*Macaca mulatta*) studied by Hilgard and Marquis (1936). Indeed, the rate of conditioning of different sorts of responses varies so much within species it is impossible to show any meaningful pattern of phyletic differences.

Nor does it seem likely that other measures of conditioning will reveal coherent patterns of interspecies differences. Hilgard and Marquis compared the changes in response topography during conditioning of lid closure in dog, rhesus monkey, and man, and concluded that "the responses of dog and man are more alike than those of man and monkey" (Hilgard & Marquis, 1936, p. 198).

A similar story may be told about recent studies of the interval between the conditioned and unconditioned stimuli most favorable for rapid learning. Noble *et al.* (1959) found the optimal CS-UCS interval for fish of the genus *Mollienisia* to be 2.0 seconds. The optimal interval in man is 0.5 second (Kimble, 1961). The results obtained from *Mollienisia* were exciting since the longer optimal interval in this form suggested a behavioral disparity which might reflect the great differences in neural organization between fish and man. However, it has since been found that the optimum interval for conditioning in rhesus monkeys is also 2.0 seconds (Noble & Harding, 1963), and is even longer than 2.0 seconds for the pig (Noble & Adams, 1963).

2. INSTRUMENTAL CONDITIONING. Goldfish, pigeons, rats, cats, dogs, squirrel monkeys (*Saimiri sciureus*), rhesus monkeys, and chimpanzees (*Pan*) have recently been tested on the Sidman (1953a, 1953b) avoidance task, in which each response postpones the delivery of shock (Appel, 1960; Behrend & Bitterman, 1963; Black & Morse, 1961; Clark, 1961; Graf & Bitterman, 1963; Kelleher & Cook, 1959; Sidman, 1955; Sidman & Boren, 1957). No interspecies differences in learning were observed. The experimenters who worked with goldfish (Behrend & Bitterman, 1963) and with chimpanzees (Clark, 1961) explicitly pointed out the absence of any important differences between learning by these species and by rats. These results are completely typical of the findings regarding avoidance learning in general. No one has seriously maintained that vertebrate species differ materially in capacity for this kind of learning.

Comparative data on the learning of simple operant responses with positive reinforcement are relatively limited. Experimenters agree that the ease or difficulty of establishing operant responses is more strongly influenced by species' structural and behavioral specializations than by their phyletic status. The details of response shaping are now seldom reported, and species can be compared only with respect to changes in the rate or accuracy of operant performance resulting from changes in the experimental situation after the operant has been stabilized.

The reasonable assumption that the details of shaping are inconsequential for comparative purposes is validated by observations such as the following: fish, chickens, ducks, pigeons, rabbits, dogs, monkeys, and chimpanzees all learn simple discriminated operants with considerable and roughly equivalent facility (Razran, 1961; Voronin, 1962). Very similar operant performances under schedules of partial reinforcement have been demonstrated in such diverse forms as the pigeon, mouse, rat, dog, cat, monkey, and chimpanzee (Ferster & Skinner, 1957).

There is little point in describing additional conditioning experiments which fail to suggest phyletic trends. The available evidence indicates that there is no systematic variation in capacity for simple classical or operant conditioning among the vertebrate species studied thus far.

B. Discrimination of Ambiguous Conditioned Stimuli

Voronin (1962) described several tests of animals' ability to develop appropriate responses when conditioned stimuli function ambiguously, as when they precede reinforcement and nonreinforcement in different contexts. These tests consistently revealed a similar pattern of interspecies differences in learning among vertebrates. For example, baboons (*Papio*) and dogs learn in 3 to 20 trials to respond to a reinforced combination of light and sound conditioned stimuli, and not to respond to unreinforced presentations of either light or sound alone. Fish failed completely to discriminate between the compound stimulus and its components presented separately. Rabbits failed to discriminate as accurately as the dogs or baboons but performed more adequately than the fish.

C. Repeated Extinctions and Reversals of Conditioned Responses

Voronin (1962) also described a series of experiments in which discriminated operants were alternately extinguished and reconditioned until the subjects learned to stop responding after a single extinction trial. The minimum number of experimental sessions required for extinction following a single failure of reinforcement was 10 for baboons, 7 for dogs, 12 for rabbits, 36 for hens, 50 for tortoises, and 68 for fish.

Comparable results were obtained in studies of serial reversals of a discriminated operant. Animals were trained to respond to one of two stimuli, and then the significance of S^D and S^Δ was reversed each time a criterion of learning was attained. Chimpanzees learned after two or three reversals to shift their responses appropriately in a single trial under the altered conditions. Dogs and baboons learned almost as quickly as chimpanzees. Rabbits and jackdaws showed some improvement in inter-task performance, but never approached the level of one-trial learning. Tortoises and fish gave no sign of learning to learn later reversals in fewer trials than were required for the first reversal.

The findings just presented and those of many other experiments (Razran, 1961; Voronin, 1962) indicate a consistent set of differences among vertebrate species in learning certain types of tasks. These tasks all involve stimuli to which responses have been reinforced, but the subject must learn not to respond to these stimuli under specific conditions. Monkeys and chimpanzees learn much more efficiently than rabbits and nonmammalian organisms, but the performance of the primates does not surpass that of dogs. Thus, studies of conditioned-response learning have not suggested any uniquely specific characteristics of learning by primates.

III. DISCRIMINATION LEARNING

A. Single Discrimination Habits

1. SPATIAL DISCRIMINATION. Spatial discrimination is ordinarily a simple and unambiguous task. The subject is confronted with two alternatives, the right and left arms of a T-maze, or objects on the right and left sides of the stimulus tray in the Wisconsin General

Table 1. Trials required by experimentally naive subjects to learn a discrimination with combined spatial and visual cues.

Species	*Age*	*N*	*Mean*	*Range*	*Reference*
Paradise fish[a]	Adult	72	34	0-170	Warren (1960c)
Goldfish[a]	Adult	6	20	15-25	Warren, unpublished data
Chickens[a]	53 Days	20	5	0-20	Warren *et al.* (1960)
Cats[b]	Adult	38	12	0-58	Cronholm *et al.* (1960)
Horses[b]	Adult	2	7.5	7-8	Warren & Warren (1962).
Raccoon[b]	Adult	1	6	—	Warren & Warren (1962)
Rhesus monkeys[c]	15 Days	10	8	0-50+	Mason & Harlow (1958)
	45 Days	10	6	0-50+	Mason & Harlow (1958)

[a] Criterion: 18 correct in 20 noncorrection trials.
[b] Criterion: 11 correct in 12 noncorrection trials, and last 8 all correct.
[c] Criterion: 18 correct in 20 correction (rerun) trials.

Test Apparatus (WGTA; see Chapter 1 by Meyer *et al.*), and responding to one side but not the other is consistently reinforced. Frequently the discriminanda differ only in spatial location, but rhesus monkeys (Warren, 1959a), cats (Warren, 1959b) and chickens (Warren *et al.*, 1960) learn spatial discriminations more readily if the right and left alternatives differ in visual characteristics than if they do not.

The results obtained from experimentally naive subjects of several species, trained to discriminate between stimuli differing in both position and brightness, are presented in Table 1. The rhesus monkeys were trained with a correction method, and one animal in each of the two age groups failed to reach criterion within the arbitrary limit of 50 trials; the means for the monkey groups are based on the scores of the successful subjects only. In contrast, the noncorrection method was used in training the nonprimates, and each individual was tested until it reached criterion. Although a bias in favor of the monkeys results from comparing correction with noncorrection trials and from excluding the scores of the monkeys that failed to learn quickly, the ranges of individual differences within species were, in fact, so great that none of the species tested can be thought to differ reliably from any other in speed of solving the simple spatial discrimination task.

2. NONSPATIAL DISCRIMINATION. In nonspatial discrimination problems, two dissimilar stimuli are each presented on either the right or left over a series of trials in a balanced irregular sequence.

The subject must suppress any tendency to respond to positional cues and must consistently select one of the stimuli, for example, black rather than white, independent of its locus in space.

There is no evidence that vertebrate species differ appreciably in the rate at which experimentally naive animals learn a nonspatial discrimination. Gardner and Nissen (1948) summarized a series of experiments with cows, horses, sheep, chimpanzees, and human idiots and imbeciles tested on a simple discrimination, between a feedbox covered with a black drape and an uncovered box. The retarded humans and the chimpanzees performed at about the same level, and both types of primates learned the discrimination more slowly than the domestic animals.

Although naive primates may not differ markedly from other mammals in the rate of learning simple positional or visual discrimination habits, a recent experiment by the writer indicates that rhesus monkeys differ markedly from cats in their responsiveness to different sorts of cues in discrimination learning. Rhesus monkeys and cats were trained to the same criterion in the WGTA with the same pair of objects differing in multiple visual dimensions. The position of the objects was varied in an irregular sequence from trial to trial, and one group of each species was required to choose consistently one of the objects and to ignore spatial cues, the usual visual discrimination task. The second group, however, was required to respond to the right or left on every trial and to ignore the objects. The naive monkeys trained on the nonspatial problem learned much more quickly than those trained on the spatial discrimination (Table II). Quite the reverse was true for the cats. The cats trained on the spatial task learned in less than half as many trials as those trained on the object discrimination. These findings do not imply that monkeys are inferior to cats in spatial learning; instead, they suggest that the untrained monkey responds so strongly to

Table II. Trials required by experimentally naive rhesus monkeys and cats to learn discrimination habits.

	Monkeys			*Cats*		
Relevant cues	*N*	*Mean*	*Range*	*N*	*Mean*	*Range*
Position	5	66	19-109	8	23	6-62
Object	5	35	12-86	10	60	1-311

object cues that it is seriously distracted when these are irrelevant and only positional cues are relevant. The cat, on the other hand, has little difficulty in suppressing responses to object cues when they are opposed to spatial cues.

Harlow, (1951) has pointed out that experimentally sophisticated monkeys respond more strongly to object than positional cues. The study just described indicates that this preferential response to object cues in the monkey exists before any formal training. Studies of maze learning by monkeys suggest that the dominance of visual over spatial cues is very general in primates. The learning curves for sparrows, rats, and monkeys trained on the Hampton Court maze are virtually identical (Bitterman, 1960, Fig. 2). Rhesus monkeys (Orbach, 1959) learn the Lashley III maze in fewer than half as many trials as rats (Lashley, 1929), but Orbach provided a clear explanation of the monkeys' superiority. "Unlike the rat in the enclosed maze, the monkeys responded during training to the visual requirements of the situation, and the learning of sequences of turns seemed completely unnecessary. At the entrance to each alley, the monkey scanned both ends, identified the next entrance, and took the appropriate path to it" (Orbach, 1959, pp. 51-52).

Species differences in initial responsiveness to visual and spatial cues in discrimination learning are not consistently correlated with problem-solving in general. Chickens, pigeons (Jones, 1954), and "maze-dull" rats (Rosenzweig *et al.*, 1960), like monkeys, all respond preferentially to visual rather than spatial cues.

Parametric comparisons of stimulus variables in discrimination learning by primates and nonprimates should reveal additional differences in the kinds of hypotheses that untrained animals of various species bring to the learning situation. Data on the relative dominance of cues for different species are needed to sensibly interpret interspecies differences in performance, but several other kinds of information are needed as well. Recent studies of the maturation of maze learning in rhesus monkeys (Zimmermann, 1963) and in kittens (Warren & Warren, unpublished) serve to illustrate this point.

The task was the closed-field intelligence test for animals, described by Rabinovitch and Rosvold (1951) and illustrated in Fig. 1. Infant rhesus monkeys and kittens were adapted to the test situation by training them to run from a fixed starting point to the

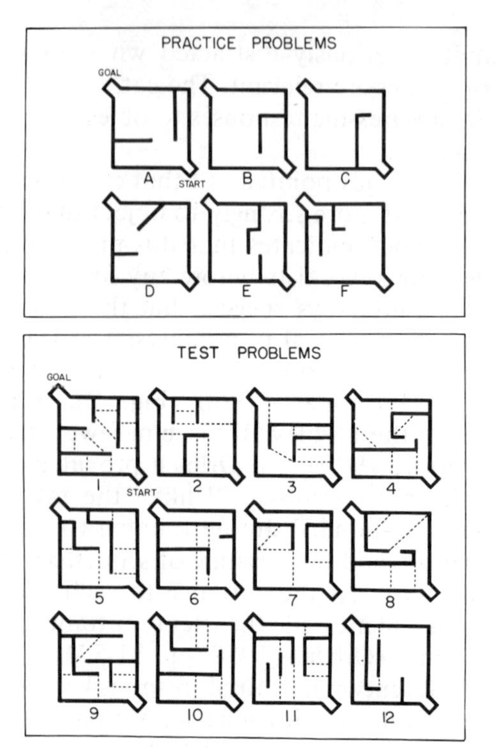

Fig. 1. The closed-field intelligence test for animals.

goal box in the opposite corner of the square enclosure and on a series of practice problems (A through F in Fig. 1). Pretraining was continued for each individual subject until it met a criterion of rapid and direct approach to the goal box. The animals were then tested on the standard series of 12 problems, consisting of different arrangements of barriers across the direct path from start to goal that are shown in the lower portion of Fig. 1. Errors consisted of deviations from the true path into the culs indicated by dashed lines in Fig. 1; deeper penetrations into the error zones were scored as two errors. Both the monkeys and the kittens were tested for 8 trials on each of two problems presented per day; performance was measured in terms of errors made on a total of 96 trials (twelve 8-trial problems). The rewards were meat for the kittens, and, for the baby monkeys, both milk and contact with a surrogate mother or a diaper. The results for five groups of four monkeys each, tested at 15, 45, 90, and 120 days

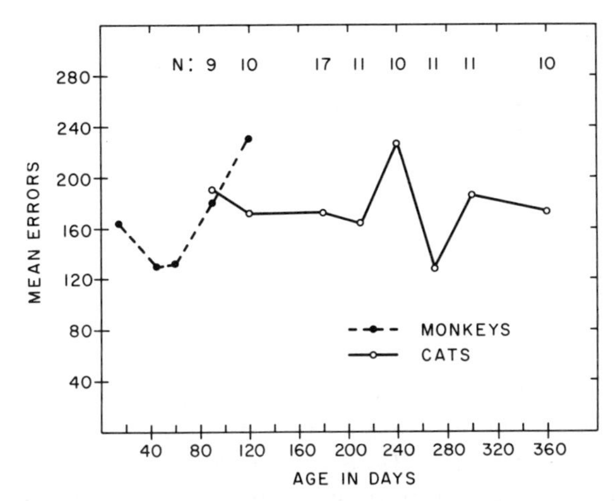

Fig. 2. Mean errors on the closed-field test of intelligence as a function of age in rhesus monkeys and cats.

of age, and for eight groups of cats, ranging in age from 90 to 360 days, are presented in Fig. 2. The highest mean error score for any group was that for the 120-day-old monkeys, but observations of the behavior of these animals made it clear that the objective error scores told little about their learning capacity, since they responded to the test apparatus as if it were a playground, often making a direct approach to the goal and removing the diaper without entering to end the trial. Instead, they romped about, exploiting the opportunities for play afforded by the maze, and making many more errors, without manifest interest in milk, even though they were severely deprived.

Clearly, any conclusion regarding either the ontogeny or phylogeny of learning based upon the performance of the monkeys tested at 120 days of age would be misleading, since the experimenters failed to provide a reward attractive enough to outweigh the chance to play in error zones. It is not intrinsically obvious in Fig. 2, but the data presented for cage-reared cats are also largely invalid for comparative purposes. Both alley cats (Warren *et al.*, 1961) and laboratory-reared kittens given regular opportunities to explore complex environments before being given this test make substantially lower error scores than the sample considered here.

The foregoing discussion is calculated to raise the question of the validity of interspecies differences in the measured aspects of learning performance. There are no pure, uncontaminated measures of learning proficiency; sensory, emotional, motivational, maturational, and experiential factors inevitably influence performance, and must always be considered carefully when comparing the learning observed in primates and other animal groups.

3. PROBABILITY LEARNING. Probability-learning experiments are characterized by the use of reinforcement ratios other than 100:0. Instead of reinforcing responses to one stimulus on every trial and never reinforcing responses to the other, both alternatives are reinforced in fixed proportions, such as 70:30 or 60:40, in a random sequence. Interest centers upon the sequential pattern of choices made by the subject; three types of response patterns or strategies have been described. "Matching" refers to the distribution of responses to the stimuli in a proportion approximating the ratio of reinforcement; matching may either be random and unsystematic, or reflect some clear pattern of sequential dependencies. "Maximizing" occurs when a subject consistently makes the more-frequently-reinforced choice, and never makes the less-frequently-reinforced choice. With any differential ratio between reinforcement of the two choices, consistent performance of the more-frequently-rewarded response results in the maximum number of reinforcements possible (hence, the name for this strategy).

Fish match randomly on both spatial and nonspatial discrimination tasks (Behrend & Bitterman, 1961; Bitterman *et al.*, 1958). Pigeons maximize on spatial discrimination tasks, but fail to do so consistently on nonspatial discriminations, and match randomly under some conditions (Bullock & Bitterman, 1962; Graf *et al.*, 1964). Rats (Bitterman *et al.*, 1958) and monkeys (Meyer, 1960; Wilson, 1960; Wilson & Rollin, 1959) usually maximize. When rhesus monkeys fail to maximize, they adopt a systematic pattern of responses such as alternation after reinforcement (Wilson *et al.*, 1964); in this one instance of nonmaximizing behavior, the monkeys responded more like humans than like fish or pigeons.

The comparative results of probability-learning experiments are similar to those obtained in many conditioning studies. Monkeys behave in a clearly more adaptive manner than nonmammalian animals, but their behavior seems not to differ in any important qualitative respect from that of rats.

4. THE INTERMEDIATE-SIZE PROBLEM. In the intermediate-size problem, three stimuli differing in size are presented simultaneously, and the subject is obliged to choose the middle-sized rather than the largest or smallest of the three stimuli. Lashley (1938b) was unable to train rats to solve the intermediate-size problem with a reasonable amount of tuition. This task is comparatively easy for chimpanzees. Six chimpanzees learned to choose the middle-sized of three stimuli differing in the ratio of 1.6 : 1 in a mean of 135 trials (Spence, 1942). Unpublished observations by Warren indicate that the intermediate-size problem is extremely difficult for cats tested with stimuli differing in the 1.6 : 1 ratio; only one of six cats learned, and he required 1,320 trials. As the difference ratio between the stimuli was increased, more of the cats learned; but even when each stimulus was three times larger than the next smaller in the series, six cats averaged 668 trials to criterion. Under the most favorable conditions investigated so far, the cats were grossly inferior to Spence's chimpanzees in rate of learning the intermediate-size problem.

Theoretical discussions (Hull, 1952; Spence, 1942) suggest that rapid solution of problems like intermediate size depends upon precise inhibitory control of choice behavior. Progressive improvement in performance on the intermediate-size problem from rats to cats to chimpanzees lends support to recent theories that emphasize the importance of inhibitory processes in the phylogeny of learning (Harlow, 1958; Harlow & Hicks, 1957; Voronin, 1962).

The cats, like Spence's chimpanzees, were tested for transposition responses after they mastered the intermediate-size problem, to determine whether they had learned to respond to the absolute or relative size of the stimuli used in original training. If an animal had been trained initially with 100-, 160-, and 256-cm^2 squares, it was tested with 160-, 256-, and 409-cm^2 squares, and all responses were reinforced. If the subject had learned to select the middle-sized stimulus, it would select 256, but if it had learned on the basis of absolute properties of the stimuli, it would continue to select 160 even though it was the smallest of the transposition series. Table III summarizes the performances of Spence's chimpanzees and the cats on the following transposition tests: (1) 10 minutes after original learning, (2) 24 hours after original learning, (3) 24 hours after being retrained to criterion on the original problem, (4) 10 minutes after reversal learning in which the subject learned to choose the

Table III. Percentage of relative and absolute choices in tests for transposition of intermediate-size learning by 6 chimpanzees and 10 cats.

	Chimpanzees		*Cats*	
Test	*Relative*	*Absolute*	*Relative*	*Absolute*
1	12	88	24	74
2	23	73	14	81
3	19	74	16	83
4	39	61	33	65
5	36	64	45	53
Mean	26	72	26	71

NOTE: Rows do not add to 100% because one of the three stimuli was not intermediate in either relative or absolute terms.

middle-sized of the original transposition set, and (5) 24 hours after reversal learning. In spite of the great difference between these species in learning, their transposition behavior is similar. Both the chimpanzees and the cats made approximately three times as many absolute as relative responses.

The obvious conclusion, that species do not vary appreciably in transfer of discrimination habits, can be generalized rather widely. A comprehensive review of studies of shape discrimination (Sutherland, 1961) reveals a remarkable degree of consistency in equivalence reactions across a wide taxonomic range. When differences in the transfer of discrimination habits are observed among species, they are frequently difficult to relate systematically to phyletic status, and appear to be more strongly influenced by differences in visual sensitivity than in learning ability.

Ontogenetic studies of monkeys support this conclusion. The generalization of shape-discrimination habits is essentially similar in infant and adult rhesus monkeys (see Chapter 11 by Zimmermann and Torrey in Volume II). Infant monkeys reared in a strictly-controlled visual environment generalize along continuum on their first exposure to stimuli other than the one used in original learning of a discriminated operant (Ganz & Riesen, 1962).

To summarize the results presented in this section, experimentally naive primates evidently do not differ conspicuously from nonprimates in learning two-choice spatial or nonspatial discriminations, or in transposition or equivalence reactions. Naive primates are, however, more responsive to object than spatial cues and differ in this respect from cats, but not from chickens or pigeons. Monkeys and rats effectively maximize the number of rewards obtained in probability-learning experiments; nonmammalian species fail to do so consistently. Finally, both rats and cats are markedly inferior to chimpanzees in performance on the intermediate-size problem; this is the first task considered that appears to differentiate between the learning capacity of primates and that of other mammals.

B. Learning Sets

There are two definitions of the phenomenon of "learning how to learn" implicit in the comparative literature: (1) increased efficiency in learning repeated reversals of the same discrimination problem (see Chapter 5 by French), and (2) progressive improvement in learning consecutive nonspatial discrimination problems (see Chapter 2 by Miles). Many important questions, empirical and theoretical, about the equivalence or nonequivalence of the two definitions remain unanswered, but studies using the techniques of repeated-reversal learning and interproblem learning have yielded evidence of an orderly phyletic trend toward progressively greater learning capacity within the vertebrate series.

1. REPEATED REVERSALS OF THE SAME PROBLEM. Fish fail to improve in learning repeated reversals of a spatial discrimination (Bitterman *et al.*, 1958; Warren, 1960c). In fact, when 20 paradise fish were trained to criterion on each of 20 positional reversals in a T-maze, the number of trials required for learning consecutive reversals *increased* progressively (Warren, 1960c).

In contrast to the results with fish, evidence of learning to learn repeated reversals with progressively fewer errors has been obtained in experiments with turtles (Kirk & Bitterman, 1963), chickens (Warren *et al.*, 1960), and pigeons (Bitterman, 1963), as well as every mammalian species studied: rats (Dufort *et al.*, 1954), cats (Cronholm *et al.*, 1960), horses and raccoons (Warren & Warren, 1962), and rhesus monkeys (Harlow, 1949). Performance on repeated reversals of a position discrimination does not vary systematically among the mammals studied; the learning functions for rats and retarded humans are quite similar (House & Zeaman, 1959, Fig. 1).

Turtles make progressively more errors in learning repeated reversals of a visual discrimination problem (Bitterman, 1963), their performance indicating "learning not to learn" in the same manner that fish fail on repeated reversals of a spatial habit.

But there is no evidence that the performance of primates differs substantially from that of birds or nonprimate mammals on repeated reversals of a nonspatial discrimination. Both chickens (Bacon *et al.*, 1962) and pigeons (Bitterman, 1963) show a progressive decrease in errors to criterion over repeated reversals, and eventually learn to reverse their responses very quickly. The performances of naive rats and squirrels (Rollin, 1963) and cats and rhesus monkeys (Warren, unpublished data) on a series of reversals of an object-quality discrimination in the WGTA are compared in Fig. 3. The curves for cats and monkeys are nearly identical. The performance of the rats and squirrels is inferior to that of the cats and monkeys, but chimpanzees (Nissen *et al.*, 1938; Schusterman, 1962) often do so badly on the first few reversals of a visual discrimination that it would be impossible to substantiate a claim that primates are more proficient on this kind of task than other mammals or birds.

2. INTERPROBLEM LEARNING. Several investigators have demonstrated the formation of learning sets by rats (Koronakos & Arnold, 1957; Weaver & Michels, 1961; Wright *et al.*, 1963), but

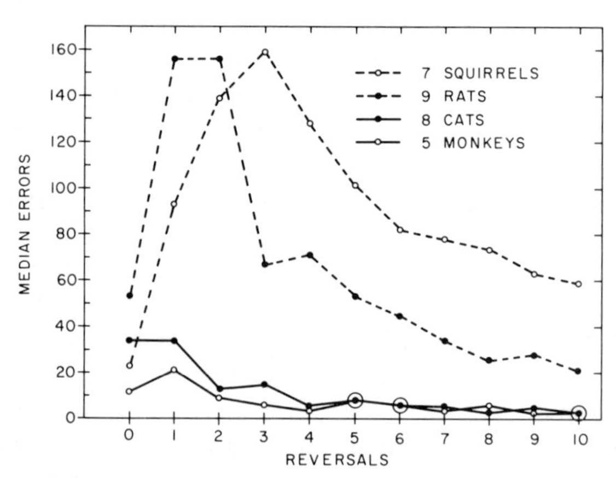

Fig. 3. Errors to criterion on repeated reversals of a nonspatial discrimination by squirrels, rats, cats, and rhesus monkeys.

underestimated the rat's capacity for interproblem learning because they used 2-dimensional pattern-stimuli instead of 3-dimensional objects. It is well known that rhesus monkeys form learning sets much more slowly when tested with patterns than with objects (see Chapter 1 by Meyer *et al.*). More satisfactory data for comparative purposes have been obtained by Tyrrell (1963), who trained rats in a modified WGTA to displace 3-dimensional objects with their heads. The objects were like those typically used in learning-set experiments with carnivores and primates. The performance of Tyrrell's rats on 80 50-trial discrimination problems was similar to that of cats tested under similar conditions by Warren and Baron (1956). Both species showed considerable intraproblem learning within each 20-problem block, and the performance of both species improved markedly from block to block. Initial stimulus preferences strongly affected the performance of both the rats and the cats, resulting in poorer performance on problems in which the subject made an error on trial 1 than on problems in which the subject made a correct response on this trial. This effect was greater for the cats; so if there is a difference between species under these conditions of testing, it is in favor of the rat. There is no convincing evidence that raccoons (Johnson & Michels, 1958; Shell & Riopelle, 1957) form learning sets more efficiently than cats or rats. The performance of these nonprimate mammals is only slightly superior to that of pigeons tested under similar conditions (Zeigler, 1961).

By far the most conspicuous variation in capability for forming learning sets occurs among the primates. Interproblem learning over 6-trial discrimination problems by four rats and three squirrels (Rollin, unpublished), cats (Meyers *et al.*, 1962), marmosets (*Callithrix*) and rhesus monkeys (Miles & Meyer, 1956), and squirrel monkeys (Miles, 1957) is plotted in Fig. 4. All of the species studied show an improvement in interproblem learning, but at markedly different rates, and attain quite different asymptotic levels of performance. The rodents' curves remain at essentially chance levels over the first 800 problems, and indicate only very slow and gradual improvement over the next 1,000 problems, the rats and squirrels averaging 64.5 and 61.3% correct responses on the last 200 problems. Their terminal level of performance is lower than that attained by cats or monkeys in many fewer problems. The rhesus monkeys are obviously superior to the squirrel monkeys, marmosets, and cats.

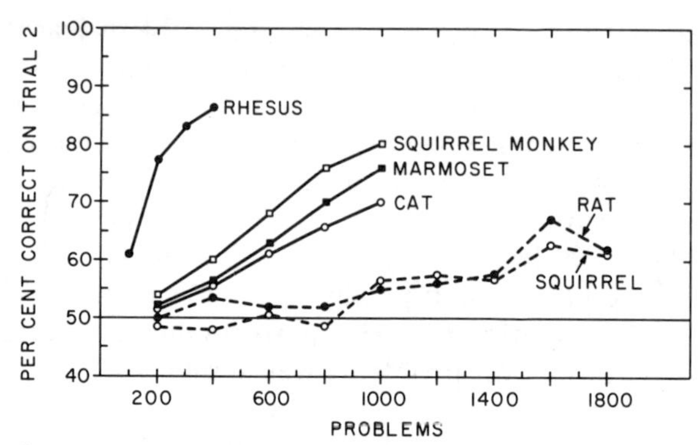

Fig. 4. Discrimination-learning-set formation by primates, carnivores, and rodents.

Learning-set curves for cebus monkeys (*Cebus albifrons*) and spider monkeys (*Ateles geoffroyi*) (Shell & Riopelle, 1958) would fall between those for squirrel monkeys and rhesus monkeys in Fig. 4.

In general, the available data suggest that the phylogenetic development of capacity for learning-set formation in mammals is best described as a continuous ʃ-function, with no sharp discontinuities between adjacent taxa, but with marked quantitative differences between the extremes of the distribution. At the lower end of the scale, rats perform as well as cats or raccoons under favorable conditions (50-trial problems), but not under more rigorous circumstances of testing (6-trial problems). The transition from the carnivore to the primitive-primate level of performance is not abrupt. Taking into consideration the many data (e.g., Warren *et al.*, 1963) showing a relation between the number of differential cues available to an animal and the rate of learning-set formation, the slight superiority of the marmosets over the cats seen in Fig. 4 can be attributed very largely to the presence of color vision in marmosets (Miles, 1958) and its absence (Meyer *et al.*, 1954) or its, at best, extremely poor development (Clayton, 1963) in cats.

The steeply-rising portion of our metaphorical ogive corresponds to the rapid and steady improvement in learning-set acquisition through the New World monkeys, to the high level represented by the rhesus monkey (Harlow, 1959) and other Old World forms like the sooty mangabey (*Cercocebus torquatus*) (Behar, 1962). The upper horizontal limb of the ʃ represents the absence of any major difference in interproblem learning between macaques and anthropoid apes (Fischer, 1962; Harlow, 1959; Hayes *et al.*, 1953; Rumbaugh & Rice, 1962).

How long the currently tidy phylogenetic sequence in learning-set proficiency will endure is a matter for conjecture; Crawford (1962) has recently reported that cynomolgus monkeys (*Macaca irus*) were inferior to spider monkeys in discrimination-learning-set formation and in learning to reverse visual discriminations in response to changed locations of the stimuli.

Primate learning, as measured by the formation of learning sets, differs quantitatively but not qualitatively from learning by rodents and carnivores. Further differences between primates and other mammals have been demonstrated in respect to forming sets for discrimination reversal to a sign, and transfer of the effects of repeated-reversal training.

Rhesus monkeys learn to reverse discriminations without error when reversal of the stimulus-reward relation is signaled by a change in the color of the tray on which the discriminanda are presented (Riopelle & Copelan, 1954). Experiments comparing the effectiveness of food and nonfood signs in reversal learning were performed with cats (Warren, 1960a) and with rhesus monkeys (Warren, 1960e). Apparatus, stimulus objects, and trial procedures were identical for both species. The stimulus objects were presented on a white tray during the discrimination phase of each problem, and the white tray was retained during the reversal phase for the no-cue group of monkeys and cats. For the cue groups, however, reversal was signaled by replacing the white tray with a black one before the first reversal trial. All of the subjects were trained to criterion on 80 discrimination and reversal problems.

The final levels of proficiency are shown in Fig. 5, which presents intraproblem learning curves for the last block of 20 problems. The curves for the monkeys are typical discontinuous functions expected from experimentally sophisticated monkeys. The no-cue group averaged 2% and 88% correct responses on the first and second reversal trials. The cue group responded to the change in the color of the test tray as a reversal cue and made 85% correct responses on the first reversal trial. In other words, changing the color of the test tray eventually becomes as effective a cue for reversal as nonreward on the first reversal trial for monkeys.

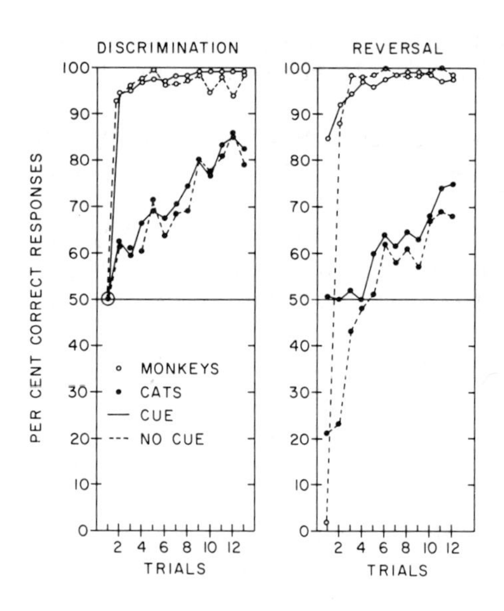

Fig. 5. Intraproblem learning curves for cats and rhesus monkeys trained on discrimination reversal to food and nonfood signs.

In both discrimination and reversal learning, the curves for the cats indicate a much more gradual and continuous improvement than is seen in the monkeys. It would be misleading to compare the functions for the cats and monkeys in absolute terms because the previous histories of the groups were not identical, and the cats, of course, could not get color cues from the stimulus-objects as the monkeys could. But the cue cats had precisely the same number of experiences with the exchange of a black for a white tray as a cue for reversal, and the fact that they were much more successful than the no-cue cats on reversal trials 1 and 2 shows that they were sensitive to the tray cue. Therefore, the gross inferiority of the cue cats to the cue monkeys indicates a substantially superior ability of monkeys to form a set for discrimination reversal to a sign. Indeed, the chance performance of the cue cats over the first four reversal trials, and their failure to differ reliably from the no-cue cats in number of errors to criterion, suggest that changing the color of the test tray has the effect of distracting stimulus rather than of a cue (Warren, 1960a).

Chimpanzees trained on repeated reversals of three visual discrimination habits showed very great facilitation when subsequently tested on a series of 6-trial discrimination problems, averaging about 90% correct on the first 30 problems (Schusterman, 1962). The transfer effect was specific to the training on reversals, since a group trained to alternate between objects performed no better than naive animals on the 6-trial problems. Schusterman attributed the superiority of the reversal group's learning-set formation to these animals' acquisition of a "win-stay, lose-shift" strategy with respect to objects during reversal training (see Chapter 3 by Levine).

I have performed a very similar experiment with three groups of cats. The control group of 11 cats, without any prior training, was trained to a criterion of 10 consecutive correct responses on each of 80 discriminations between stimuli differing in many visual dimensions. Two experimental groups of cats were trained on the same discrimination problems as the controls, after they had been pretrained on tasks calculated to produce positive or negative transfer to the learning-set series. Eight cats were pretrained on 60 reversals of a visual discrimination habit with a single pair of objects. As in learning-set training, only responses to objects were consistently rewarded; so this group, the object group, was expected to show positive transfer. The other experimental group, the position group, consisted of eight cats pretrained on 60 reversals with the same objects used in pretraining the object group. The positions of the objects were varied randomly from right to left as in a visual discrimination, but object cues were irrelevant, and responding consistently to the right or left was rewarded. Thus the position group was trained to ignore visual cues in favor of positional cues, and should have formed habits that would interfere with subsequent learning-set formation.

Both groups learned to solve the repeated reversals with increasing efficiency and averaged about 4 errors to a criterion of 10 consecutive correct responses on the last 10 reversals presented. A portion of the interreversal learning curve for the object group is shown in Fig. 5. The median number of trials in pretraining was 1,202 for the position group and 1,458 for the object group.

When the two experimental groups were tested on the series of 80 nonspatial discrimination problems, however, their performances did not differ reliably from one another nor from that of the control group; all three groups showed a progressive reduction in the number of trials to criterion, but there was no evidence of differential transfer effects. The implication of these results is clear. Extended training on repeated reversals failed to influence subsequent learning-set performance of cats, although similar pretraining resulted in conspicuous positive transfer in Schusterman's chimpanzees. This discrepancy suggests that primates and nonprimates may differ in the types of strategies they develop on objectively similar discrimination tasks. Further research on the transfer of learning sets is badly needed.

The major points made in the discussion of learning-set formation by primates and other vertebrates may be summarized quite succinctly. Mammals and birds differ from fish and reptiles in being able to learn repeated discrimination reversals in progressively fewer trials, but primates are not markedly more proficient than other mammals or birds. The variation among mammals in capacity for interproblem learning, the capacity to learn consecutive nonspatial discrimination problems with increasing efficiency, appears to be quantitative rather than qualitative. All of the species tested have shown some capacity for learning to learn, but no nonprimate mammal yet tested has approached the level of one-trial learning observed in the rhesus monkey. Cats fail to learn discrimination reversal to a sign within a number of problems sufficient for monkeys to form such a set, and cats fail to transfer training on repeated reversals of a discrimination habit to an interproblem-learning task. Chimpanzees trained on repeated reversals of three problems show very strong positive-transfer effects.

IV. DOUBLE ALTERNATION

The subject must learn to make a series of right and left responses in a constant temporal sequence, typically RRLL, in order to solve the double-alternation problem (see Chapter 5 by French). Successful double alternation was once presumed to occur in the absence of differential exteroceptive or kinesthetic cues. In other words, it was believed to depend upon symbolic or representational processes (Hunter, 1928) analogous to counting in verbal humans (Gellermann,

1931b), and "higher" than those involved in the solution of single alternation (RLRL). Single alternation was assumed to be a simple problem that could be learned readily on the basis of differential kinesthetic cues. The status of double alternation as a measure of symbolic behavior was supported by the phyletic evidence. Rats failed to learn double alternation in the temporal maze (Hunter, 1920) or learned slowly after elaborate preliminary training (Hunter & Nagge, 1931). Raccoons (Hunter, 1928), cats (Karn, 1938; Karn & Patton, 1939), and dogs (Karn & Malamud, 1939) performed more adequately than rats, but were inferior to rhesus monkeys (Gellermann, 1931a, 1931c).

This elegant hierarchical order of capacity in mammals rested on a very flimsy foundation of facts. Most of the species studied were represented by only one or two subjects, and it was impossible to estimate the range of individual differences within species in capacity for double-alternation learning. More adequate samples of rhesus monkeys (Warren & Sinha, 1959), cats, (Warren, 1961), and raccoons (Johnson, 1961) have recently been tested on double alternation in the WGTA under very similar experimental conditions. All were trained on sequences of four responses, with responses in RRLL sequence rewarded as described in detail by Stewart and Warren (1957). The results are shown in Fig. 6 as cumulative percentages of subjects meeting criterion (80% correct over 50 sequences) after the number of sequences indicated on the abscissa. The curve for the monkeys ends abruptly because the animals were

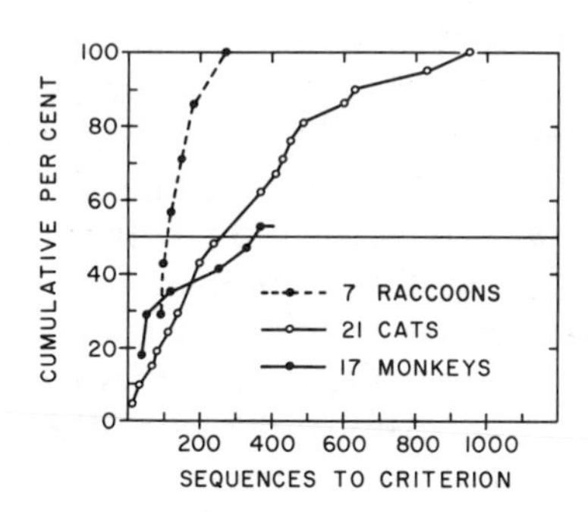

Fig. 6. Percentages of raccoons, of cats, and of rhesus monkeys having met a criterion of double-alternation learning.

tested on a maximum of 450 sequences. The median number of sequences to criterion was 110 for the raccoons, 270 for the cats, and 370 for the monkeys. Individual differences within species, however, were great enough to preclude any inference of reliable differences between species. Some monkeys and cats solve double alternation almost immediately, while others require substantially more extensive training.

The distribution of double-alternation scores for the rhesus monkeys suggests a resolution of an annoying discrepancy in the primate literature. No one, to the best of my knowledge, has ever succeeded in replicating Gellermann's (1931c) results on rapid double-alternation learning by monkeys. Extremely slow and imperfect learning has been observed in small samples of rhesus (Leary *et al.*, 1952; Warren *et al.*, 1957) and cynomolgus (Warren, unpublished data) macaques, and gibbons (*Hylobates*) (Schusterman & Bernstein, 1962). The pattern of variation among the rhesus monkeys studied by Warren and Sinha suggests that Gellermann was unusually fortunate in his sampling and worked with representatives of the rather small minority of monkeys which are highly competent at double-alternation learning, and that later workers failed to replicate his results because their samples included only monkeys of average competence and none of the gifted minority.

The data presented in Fig. 6 demonstrate that primates and carnivores do not differ significantly in learning of double-alternation sequences of four responses, and Stewart and Warren (1957) have shown that some cats, like Gellermann's monkeys, can perform adequately on more extensive double-alternation sequences of eight responses. The observations that rabbits can learn double alternation in the WGTA at least as rapidly as cats (Livesey, 1964) and that rats can learn double alternation readily in the Skinner box (Schlosberg & Katz, 1943; G. Heise, personal communication) complete the demolition of the alleged correlation between phyletic status and double-alternation capability in mammals.

There are additional grounds for rejecting claims that double alternation is a test of symbolic behavior. Rhesus monkeys deprived of most of their cerebral cortex are not significantly impaired on this task relative to intact controls (Warren *et al.*, 1957). Yamaguchi and Warren (1961) found that cats learn double alternation reliably more rapidly than single alternation, and presented detailed analyses indicating that double alternation is learned as a highly specific serial order (see Chapter 5 by French). Therefore, the relative difficulty of double and single alternation varies among species as a function of characteristic differences in sequential-response preferences, and not as a function of general capacity for problem solving.

It is by now patent that the only reason for treating double alternation in a separate section of the chapter is historical precedent. Empirically, the results obtained in testing primates and other mammals on this task would dictate its inclusion in Section III, A, since it is no more successful than simple discrimination problems in differentiating the performance of primates from that of other mammals.

V. DELAYED RESPONSE

Like double alternation, delayed-response performance was once thought to imply the presence of symbolic or ideational processes in animals. This belief was also supported by data showing that delayed-response performance was correlated with phyletic status among the mammals (see Chapter 4 by Fletcher). Both notions were severely criticized by Maier and Schneirla (1935), who pointed out that every species studied could delay successfully for hours, indeed for days, if tested with distinctively different response-alternatives, and that no mammal could long delay its responses if the alternatives lacked distinctiveness.

Until recently, conservatives could object to the heterogeneous tests that Maier and Schneirla accepted as valid measures of delayed-response capability, and maintain that, if they were tested under strictly comparable conditions, nonprimate mammals would be found inferior to primates in terms of the maximum delay possible in delayed-response tests. But raccoons (Michels & Brown, 1959) and cats (Warren *et al.*, 1962) can successfully delay their responses for at least 40 seconds in the WGTA under conditions approximating those of experiments with primates. Although no effort was made to determine precisely the upper limit of the carnivores' capacity for delaying responses, the high levels of performance observed with 40-second delays suggest that primates and carnivores may not differ materially in respect to the maximum delay possible in the WGTA.

Primates and nonprimates also seem not to differ in some other aspects of delayed-response proficiency. Intersubject variability among 17 rhesus monkeys trained on 5-second delayed response was so great that French and Harlow (1962) published individual learning curves for their animals, because they felt that any single learning function based upon pooled data would be misleading. The distribution of individual differences was similar to the distributions of individual scores of monkeys and cats on double alternation (see Section IV). Comparison of the individual monkeys' delayed-response data provided by French and Harlow with the data for 10 cats trained on the same problem (Warren, 1964a) reveals that 6 of 17 monkeys failed to reach 80% correct responses in as few trials as the median cat. Primates and carnivores apparently do not differ substantially in capacity for rapid learning of the delayed-response task, a conclusion supported by the observation that under particularly favorable conditions both cats and dogs learn delayed response in a single testing session (Lawicka, 1959).

It has also proved impossible to differentiate between primates and other mammals in terms of the subjects' behavior during the delay period. New World monkeys adopt overt bodily orientations during the delay interval (French, 1959; Meyers *et al.*, 1962; Miles, 1964); cats and dogs do not (Lawicka, 1959; Meyers *et al.*, 1962). Thus, there is no consistent difference between primates and carnivores in (1) reliance on bodily orientation during the delay period, (2) rate of learning the delayed-response task, or (3) length of maximum delay. But level of performance at a given delay seems to differentiate at least some species tested under at least one standard procedure (see Chapter 4 by Fletcher).

Continuing behavioral analysis has removed delayed response progressively further from the category of "symbolic" behavior. Harlow (1951) interpreted delayed response as a type of memory test, and stated, "Successful delayed response performance is possible only if an animal learns discrimination *reversal* problems in a *single* trial to an implicit (secondarily reinforced) reward and retains this learning for a period defined by the delay" (Harlow, 1951, p. 229). French (1959) showed that this hypothesis attributes too much to an animal that solves delayed response, since he demonstrated that squirrel monkeys learn only to adopt bodily orientations toward the baited locus in delayed response, unless forced to do otherwise by special experimental procedures. Harlow's explanation of delayed response in terms of one-trial reversal learning fails completely to apply to delayed-response learning by cats and raccoons, because there is no evidence of consistent one-trial *discrimination* or *reversal* learning in these forms (see Section III, B). Konorski and Lawicka (1964) have shown that many features of delayed-response performance in carnivores may be explained satisfactorily by treating delayed response as an instance of trace conditioning. (Also see Chapter 4 by Fletcher for a new analysis of the delayed-response problem.)

VI. MULTIPLE-SIGN LEARNING

The capacity for solving complex multiple-sign problems (see Chapter 5 by French) is not restricted to primates. Pigeons have solved the conditional-discrimination and matching-to-sample problems (Blough, 1956, 1957, 1959; Ferster, 1960; Ferster & Appel, 1961; Ginsburg, 1957; Skinner, 1950; Zimmerman & Ferster, 1963), and canaries have solved the oddity problem (Pastore, 1954). Rats have solved both oddity and conditional-discrimination tasks (Lashley, 1938a; North *et al.*, 1958; Wodinsk & Bitterman, 1953). Manifold differences in experimental procedure, however, preclude direct comparisons between the experiments with birds and rats and those with primates.

Cats have been trained on multiple-sign problems in the WGTA under conditions very much like those of experiments with rhesus monkeys; the remainder of this section is concerned with the comparison of oddity and conditional-discrimination learning by rhesus monkeys and cats, tested under very similar conditions.

A. Oddity

Many cats fail to master the oddity problem (Boyd & Warren, 1957; Warren, 1960b), even when given many more trials than are required for learning by rhesus monkeys (Meyer & Harlow, 1949). Of the cats that solve a single oddity problem, most fail to generalize the oddity principle. On the other hand, one cat formed a highly efficient set for the solution of oddity problems, and attained a final level of performance within the range of performance of rhesus monkeys trained under similar conditions (Warren, 1960b).

The proportion of monkeys that learn the generalized oddity principle is far higher than the proportion of cats, but some individuals of both species can reach the same final level of efficiency.

B. Conditional Discrimination

In order to determine whether nonprimate mammals could discriminate stimuli presenting multiple, ambivalent cues, Joshi and Warren (1959) tested cats on a complex conditional-discrimination problem under conditions almost identical to those of an earlier experiment with rhesus macaques (Noer & Harlow, 1946). The stimuli were large white (W), large black (B), small white (w), and small black, (b) wooden objects, which were paired in four configurations (+ and – denote the positive and negative stimulus in each pair):

1. b+ and w–
2. W+ and B–
3. w+ and W–
4. B+ and b–

The final stage of training required the subjects to respond appropriately to all four configurations, presented in random sequence within a single testing session. Each object was positive in one context and negative in another, so that accurate performance depended on varying responses to each object in terms of the other discriminandum presented on any particular trial. The final stage was reached through a sequence of part problems which is shown in the second column of Table IV. This sequence and most other features were identical to those in the experiment with monkeys. The criterion of learning at each step in training was 45 correct responses in 50 consecutive noncorrection trials (2 days of testing).

Table IV also gives the median number of errors to criterion made by the monkeys and cats at each stage of learning. Medians must be used because two of the monkeys required special remedial

Table IV. Discrimination of ambivalent cues by rhesus monkeys and cats.

		Median errors	
Test	*Configurations*	*6 Monkeys*	*6 Cats*
I	1	6	55
II	2	17	112
III[a]	1,2	8	43
III[b]	1,2	2	7
IV	3	8	35
V	4	13	57
VI[a]	3,4	26	211
VI[b]	3,4	3	18
VII	2,3,4	44	30
VIII	1,2,3,4	428	40

[a] Trials presented in alternate groups of five.
[b] Trials presented in balanced irregular sequence.

training to learn Test VII and three monkeys failed to reach criterion on Test VIII. All of the cats learned every test, and none required any special training. The monkeys made substantially fewer errors than the cats in learning the first six tests, but the monkeys made more than 10 times as many errors as the cats on Test VIII, every cat making fewer errors than any of the monkeys at this stage. Joshi and Warren speculated that these results were artifactual in the sense that they were specific to the conditions imposed by the particular experimental design employed and possibly reflected species differences in the way that cats and monkeys learn this one particular problem. No claim that cats are peculiarly gifted in capacity for solving complex conditional-discrimination problems was made.

As a check on the general validity of the paradoxical findings just given, groups of rhesus monkeys (Warren, 1960d) and cats (Warren, 1961) with extensive experience in visual-discrimination learning were trained on a conditional-discrimination problem, without the sequence of pretraining used in the above experiment. The stimuli were a square and a triangle. When these forms were both large (100 cm^2 in area), one was correct; but when they were both small (12.5 cm^2), the other was correct. From the outset of training, the size of the pair of figures was varied from trial to trial in an irregular sequence. Each size was presented on half the trials in a given test session, and the positive stimulus appeared equally often on the right and on the left. Both the monkeys and the cats were trained to a criterion of 20 correct responses within a block of 24 trials.

Figure 7 shows the rates of learning. Seven of the 13 monkeys reached criterion in the first 24 trials, and none required more than 48 trials to learn. Median trials to criterion for the cats was 180; however, four cats' scores fall within the range for the monkeys. These data reveal a marked quantitative superiority of rhesus monkeys over cats in learning a single conditional discrimination, but the overlapping ranges of individual scores demonstrate that the difference between these species is not all-or-none.

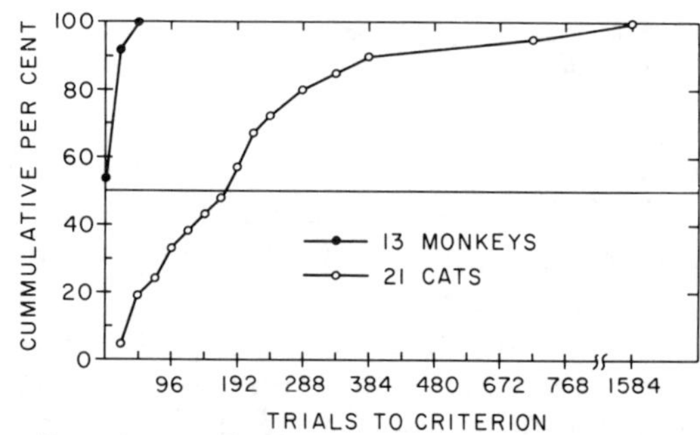

Fig. 7. Percentages of rhesus monkeys and of cats having met criterion on a conditional-discrimination problem.

Nonprimates have not yet shown interproblem learning, however. Rats (Lashley, 1938a) and cats (Warren, 1964a) have shown no interproblem improvement in performance over a series of conditional-discrimination problems. Rhesus monkeys, in contrast, form conditional-discrimination-learning sets with considerable facility (Warren *et al.*, 1963). The performance of four rhesus monkeys tested on 60 24-trial conditional discriminations between geometrical forms, with a difference in surface area (36 cm^2 versus 81 cm^2) as the conditional cue, is summarized in Fig. 8. Significant interproblem learning was observed; the monkeys made 66% and 80% correct responses on the first and last 10 conditional discriminations. The intraproblem learning curves show that the animals learned the conditional problems slowly and gradually in comparison to the

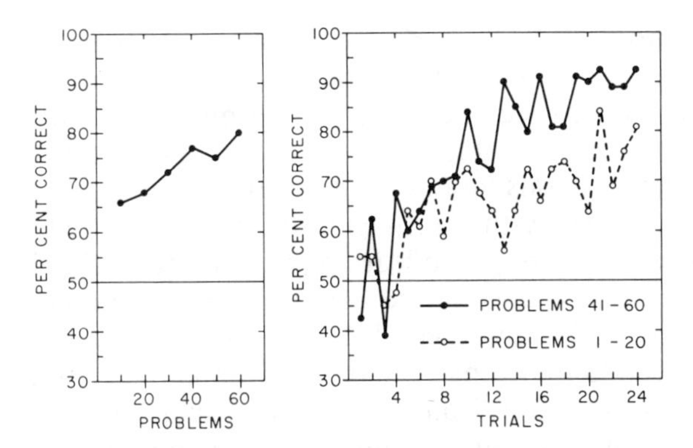

Fig. 8. Formation of a conditional-discrimination-learning set by rhesus monkeys. Left: Interproblem learning. Right: Intraproblem learning.

rapid, discontinuous solution of simultaneous discrimination problems by monkeys.

But further research (Warren, 1964b) indicates that Fig. 8 provides only a minimal estimate of the sophisticated rhesus macaque's capacity for solving conditional-discrimination problems. Much more rapid learning is observed when, for example, differences in color or orientation of the stimuli in the horizontal and vertical planes are made the conditional cues. The effect is probably related to the greater discriminability of these as opposed to size cues (see Chapter 1 by Meyer *et al.*).

The available evidence points toward the same conclusion about conditional-discrimination learning as about simple discrimination learning: nonprimate mammals may learn single conditional-discrimination problems at least as readily as primates, but primates clearly surpass all other forms in their capacity for rapid interproblem learning.

VII. CONCLUSIONS

No one can yet provide a definitive answer to the question "In what ways does learning in primates differ from learning in other vertebrates?" Far too little is known about learning in nonprimate species and most species of primates, particularly the more primitive primates. Also, it is safe to assume that the most favorable conditions for learning, and hence the limits of learning and problem-solving ability, remain to be established in even such intensively-studied species as the rat, rhesus monkey, and chimpanzee.

One can list with confidence the ways in which learning in primates does *not* differ from learning in other taxa: 1. The evidence fails to indicate any meaningful variation among vertebrates in the acquisition of single simple conditioned responses or discrimination habits by experimentally naive subjects. 2. Mammals, both primates and nonprimates, differ from nonmammalian forms in probability learning and in reversal learning. 3. Primates and nonprimate mammals do not differ qualitatively in their capacity for forming discrimination-learning sets, for performing delayed response or double alternation, or for solving individual conditional-discrimination or oddity problems.

This leaves a surprisingly short list of learning problems on which primates appear to be superior to nonprimate mammals: 1. Old World primates are *quantitatively* superior to nonprimate mammals in the speed with which they form learning sets, in the asymptotic level of performance attained on learning-set problems (no nonprimate animal has yet shown one-trial solution of visual discrimination problems), and in the rate at which they solve exceptionally difficult discrimination problems such as intermediate size. 2. Chimpanzees are qualitatively superior to cats in the generalization and transfer of learning sets (see Section III, B, 2). 3. Rhesus monkeys are qualitatively superior to cats in learning discrimination reversal to a sign and in forming sets for conditional-discrimination learning.

These conclusions must be regarded as tentative for two reasons. Generalizations of negative results are very hazardous; it is quite conceivable that dogs or dolphins would succeed where cats have failed, or that cats tested under more appropriate conditions would perform more adequately than the groups discussed in this chapter. In either event, the suggested qualitative differences between primates and other mammals would vanish. In the second place, the very similar learning-set performance of cats and marmosets raises considerable doubt about differences between orders in learning capacity. Differences between New World monkeys and nonprimate mammals probably will be less impressive on complex learning-set problems than are differences between cats and rhesus macaques or chimpanzees. Learning performances of primitive primates, like the lemur, probably resemble those of carnivores more than those of advanced primates.

The data summarized in this chapter point toward an important conclusion about learning theory and comparative psychology. The qualitative differences in learning between mammals and nonmammals are much greater and more significant than learning theorists (Hull, 1945; Skinner, 1956) have recognized. On the other hand, the substantial qualitative similarities in learning by mammals in general, as opposed to nonmammals, clearly indicate that the differences in learning between primates and other mammals are not so great as they seemed to many primatologists a few years ago.

REFERENCES

Appel, J. B. (1960). Some schedules involving aversive control. *J. exp. Anal. Behav.* **3**, 349.

Bacon, H. R., Warren, J. M., & Schein, M. W. (1962). Non-spatial reversal learning in chickens. *Anim. Behav.* **10**, 239.

Behar, I. (1962). Evaluation of cues in learning set formation in mangabeys. *Psychol. Rep.* **11**, 479.

Behrend, Erika R., & Bitterman, M. E. (1961). Probability-matching in the fish. *Amer. J. Psychol.* **74**, 542.

Behrend, Erika R., & Bitterman, M. E. (1963). Sidman avoidance in the fish. *J. exp. Anal. Behav.* **6**, 47.

Bitterman, M. E. (1960). Toward a comparative psychology of learning. *Amer. Psychologist* **15**, 704.

Bitterman, M. E. (1963). Species-differences in learning: fish, reptile, bird, and rat. Paper read at Amer. Psychol. Assn., Philadelphia, Pennsylvania.

Bitterman, M. E., Wodinsky, J., & Candland, D. K. (1958). Some comparative psychology. *Amer. Psychol.* **71**, 94.

Black, A. H., & Morse, Patricia (1961). Avoidance learning in dogs without a warning stimulus. *J. exp. Anal. Behav.* **4**, 17.

Blough, D. S. (1956). Technique for studying the effects of drugs on discrimination in the pigeon. *Ann. N. Y. Acad. Sci.* **65**, 334.

Blough, D. S. (1957). Some effects of drugs on visual discrimination in the pigeon. *Ann. N. Y. Acad. Sci.* **66**, 733.

Blough, D. S. (1959). Delayed matching in the pigeon. *J. exp. Anal. Behav.* **2**, 151.

Boyd, B. O., & Warren, J. M. (1957). Solution of oddity problems by cats. *J. comp. physiol. Psychol.* **50**, 258.

Bullock, D. H., & Bitterman, M. E. (1962). Probability-matching in the pigeon. *Amer. J. Psychol.* **75**, 634.

Clark, F. C. (1961). Avoidance conditioning in the chimpanzee. *J. exp. Anal. Behav.* **4**, 393.

Clayton, K. N. (1963). Successful performance by cats on several color discrimination problems. *Amer. Psychologist* **18**, 407. (Abstract.)

Crawford, F. T. (1962). Reversal learning to spatial cues by monkeys. *J. comp. physiol. Psychol.* **55**, 869.

Cronholm, J. N., Warren, J. M., & Hara, K. (1960). Distribution of training and reversal learning by cats. *J. genet. Psychol.* **96**, 105.

Dufort, R. H., Guttman, N., & Kimble, G. A. (1954). One-trial discrimination reversal in the white rat. *J. comp. physiol. Psychol.* **47**, 248.

Ferster, C. B. (1960). Intermittent reinforcement of matching to sample in the pigeon. *J. exp. Anal. Behav.* **3**, 259.

Ferster, C. B., & Appel, J. B. (1961). Punishment of S^{Δ} responding in matching to sample by time out from positive reinforcement. *J. exp. Anal. Behav.* **4**, 45.

Ferster, C. B., & Skinner, B. F. (1957). "Schedules of Reinforcement." Appleton-Century-Crofts, New York.

Fischer, Gloria J. (1962). The formation of learning sets in young gorillas. *J. comp. physiol. Psychol.* **55**, 924.

French, G. M. (1959). Performance of squirrel monkeys on variants of delayed response. *J. comp. physiol. Psychol.* **52**, 741.

French, G. M., & Harlow, H. F. (1962). Variability of delayed-reaction performance in normal and brain-damaged rhesus monkeys. *J. Neurophysiol.* **25**, 585.

Ganz, L., & Riesen, A. H. (1962). Stimulus generalization to hue in the dark-reared macaque. *J. comp. physiol. Psychol.* **55**, 92.

Gardner, L. Pearl, & Nissen, H. W. (1948). Simple discrimination behavior of young chimpanzees: comparisons with human aments and domestic animals. *J. genet. Psychol.* **72**, 145.

Gellermann, L. W. (1931a). The double alternation problem: I. The behavior of monkeys in a double alternation temporal maze. *J. genet. Psychol.* **39**, 50.

Gellermann, L. W. (1931b). The double alternation problem: II. The behavior of children and human adults in a double alternation temporal maze. *J. genet. Psychol.* **39**, 197

Gellermann, L. W. (1931c). The double alternation problem: III. The behavior of monkeys in a double alternation box-apparatus. *J. genet. Psychol.* **39**, 359.

Ginsburg, N. (1957). Matching in pigeons. *J. comp. physiol. Psychol.* **50**, 261.

Graf, V., & Bitterman, M. E. (1963). General activity as instrumental: Application to avoidance training. *J. exp. Anal. Behav.* **6**, 301.

Graf, V., Bullock, D. H., & Bitterman, M. E. (1964). Further experiments on probability-matching in the pigeon. *J. exp. Anal. Behav.* **7**, 151.

Harlow, H. F. (1949). The formation of learning sets. *Psychol. Rev.* **56**, 51.

Harlow, H. F. (1951). Primate learning. *In* "Comparative Psychology" (C. P. Stone, ed.), 3rd ed., pp. 183-238. Prentice-Hall, New York.

Harlow, H. F. (1958). The evolution of learning. *In* "Behavior and Evolution" (Anne Roe & G. G. Simpson, eds.), pp. 269-290. Yale Univer. Press, New Haven, Connecticut.

Harlow, H. F. (1959). Learning set and error factor theory. *In* "Psychology: A Study of a Science" (S. Koch, ed.), Vol. 2, pp. 492-537. McGraw-Hill, New York.

Harlow, H. F., & Hicks, L. H. (1957). Discrimination learning theory: uniprocess vs. duoprocess. *Psychol. Rev.* **64**, 104.

Harris, J. D. (1943). The auditory acuity of pre-adolescent monkeys. *J. comp. Psychol.* **35**, 255.

Hayes, K. J., Thompson, R., & Hayes, Catherine (1953). Discrimination learning set in chimpanzees. *J. comp. physiol. Psychol.* **46**, 99.

Hilgard, E. R., & Marquis, D. G. (1936). Conditioned eyelid responses in monkeys, with a comparison of dog, monkey, and man. *Psychol. Monogr.* **47**, No. 2 (Whole No. 212), 186-198.

House, Betty J., & Zeaman, D. (1959). Position discrimination and reversals in low-grade retardates. *J. comp. physiol. Psychol.* **52**, 564.

Hull, C. L. (1945). The place of innate individual and species differences in a natural-science theory of behavior. *Psychol. Rev.* **52**, 55.

Hull, C. L. (1952). "A Behavior System." Yale Univer. Press, New Haven, Connecticut.

Hunter, W. S. (1920). The temporal maze and kinesthetic sensory processes in the white rat. *Psychobiology* **2**, 1.

Hunter, W. S. (1928). The behavior of raccoons in a double alternation temporal maze. *J. genet. Psychol.* **35**, 374.

Hunter, W. S., & Nagge, J. W. (1931). The white rat and the double alternation temporal maze. *J. genet. Psychol.* **39**, 303.

Johnson, J. I., Jr. (1961). Double alternation by raccoons. *J. comp. physiol. Psychol.* **54**, 248.

Johnson, J. I., Jr., & Michels, K. M. (1958). Learning sets and object-size effects in visual discrimination learning by raccoons. *J. comp. physiol. Psychol.* **51**, 376.

Jones, L. V. (1954). Distinctiveness of color, form, and position cues for pigeons. *J. comp. Physiol. Psychol.* **47**, 253.

Joshi, B. L., & Warren, J. M. (1959). Discrimination of ambivalent cue stimuli by cats. *J. Psychol.* **47**, 3.

Karn, H. W. (1938). The behavior of cats on the double alternation problem in the temporal maze. *J. comp. Psychol.* **26**, 201.

Karn, H. W., & Malamud, H. R. (1939). The behavior of dogs on the double alternation problem in the temporal maze. *J. comp. Psychol.* **27**, 461.

Karn, H. W., & Patton, R. A. (1939). The transfer of double alternation behavior acquired in a temporal maze. *J. comp. Psychol.* **28**, 55.

Kelleher, R. T., & Cook, L. (1959). An analysis of the behavior of rats and monkeys on concurrent fixed-ratio avoidance schedules. *J. exp. Anal. Behav.* **2**, 203.

Kimble, G. A. (1961). "Hilgard and Marquis' Conditioning and Learning," 2nd ed. Appleton-Century-Crofts, New York.

Kirk, K. L., & Bitterman, M. E. (1963). Habit reversal in the turtle. *Quart. J. exp. Psychol.* **15**, 52.

Konorski, J., & Lawicka, W. (1964). Analysis of errors by prefrontal animals on the delayed-response test. *In* "The Frontal Granular Cortex and Behavior" (J. M. Warren & K. Akert, eds.), pp. 271-294. McGraw-Hill, New York.

Koronakos, C., & Arnold, W. J. (1957). The formation of learning sets in rats. *J. comp. physiol. Psychol.* **50**, 11.

Lashley, K. S. (1929). "Brain Mechanisms and Intelligence." Univer. Chicago Press, Chicago, Illinois.

Lashley, K. S. (1938a). Conditional reactions in the rat. *J. Psychol.* **6**, 311.

Lashley, K. S. (1938b). The mechanism of vision: XV. Preliminary studies of the rat's capacity for detail vision. *J. gen. Psychol.* **18**, 123.

Lawicka, W. (1959). Physiological mechanism of delayed reactions: II. Delayed reactions in dogs and cats to directional stimuli. *Acta Biol. exp.* **19**, 199.

Leary, R. W., Harlow, H. F., Settlage, P. H., and Greenwood, D. D. (1952). Performance on double-alternation problems by normal and brain-injured monkeys. *J. comp. physiol. Psychol.* **45**, 576.

Livesey, P. J. (1964). A note on double alternation by rabbits. *J. comp. physiol. Psychol.* **57**, 104.

Maier, N. R. F., & Schneirla, T. C. (1935). "Principles of Animal Psychology." McGraw-Hill, New York.

Mason, W. A., & Harlow, H. F. (1958). Performance of infant rhesus monkeys on a spatial discrimination problem. *J. comp. physiol. Psychol.* **51**, 71.

Meyer, D. R. (1960). The effects of differential probabilities of reinforcement on discrimination learning by monkeys. *J. comp. physiol. Psychol.* **53**, 173.

Meyer, D. R., & Harlow, H. F. (1949). The development of transfer of response to patterning by monkeys. *J. comp. physiol. Psychol.* **42**, 454.

Meyer, D. R., Miles, R. C., & Ratoosh, P. (1954). Absence of color vision in cat. *J. Neurophysiol.* **17**, 289.

Meyers, W. J., McQuiston, M. D., & Miles, R. C. (1962). Delayed-response and learning-set performance of cats. *J. comp. physiol. Psychol.* **55**, 515.

Michels, K. M., & Brown, D. R. (1959). The delayed-response performance of raccoons. *J. comp. physiol. Psychol.* **52**, 737.

Miles, R. C. (1957). Learning-set formation in the squirrel monkey. *J. comp. physiol. Psychol.* **50**, 356.

Miles, R. C. (1958). Color vision in the marmoset. *J. comp. physiol. Psychol.* **51**, 152.

Miles, R. C. (1964). Learning by squirrel monkeys with frontal lesions. *In* "The Frontal Granular Cortex and Behavior" (J. M. Warren & K. Akert, eds.), pp. 149-167. McGraw-Hill, New York.

Miles, R. C. & Meyer, D. R. (1956). Learning sets in marmosets. *J. comp. physiol. Psychol.* **49**, 219.

Nissen, H. W., Riesen, A. H., & Nowlis, V. (1938). Delayed response and discrimination learning by chimpanzees. *J. comp. Psychol.* **26**, 361.

Noble, M., & Adams, C. K. (1963). Conditioning in pigs as a function of the interval between CS and US. *J. comp. physiol. Psychol.* **56**, 215.

Noble, M., & Harding, G. E. (1963). Conditioning in rhesus monkeys as a function of the interval between CS and US. *J. comp. physiol. Psychol,* **56**, 220.

Noble, M., Gruender, Anne, & Meyer, D. R. (1959). Conditioning in fish (*Mollienisia* sp.) as a function of the interval between CS and US. *J. comp. physiol. Psychol.* **52**, 236.

Noer, Mary C., & Harlow, H. F. (1946). Discrimination of ambivalent cue stimuli by macaque monkeys. *J. gen. Psychol.* **34**, 165.

North, A. J., Maller, O., & Hughes, C. (1958). Conditional discrimination and stimulus patterning. *J. comp. physiol. Psychol.* **51**, 711.

Orbach, J. (1959). Disturbances of the maze habit following occipital cortex removals in blind monkeys. *A. M. A. Arch. Neurol. Psychiat.* **81**, 49.

Pastore, N. (1954). Discrimination learning in the canary. *J. comp. physiol. Psychol.* **47**, 389.

Rabinovitch, M. S., & Rosvold, H. E. (1951). A closed-field intelligence test for rats. *Canad. J. Psychol.* **5**, 122.

Razran, G. (1961). The observable unconscious and the inferrable conscious in current Soviet psychophysiology: Interoceptive conditioning, sematic conditioning, and the orienting reflex. *Psychol. Rev.* **68**, 81.

Riopelle, A. J., & Copelan, E. L. (1954). Discrimination reversal to a sign. *J. exp. Psychol.* **48**, 149.

Rollin, A. R. (1963). Successive object discrimination reversals by squirrels. Paper read at East. Psychol. Ass., New York.

Rosenzweig, M. R., Krech, D., & Bennett, E. L. (1960). A search for relations between brain chemistry and behavior. *Psychol. Bull.* **57**, 476.

Rumbaugh, D. M., & Rice, Carol P. (1962). Learning-set formation in young great apes. *J. comp. physiol. Psychol.* **55**, 866.

Schlosberg, H., & Katz, A. (1943). Double alternation lever-pressing in the white rat. *Amer. J. Psychol.* **56**, 274.

Schusterman, R. J. (1962). Transfer effects of successive discrimination-reversal training in chimpanzees. *Science* **137**, 422.

Schusterman, R. J., & Bernstein, I. S. (1962). Response tendencies of gibbons in single and double alternation tasks. *Psychol. Rep.* **11**, 521.

Shell, W. F., & Riopelle, A. J. (1957). Multiple discrimination learning in raccoons. *J. comp. physiol. Psychol.* **50**, 585.

Shell, W. F., & Riopelle, A. J. (1958). Progressive discrimination learning in platyrrhine monkeys. *J. comp. physiol. Psychol.* **51**, 467.

Sidman, M. (1953a). Avoidance conditioning with brief shock and no exteroceptive warning signal. *Science* **118**, 157.

Sidman, M. (1953b). Two temporal parameters of the maintenance of avoidance behavior by the white rat. *J. comp. physiol. Psychol.* **46**, 253.

Sidman, M. (1955). Some properties of the warning stimulus in avoidance behavior. *J. comp. physiol. Psychol.* **48**, 444.

Sidman, M., & Boren, J. J. (1957). A comparison of two types of warning stimulus in an avoidance situation. *J. comp. physiol. Psychol.* **50**, 282.

Skinner, B. F., (1950). Are theories of learning necessary? *Psychol. Rev.* **57**, 193. (Reprinted in "Cumulative Record," pp. 39-69. Appleton-Century-Crofts, New York, 1959).

Skinner, B. F. (1956). A case history in scientific method. *Amer. Psychologist* **11**, 221. (Reprinted in "Cumulative Record," pp. 76-100. Appleton-Century-Crofts, New York, 1959. Also in "Psychology: A Study of a Science" [S. Koch, ed.], Vol. 2, pp. 359-379. McGraw-Hill, New York, 1959.)

Spence, K. W. (1942). The basis of solution by chimpanzees of the intermediate size problem. *J. exp. Psychol.* **31**, 257. (Reprinted in "Behavior Theory and Learning," pp. 339-358. Prentice-Hall, Englewood Cliffs, New Jersey, 1960.)

Stewart, C. N., & Warren, J. M. (1957). The behavior of cats on the double-alternation problem. *J. comp. physiol. Psychol.* **50**, 26.

Sutherland, N. S. (1961). The methods and findings of experiments on the visual discrimination of shape by animals. *Exp. Psychol. Soc. Monogr.* **1**, 1.

Tyrrell, D. J. (1963). The formation of object discrimination learning sets by rats. Paper read at East. Psychol. Ass., New York.

Voronin, L. G. (1962). Some results of comparative-physiological investigations of higher nervous activity. *Psychol. Bull.* **59**, 161.

Warren, J. M. (1959a). Solution of object and positional discriminations by rhesus monkeys. *J. comp. physiol. Psychol.* **52**, 92.

Warren, J. M. (1959b). Stimulus perseveration in discrimination learning by cats. *J. comp. physiol. Psychol.* **52**, 99.

Warren, J. M. (1960a). Discrimination reversal learning by cats. *J. genet. Psychol.* **97**, 317.

Warren, J. M. (1960b). Oddity learning set in a cat. *J. comp. physiol. Psychol.* **53**, 433.

Warren, J. M. (1960c). Reversal learning by paradise fish (*Macropodus opercularis*). *J. comp. physiol. Psychol.* **53**, 376.

Warren, J. M. (1960d). Solution of sign-differentiated object and positional discriminations by rhesus monkeys. *J. genet. Psychol.* **96**, 365.
Warren, J. M. (1960e). Supplementary report: Effectiveness of food and nonfood signs in reversal learning by monkeys. *J. exp. Psychol.* **60**, 263.
Warren, J. M. (1961). Individual differences in discrimination learning by cats. *J. genet. Psychol.* **98**, 89.
Warren, J. M. (1964a). The behavior of carnivores and primates with lesions in the prefrontal cortex. *In* "The Frontal Granular Cortex and Behavior" (J. M. Warren & K. Akert, eds.), pp. 168-191. McGraw-Hill, New York.
Warren, J. M. (1964b). Additivity of cues in conditional discrimination learning by rhesus monkeys. *J. comp. physiol. Psychol.* **58**, 124.
Warren, J. M., & Baron, A. (1956). The formation of learning sets by cats. *J. comp. physiol. Psychol.* **49**, 227.
Warren, J. M., & Sinha, M. M. (1959). Interactions between learning sets in monkeys. *J. genet. Psychol.* **95**, 19.
Warren, J. M., & Warren, Helen B. (1962). Reversal learning by horse and raccoon. *J. genet. Psychol.* **100**, 215.
Warren, J. M., Leary, R. W., Harlow, H. F., & French, G. M. (1957). Function of association cortex in monkeys. *Brit. J. Anim. Behav.* **5**, 131.
Warren, J. M., Brookshire, K. H., Ball, G. G., & Reynolds, D. V. (1960). Reversal learning by white leghorn chicks. *J. comp. physiol. Psychol.* **53**, 371.
Warren, J. M., Warren, Helen B., & Akert, K. (1961). *Umweg* learning by cats with lesions in the prestriate cortex. *J. comp. physiol. Psychol.* **54**, 629.
Warren, J. M., Warren, Helen B., & Akert, K. (1962). Orbitofrontal cortical lesions and learning in cats. *J. comp. Neurol.* **118**, 17.
Warren, J. M., Grant, R., Hara, K., & Leary, R. W. (1963). Impaired learning by monkeys with unilateral lesions in association cortex. *J. comp. physiol. Psychol.* **56**, 241.
Weaver, L. A., Jr., & Michels, K. M. (1961). Methodological factors affecting the formation of learning sets by rats. *Anim. Behav.* **9**, 4.
Wilson, W. A., Jr. (1960). Supplementary report: Two-choice behavior of monkeys. *J. exp. Psychol.* **59**, 207.
Wilson, W. A., Jr., & Rollin, A. R. (1959). Two-choice behavior of rhesus monkeys in a noncontingent situation. *J. exp. Psychol.* **58**, 174.
Wilson, W. A., Jr., Oscar, Marlene, & Bitterman, M. E. (1964). Probability-learning in the monkey. *Quart. J. exp. Psychol.* **16**, 163.
Wodinsky, J., & Bitterman, M. E. (1953). The solution of oddity-problems by the rat. *Amer. J. Psychol.* **66**, 137.
Wright, P. L., Kay, H., & Sime, M. E. (1963). The establishment of learning sets in rats. *J. comp. physiol. Psychol.* **56**, 200.
Yamaguchi, S., & Warren, J. M. (1961). Single versus double alternation learning by cats. *J. comp. physiol. Psychol.* **54**, 533.

Zeigler, H. P. (1961). Learning-set formation in pigeons. *J. comp. physiol. Psychol.* **54**, 252.
Zimmerman, J., & Ferster, C. B. (1963). Intermittent punishment of S^{Δ} responding in matching to sample. *J. exp. Anal. Behav.* **6**, 349.
Zimmermann, R. R. (1963). The performance of baby monkeys on a closed-field intelligence test for rats. Paper read at East. Psychol. Ass., New York.

SUGGESTIONS FOR FURTHER READING

Corning, W. C., & Ratner, S. C. (Eds.) *Chemistry of learning invertebrate research*. New York: Plenum Press, 1967.

Konorski, J. *Integrative activity of the brain*. Chicago: University of Chicago Press, 1967.

Kutscher, C. L. *Readings in comparative studies of animal behavior*. Waltham, Mass.: Xerox College Publishing, 1971.

Maier, N. R. F., & Schneirla, T. C. *Principles of animal psychology*. New York: McGraw-Hill, 1935.

Rosenthal, R. (Ed.) *Clever Hans, the horse of Mr. Von Osten*. New York: Holt, Rinehart & Winston, 1965.

Sutherland, N. S., & Mackintosh, N. J. *Mechanisms of animal discrimination learning*. New York: Academic Press, 1971.

Thorndike, E. L. *Animal intelligence: Experimental studies*. New York: Hafner, 1965. Facsimile of 1911 edition.

Thorpe, W. H. *Learning and instinct in animals*. Cambridge, Mass.: Harvard University Press, 1956.

Tolman, E. C. *"Insight" in rats*. Berkeley: University of California Press, 1930.

Tolman, E. C. *Purposive behavior in animals and men*. New York: Century Co., 1932.

Yerkes, R. M. *Chimpanzee intelligence and its vocal expressions*. Baltimore: Williams and Wilkins, 1925.

INDEX

ACTH and crowding stress, 265-266
Adrenals and stress, 243-248
Aggregations, 179
Agonistic behavior, 139-161, 176-177
Alarm substances, 358-359
Ambiguity, in signals, 274-277
Ambivalence, 67
Analysis, of behavior, 57-59
Appetitive behavior, 12
Attachment, in human infant, 501-506
Attack-escape theory, 151-155
Auditory communication, 312-320
Behavior and crowding stress, 248-251
Behaviorism, 8
Bird song, evolution, 320-330
Birds, displays, 303-307
Brain development, 542
Brain stimulation, 132-137, 139-161
Bruce effect, 355-356
Canalization, 532-534
Care-dependency relationships, 180
Care-giving behavior, 176
Chemical communication, 291-297, 347-368
Classical conditioning, 561-563, 609-610
Communication, origins of, 331-336
Communication and pheromones, 356-368
Comparative learning studies, 587-608, 609-639
Comparative method, 30-48
Compromise movements, 3
Concept formation, 579-581
Conspicuous structures and evolution, 37
Consummatory act, 12
Contact reinforcement and imprinting, 493-496
Contactual behavior, 175
Convergence, in behavior, 41
Coordination and evolution, 393-395
Courtship, effects of, 125-131
Courtship, evolution of, 34-39
Critical distance, 170
Critical period, 534-536, 542-545
Cross-correlation sequence, 63
Cross-fostering effects, 448-470
Crowding stress, 241-270
Decortication and learning, 598
Delayed-response learning, 631-633
Deprivation studies, 33, 50, 99-105

Derived activities, 3, 87, 93-97, 106-110
Development, of behavior, 473-547
Developmental patterns, 475
Dialect learning, 324
Discrimination reversal learning, 576-577
Diseases and crowding stress, 247-248
Displacement activities, 4, 36, 72-74, 162-165, 334
Displays, 3
Displays, development of, 477-485
Displays, function of, 39
Displays, of rat, 66-80
Displays and communication, 297-312
Distance ambivalence, 75-78, 82
Dominance-subordination relationships, 179
Double-alternation learning, 628-631
Early experience and behavior, 473-547
Ecology and populations, 241-270
Ecology and reproduction, 238-240
Ecology and ritualization, 272-285
Eliminative behavior, 176
Emancipation, 38
Epimeletic behavior, 176
"Erbköordination," 15
Et-epimeletic behavior, 176
Ethogram, 1
Ethogram, of rat, 71
Ethologizing, 27
Ethology, history of, 1, 5-14
Evolution, of behavior, 31-32
Evolution, of bird song, 320-330
Evolution and pheromones, 363-365
Evolution and ritualization, 272-285
Experiential deprivation, 526-527
Experiential enrichment, 527-529
Exploratory behavior, 536-539
Exploratory behavior, genetics, 426-429
Exposure learning, 555
Fear and imprinting, 496-498
"Fear period," 539
Fighting, release of, 17
Fighting and adrenal weight, 250
Fish ethology, 14-22
Fixed-action pattern, 2, 11, 32
Flight distance, 170
Food-soliciting, 96
Fright substance, 294
Gene pools, evolution of, 442-445
Genes and behavior, 49-53, 386-389
Genes and evolution, 381-402
Genes and nervous system, 383-385
"Genetic assimilation," 395
Genetics and behavior, 377-469
Genetics and cross-fostering, 464, 468
Genetics and crowding stress, 264-265
Genotype and behavior, 408-419
Genotype-environment interaction, 524-547
Gestalt psychology, 8
Gyandromorphs, behavior, 389-391
Habit reversal, 591
Habitat selection and isolation, 401-402
Habituation, 559-561
"Handling" effects, 527-529
Heterogenous summation, 2
Heterosis, 421-446
Honey-bee dance, 273
Hormones and dominance, 192-230
Hormones and incubation behavior, 125-131
Hormones and population regulation, 241-270
Hybrid mouse behavior, 421-446
"Hybrid vigor," 437
Hypothalamus stimulation, 132-137
Incomplete movements, 3
Imprinting, 184, 486-507
Imprinting and cross-fostering, 448-470
Incubation behavior, 125-131
Individual differences, communication, 281

Induction, 532-534
Information theory, 274
Ingestive behavior, 176
Inguinal response, ontogeny, 98-109
Inheritance of behavior, 33-34, 377-469
Inheritance of behavior patterns, 395-397
"Innate," definition of, 478
Innate releasing mechanism (IRM), 2, 11
Innate vs. learned, 25, 33, 49-53, 226, 382
Insect behavior, evolution, 381-402
Insects, communication, 299-301
Insight, 574, 581-583
Instinctive behavior, 49-53
Instrumental conditioning, 563-567, 610-611
Intention movements, 36, 171, 333
Intermediate inheritance, 433-455
Intermediate size problem, 619-621
Interproblem learning, 622
Interspecies differences, 40-41
Intraspecies recognition, 277-278
Investigative behavior, 536-539
Isolating mechanisms, 275-277
Isolation and dominance, 192-230
Isolation and imprinting, 491-492, 498-500
Isolation effects, 526-527, 537
Isolation-rearing effects, 478-485
Language, 336-340
Leader-follower relationships, 179
Learning, 555-639
Learning, in fish, 20-21
Learning, types of, 555
Learning and brain stimulation, 132-137
Learning and dominance, 182, 192-230
Learning sets, 578-579, 621-628
Lee-Boot effect, 352-353
Leerlauf reaction, 2
Mammals, displays, 307-312
Maze learning, 567-569
Methods, of ethology, 57-59
Mice, behavior genetics, 408-419, 421-446
Microevolution, 32
Models, experiments with, 98-109, 116,123
Motivation and brain stimulation, 132-137
Mounting behavior, 74-75
Multiple-sign learning, 633
Mutual care, 180
Mutual defense, 180-181
Neurobehavioral development, 524-547
Neuroethology, 139-161
"Noncontact" species, 171
Nonspatial discrimination learning, 613-618
Observational (imitative) learning, 555
Observational learning, 574-575
Olfactory communication, 291-297
Ontogeny, 1
Ontogeny, bird song, 329
Ontogeny, chick behavior, 195-199
Ontogeny of behavior, 98-109
Overdominance, 436
Pathway analysis, 71
Patterning of development, 529-532
Pecking, in gull chicks, 50
Peck-order studies, 192-230
Penile display, 96, 111
Perceptual homeostasis, 537
Pheromones, 347-368
Pheromones and recognition, 362-363
"Phylogenetic filtration," 601
Phylogeny, 1
Phylogeny, of learning, 587-608
Phylogeny and ritualization, 272-285
Physiology of crowding stress, 243-248
Play behavior, 513-522
Population cycles, 241-270

Population heterosis, 436, 439
Pregnancy block, 355-356
Prenatal effects, 528
Primate learning, 609-639
Principle of antithesis, 332, 334
Probability learning, 575-576, 594, 618
Proxemics, 171
Rat, social behavior, 61-85
Reaction-specific energy, 2
Redirected behavior, 4, 36
Releasers, 2, 12, 116-123
Releasing mechanism and evolution, 392-393
Reproduction and adaptation, 238-240
Reproduction and crowding, 245-247
Reproductive isolation, 40, 275-277, 397-400
Ring dove courtship, 125-131
Ritualization, 3, 272-285, 392-395
Ritualized fighting, 237, 279-280
RNA and learning, 566
Scent glands, canids, 90-91
Schematization, of movements, 37
Schooling, of fish, 17-18
Sensitive periods, 542-545
Sequences, in ontogeny, 529-532
Sex-attractants, 357-358
Sexual behavior, 176
Sexual behavior and cross-fostering, 457-470
Sexual behavior and imprinting, 500-501
Sexual behavior and releasers, 116-123
Sexual isolation, 397-400
Sexual relationships, 180
"Shock disease," 244
Sign stimuli, 2
Signals and distance, 170-171
Simultaneous combination, 3
Smiling response, 502-503
Social behavior, rat, 61-85
Social deprivation and dominance, 192-230
Social facilitation, 19
Social inertia and aggression, 220-223
Social investigation, 87-92
Social isolation, 478-485
Social organization, 169-271
Social organization, analysis of, 173-189
Social organization, development of, 192-230
Social preferences and cross-fostering, 448-470
Social rank and crowding, 248
"Social releaser," 89, 99-105
Social relationships, 178-181
Social signals, canids, 87-114
Social system, Wildebeest, 234-236
Socialization (*see* Imprinting)
Socialization, 184-185, 535-539
Socioecology, 169
Socio-infantile signals, 87-114
Socio-infantile-sexual signals, 97
Socio-sexual signals, 87-114
Song development, 34
Space and territory, 169-170
Spatial discrimination learning, 612-613
"Specialist" learners, 556
Speciation and ritualization, 272-285
Specific-action potential, 2, 11
Stickleback behavior, 14-16
"Stimulus bound" behavior, 132-137
Supranormal releaser, 2
Systematics, of behavior, 42-43
Taste communication, 291-297
Territorial behavior, Wildebeest, 236-238
Territoriality, of fish, 18-19
Territoriality and pheromones, 360-362
Threat displays, evolution of, 34-39
Threshold, changes in evolution, 37
Tool using, 583-584
Trail substances, 359-360
Trophallaxis, 180

"Typical form," of displays, 280
Typical intensity, 280
Umwelt, 2
Unitary drives, 152
Urination, social, 96-97
Vacuum reaction, 2
Visual communication, 297-312
Whitten effect, 353-354
Wildebeest, behavior, 234-240
Zoosemiotics, 171